D1615181

Engineering Principles of Agricultural Machines

ASAE Textbook Number 6
Published by the
American Society of Agricultural Engineers

Pamela DeVore-Hansen, Editor
Books & Journals
June 1993

ENGINEERING

PRINCIPLES

OF

AGRICULTURAL

MACHINES

Ajit K. Srivastava
Michigan State University

Carroll E. Goering
University of Illinois

Roger P. Rohrbach
North Carolina State University

For information, contact:

ASAE
2950 Niles Road
St. Joseph, Michigan 49085-9659 USA
Phone 616.429.0300 Fax 616.429.3852 E-mail: hq@asae.org

ASAE Textbook Number 6
LCCN 92-73957; ISBN 0-929355-33-4

Pamela DeVore-Hansen, Editor
Information Publishing Group

Preface

Engineering Principles of Agricultural Machines is written as a textbook for a course in agricultural machines in an engineering program. The book is designed to be used in an upper level undergraduate course. The prerequisites are statics, strength of materials, and differential equations. However, knowledge of dynamics and fluid mechanics would be helpful. The book may also be used in a lower division course by not covering the theoretical part of each chapter without loss of continuity.

The objectives of the book are: 1) to discuss the methods and equipment used to accomplish the various operations employed in production agriculture; 2) to present agricultural machines as a system of sub-components performing different functions; and 3) to present the engineering principles governing the operation of machines used in agricultural production.

The concept of dividing a machine into subsystems is discussed in Chapter 1. Every agricultural machine can be divided into functional, power, and framing subsystems. This book focuses on the functional systems and the power systems. Chapters 2, 3, and 4 cover the power systems. Chapters 4 through 10 discuss machines used for production operations from tillage to harvesting. Chapter 11 covers materials handling while machinery management is covered in Chapter 12. An approach to teaching agricultural machines by preparing a "process diagram" is presented in this book. A "process diagram" breaks a machine down into several functional processes, for example, a sprayer may be divided into processes of pumping, mixing and agitation, metering, and atomization. The instructors are encouraged to use this approach as it provides a common thread while discussing different machines. An effort has been made to maintain uniformity of format in Chapters 5 through 11. The material is generally presented under the titles of methods and equipment, functional processes, and performance. The book does not cover the framing subsystems.

The authors would like to acknowledge those individuals who have contributed in so many ways in completing this book. First of all we would like to acknowledge Prof. Emeritus Robert Kepner, author of *Principles of Farm Machinery* for giving us a blanket permission to use material from his book. Many figures and, in certain instances, verbatim textual material from his book has been used.

We also drew heavily from Prof. Sverker Persson's book entitled *Mechanics of Cutting Plant Materials* in Chapter 8. We relied on *Agricultural Electrification* by T. C. Surbrook and R. C. Mullins for

v

material on electric motors. We would like to thank those individuals who conducted an early in-depth review of the individual chapters of the book. They are Dr. Ken VonBergen, University of Nebraska, and Dr. Bob Wilkinson, Michigan State University – chapters on power; Prof. Ralph Alcock, South Dakota State University, and Prof. Larry Wells, University of Kentucky – chapter on tillage; Mr. Dave Wolak, Deere and Company, and Prof. Larry Shaw, University of Florida – chapter on planting; Prof. Loren Bode, University of Illinois, and Dr. Fred Bouise, USDA-ARS – chapter on chemical application; Dr. Al Rotz, USDA-ARS, and Dr. Kevin Shinners, University of Wisconsin – chapter on forage harvesting; Mr. Jim Hall and Mr. Neil West, Deere and Company – chapter on grain harvesting; Prof. Gerald Brusewitz, Oklahoma State University, Prof. Larry Shaw, University of Florida, and Dr. David Nahir, Bet-Dagan, Israel – chapter on fruit and vegetable harvesting; Dr. Ken Hellevang, North Dakota State University and Prof. Gerry Rehkugler, Cornell University – chapter on materials handling; and Prof. Jim Frisby, University of Missouri, and Prof. John Siemens, University of Illinois – chapter on machinery management.

Dr. Steve Borgelt, University of Missouri, Prof. Mark Schrock, Kansas State University, Prof. Larry Shaw, University of Florida, Dr. Kevin Shinners, University of Wisconsin, and Dr. Dan Humburg, South Dakota State University, used an early draft copy in the classroom and gave us constructive feedback. We appreciate the overall review of the book for ASAE completed by Prof. Leonard Bashford, University of Nebraska, Dr. Kevin Shinners, University of Wisconsin, and Dr. Dennis Buckmaster, Pennsylvania State University. We consider the comments made by the reviewers valuable and made a sincere effort to incorporate them in the manuscript.

We encourage the instructors who use this book to give us feedback related to errors that they may find and to give us suggestions for improving the book in a later edition by contacting the senior author.

Ajit K. Srivastava
Carroll E. Goering
Roger P. Rohrbach

Table of Contents

Chapter 1
Introduction

Chapter 2
Power for Agricultural Machines

Chapter 3
Transmission of Power

Chapter 4
Tractor Hitching, Traction, and Testing

Chapter 5
Soil Tillage

Chapter 6
Crop Planting

Chapter 7
Chemical Application

Chapter 8
Hay and Forage Harvesting

Chapter 9
Grain Harvesting

Chapter 10
Fruit, Nut, and Vegetable Harvesting

Chapter 11
Conveying of Agricultural Materials

Chapter 12
Machinery Management

1

Introduction

Reasons for Mechanization

Several factors have contributed to the mechanization of agriculture. Reduction of human drudgery, increase in productivity, and need to reduce peak labor demands are among the most significant. Agricultural work is physically demanding and the working conditions are adverse. Mechanization reduces human drudgery. It is less strenuous to drive a tractor than to till the soil with a spade all day long. A tractor pulling a plow can cultivate a larger area than a human with a spade in the same time thereby increasing productivity and timeliness of the operation. Timeliness is an important factor in agricultural production. Completing certain farming operations such as planting and harvesting in a timely manner increases yields considerably. The labor demand fluctuates during farming. More labor is needed during planting and harvesting than during other periods of plant growth. This fluctuating labor demand creates logistics problems from the point of view of labor management. With mechanization it is possible to reduce peak labor demand and maintain a more stable labor force.

1.1 History of Mechanized Agriculture

Even though great changes have taken place in the field of agriculture, soil still has to be tilled; seeds still have to be planted in the soil; the growing crop still has to be tended and cared for; and the crops still have to be harvested and threshed. However, the manner in which these operations are performed have changed drastically.

One of the earliest plows used to till soil was a wooden plow pulled either by human or animal power. As we learned to work with steel, moldboard plows were developed. The moldboard plow was a major development, since it turned the soil and provided for weed control and soil aeration. The seeds were planted by broadcasting them by hand. Major development in planting occurred when we learned to plant seeds in rows using dibble sticks in the early stages and later on with planters. Planting in rows had the advantage of controlling plant population and better weed control during the plant growth period.

Crop harvesting was done by hand using sickle or scythe. The cut crop was bundled and carried to a central location where it was threshed by either beating it with a stick or by having hooved animals walk on it. The threshed crop was separated from chaff and straw by winnowing in natural wind. The threshed crop mixture would be slowly dropped from a height and the wind would blow the chaff and small pieces of straw away leaving the clean grains to fall down in a pile. The process was repeated until the grain was clean. Later, the grain was cut by mowers that used a reciprocating sicklebar. The crop was still bundled by hand. Reapers combined the cutting and binding process in one machine. The development of steam engines made it possible to develop stationary threshers. Stationary threshers were used to thresh a bundled crop at a central location. The cleaning operation was still done by winnowing but it was done by a fan instead of the natural wind. The development of the internal combustion engine made it possible to combine the cutting, threshing, and cleaning functions. The name "combine" became popular because the machine combined the three operations.

The power for farming operations was primarily human labor. Later, animals were used as the source of power. Primarily horses, water buffalos, oxen, camels, and even elephants were used as power sources. Mechanical power became the primary source with the development of steam engines in 1858. In 1889 the first tractor with internal combustion engine was built. The tractors powered by internal combustion engines, were lighter and more powerful. In the 1930s the high compression diesel engine was adopted for the tractor and became very popular. Today's modern tractor is a very sophisticated machine with hydrostatic drive, electrohydraulic servo control for draft and depth, with ergonomically designed climate control operators' station.

It must be pointed out that in many parts of the world, especially the Third World countries, both manual labor and animal power continues to be the major source of power for farming operations. Even in the most advanced countries, manual labor is still used for fresh market fruit and vegetable harvesting operations because of the delicate nature of the products. The level of mechanization is dependent upon the availability of human labor and the level of industrialization within each country.

Mechanization of agriculture made it possible for other industries to develop by reducing labor needs and by making it available to other industries. In 1870 over half of the entire United States labor force was engaged in farming. One out of twelve laborers in 1960 and one out of twenty-six laborers in 1976 was engaged in farming operation, due to agricultural mechanization. One United States farmer now produces enough food for 60 people and one farm family can manage up to 1200 ha of farmland. Today, agricultural products are the second largest export commodity in the United States.

Mechanized agriculture is energy and capital intensive. Energy costs and the availability of capital to buy machines determines the level of mechanization in a society.

The area of agricultural mechanization is very dynamic. Technological advancement and concerns for energy and the environment continue to impact agriculture including mechanization.

1.2 Farming Operations and Related Machines

Plants are the primary production units of agriculture. They receive carbon dioxide from the air through their leaves, and receive water and nutrients from the soil through their roots. Using carbon dioxide, water, and nutrients along with solar energy, plants produce seeds, fruits, roots, fibers or oils which people can use.

The growth of plants happens in nature without any human intervention. However, agriculture arises when people exert control over plant growth. Machines are used as an extension of people's ability to produce and care for plants. This book will focus on many of the machines which are used by farmers to produce crops in plant agriculture.

A crop is a group of similar plants which are growing within the same land area. For example, if a farm produces rice and wheat, that farm is said to produce two crops. A farmer must complete certain operations in order to successfully produce a crop. The first operation is a mechanical stirring of the soil, called tillage, to prepare the seed bed. The second operation is called planting and it places the seeds in the tilled soil at the correct depth with the appropriate spacing between seeds. When the required soil temperature and soil water content are present, the seeds will germinate to form plants. For some crops the seeds are planted in a small area called a nursery and then the seedlings (small plants) are transplanted to the fields where they will grow to maturity.

As the plants grow to maturity the farmer must protect them from pests such as weeds (unwanted plants), insects, animals, and diseases. Chemicals are frequently used to control weeds, insects, and disease. Mechanical cultivation (tillage between the plants) is used to control weeds in some cases. Fences and/or noise-making devices may be used for protection from animals.

The final crop production operation is the harvesting of the plant parts which have economic value for the farmer. In some cases, more than one part of the plant may have economic value. For example, a farmer may use rice straw (stems and leaves) as an energy resource after the rice seeds have been removed from the plants. In other cases, the crop residue (unused plant parts) is stirred into the soil during tillage for the next crop.

The period of time on the calendar which passes from the beginning of the planting operation until the end of the harvest operation is called the growing season. The weather in some tropical farming areas is such that the growing season is continuous. In these areas, a crop can be planted any time during the year, and it can be harvested whenever it is mature. In many farming areas, the growing season is restricted because of weather conditions. For example, the planting operation may begin during spring when the soil temperature is increasing, and the harvest operation is completed during fall before cold weather begins. In other climates, the growing season depends on rainfall patterns with the planting operation done at the beginning of the rainy season so that the plants have adequate water for growth. Some farming areas have weather conditions which cause a short growing season that allows only one crop per calendar year, while other areas have a longer growing season which allows two or more crops each year from a given field. When the growing season is weather dependent, the planting and harvesting operations are very labor intensive to complete these operations in a timely way. If planting and harvesting are not completed in a timely way, the crop yield will be lowered.

TABLE 1.1 EXAMPLE OF A CROP ROTATION WHICH CONTAINS FOUR CROPS

Year	Area 1	Area 2	Area 3	Area 4
1	Crop A	Crop B	Crop C	Crop D
2	Crop B	Crop C	Crop D	Crop A
3	Crop C	Crop D	Crop A	Crop B
4	Crop D	Crop A	Crop B	Crop C

Agricultural crops, such as rice, are annual plants which have one harvest after each planting. The annual plants die after they reach maturity and a new crop must be planted before another harvest can be achieved. Crops like hay (used for livestock feed) are perennial plants which live for several years and can be harvested several times after a single planting operation.

Field crops include grains, beans, hay, and sugar beets while horticultural crops include fruit and vegetables. The type of crops which farmers choose for their own farm depends on soil type, climate, labor availability, machine availability, profit potential, social customs, government programs, and the farmer's skills. Many farmers produce more than one type of crop during each calendar year. For example, a farm may be divided into four land areas with a different crop grown on each of the four land areas. Alternating these crops in a fixed sequence is called a crop rotation and an example is illustrated in table 1.1. Using a crop rotation spreads the farmer's work load over a longer period of time and reduces the economic risk in case one crop fails. A good crop rotation can also improve crop yield and the soil.

1.3 Functional Analysis of Agricultural Machines

An agricultural machine has several components that work together as a system in order for the machine to perform in the intended manner. Any machine, however simple, may be divided into many subcomponents. In order to understand how a machine works, it is essential to consider the machine as a collection (or system) of several subsystems. In this section, we will learn how to identify the various systems found in a modern agricultural machine and the functions performed by the subsystems.

An agricultural machine may be divided into two subsystems: either process systems or support systems. The process systems are those components of the machine that actually perform the functions that the machine is designed to perform, i.e., cut, separate, mix, etc. The support systems are the parts that support or aid the process systems in performing their function. The support systems may be categorized as framing, power or control systems. The framing systems consists of all structural parts of the machine whose

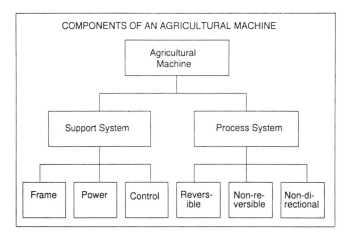

Figure 1.1–Systems of agricultural machines.

functions are to hold all parts of the machine together so that they may function properly. The power system supplies the power to the process systems. Power to operate would normally be produced and transmitted by the power system. Self-propelled machines contain both the power source (engine) and the power transmission devices (drive train). Many other machines, which depend on the tractor as a power source, contain power transmission devices such as chains, belts, gears, pto shafts, etc. Together these devices form the power system which drives the process system. The function of the control system is to provide control over the process system. Controls may be automatic or manual.

Like support systems, process systems may be divided into three types. These are reversible, non-reversible and non-directional. Reversible processes are those that can be reversed such as separation, compaction, etc. Non-reversible processes are those that cannot be reversed, for example, cutting, grinding, etc. Non-directional processes are those that have no direction. Examples of these processes are conveying, metering, or storing materials.

A breakdown of the types of systems found in an agricultural machine is given in figure 1.1. This illustration should aid in developing the concept of the agricultural machine as a system.

1.3.1 Basic Processes of Agricultural Machines

In this book we will concentrate on the process system of agricultural machines. The process system of a machine includes all parts that perform reversible, non-reversible, or non-directional processes, whereas these processes are the functions the machine was designed to perform. For example, the conventional square hay baler was designed to package hay material. In order to perform this

TABLE 1.2 BASIC PROCESSES OF AGRICULTURAL MACHINES

Reversible Processes	
Mix	Separate
Fluff	Pack
Pickup	Deposit
Scatter	Position

Non-Reversible Processes
Dissociate
Cut
Crush
Grind

Non-Directional Processes
Convey
Meter
Store

task, several processes must occur to the hay material. They include non-reversible processes such as cutting, reversible processes such as pick-up and compaction, and non-direction processes such as conveying and metering the hay.

There are 15 processes commonly found in agricultural machines. They include eight reversible, four non-reversible, and three non-directional processes. Each of the processes are listed under the appropriate category in table 1.2. The reversible processes are listed in pairs under the appropriate category in the table. The list is not meant to be comprehensive. It includes most commonly found processes in modern agricultural machines.

1.3.2 Process Diagrams

A tool which can be helpful in understanding the operation of agricultural machines is to draw a diagram of the processes that occur in a machine. A diagram is formed by following the flow of material through a machine and listing the processes in the order in which they occur. The processes can be connected with lines to indicate the flow of the material through the machine.

Any of the processes can occur either totally within the machine or with machine mobility as part of the process. For example, the forward motion of a baler is essential to pick up hay. However, after hay is picked up, it will be baled regardless of the forward motion of the machine. When machine mobility is a part of the process, the process should be enclosed in a box. A process occurring totally within the machine should be enclosed in a circle or an ellipse.

A few examples should be helpful in understanding the concept of process diagramming. A good first example is the moldboard plow. The first step is to determine what processes occur as the plow moves through the soil. As the plow moves forward, the soil is cut, picked up, positioned, and deposited. The second step is to determine

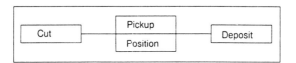

Figure 1.2–Process diagram of a plow.

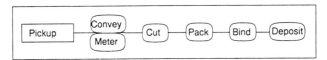

Figure 1.3–Process diagram of a hay baler.

whether the processes are dependent upon forward motion. In the case of a moldboard plow, all functions would cease as soon as the plow is stopped. The process diagram for the moldboard plow is given in figure 1.2. The processes of pickup and positioning occur simultaneously and therefore are diagrammed as a pair.

A more complex machine to diagram is the conventional hay baler. The processes which occur in the machine are pickup, conveying, metering, cutting, packing, binding, conveying, and depositing. The process which is dependent upon forward motion of the baler is pickup. The process diagram is given in figure 1.3.

The concepts of machine systems and process diagraming are introduced here as tools to aid students in learning more about the makeup and operation of agricultural machines. It is hoped that these concepts would provide a new and more interesting view to study agricultural machines.

2

Power for Agricultural Machines

Introduction

The earliest farm equipment made use of human power and, for a period in the 19th and 20th centuries, animals supplied the power needs of farm equipment. Modern agricultural equipment, however, is powered by internal combustion (IC) engines and, since the 1970s, nearly all new agricultural engines have been compression ignition (CI) engines which burn diesel fuel. The engine can be a part of the machine itself, as on a self-propelled combine, or can provide the power for an agricultural tractor. Electric motors are often chosen over engines for applications in which an electrical power supply is available. Compared to engines, electric motors are quieter, more readily adaptable to automatic or remote control, and do not produce exhaust emissions. Thus, various types of electric motors will be discussed in this chapter.

2.1 Diesel Power

Engines consume fuel to produce power. The power is delivered to some load through the crankshaft and flywheel of the engine. Much of the energy in the fuel is lost before it is converted to useful power. The purpose of this section is to clarify the processes by which an IC engine produces power and to provide insights into how engines may be made to operate efficiently. By reading this section, you will also learn the important terminology of diesel engines.

2.1.1 The Power in Fuel

Liquid fuels are a highly concentrated form of chemical energy storage. Burning the fuel at even a modest rate releases a large amount of power, which can be calculated using equation 2.1:

$$P_{fe} = \frac{H_g \, \dot{m}_f}{3600} \qquad (2.1)$$

where
P_{fe} = fuel equivalent power (kW)
H_g = gross heating value of the fuel (kJ/kg)
$\dot{m}_f$ = fuel consumption rate (kg/h)

The heating values are measured by burning a sample of fuel in a calorimeter. The heating values are defined as gross (H_g) or net (H_n) depending on whether the water created in combustion is recovered as liquid or vapor, respectively. The terms higher and lower are sometimes used instead of gross and net, respectively. Heating values tabulated in books (see table 2.1) are gross values unless otherwise indicated. Less than half of the fuel equivalent power is available for useful work at the flywheel of an engine (see fig. 2.1). In the remainder of section 2.1, the various power losses are identified.

2.1.2 Combustion

Combustion is a very complex process, particularly in a CI engine. The fuel must vaporize and mix with air to form a combustible mixture. Burning of the fuel-air mixture generates exhaust emissions, but also generates increased pressure to drive the pistons. The rate of pressure rise affects engine performance and durability.

Combustion chemistry. Insights which are very useful in understanding engines can be obtained by making two simplifying assumptions regarding combustion chemistry. The first is that all of

TABLE 2.1 COMPARISON OF PROPERTIES OF SEVERAL FUELS

Fuel	API Gravity Degree	Density (kg / m³)	Higher Heating Value (kJ / kg)	Research Octane No.	Boiling Range (° C)	Formula	Stoichiometric Air-Fuel Ratio
Butane	112	580	49,500	98	0	C_4H_{10}	15.5
Propane	146	509	50,300	111	– 42	C_3H_8	15.7
Regular gasoline	61	735	47,600	93	30-230	C_6H_{18}	15.2
No. 1 diesel	40	823	45,700	40*	160-260	$C_{12}H_{26}$	15.0
No. 2 diesel	38	834	45,500	40*	200-370	$C_{16}H_{34}$	15.0
Methyl alcohol	--	792	22,700	110	65	CH_4O	6.49
Ethyl alchol	--	785	29,700	110	78	C_2H_6O	9.03
Butyl alcohol	--	805	36,100	--	118	$C_4H_{10}O$	11.2

* Minimum cetane ring for diesel fuel.

the hydrogen in the fuel links with oxygen to form water. The second is that all of the carbon in the fuel is converted to carbon dioxide (CO_2) and carbon monoxide (CO), so that no free carbon appears in the combustion products. Most conventional, petroleum-based engine fuels are mixtures of a variety of hydrocarbon molecules, but representative molecules are given in table 2.1 for each of the common petroleum-based fuels. Alcohols which may become engine fuels of the future are also listed. Atomic weights of 12 for carbon, 1 for hydrogen, 16 for oxygen, and 14 for nitrogen may be used in the combustion calculations. Although various gases are in the earth's atmosphere, it is common practice in combustion calculations to neglect all gases except oxygen and nitrogen. The composition of earth's atmosphere is such that 3.76 molecules of nitrogen (N_2)

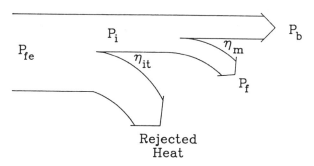

P_b = Fuel Equivalent Power, kW
P_i = Indicated Power, kW
P_f = Friction Power, kW
P_b = Brake Power, kW
η_{it} = Indicated Thermal Efficiency, decimal
η_m = Mechanical Efficiency, decimal

Figure 2.1–Energy flows through an engine.

accompany every molecule of oxygen (O_2). Combustion chemistry then becomes a simple matter of counting atoms, as indicated in example problem 2.1.

Example Problem 2.1

Calculate the stoichiometric (chemically correct) air/fuel ratio when diesel fuel is burned with air. Also analyze the products of combustion.

Solution. From table 2.1, the cetane molecule ($C_{16}H_{34}$) is used to represent diesel fuel. Under the standard simplifying assumptions, the complete combustion reaction becomes:

$$C_{16}H_{34} + 24.5\ O_2 + 92.12\ N_2 \geq 92.12\ N_2 + 16\ CO_2 + 17\ H_2O$$

The reaction is balanced on the basis of one molecule of fuel. The hydrogen balance determines the amount of water in the combustion products, while the carbon balance determines the amount of CO_2. Then enough O_2 must be supplied to form the CO_2 and H_2O; each mole of O_2 is accompanied by 3.76 moles of N_2. The nitrogen is nearly inert and simply appears in the combustion products. The stoichiometric air/fuel ratio is:

$$A/F = (24.5 \cdot 32 + 92.12 \cdot 28)/(16 \cdot 12 + 34 \cdot 1) = 14.9$$

Note that 17 moles of water appear in the exhaust for each mole of fuel burned or, on a mass basis, 1.35 kg of water appear per kilogram of fuel burned. The difference between the gross and net heating values of the fuel is exactly equal to the latent energy of the water produced by combustion, i.e., the energy needed to convert that liquid water to vapor. A major reason why quick warm-up of engines is important is to cause the combustion water to exit the engine as vapor rather than liquid. If the fuel contains sulphur impurities, the sulphur compounds created in combustion can react with liquid water to form sulfuric acid and corrode the engine.

Engine exhaust gases are normally analyzed on a dry, volume basis. Since the exhaust gases are intermingled at the same temperature and pressure, each molecule occupies the same volume according to Avogadros Law. Thus, the analysis of the dry exhaust gases in example problem 2.1 is:

$92.12/(92.12 + 16) = 0.852$ volume fraction (85.2%) is occupied by N_2,

and

$16/(92.12 + 16) = 0.148$ volume fraction (14.8%) is occupied by CO_2.

The equivalence ratio, ϕ, is a measure of mixture richness. It is defined as follows:

$$\phi = \frac{(F/A)_{actual}}{(F/A)_{stoichiometric}}$$
(2.2a)

or

$$\phi = \frac{(A/F)_{stoichiometric}}{(A/F)_{actual}}$$
(2.2b)

Note that the F/A ratio is just the inverse of the A/F ratio. Thus, in example problem 2.1, the stoichiometric ratios were A/F = 14.9 or F/A = 0.0671. An air-fuel mixture is rich if $\phi > 1$, stoichiometric if $\phi = 1$ or lean if $\phi < 1$. A rich mixture contains more fuel than the available oxygen can combust, while a lean mixture contains more oxygen than is theoretically needed to combust all of the fuel. When $\phi > 1$, not enough oxygen is available to convert all of the carbon in the fuel to CO_2; consequently, CO appears in the exhaust. When $\phi < 1$, not all of the oxygen is needed in combustion and free oxygen appears in the exhaust products.

The following generalized combustion reaction is valid for any air-fuel mixture under the two simplifying assumptions given earlier:

$$C_xH_yO_z + \frac{\Psi_1}{\phi} O_2 + 3.76 \frac{\Psi_1}{\phi} N_2 \Rightarrow$$

$$3.76 \frac{\Psi_1}{\phi} N_2 + \Psi_2 CO_2 + \Psi_3 CO + \Psi_4 O_2 + \frac{y}{2} H_2O$$
(2.3)

where
    x = number of carbon atoms in fuel molecule
    y = number of hydrogen atoms in fuel molecule
    z = number of oxygen atoms in fuel molecule

$\Psi_1 = x + y/4 - z/2$

$$\Psi_2 = \begin{cases} x, & \phi \le 1 \\ x - 2\Psi_1(1 - 1/\phi), & \phi > 1 \end{cases}$$

$$\Psi_3 = \begin{cases} 0, & \phi \le 1 \\ 2\Psi_1 (1 - 1/\phi), & \phi > 1 \end{cases}$$

$$\Psi_4 = \begin{cases} \Psi_1 (1/\phi - 1), & \phi < 1 \\ 0, & \phi \ge 1 \end{cases}$$

Note that the combustion reaction 2.3 accommodates oxygenated fuels, such as the alcohols in table 2.1. The number of carbon, hydrogen, and oxygen atoms need not be integer numbers. The actual air/fuel ratio for the combustion is:

$$A/F = \frac{137.3 \cdot \psi_1}{\phi \cdot (12\ x + y + 16\ z)} \tag{2.4}$$

The theoretical concentrations of the *dry* exhaust products on a volume basis are:

$$\text{Conc. } N_2 = 3.76\,\Psi_1 / (\phi\ T) \tag{2.5a}$$

$$\text{Conc. } CO_2 = \psi_2 / T \tag{2.5b}$$

$$\text{Conc. } CO = \psi_3 / T \tag{2.5c}$$

$$\text{Conc. } O_2 = \psi_4 / T \tag{2.5d}$$

where $T = \psi_2 + \psi_3 + \psi_4 + 3.76\psi_1/\phi$.

Equations 2.5a through 2.5d give good approximations to actual exhaust emissions, except that minute amounts of other gases also appear. A small amount of oxygen and nitrogen react with each other to form oxides of nitrogen, i.e., NO and NO_2. The combined NO and NO_2 gases are commonly referred to as NO_x. Also, because ϕ is typically not uniform throughout all of the combustion chambers of an actual engine, small amounts of CO and O_2 may appear in the exhaust whether the overall ϕ is less than or greater than one. Some free carbon may also appear, as well as trace amounts of unburned hydrocarbons (HC), hydrogen and other gases.

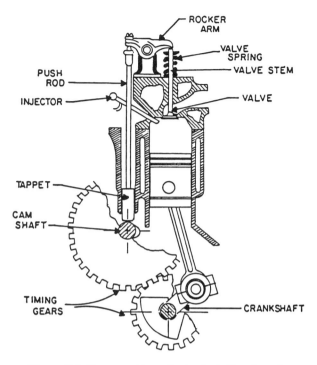

Figure 2.2–Cross-section of a typical diesel engine.

Energy release in combustion. The purpose of the combustion reaction is to release energy to drive the pistons. A cross-section of a typical diesel engine is shown in figure 2.2. The combustion process can be carried out in either two or four strokes of the piston, but the four-stroke cycle is most common. Unless otherwise indicated, all engines discussed in this book will be assumed to use the four-stroke cycle.

Through a combined experimental and analytical technique, it is possible to infer the rate of energy release throughout the combustion process. The technique relies on measurement of combustion chamber pressures in a running engine while simultaneously measuring the crankshaft rotation and computing the volume within the combustion chamber. The spatially averaged temperature in the combustion chamber can be calculated from the pressure and volume. Then, from changes in pressure, volume and temperature, the heat loss through the chamber walls, work done on the piston, and changes in internal energy of the mixture in the combustion chamber can be calculated. The energy released from the fuel is equal to the sum of the heat loss, work and increases in internal energy. Figure 2.3 shows a typical energy release diagram for a diesel engine; the rate of energy release is plotted versus crankshaft position.

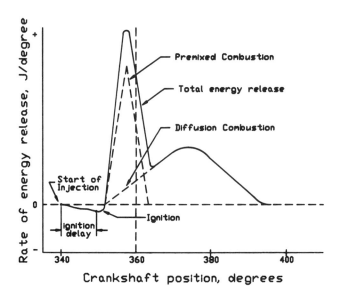

Figure 2.3–Rate of energy release from fuels in a compression-ignition engine.

In a diesel engine, air without fuel is taken in during the intake stroke and compressed. Late in the compression stroke, at approximately 20° before HDC (Head Dead Center), injection of fuel into the combustion chamber begins. An apparent negative energy release rate appears initially as energy is withdrawn from the chamber to evaporate the injected fuel. The evaporated fuel mixes with air and undergoes certain prereactions during an ignition delay period. Then ignition occurs and all of the air-fuel mixture prepared during the ignition delay burns suddenly to produce a sharp, triangular-shaped energy release pattern identified as premixed combustion. For combustion to continue, fuel vapor and air must diffuse toward each other across the regions burned out in the premixed combustion. The rate of diffusion limits the latter combustion, which is identified as diffusion combustion. The total energy release is the sum of the premixed and diffusion combustion. Premixed combustion is efficient and, except for the production of NO_x, is also clean combustion. However, the rapid release of energy produces the greatest stress on the engine and also most of the combustion noise. The slower diffusion burning is quieter and less stressful on the engine, but produces exhaust smoke and most of the CO emissions and is less efficient. Using fuels of higher cetane rating and less-advanced injection timing shifts more of the combustion from the premixed to the diffusion mode; the converse is also true.

In a diesel engine, the air supply is never throttled to control the engine speed. Rather, control is achieved by controlling only the fuel delivery rate. Consequently, ϕ is close to zero when the engine is idling without load and increases as more fuel is injected with increasing load. To limit smoke emissions and avoid excessive engine temperatures, it is necessary to operate a diesel engine with ϕ below approximately 0.7. As reaction 2.3 and equation 2.5d would show, considerable free oxygen appears in the exhaust when $\phi=0.7$ or less. Engine users sometimes increase the fueling rate to diesel engines to take advantage of the extra oxygen and boost the power output of the engine, but at the cost of reduced engine life. For their own protection, engine manufacturers put a seal on the injector pumps of their engines; if the seal is broken to increase the fueling rate, the engine warranty is automatically voided.

2.1.3 Thermodynamic Limits to Engine Performance

The effective pressure that can be obtained from fuel to drive the pistons and also the combustion efficiency have thermodynamic limits which are defined in this section. The engine is designed to carry out the combustion cycle in four strokes of the piston. As is required in an engine with a four-stroke cycle, the timing gears in figure 2.2 are arranged such that the crankshaft makes two revolutions for each revolution of the camshaft. Valve timing in a four-stroke cycle is shown on a valve-timing spiral, as illustrated in figure 2.4. Valve timing is designed to maximize airflow through the engine and may differ somewhat from that shown in figure 2.4. The cycle begins just before HDC (Head Dead Center) with the opening of the intake valve, and the air intake process ends well after CDC (Crank Dead Center) with the closing of the intake valve. As the piston approaches HDC on the compression stoke, fuel is injected and, after a short delay, ignites and forces the piston down on the power stroke. The exhaust process begins with the opening of the exhaust valve late in the power stroke and ends with the closing of the exhaust valve soon after HDC. Thus, the four strokes of the cycle are intake, compression, power and exhaust. Note that there is valve overlap, i.e., both valves are open simultaneously during a brief part of the cycle. Alternate terms used in the literature are TDC (Top Dead Center) instead of HDC and BDC (Bottom Dead Center) instead of CDC.

The dual cycle of figure 2.5 is the best thermodynamic model of the modern diesel engine. It illustrates the theoretical variations in combustion gas pressure and cylinder volume during an engine cycle. The dual cycle is a combination of the Otto cycle, which represents spark-ignition engines, and the original Diesel cycle which Dr. Rudolph Diesel proposed to represent his engine. Parameter Υ defines the relative proportion of energy input to the dual cycle at constant pressure, i.e.:

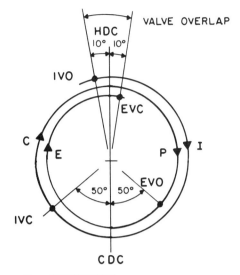

C   = COMPRESSION
E   = EXHAUST
P   = POWER
I   = INTAKE
IVO = INTAKE VALVE OPENS
IVC = INTAKE VALVE CLOSES
EVO = EXHAUST VALVE OPENS
EVC = EXHAUST VALVE CLOSES

Figure 2.4–Valve timing spiral showing typical valve timing.

$$\Upsilon = \frac{q_p}{q_p + q_v} \qquad (2.6)$$

where
$\quad q_p$ = energy input at constant pressure
$\quad q_v$ = energy input at constant volume

When $\Upsilon = 0$, the dual cycle becomes the Otto cycle with points 2a and 3 becoming coincident (fig. 2.5). When $\Upsilon = 1$, the dual cycle becomes the original diesel cycle with points 2 and 2a becoming coincident.

In the dual cycle, 0-1 is the intake process, followed by compression, 1-2. Process 2-2a is energy input to the cycle at constant volume and 2a-3 is constant-pressure energy input. Work is extracted from the cycle between points 2a and 4, followed by heat rejection, 4-1. Process 1-0 is exhaust, at which point the cycle starts over. The cylinder volume at CDC, V_1, is the maximum gas volume. The cylinder volume at HDC, V_2, is called the clearance volume. The displacement of a single cylinder is:

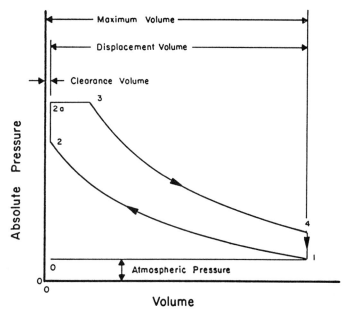

Figure 2.5–The theoretical dual cycle.

$$V_c = V_1 - V_2 \qquad (2.7)$$

The displacement, V_e, of a multi-cylinder engine is simply V_c times the number of cylinders. The compression ratio of the engine is:

$$r = \frac{V_1}{V_2} \qquad (2.8)$$

The cycle mean effective pressure is the net area within the p-v diagram of figure 2.5 divided by V_c. Multiplying the cycle mean effective pressure by the piston area and stroke length gives the actual work performed by each power stroke. The cycle mean effective pressure can be calculated from:

$$\frac{P_{cme}}{P_1} = \frac{r - r^k + r\,r_{co}\Theta_r - r^{2-k}\,r_{co}^k\,\Theta_r + (k-1)\,r \cdot \Theta_r(r_{co}-1)}{(k-1)(r-1)} \qquad (2.9)$$

where

P_{cme} = cycle mean effective pressure (kPa)

P_1 = absolute pressure at beginning of compression (kPa)

Θ_r = $\lambda(\Theta_3 / \Theta_1) + r^{k-1}/(\lambda + 1)$

λ = $k(\Upsilon^{-1} - 1)$

$$r_{co} = (\lambda + 1)/(\lambda + (\Theta_1/\Theta_3)\, r^{k-1}) = \text{fuel cut-off ratio}$$
$$k = 1.4 \text{ for air standard cycle}$$

The pressure, p_1, is very nearly equal to the atmospheric pressure unless the engine is turbocharged. The fuel cut-off ratio is defined as the proportion of the power stroke during which energy is being released into the cycle from the burning fuel. The cycle efficiency can be calculated from:

$$\eta_{cy} = 1 - \frac{\Upsilon\,(r_{co}^{k} - 1) + k\,(r_{co} - 1)\,(1 - \Upsilon)}{k \cdot (r_{co} - 1)}\, r^{1-k} \qquad (2.10)$$

The theoretical values, p_{cme} and η_{cy}, cannot be achieved in practice, but are thermodynamic upper limits and targets against which practical designs can be compared.

Example Problem 2.2

Assume that the compression ratio of a NA (naturally aspirated, i.e., not turbocharged) diesel engine is r=14.5. For typical conditions, estimate the cycle mean effective pressure and the cycle efficiency if $\Upsilon = 0.2$.

Solution. An estimate is needed for the ratio, Θ_3/Θ_1. If the ambient temperature is 27° C, then $\Theta_1 = 300°$ K. It is common practice to estimate Θ_3 as being equal to the equilibrium flame temperature for hydrocarbon fuels, i.e., $\Theta_3 = 2700°$ K. Thus, for a NA diesel engine, a good estimate is $\Theta_3/\Theta_1 = 9$. Then, using equations 2.9, 2.10, and the supplementary equations that support them:

$$\Theta_r = 8.078$$
$$r_{co} = 1.114$$
$$p_{cme}/p_1 = 11.36$$
$$\eta_{cy} = 0.655$$

Theoretically, the specified cycle can convert 65.5% of the input energy to useful work. For a NA diesel engine, p_1 is approximately equal to barometric pressure or, approximately, $p_1 = 100$ kPa. Then $p_{cme} = 1136$ kPa. Because of friction and other losses, the theoretical efficiency and mean effective pressure cannot be achieved in practice, but it is possible to achieve at least 75% of the theoretical values.

2.1.4 Heat Losses and Power at the Pistons

Energy is liberated from the fuel when combustion reaction 2.3 occurs. The released energy causes a sharp rise in cylinder pressure but the pressure diminishes as the piston moves toward CDC. Through proper instrumentation, it is possible to obtain a plot similar to figure 2.5, except that actual (not theoretical) cylinder pressure is plotted versus volume. Historically, cylinder pressures were plotted on indicator diagrams and thus the net area within the actual p-v diagram, divided by V_c, is called the indicated mean effective pressure, p_{ime}. Multiplying p_{ime} by the top area of the piston gives the average force exerted on the piston during the power stroke. Multiplying force by the stroke length gives the work per stroke and multiplying by the number of strokes per unit time gives the indicated power for a single-cylinder engine. Finally, multiplying by the number of cylinders gives the indicated power for the entire engine. Note, however, that the product of piston area times stroke times number of cylinders gives the engine displacement, V_e. Thus, the indicated power (power generated at the head of the pistons) for an engine can be calculated from:

$$P_i = \frac{p_{ime} \, V_e \, n_e}{2 \cdot 60{,}000} \qquad (2.11)$$

where

P_i = indicated power (kW)
p_{ime} = indicated mean effective pressure (kPa)
V_e = engine displacement (L)
n_e = engine speed (rev/min)

The factor 2 is in the denominator of equation 2.11 because two revolutions of the crankshaft are required for each power stroke in a four-stroke cycle engine. The factor, 60,000, is simply a units constant. Equation 2.11 brings out the important point that only three ways are available to increase engine power. They are, increase the size (V_e) of the engine, increase its speed (n_e), or increase the pressure levels (p_{ime}) in the engine.

The indicated power is always less than the fuel equivalent power. The indicated thermal efficiency of an engine is defined as:

$$\eta_{it} = \frac{P_i}{P_{fe}} \qquad (2.12)$$

The fraction, $(1-\eta_{it})$, of P_{fe} is not converted into work but is rejected as heat (fig. 2.1). Some of the rejected heat can be recovered using heat exchangers if there is a need for heat in the vicinity of the engine; else the heat is lost. The cycle efficiency, η_{cy}, is an upper limit for η_{it} and a target against which achieved values of η_{it} can be compared.

2.1.5 Mechanical Losses and Power at the Flywheel

After combustion and mechanical losses are subtracted, the remaining power reaching the flywheel is called flywheel power. The earliest devices used to measure engine power were called prony brakes, and thus flywheel power is more commonly called brake power. With modern technology, a device called a dynamometer is used to measure the torque and speed of the power shaft connected to the engine flywheel. If T_b is the torque in a shaft, the work accomplished per revolution of the shaft is equal to $2\pi \cdot T_b$. Then, since the engine speed gives the revolutions per unit of time, the brake power can be calculated from the following equation:

$$P_b = \frac{2\,\pi\,T_b\,n_e}{60,000} \qquad (2.13)$$

where
  P_b = brake power (kW)
  T_b = engine brake torque (N·m)

The factor, 60,000, is a units conversion factor. The mechanical efficiency, η_m, is the fraction of P_i that is converted to brake power (fig. 2.1), i.e.:

$$\eta_m = \frac{P_b}{P_i} \qquad (2.14)$$

By definition, all of the indicated power not converted to brake power is called friction power, i.e.:

$$P_f = P_i - P_b \qquad (2.15)$$

What is included in friction power? All the friction of moving parts in the engine is included, as the name implies, but power to operate the fan, oil pump, alternator, and other engine accessories is also included.

Engine users are interested in the overall efficiency of the engine in converting fuel equivalent power to brake power. The overall efficiency is called the brake thermal efficiency, i.e.:

$$\eta_{bt} = \frac{P_b}{P_{fe}} \qquad (2.16a)$$

It is easy to show that the following equation is true:

$$\eta_{bt} = \eta_{it} \cdot \eta_m \qquad (2.16b)$$

Thus, for good overall efficiency, engine designers must design an efficient combustion process (high η_{it}) and a high percentage of the resulting power must be transmitted to the flywheel (high η_m).

Equation 2.11 shows that, for a given engine running at a given speed, P_i is proportional to p_{ime}. Engine designers have broadened that concept in defining brake mean effective pressure, p_{bme}, as:

$$p_{bme} = \frac{2 \cdot 60{,}000 \, P_b}{V_e \, n_e} \qquad (2.17)$$

and in defining friction mean effective pressure, p_{fme}, as:

$$p_{fme} = \frac{2 \cdot 60{,}000 \, P_f}{V_e \, n_e} \qquad (2.18)$$

In a diesel engine, p_{fme} is almost entirely a function of speed, i.e.:

$$p_{fme} = C_0 + C_1 \, n_e + C_2 \, n_e^2 \qquad (2.19)$$

where C_0, C_1, and C_2 are constants that vary from engine to engine. The following approximate values were presented by the Society of Automotive Engineers (SAE) for the purpose of estimating the mechanical efficiency of a diesel engine:

C_0 = 139.3 kPa
C_1 = −0.0259 kPa·rev/min
C_2 = 22.97 × 10^{-6} kPa/(rev/min)^2

More accurate values can be obtained for a specific engine by fitting a curve to friction mean effective pressure values at various engine speeds. An important practical consequence of equation 2.19 is that engine friction power can be reduced and engine efficiency can be increased by running engines at reduced speeds.

The reader is encouraged to derive a relationship between the several mean effective pressures and to express η_m in terms of mean effective pressures.

2.1.6 Engine Torque and Efficient Engine Loading

Combining equations 2.1, 2.12, 2.13, 2.15, and 2.18 provides an equation which gives insights into how an engine produces torque, i.e.:

$$T_b = \frac{H_g\,\eta_{it}}{4\,\pi}\left(\frac{C_f\,\dot{m}_f}{n_e}\right) - \frac{V_e}{4\,\pi}\,p_{fme} \qquad (2.20)$$

where

C_f = $2*1000/60$ = units conversion factor
$(C_f*\dot{m}_f/n_e)$ = grams of fuel injected per engine cycle

In equation 2.20, The term between the equal sign and the minus sign is called indicated torque, while the last term in the equation is friction torque. Thus, the net or brake torque is the indicated torque minus the friction torque. Since H_g (the heating value of the fuel) is constant and η_{it} varies only a little with changes in torque and speed, the indicated torque varies nearly proportionally with the quantity of fuel injected into each engine cycle. As explained in section 2.1.7, the quantity of fuel injected into each cycle is controlled by an engine governor.

Combining equations 2.12, 2.15, and 2.16a gives the following alternate equation for brake thermal efficiency:

$$\eta_{bt} = \eta_{it}\,P_b/(P_b + P_f) \qquad (2.16c)$$

Figure 2.6 is a plot of equation 2.16c and illustrates the relationship of engine efficiency to load. All engines are most efficient at full load and are especially inefficient as the engine load approaches zero.

Engine designers have developed the term SFC (Specific Fuel Consumption) to indicate how much fuel is burned by an engine to accomplish a given amount of work. It is defined as:

$$SFC = \frac{\dot{m}_f}{\text{power}} \qquad (2.21)$$

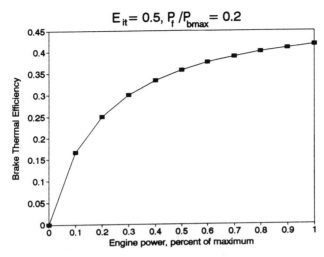

Figure 2.6–Variation of brake thermal efficiency with engine load.

Because of losses in the transmission of power, it is important to use an adjective with SFC to indicate the point of power measurement. The two most common SFC terms in the literature are BSFC (for Brake SFC, i.e., when the denominator of equation 2.21 is brake power) and ISFC (for Indicated SFC). Like η_{bt}, BSFC is an indicator of overall engine efficiency, except that BSFC is lowest when the engine is most efficient.

2.1.7 Control of Engine Speed

It is desirable to perform many agricultural operations at nearly constant speed. Governors control speed by reducing fuel delivery to the engine when the speed is too high and increasing fuel delivery when the speed is too low. A flyweight governor is illustrated in figure 2.7. The flyweights are hinge-connected to the governor shaft, which typically rotates at one half of crankshaft speed. In the unit shown in figure 2.7a, centrifugal force from increasing engine speed causes the weights to swing outward and the flyweight linkage forces the thrust bearing downward. The governor linkage rotates counterclockwise, stretching the spring and reducing fuel delivery. Conversely, reductions in engine speed allow the spring to contract, forcing the flyweights inward and increasing fuel delivery.

The force induced on the thrust bearing by centrifugal force on the flyweights varies proportionally with the radius of the path of the flyweights and with the square of the engine speed. Figure 2.7b shows curves for the limiting cases when the path radius is smallest

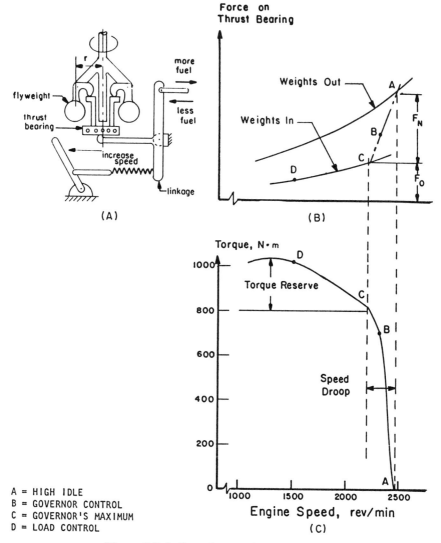

A = HIGH IDLE
B = GOVERNOR CONTROL
C = GOVERNOR'S MAXIMUM
D = LOAD CONTROL

Figure 2.7–Action of an engine governor.

(weights in) and largest (weights out). The governor can only operate between these two limiting curves.

If an ungoverned engine was receiving fuel at even a moderate rate and was running without load, the speed would quickly become excessive and destroy the engine. In a governed engine, however, the flyweights would swing out to their limit and fuel delivery would fall to a level sufficient to provide only the friction power of the engine. The engine would operate at point A on figures 2.7b and 2.7c, which is called the High Idle point because the speed is high and the engine is idling (not doing any work). As an increasing torque load is applied to the engine, the flyweights move inward to increase the stroke of the fuel injector pump and supply the fuel needed to provide that torque (see eq. 2.20). At point C in figure 2.7, the flyweights are at their innermost position and cannot move the governor linkage or increase the injector pump stroke any further; thus Point C is called Governor's Maximum. With further increases in torque, the speed begins to fall rapidly because the governor cannot increase the fuel delivery per cycle. At points to the left of point C in figure 2.7c, speed is controlled only by the torque load on the engine. Thus, the engine is under governor control at points between A and C and under load control at points to the left of point C. Torque increases are possible in the load-controlled range because friction torque declines with speed (see eq. 2.20) and because injector pumps gain somewhat in pumping efficiency as speed decreases.

Governors cannot maintain perfectly uniform speed, even in the governor-controlled range. The governor regulation, as calculated in equation 2.22, is a measure of how closely the governor controls the engine speed.

$$\text{Reg}_g = \frac{200\left(n_{HI} - n_{GM}\right)}{\left(n_{HI} + n_{GM}\right)} \tag{2.22}$$

where

Reg_g = governor regulation (%)
n_{HI} = engine speed at high idle (rev/min)
n_{GM} = engine speed at governor's maximum (rev/min)

The curves in figures 2.7b and 2.7c show the governor controlling the engine at one speed setting. By moving the hand lever to the right, the operator can decrease the initial tension in the governor spring and thereby decrease the speed required to move the flyweights outward. The effect is to move curve ABC to the left, where it meets the load-control curve at some higher value of torque (see fig. 2.8a). Conversely, if the linkage stop will permit it, the operator can increase the speed setting of the engine by moving the speed control lever to the left. Manufacturers typically rate their engines at the governor's maximum speed which corresponds to the fastest setting of the governor. In figure 2.8, for example, the highest governor's maximum speed is at 2200 rev/min and that would be the rated speed of the engine.

As shown in figure 2.7c, torque reserve is defined as the difference between the peak torque of the engine and the torque at rated speed. Large torque reserve is desirable to prevent the engine from stalling during momentary overloads. Torque reserve is expressed as a percentage of rated torque. In figure 2.7c, for example, the peak torque is 1020 N·m and the rated torque is 820 N·m, so the torque reserve would be 24.4%. It is also desirable for the torque peak to be well to the left of governor's maximum. In figure 2.7c, the torque peak is at 1300 rev/min while rated speed is 2200 rev/min. Therefore, the torque peak appears at 59% of rated speed.

Figure 2.8b shows a power versus speed curve that results from the torque versus speed curve of figure 2.8a. From equation 2.13, the power rises nearly linearly with torque in the governor-controlled range because the speed varies little. Torque varies only modestly in the load-controlled range, so power falls in nearly direct proportion to the fall in speed. Some engine manufacturers market "constant power" engines; these are engines with sufficient torque rise to offset the falling speed in the load-controlled range, so that the power doesn't begin to fall until operation has moved some distance into the load-controlled range.

2.1.8 Turbocharging and Intercooling Engines

Power generation in an engine increases in proportion to the fueling rate, as indicated by equation 2.1. To keep the equivalence ratio below 0.7, as indicated in section 2.1.2, the air delivery rate must be much larger than the fuel delivery rate; thus it is air-handling capacity that truly limits the power producing capacity of an engine. The air handling capacity can be calculated using the following equation:

$$\dot{m}_a = C_a \, V_e \, n_e \, \rho_a \, \eta_v \qquad\qquad (2.23)$$

where

$\dot{m}_a$ = air handling capacity (kg/h)
C_a = 0.03 = constant to convert units
V_e = engine displacement (L)
n_e = engine speed (rev/min)
ρ_a = density of the air entering the engine (kg/m^3)
η_v = volumetric efficiency of the engine (a decimal)

Volumetric efficiency is a measure of the air-pumping efficiency of an engine. It is equal to ratio of the actual air handling capacity divided by the theoretical capacity that could be obtained at the same engine speed if each cylinder filled entirely with atmospheric air during each intake stroke. If the engine has no turbocharger, pressure drops in the intake system cause the volumetric efficiency to be less than one. Conversely, a turbocharger delivers pressurized air for intake and the volumetric efficiency can be greater than one. The following

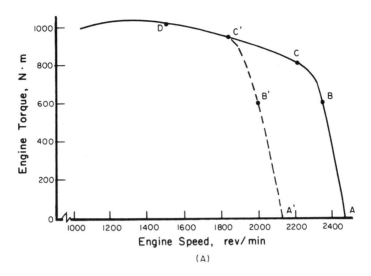

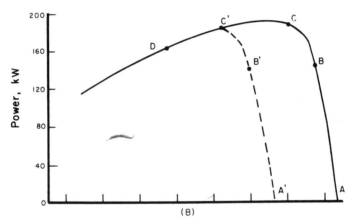

Figure 2.8–Torque-speed and power-speed curves for a governed engine.

equation, which was derived from the ideal gas law, can be used to calculate ρ_a if the barometric pressure and the ambient temperature are known:

$$\rho_a = \frac{29\, p_a}{8.314\, \Theta_a} \qquad (2.24)$$

where
    p_a= air pressure, i.e., barometric pressure (kPa)
    Θ_a= ambient air temperature (° K)

Under most atmospheric conditions, ρ_a will be between 1.1 and 1.2 kg/m^3.

The volumetric efficiency of a typical naturally-aspirated (NA) diesel engine is approximately 0.85; the air-handling capacity of a NA diesel engine can only be increased by increasing the displacement or the engine speed. However, the volumetric efficiency and air-handling capacity can be greatly increased by adding a turbocharger to the engine.

Operation of turbochargers. A turbocharger consists of a compressor directly coupled to an exhaust-driven turbine as illustrated conceptually in figure 2.9. Ambient air enters the compressor at point 1 and is compressed before entering the intake manifold at point 2. Hot exhaust gases in the exhaust manifold at point 3 drive the turbine before exiting at point 4. Thus, the turbocharger uses energy extracted from the engine exhaust to pressurize the air entering the combustion chamber. The boost is the increase in pressure provided by the compressor, i.e.:

$$\text{boost} = p_2 - p_1 \tag{2.25}$$

where p_1 and p_2 are the absolute pressures at points 1 and 2, respectively. The pressure ratio across the compressor, p_{rc}, is also important and is defined as:

$$p_{rc} = \frac{p_2}{p_1} \tag{2.26}$$

The temperature ratio across the compressor, Θ_{rc}, can be calculated from the following equation:

$$\Theta_{rc} = \frac{\Theta_2}{\Theta_1} = 1 + \frac{p_{rc}^{0.286} - 1}{\eta_c} \tag{2.27}$$

where η_c = compressor efficiency.

A turbocharger is ineffective when the engine is idling. The turbocharger becomes increasingly effective as load is put on the engine, because the fraction $(1-\eta_{it})$ of the increased fuel supplied is available to drive the turbine; the turbocharger reaches maximum effectiveness near governor's maximum. When the engine is well loaded, the volumetric efficiency of the engine can be estimated with acceptable accuracy using the following equation:

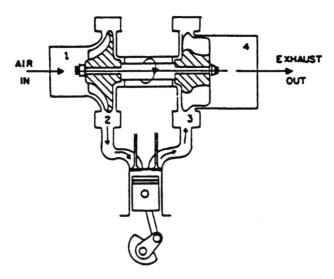

Figure 2.9–The concept of a turbocharger.

$$\eta_v = p_{rc}/\Theta_{rc} \qquad\qquad (2.28a)$$

Equation 2.28 fails when the engine is idling, but then η_v is close to 0.85. Example problem 2.3 illustrates the use of equations 2.23 through 2.28a.

Example Problem 2.3

A turbocharger is to be fitted to a 6.5 L engine. A boost pressure of 110 kPa is desired when the engine is running under full load at 2200 rev/min. The map of the turbocharger compressor is shown in figure 2.10. Ambient conditions are 27° C and 100 kPa. Determine the compressor (a) airflow, (b) efficiency, and (c) speed.

Solution. From equation 2.24, the ambient air density is:

$$\rho_a = 29 \cdot 100/(8.314 \cdot [273 + 27]) = 1.16 \text{ kg/m}^3$$

From equations 2.25 and 2.26, the desired pressure ratio across the compressor is:

$$p_{rc} = (p_1 + \text{boost})/p_1 = (100 + 110)/100 = 2.1$$

The remainder of the problem must be solved by iteration, because the compressor efficiency, engine volumetric efficiency and engine airflow are all unknown and interdependent. Begin by assuming a compressor efficiency of 70%. Then, from equation 2.27, the initial estimate of the temperature ratio is:

$$\Theta_{rc} = 1 + (2.1^{0.286} - 1)/0.7 = 1.338$$

The estimated volumetric efficiency is, from equation 2.28a:

$$\eta_v = 2.1/1.338 = 1.57$$

Finally, from equation 2.23, the initial estimate of airflow into the engine is:

$$\dot{m}_a = 0.03 \cdot 6.5 \cdot 2200 \cdot 1.16 \cdot 1.57 = 781 \text{ kg/h}$$

Now we can check on the accuracy of the initial choice of compressor efficiency. From figure 2.10, when the pressure ratio is 2.1 and the airflow is 781 kg/h, the corresponding compressor efficiency is 72%. Using the new value for compressor efficiency, the new estimate of temperature ratio is 1.328, the new volumetric efficiency is 1.58, and the new airflow is 787 kg/h. From figure 2.10, the compressor efficiency corresponding to pressure ratio of 2.1 and airflow of 787 kg/h is very close to 72%, so no further iteration is needed. Thus (a) the airflow into the turbocharged engine would be 787 kg/h, (b) the compressor efficiency would be 72%, and (c) interpolating between the adjacent speed curves on figure 2.10, the compressor speed would be approximately 51 000 rev/min. It should be noted that pressure ratio-airflow combinations to the left of the surge curve in figure 2.10 produce unstable, surging airflow and are therefore unacceptable. The solution to example problem 2.3 was to the right of the surge curve and is therefore acceptable.

Selection of the compressor operating point does not complete the problem of fitting a turbocharger to an engine; it is also necessary to select a compatible operating point for the turbine. The turbine must rotate at the same speed as the compressor while supplying the power necessary to drive the compressor. In addition, the flow rate through the compressor is $\dot{m}_a(1+FA)$, where FA is the fuel-air ratio of the turbocharged engine, that is, the mass airflow rate divided by the mass fuel flow rate. A turbine map (not shown in this book) is used to ensure that the values selected for turbine flow rate, pressure ratio, speed and efficiency are mutually compatible.

Intercoolers. Equation 2.27 can be used to show that the temperature of the air leaving the compressor can be very hot, i.e., well above the boiling point of water. An intercooler (sometimes called an aftercooler) may be used to reduce the temperature of the compressed air. An intercooler is a heat exchanger through which the compressed air is passed in giving up heat energy to a secondary fluid. The engine coolant is the most common secondary fluid used, but ambient air is used in some intercoolers. Intercooling is a

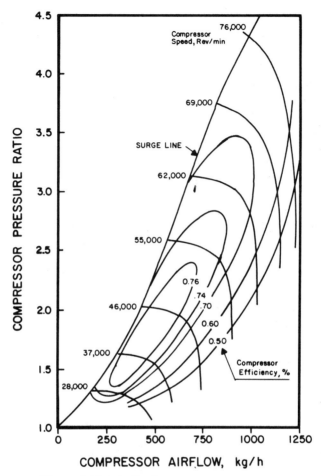

Figure 2.10–A turbocharger compressor map.

constant-pressure process. When an intercooler is used, the volumetric efficiency of the turbocharged, intercooled engine can be estimated using the following equation:

$$\eta_v = \frac{p_{rc}}{\Theta_{rc}} \cdot \frac{\Theta_2}{\Theta_{2i}} \qquad (2.28b)$$

where

Θ_2 = temperature of air leaving compressor (° K)

Θ_{2i} = temperature of air leaving intercooler (° K)

Turbocharging and intercooling for versatility. In recent years, engine manufacturers have used turbocharging and intercooling to reduce the costs of manufacturing a family of engines and of maintaining an inventory of replacement parts for the engines. The procedure is illustrated in example problem 2.4.

Example Problem 2.4

An engine manufacturer wants to provide four engine models from one basic design of a 6-cylinder, 7.636 L, diesel engine that is to run at a rated speed of 2200 rev/min. The desired power levels of the four engines are to increase in approximately 15 kW increments from a base level of 75 kW for the NA version of the engine. How might turbocharging and intercooling be used to accomplish the objective? The intercooler is to use the engine coolant as the secondary fluid, and the thermostat provides a coolant temperature of 90° C. Tests have shown that the NA engine can achieve BSFC of 0.3 kg/kW·h.

Solution. The assumed atmospheric conditions will be 300° K and 100 kPa. Thus, from equation 2.24, the ambient air density is:

$$\rho_a = (29/8.314)\,(100/300) = 1.16 \text{ kg/m}^3$$

Assuming $\eta_v = 0.85$ for the base, NA engine, equation 2.23 gives the air consumption as:

$$\dot{m}_a = 0.03 \cdot 7.636 \cdot 2200 \cdot 1.16 \cdot 0.85 = 497 \text{ kg/h}$$

The fuel consumption of the 75 kW, NA engine would be:

$$\dot{m}_f = P_b \cdot \text{BSFC} = 75 \cdot 0.3 = 22.5 \text{ kg/h}$$

The stoichiometric air-fuel ratio for diesel fuel is 14.9 (see example problem 2.1) and the actual air-fuel ratio is 497/22.5 = 22.1. Thus, from equation 2.2b, ϕ for the NA engine is:

$$\phi = 14.9/22.1 = 0.674$$

This ϕ is well below the recommended maximum of 0.7 discussed in section 2.2.3.

For the 120 kW engine, assume that a turbocharger is added to provide a boost of 90 kPa. Then, from equations 2.25 and 2.26, $p_{rc} = 1.9$. A reasonable value for compressor efficiency is $\eta_c = 0.7$ and, from equation 2.27:

$$\Theta_{rc} = \Theta_2/\Theta_1 = 1 + (1.9^{0.286} - 1)/0.7 = 1.288$$

Since $\Theta_1 = 300°$ K (27° C), note that the temperature of the air leaving the compressor would be $1.288 \cdot 300 = 386°$ K (113° C), which is very hot. Thus an intercooler will be added; it can reduce the air temperature to within approximately 10° C of the coolant temperature, i.e., to 100° C (373° K). From equation 2.28b, the estimated volumetric efficiency of the 120 kW, turbocharged, intercooled (TC, IC) engine would be:

$$\eta_v = (1.9/1.288)\,(386/373) = 1.53$$

Then, using the new value for η_v in equation 2.23, the air consumption of the TC, IC engine would be 895 kg/h. Assuming the BSFC remained at 0.3 kg/kW·h, the approximate fuel delivery rate would be:

$$\dot{m}_f = P_b \text{ BSFC} = 120 \cdot 0.3 = 36 \text{ kg/h}$$

After the engine was constructed, the actual fueling rate could be adjusted to produce exactly the 120 kW of brake power desired. The ϕ corresponding to the 36 kg/h fueling rate would be:

$$\phi = 14.9/(895/36) = 0.60$$

The proposed increase in fueling rate, from 22.5 kg/h for the 75 kW, NA version to 36 kg/h for the 120 kW, TC, IC engine, would be acceptable since ϕ would remain below 0.7.

The intermediate sized engines (90 and 105 kW) could be achieved by using appropriate fueling rates; the rates would be approximately $90 \cdot 0.3 = 27$ kg/h and $105 \cdot 0.3 = 31.5$ kg/h for the 90 and 105 kW engines, respectively. These fueling rates, being less than the 36 kg/h used for the 120 kW engine, would reduce the turbocharger boost below 90 kPa and the temperature of the air leaving the compressor (Θ_2) would fall below the 113° C calculated for the TC, IC engine. If Θ_2 fell close to 100° C or below, not enough temperature differential above the coolant temperature would exist to permit cooling of the air. Thus, intercooling would probably be impractical except for the 120 kW engine.

In summary, a family of four engines ranging from 75 to 120 kW in power could be obtained from one basic engine. The family would include a 75 kW NA engine, 90 and 105 kW TC engines and a 120 kW TC, IC engine. The advantage would be that all four engines would share a common inventory of parts except that a larger injector pump and fuel injectors might have to be used on the largest engines. The three smaller engines would be over-designed, since they would have to have the same strength as the 120 kW engine. That disadvantage would be more than offset by the greatly reduced parts inventory that was achieved, and thus engine manufacturers have adopted the strategy of example problem 2.4.

2.2 Electric Motors

Electric motors are devices that convert electric power into mechanical power. Unlike engines, which will stall and stop consuming fuel when overloaded, an electric motor will continue to absorb electricity when overloaded. To prevent self-destruction, therefore, means must be provided to prevent an electric motor from overheating and breaking down the insulation on the windings. Typically, a thermal protector is provided to disconnect the electrical power when the windings reach a limiting temperature.

2.2.1 Motor Components

A wide variety of electric motors are in commercial use, but all motors have certain features in common. A frame holds all parts in their proper orientation. Bearings (sleeve, roller, or ball) hold the rotating shaft in the frame. The stator includes electrical windings on a laminated magnetic core. The windings are arranged to provide at least two electrical poles, that is, a north and a south pole. Electric current flowing through the windings produces a magnetic field across a rotor, which rotates with the motor shaft. A fan within motors helps to provide cooling. The housings of some electric motors have external fins to aid in cooling. A terminal housing with a removable cover is attached to motors to allow access to the certain wires within the motor. On most motors, a means of terminating an equipment grounding wire is provided in the terminal housing. Finally, information relating to the internal wiring and the motor application is given on a nameplate attached to the motor.

2.2.2 Motor Classifications

There are four classification systems that help to describe the differences between motors. First, motors can be classified as to the type of electrical power required, that is, alternating current (ac) or direct current (dc). Secondly, ac electrical power can be single-phase (1-) or three-phase (3-). The rotor can be designed as a squirrel cage or a wound rotor. The squirrel cage design is less expensive because it has no windings; rather, induced currents flow in the bars and end plates (fig. 2.11). A wound rotor has many loops of wire wrapped on the rotor; the wound rotor in figure 2.12 is for a dc motor used as an electric starter, but ac motors with wound rotors are also available. The loops terminate at commutator segments on which stationary brushes can ride to make electrical contact with the loop connected to a particular set of commutators. Rotors containing such windings and commutators are called armatures. Finally, motors can be classified as induction or synchronous motors. Synchronous motors turn at a speed that is governed by the frequency of the electrical voltage and the number of poles but is independent of motor load. Conversely, loading of induction motors causes slippage which in turn causes the rotor to turn slower than the synchronous speed. Most of the rest of this chapter is concerned with ac, induction-type motors with a squirrel-cage rotor, since these motors are in the most widespread use. Smaller motors of this design run on single-phase power, while three-phase power is used for larger motors. The dc motors will also be discussed. Other types of electrical motors will be described only briefly.

2.2.3 Principle of Operation of Induction Motors

The motor of figure 2.13 is not a practical motor, but it illustrates the principle of operation of induction motors. A squirrel-cage rotor similar to the one in figure 2.11 is surrounded by a permanent magnet with two poles (one a North pole and the other a South pole). The rotor in this case is made from aluminum, a material that conducts electrical current but is not attracted to magnets. Imagine that the rotor is initially stationary, but the permanent magnet is made to rotate clockwise, as indicated by the arrows. The rotor is thus positioned in a rotating magnetic field. Due to the relative motion between the rotor and rotating field, the aluminum bars in the rotor cut across the magnetic lines of force flowing from the north pole to the south pole and electrical currents are induced in the bars. The currents flow toward the reader in the conductors nearest the north pole (as indicated by the dots) and away from the reader in the conductors nearest the south pole (as indicated by the plus signs). These induced currents in turn generate magnetic fields around each conductor; these circular fields are counterclockwise about the conductors nearest the north pole. The counterclockwise fields add to the rotating flux field on the left side of each conductor and subtract on the right side. Consequently, the bars tend to move to the right into the weaker flux field. Near the south pole, similar logic shows that the bars tend to move to the left into a weaker flux field. The net result is that the rotor rotates clockwise, that is, in the same direction that the magnetic flux field is rotating. However, the rotor cannot attain the same rotational speed as the rotating magnetic field or there would be no relative motion to induce currents in the bars of the squirrel cage.

The motor in figure 2.14 is similar to the one in figure 2.13, except that the outer frame is now held stationary (it becomes a stator) and the permanent magnets are replaced with electromagnets wired in series. The electromagnets are connected to a source of alternating current. Thus, as the ac current goes through a full sine wave, the top electromagnet starts at zero magnetism, builds to a strong north pole, diminishes to zero, builds to a strong south pole,

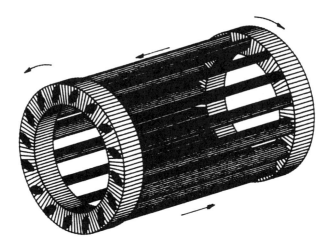

Figure 2.11–A squirrel-cage rotor of an electric motor.

diminishes to zero again and the cycle repeats. Because of the arrangement of the windings, the bottom magnet is going through a similar pattern, except that its magnetic polarity is opposite that of the top magnet. Note that, along a vertical line through the center of the squirrel-cage rotor, the variation of the magnetic field is the same as if the permanent magnet of figure 2.13 was rotating, that is, the magnetic flux builds to a maximum in the downward direction, diminishes to zero, builds to a maximum in the upward direction, diminishes to zero, etc. Thus, the motor of figure 2.14 can be viewed as having a rotating field. The synchronous speed, that is, the speed at which the field appears to rotate, can be calculated by using the following equation:

$$n_s = \frac{120f}{\lambda_p} \qquad\qquad (2.29)$$

where
n_s = synchronous speed (rev/min)
f = line frequency (Hz)
λ_p = number of poles

In the United States, the standard line frequency is 60 Hz. Then, for the motor of figure 2.13 with two poles, the synchronous speed would be 3600 rev/min. The rotor cannot turn as fast as the synchronous speed in an induction motor, that is, there is some slip, defined as:

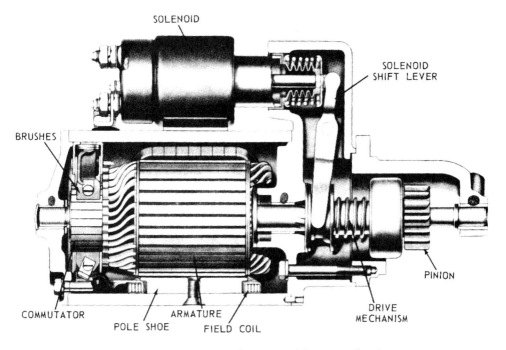

SOLENOID

SOLENOID
SHIFT LEVER

BRUSHES

PINION

COMMUTATOR

ARMATURE

POLE SHOE

FIELD COIL

DRIVE
MECHANISM

Figure 2.12–An electric motor with a wound rotor.

$$s = \frac{n_s - n_r}{n_s} \qquad (2.30)$$

where
    s = slip (decimal)
    n_r = rotor speed (and shaft speed, rev/min)

Combining equations 2.29 and 2.30 gives the following equation for rotor speed:

$$n_r = \frac{120f\,(1-s)}{\lambda_p} \qquad (2.31)$$

The slip s=1.0 at startup and declines to some small value when the motor reaches full speed. For example, if the two-pole motor of figure 2.14 was driven with 60 Hz ac current and the slip was 4.17%, the rotor speed would be 3450 rev/min. Note that, if the bottom pole in figure 2.14 was positioned 90° from the top pole instead of 180°, the magnetic field would rotate only half a revolution in each voltage cycle. Another set of poles could be added to allow the magnetic field

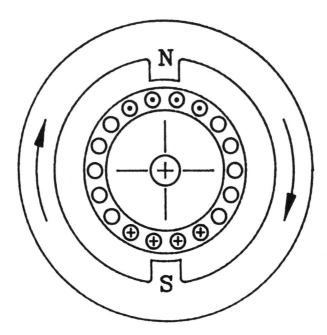

Figure 2.13–Illustration of the principle of operation of an induction motor.

to complete the full revolution in two voltage cycles. Doubling the number of stator poles to four would reduce the synchronous speed to 1800 rev/min and, if the slip was 4.17%, the rotor speed would be 1725 rev/min.

The motor of figure 2.14 has no provision for starting the rotor into motion. Once started, the rotor would continue to run in the initial direction because of the alternating magnetic field. As explained in the next section, there are various types of single-phase induction motors, each differing in the means used to start the rotor into motion.

2.2.4 Types of Single-Phase Induction Motors

Split-phase induction motors. The motor of figure 2.15a is called a split-phase motor. A set of starting windings has been added on poles that are rotated 90° from the running windings. Compared to the running windings, the starting windings have fewer turns of higher-resistance wire. Because of the lower resistance and higher inductance of the starting windings, the current in the starting windings is displaced in phase from the running windings (see fig. 2.15b). Consequently, a clockwise-rotating magnetic field is established that starts the rotor into clockwise motion. A centrifugal switch in series with the starting windings opens when the motor has

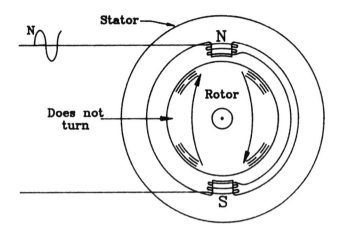

Figure 2.14–Illustration of an induction motor without starting means (Adapted from Surbrook and Mullin, 1985).

attained sufficient speed and the motor then continues to run as an ordinary induction motor. If the leads are brought out to the terminal housing, the direction of rotation can be reversed by reversing the leads, A and B, of the start-windings circuit. The split phase motor is generally available in sizes from 0.04 to 0.25 kW (1/20 to 1/3 hp). Compared to other single-phase induction motors, it has higher starting current and lower starting torque. It is best suited to fans and other machines that do not start under heavy load.

Capacitor-start, induction-run motors. A capacitor-start, induction-run motor is illustrated in figure 2.16a. An electrolytic capacitor has been inserted in series with the starting windings to shift the phase of the starting current as shown in figure 2.16b. The electrolytic capacitor is not designed for continuous duty and thus, when the motor reaches 75 to 80% of synchronous speed, a centrifugal switch opens and disconnects the start-winding circuit. Comparing figures 2.15b and 2.16b shows that the capacitor-start motor has much lower starting current than the split-phase motor; typically, the starting current of the capacitor-start motor is three to four times that required for running. The starting torque capability of the capacitor-start motor typically is about twice that of a split-phase motor. The capacitor-start, induction run motor is available in sizes from 0.13 to 2.3 kW (1/6 to 3 hp) and is the most widely used motor for farm equipment. As with the split-phase motor, the direction of rotation can be reversed by reversing the leads, A and B, to the starter-winding circuit.

Two-value-capacitor induction-run motors. A schematic diagram of a two-value capacitor induction motor (also called a capacitor-start, capacitor-run motor) is shown in figure 2.17. The auxiliary winding used for starting is also used for running. An oil-filled capacitor (C_r) capable of continuous operation is placed in series with the auxiliary winding. An electrolytic capacitor (C_s) is connected in parallel with the oil-filled capacitor while starting but is disconnected by a centrifugal switch when the motor comes up to speed. The two-value-capacitor induction motor is commonly available in sizes up to 7.5 kW (10 hp) and develops high starting torque. Again, the direction of rotation can be reversed by reversing the leads, A and B, to the auxiliary-coil circuit.

Repulsion-start induction-run motors. A repulsion-start, induction-run motor is illustrated schematically in figure 2.18. Unlike the previous induction motors, the repulsion-start motor does not use auxiliary starting windings on the stator. Instead, a wound rotor is used. Unlike the squirrel-cage rotor in which all of the conductor bars are shorted together by washer-shaped end plates, the conductors of the wound rotor are brought out to commutator segments, that is, the rotor is an armature. The two brushes which ride on opposite sides of the commutator are shorted together, as shown in figure 2.18. Thus, at any instant, one set of windings on the armature are connected into a coil whose axis is tilted relative to the axis of the stator winding. The stator magnetic field induces a current in the coil on the armature which, in turn, generates a magnetic flux from the armature coil. The repulsion of the stator and armature electromagnets forces the armature to turn. After the motor comes up to speed, a centrifugal device shorts all of the commutator segments together and the motor runs similar to a squirrel-cage induction motor. The direction of rotation can be changed by shifting the angle of the brushes relative to the axis of the stator coil. The repulsion-start, induction run motor develops very high starting torque with relatively low starting current and is available in sizes from 0.37 to 7.5 kW (1/2 to 10 hp). However, because of the high cost of manufacturing the armature, the repulsion-start, induction-run motor is less widely used than the capacitor-start and two-value-capacitor motors.

2.2.5 Three-Phase Induction Motors

Single-phase motors become impractical in sizes much above 7.5 kW (10 hp) and, for larger power requirements, three-phase motors become the practical choice. Three-phase, induction-type motors are available in sizes up to 150 kW (200 hp). A three-phase induction motor is illustrated in figure 2.19a. The rotor has the squirrel cage design of figure 2.11. The voltage to the motor (fig. 2.19b) is supplied through the three electrical conductors of a three-phase line. The voltage waveform BB_1 lags AA_1 by one third of

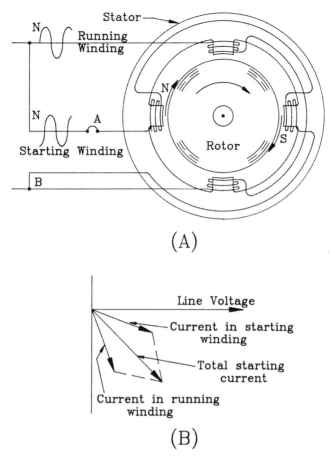

(A)

(B)

Figure 2.15–Illustration of a split-phase induction motor (Adapted from Surbrook and Mullin, 1985).

the wavelength or 120° or, for 60 Hz voltage, by 0.0056 s; Voltage CC_1 lags AA_1 by 240° or 0.0111 s. As waveform AA_1 goes through its sinusoidal variation, electromagnet A in figure 2.19a builds from zero to a strong north pole, diminishes to zero, builds to a strong south pole, diminishes to zero and so forth. Electromagnets B and C follow a similar pattern except for their respective phase delays. Thus, the north pole of the magnetic field across the rotor appears to rotate from electromagnet A to B to C to A and so forth, that is, the field appears to rotate clockwise. Thus, as was discussed in section 2.3.3, the rotor also rotates clockwise. The synchronous speed, slip and rotor speed can be calculated by using equations 2.29, 2.30, and 2.31, respectively. Thus, for 60 Hz current, the synchronous speed would be 3600 rev/min for the two-pole motor shown in figure 2.19a. If the slip at full load was 4.17%, the rotor would turn at 3450 rev/min at

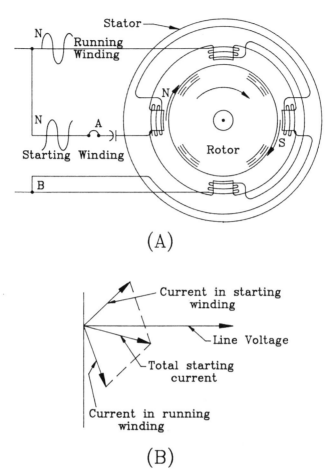

Figure 2.16–Illustration of a capacitor-start induction
motor (Adapted from Surbrook and Mullin, 1985).

full load. A four-pole motor uses twice as many windings to create
two sets of north and south poles simultaneously. As was described
in section 2.3.3, the magnetic field then rotates half way around the
stator in each cycle of voltage and the synchronous speed becomes
1800 rev/min.

The direction of rotation of the three-phase induction motor can
be reversed by reversing any two of the three leads to the motor.
Some contemplation will show that reversing any two leads reverses
the direction of rotation of the magnetic field and thus reverses the
direction of rotation of the rotor.

Three-phase electricity from the electric power grid is provided
for either wye or delta connection and motors are available for either
type of power. Figure 2.20a shows a wye-type motor while a delta-
type motor is shown in figure 2.20b.

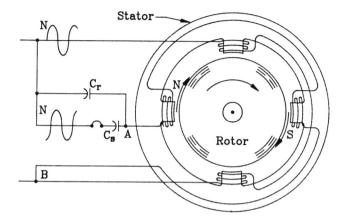

Figure 2.17–Illustration of a two-valve capacitor, induction-run motor (Adapted from Surbrook and Mullin, 1985).

2.2.6 Dual-Voltage Motors

Many motors are designed to be operated at either of two different voltages. For example, the three-phase motors of figure 2.21 can be connected to operate on 230-V or 460-V electrical power. Note that two separate coils are wrapped on each electromagnet and all leads are brought out to the terminal housing on the motor. The numbering diagrams beside each motor show how to connect the

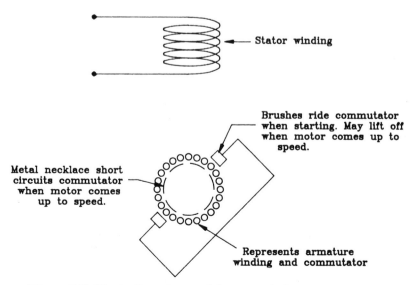

Figure 2.18–Illustration of a repulsion-start, induction-run motor.

coils. The lower voltage can be used when the two coils on each electromagnet are connected in parallel and the coils are connected in series to permit use of the higher voltage. Many single-phase motors are similarly designed for dual-voltage operation. For a given power output, the current draw of the motor will be only half as large when the higher voltage is used; thus, whenever the higher voltage is available, it should be used.

2.2.7 Torque-Speed Characteristics of Induction Motors

The torque produced by a motor must be sufficient to start the connected machine and keep it operating under normal loading. Figure 2.22 shows variations in torque as three-phase and single-phase motors accelerate from rest. The locked-rotor torque (fig. 2.22a), defined as the torque at zero speed, must be large enough to start the machine in motion. Once started, the motor will stall if the load exceeds the breakdown torque. Motor manufacturers do not indicate the breakdown torque on the nameplate, but do use it in rating the power capacity of the motor. Note that the rotor cannot achieve synchronous speed while producing torque, that is, there must be some slip. Thus, full-load torque is produced at a rated speed slightly below the synchronous speed. The motor speed will fall below rated speed when the load is increased above the full-load torque but will regain the speed when the load is reduced. Due to the steepness of the curve near the rating point, moderate increases in torque load produce only small decreases in speed; thus the power output increases with increased load until the speed begins to drop more rapidly near the point of breakdown torque. To prevent overheating and damage to a motor, it should never be loaded so heavily that the point of operation approaches the breakdown point.

The torque characteristic of single-phase motors combines two separate curves (fig. 2.22b). Starting from rest, the torque output of the motor is produced by the combined effects of the starting and running windings. After the centrifugal switch opens and the starting winding is disconnected, only the running winding remains to produce torque. Otherwise, the terminology and description of the torque characteristics of the single-phase and three-phase motors are similar.

2.2.8 Motor Name-Plate Information

Design and rating standards developed by the National Electrical Manufacturer's Association (NEMA) permit the comparison of motors from different manufacturers. Information on the nameplate may include any or all of the following: *Volts*, the proper operating voltage, may be either a single value or, for dual-voltage motors, a dual value. *Amps* is the full-load current draw in

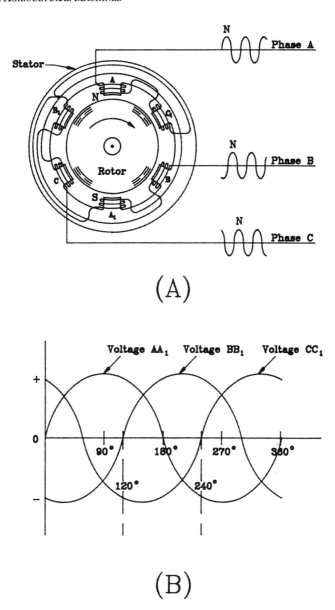

**Figure 2.19–Illustration of a three-phase induction
motor (Adapted from Surbrook and Mullin, 1985).**

amperes with the proper voltage supply. When a dual number is
listed, the motor will draw the smaller amperage when connected to
the higher voltage source. *Rev/min* is the rotor speed when the motor
runs at the full-load point on the torque-speed curve (fig. 2.22). *Hz* is
the design operating frequency of the electrical supply. In the United
States, it is 60 cycles per second. A standard frequency of 50 cycles

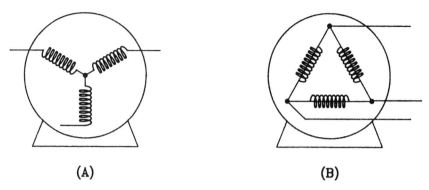

(A)   **(B)**

Figure 2.20–Three phase induction motors with (a) wye and (b) delta connections (Adapted from Surbrook and Mullin, 1985).

per second is used in some counties. *FR* is one of the standard frame numbers used by manufacturers to ensure interchangeability. For motors with power ratings below 0.75 kW (1.0 hp), common frame numbers are 42, 48, and 56. The frame number divided by 6.3 (16) gives the height in cm (in.) from the bottom of the mounting to the shaft centerline. Letters may be added to specify the type of mounting, for example, T-frame or the heavier U-frame. A replacement motor with the same frame number as the original motor will fit on the same mounting. *Duty* indicates whether the motor is rated for continuous or intermittent; *Hours* may be used to indicate the length of time the motor can be operated safely during intermittent duty. *Temperature rise* (° C) may be stated as the allowable temperature rise above a 40° C (104° F) ambient temperature while the motor is operating at full load. Often, a motor can be operated at 10 to 15% overload without damage, but the motor temperature should never exceed 55° C (131° F). If, while operating, a motor is not too hot to touch, it is not overheated. As an alternative to temperature rise, the allowable *ambient temperature* may be listed. Then the motor can be operated at full load in environments with temperatures below the stated ambient temperature. The service factor, SF, is multiplied by the rated power to obtain the permissible loading. For example, a service factor of 1.10 means the motor could be operated at 10% overload without overheating. Service factors for farm-duty motors can be 1.35 or more. *Insulation class* is a temperature-resistance rating of the insulation on the wires in the motor. Typical classes are A, B, F, or H, where class A is the lowest temperature rating. Class A or B insulation is used in most farm-duty motors. The *code letter* is used to determine the maximum rating of the motor branch-circuit protection and is based on the locked-rotor current drawn by the motor. The following equation may

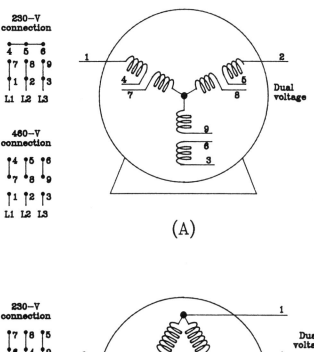

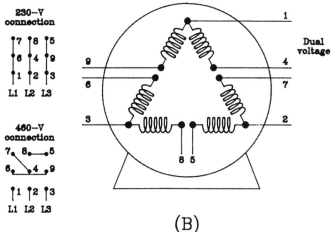

Figure 2.21–Three-phase motors with dual voltage connections (After Surbrook and Mullin, 1985).

be used to calculate the locked-rotor starting current from the code letter:

$$\text{Amps} = \frac{1000 \, \text{kVA} \cdot \text{hp}}{\text{volts} \cdot C_{ph}} \qquad (2.32)$$

where
  Amps = starting current in amperes (A)
  kVA = rating from the National Electric Code (NEC)

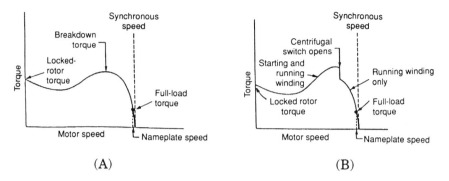

Figure 2.22–Torque-speed characteristics of induction motors (After Surbrook and Mullin, 1985).

hp   = rated power from nameplate (in hp)
volts = supply voltage in volts
C_{ph} = constant = 1.0 for single-phase motor or 1.73 for three-phase motor

Example Problem 2.5

A 50 hp, three-phase, 230/460 V motor with a code letter G on the nameplate. Determine the starting currents when the motor is used at 230 V and at 460 V.

Solution. Table 430-7(b) of the NEC lists the kilovolt-amperes/hp for code letter G as 5.6 to 6.29. Thus, from equation 2.32, the minimum locked-rotor starting current while operating at 230 V would be:

$$\text{Amps} = \frac{1000 \cdot 5.6 \cdot 50}{230 \cdot 1.73} = 704\text{A}$$

Using the same equation at the higher end of the range, the maximum locked-rotor starting current would be 790 A. These are very high starting currents. The starting currents could be reduced to the range, 352 - 395 A by using the motor on a 460-V supply.

A *design* letter may be given on the nameplate as an indication of the starting-to-rated currents and starting-to-rated torques. The five classes for squirrel-cage motors are A, B, C, D, and F, with A and B being the most common. Design A has starting current 6 to 7 times rated current and starting torque 150% of rated. Design B has starting current 5.5 to 6 times rated current and starting torque 150% of rated. A *thermal protection* indication on the nameplate indicates the motor is equipped with such protection to prevent overheating the windings. Protection may be provided by sensing motor current or temperature in the windings and shutting off the motor when either becomes excessive. After shutdown, the motor must be reset manually unless it is equipped with an automatic reset.

2.2.9 Motor Starters

The starting current of squirrel-cage motors can be up to seven times higher than the running current and, as example problem 2.5 indicates, the starting current for large electric motors can be very high. The high starting current can cause an excessive voltage drop on the electric supplier's power lines, thus interfering with neighboring customers. Means are available to reduce the excessive starting current. Sometimes it is possible to start the motor under zero load and then apply the torque load after the motor is running. Also, autotransformers can be used to temporarily reduce the supply voltage at starting and thus reduce the starting current; other types of starters are also available for reducing the starting current. When starting current is not excessive, a simple across-the-line starter can be used. Typically, across-the-line starters are used for motors up to 22 kW (30 hp) in size.

2.2.10 Motor Enclosures

Motors used in agricultural applications are often exposed to a harsh environment, including dust, high humidity, combustible vapors, and rodent and insect pests. Thus, the design of the motor enclosure is important. Available enclosures include open, drip-proof, splash-proof, totally enclosed and explosion-proof. Open enclosures are least expensive but offer the least protection. The openings for ventilation air for drip-proof motors are designed to prevent entry of rain, but not of dust. Air openings in splash-proof motors are even more secluded to reduce the possibility of liquids splashing into the motor. Totally enclosed motors prevent the entry of dust; cooling air is circulated within the motor but heat can only be dissipated by conduction through the enclosure. A fan may be located externally on the motor shaft to blow air over the exterior of the enclosure for cooling. Explosion-proof motors are totally enclosed and are designed to prevent the entry of combustible vapors into the interior of the motor; they are used on fuel-dispensing pumps and for other applications where combustible vapors may be present.

2.2.11 Variable-Speed Electric Motors

Although ac induction motors are designed to run at constant speed, permanent split-capacitor motors are capable of some speed variation, as shown in figure 2.23. The torque-speed curve for the load is shown superimposed on the torque-speed curves for the motor at two different supply voltages. By reducing the supply voltage from V_A to V_B, the operating speed is reduced from n_A to n_B. Notice that the motor has less torque available as the speed is reduced and therefore, as shown by equation 2.13, the power output falls rapidly as the supply voltage is reduced. Thus, the technique will work only if the power demand of the driven machine falls rapidly at decreased speed. A fan represents such a load and thus the technique of figure 2.23 is sometimes used to provide variable-speed fans.

As equation 2.31 indicates, the speed of an induction motor is proportional to the frequency of the supplied electrical power. Based on equation 2.31, a special controller may be used to control the speed of three-phase induction motors. The controller rectifies the ac voltage to direct current and then inverts it back to ac current at a controllable frequency. When frequency is reduced, the voltage is also reduced to prevent overheating of the motor. The controller generally maintains constant output torque from the motor. Thus, as shown by equation 2.13, the power output varies proportionally with the motor speed. Using the controller, the motor speed typically can be controlled from 20% to 110% of the motor nameplate speed, and wider variation is also possible.

A multiple-speed induction motor can be achieved by electrical switching to change the number of stator poles. If the shaft of the two-pole motor turned at 3450 rev/min, for example, equation 2.31 indicates that switching it to a four-pole motor would reduce the speed to 1725 rev/min. Other speed ratios are also possible; for example, it is possible to switch between four and six poles or between two and six poles. Note that switching the number of poles provides only two discrete speeds, whereas the previously mentioned techniques permit infinitely-variable speed changes.

A motor in which a wound rotor is connected in series with the stator coils is called a universal motor because it will operate on either ac or dc electrical power. The speed of a universal motor can be reduced by reducing the electric current supplied to the motor, for example, by lowering the supply voltage. An electric drill motor is an example of a universal motor. Speed control of the drill motor is achieved by use of an SCR (Silicon-Controlled Rectifier) to control the ac input current. Variable speed could also be obtained by operating a universal motor on a variable-voltage dc supply, but ac current is more widely available than dc current.

2.2.12 Motor Efficiency

Not all of the electrical power delivered to a motor is converted to mechanical power. The most important losses are in the windings, in the magnetic core and in mechanical friction. The power efficiency of a motor can be calculated by using the following equation:

$$\eta_m = \frac{2 \pi T_m n_m}{60 C_{ph} V I \cos(\phi)} \qquad (2.33)$$

where

η_m = power efficiency of the motor (decimal)
T_m = motor output torque in N·m
n_m = motor shaft speed in rev/min
V = voltage supplied to the motor (V)
I = current draw by the motor (A)
ϕ = phase angle between the voltage and current
C_{ph} = 1.0 for single-phase motors, or 1.73 for three-phase motors

A motor running without load must absorb electrical power to overcome mechanical friction and thus its no-load power efficiency is zero. Most motors are designed to achieve peak efficiency at 80 to 120% of rated load. The following example problem illustrates the calculation of power efficiency.

Example Problem 2.6
A single-phase, 115 V electric motor absorbs 7.8 A while running at 1725 rev/min and developing 3.1 N·m of torque. The phase angle between the voltage and current is 38°. Calculate the power efficiency of the motor.
Solution. All of the data required in equation 2.33 are given in the problem statement. The solution is:

$$\eta_m = \frac{2 \pi \; 3.1 \cdot 1725}{60 \cdot 115 \cdot 7.8 \cos(38)} = 0.79$$

Thus, the power efficiency of the motor is 79%.

Problems

2.1 (a) Determine the concentrations of N_2, CO, CO_2, and O_2 in the exhaust on a dry, volume basis when butane is combusted in air. Let ϕ vary from 0 to 1.5 in increments of 0.1 and plot the concentrations of the exhaust constituents versus ϕ. Note that use of a computer spreadsheet will greatly simplify the calculations. Repeat part (a) except with (b) propane (c) regular gasoline (d) methanol (methyl alcohol) (e) ethanol (ethyl alcohol) (f) butanol (butyl alcohol) as fuel.

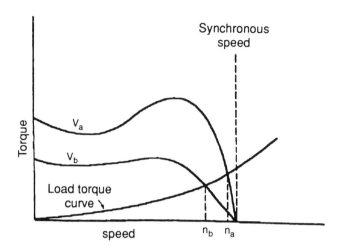

Figure 2.23–Illustration of means of changing speed of induction motors (After Surbrook and Mullin, 1985).

(g) repeat part (a) except use No. 1 diesel as the fuel, and mark the typical range of ϕ values for diesel engines on the graph. (h) repeat part (g) except use No. 2 diesel as the fuel.

2.2   Let the maximum instantaneous pressure in the dual cycle be p_{peak}. It can be shown that:

$$p_{peak} / p_1 = (r / r_{co})(\Theta_3 / \Theta_1)$$

Given a dual cycle with $\Theta_3/\Theta_1 = 9$, and compression ratios ranging from 14 to 30, plot p_{cme}/p_1 and p_{peak}/p_1, both versus compression ratio. Show curves for Υ values of 0.1 and 0.2. Considering that engine stress increases with p_{peak} while cycle work increases with p_{cme}, what conclusions can you draw from your plots concerning desirable values for r and Υ?

2.3   Given a dual cycle with $\Theta_3/\Theta_1 = 9$, and compression ratios ranging from 14 to 30, plot η_{cy} versus compression ratio. Include curves for $\Upsilon = 0.1$ and 0.2. Which is more influential on increasing η_{cy}, increasing r or reducing Υ?

2.4   A six-cylinder, turbocharged diesel engine has a displacement of 8.268 L and a compression ratio of 17.3:1. While running at 2200 rev/min engine speed, it produces 634 N·m of torque while consuming No. 2 diesel fuel at the rate of 30.6 kg/h. Through a study of the friction characteristics of the engine, it is determined that the constants in equation 2.19 for this engine are:

$C_0 = $ 77.0 kPa
$C_1 = $ −0.0143 kPa/(rev/min)
$C_2 = $ 1.271E − 5 kPa/(rev/min)^2

Making use of data given in this problem and in table 2.1, calculate the (a) brake, (b) friction, and (c) indicated mean effective pressures. Also calculate the (d) fuel equivalent, (e) indicated, (f) brake, and (g) friction power. Finally, calculate the (h) indicated thermal, (i) mechanical, and (j) brake thermal efficiencies, and (k) the BSFC (brake specific fuel consumption).

2.5   Continue problem 2.4 by assuming that the torque is increased sufficiently to maintain constant brake power while the engine speed is reduced to 1800 rev/min. You may also assume that the indicated thermal efficiency remains constant during the change in speed (this is a reasonably accurate assumption). For the engine running at 1800 rev/min as described, calculate the (a) brake (b) friction and (c) indicated mean effective pressures, the (d) indicated and (e) fuel equivalent power, (f) the brake thermal efficiency, (g) the new rate of fuel consumption, and (h) the new BSFC. (i) Comparing results from problems 2.4 and 2.5, does the engine run more efficiently at the lower or higher speed? Why?

2.6   (a) Derive the following equation:

$$BSFC = \frac{3600}{\eta_{it} \, H_g} \left(1 + \frac{P_f}{P_b} \right)$$

(b) Assume that the indicated thermal efficiency is 0.45 and take the heating value of no. 2 diesel fuel from table 2.1. Engine load is to be varied from zero to a maximum while speed remains constant. Thus, friction power will also remain constant. You can estimate the friction power, P_f, from the following equation:

$$P_f = P_b \left(\frac{1 - \eta_m}{\eta_m} \right)$$

Let the maximum brake power, P_b, be 100 kW and, at maximum brake power, assuming that the mechanical efficiency is 0.8, calculate the friction power. Then make a plot of BSFC versus percent of maximum brake power. Note that BSFC becomes infinite at zero brake power, so let the percent brake power vary from 10% to 100%. Your graph will show the characteristic shape when BSFC is plotted versus brake power.

2.7   Rework example problem 2.3, except assume the engine displacement is 7.0 L and the engine speed is 2000 rev/min.

2.8   A four-pole, single-phase induction motor runs at 1750 rev/min while being supplied with 60 Hz electrical power. Calculate (a) the synchronous speed and (b) the slip.

2.9   Rework problem 2.8, except assume the motor runs at 1730 rev/min.

2.10   A 37.3 kW (50 hp) electric motor runs on 230/460 V ac, 60 Hz, three-phase power. It draws 119.6/59.8 A at full load while running at 1775 rev/min. Its code letter is G and its service factor is 1.15. Assuming the motor is connected for 460-V operation, calculate (a) the full-load torque, (b) the locked-rotor starting current, (c) the ratio of starting current to full-load current, (d) the maximum allowable power output, and (e) the power efficiency at full load if the phase angle between the current and voltage is 35°. (f) Is this motor suitable for an across-the-line starter, or should a reduced-current starter be used? (g) How many poles does this motor have? Table 430-7b in the National Electrical Code is useful for calculating the locked-rotor starting current of electric motors. The table below shows the data for the most common code letters

Code Letter	KV-A / hp
G	5.6-6.29
H	6.3-7.09
J	7.1-7.99
K	8.0-8.99
L	9.0-9.99

2.11   Rework problem 2.10, except use a 0.75 kW (1.0 hp) motor that runs on 115/230 V ac, 60 Hz, single-phase power, draws 12.8/6.4 A at full load while running at 1725 rev/min, has code letter K and service factor 1.25. Assume the motor is connected for 115 V ac operation.

2.12   Rework problem 2.10, except use a 0.25 kW (1/3 hp) motor that runs on 115/230 V ac, 60 Hz, single-phase power, draws 6.0/3.0 A at full load while running at 3450 rev/min, has code letter L and service factor 1.75. Assume the motor is connected for 115 V ac operation.

3

Transmission of Power

Introduction

In Chapter 1 we introduced the concept of support and process systems of an agricultural machine. In Chapter 2 we presented the main sources of power for agricultural machines, i.e., the diesel engine for self-propelled machines and the electrical motor for many stationary machines used on the farmstead. Pull-type machines must receive propulsion and rotary power from the tractor. Power is transmitted from the tractor to the machine by means of traction, power-take-off drive (pto) and/or by fluid power. Rotary power is also transmitted by means of belts and chains. Topics related to rotary and fluid power transmission are presented here.

3.1 Mechanical Power Transmission

3.1.1 V-Belt Drives
V-belts are employed extensively in agricultural machinery applications in which it is not necessary to maintain exact speed ratios. V-belts tend to cushion shock loads, do not

require lubrication, and are less critical to misalignment than are other types of drives. They can be operated at speeds as high as 33 m/s, although speeds in agricultural machinery applications seldom exceed 15 m/s. V-belts are not suitable for heavy loads at low speeds.

V-belts may be used singly or in matched sets, although single belts are the most common on agricultural machines. Banded, multiple V-belts are sometimes employed on drives having high power requirements, pulsating load, and inherent instability problems. A banded belt consists of a matched set of two or more conventional V-belts with a thin tie band connecting their tops. Tying the strands together minimizes lateral belt whip and improves the load distribution among the belts.

Because a V-belt wedges into the sheave grooves, it can transmit a given amount of power with less overall shaft pull than a flat-belt drive. V-belts can be operated with relatively small arcs of contact, as in close-center shaft arrangements with large shaft-speed ratios. A single belt on an implement often drives several components in an arrangement known as a serpentine drive. V-belts permit considerable latitude in possible orientation and arrangement of the shafts involved in a drive.

V-belts are adaptable to clutching arrangements. A close-fitting guard may be needed to maintain proper belt orientation and move the belt away from the driver when the tension is released. Under certain conditions it is convenient or economically desirable to drive a relatively large flat pulley with V-belts from a smaller, grooved sheave. This is known as a V-flat drive.

V-belt types and standardization. Three types of V-belts specially designed for agricultural machines are known as agricultural V-belts, agricultural doubler V-belts, and adjustable-speed belts. These are illustrated in table 3.1. Banded belts made from agricultural V-belts are also available. Agricultural V-belts and double V-belts are distinguished from the corresponding cross-sectional sizes of industrial V-belts by the prefix (H).

The cross-sectional dimensions of agricultural V-belts are identical with those of industrial belts but the construction is different because of the different type of use. Agricultural V-belts are more likely to be subjected to excessive shock loads, heavy pulsating loads, and other adverse conditions. Whereas V-belts in an industrial drive are expected to last for several years of continuous operation, a life expectancy of 1000-2000 h is adequate for most farm machinery applications. Hence, agricultural V-belt loadings can be higher than in industrial applications.

Double V-belts are employed in serpentine drives where the direction of rotation of one or more shafts is reversed, thus requiring

TABLE 3.1. AGRICULTURAL V-BELT CROSS-SECTIONAL DIMENSIONS, SHEAVE GROOVE ANGLES, AND DIFFERENCES BETWEEN SHEAVE EFFECTIVE OUTSIDE DIAMETERS AND PITCH DIAMETERS*

Type	Belt Cross Section	Nominal Belt Width (mm)	Nominal Belt Width (in.)	Nominal Belt Depth (mm)	Nominal Belt Depth (in.)	Sheave Groove Angle (deg.)†	Effective OD Minus PD for Std-Groove Sheave (mm)	Effective OD Minus PD for Std-Groove Sheave (in.)
Conventional V-belts								
	HA	12.7	0.50	7.9	0.31	30-38	6.35	0.250
	HB	16.7	0.66	10.3	0.41	30-38	8.89	0.350
	HC	22.2	0.88	13.5	0.53	30-38	10.16	0.400
	HD	31.8	1.25	19.0	0.75	30-38	15.24	0.600
	HE	38.1	1.50	23.0	0.91	32-38	20.32	0.800
Double V-belts								
	HAA	12.7	0.50	10.3	0.41	30-38	6.35	0.250
	HBB	16.7	0.66	13.5	0.53	30-38	8.89	0.350
	HCC	22.2	0.88	17.5	0.69	30-38	10.16	0.400
	HDD	31.8	1.25	25.4	1.00	30-38	15.24	0.600
Adjustable-speed V-belts								
	HI	25.4	1.00	12.7	0.50	26	7.6	0.30
	HJ	31.8	1.25	15.0	0.59	26	9.4	0.37
	HK	38.1	1.50	17.5	0.69	26	11.4	0.45
	HL	44.4	1.75	19.8	0.78	26	13.2	0.52
	HM	50.8	2.00	22.2	0.88	26	15.2	0.60

*   ASAE Standard S211.3.
†   For V-belts and double V-belts, sheave groove angle increases as diameter is increased.

that power be transmitted to grooved sheaves from both the inside and outside of the belt. Adjustable-speed belts are discussed on page 67.

The American Society of Agricultural Engineers (ASAE) has established a standard for agricultural V-belts. This standard covers cross-sectional dimensions (table 3.1), belt lengths generally available, groove specifications, minimum diameters for idlers, procedures and examples for calculating required belt lengths, installation and take-up allowances, twisted-belt drives, and belt-measuring specifications.

The ASAE standard is similar in many respects to the standard established by the Rubber Manufacturers Association (RMA) for industrial V-belts. There are minor differences in groove dimensions and in available belt lengths. The RMA standard specifies pitch lengths for belts, whereas the ASAE standard specifies effective outside lengths. The RMA standard is intended primarily for two-sheave drives and includes formulas and charts for power ratings. The ASAE standard covers a broad range of drive configurations and does not include power ratings. In designing an agricultural drive, the allowable load is related to the expected number of hours of actual operation for a specific drive.

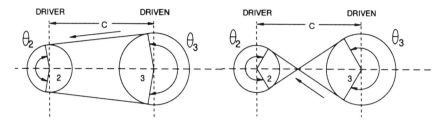

Figure 3.1–Geometry of V-belt drives.

V-belt drive geometry. Belts are generally used to connect parallel shafts so that the sheaves rotate in the same direction or in the opposite direction as shown in figure 3.1. The angle of wrap is defined as the angle of belt contact around the sheave. For the open belt drive, the angles of wrap (rad) are:

$$\theta_2 = \pi - 2 \sin^{-1} \frac{D_3 - D_2}{2C} \tag{3.1}$$

$$\theta_3 = \pi + 2 \sin^{-1} \frac{D_3 - D_2}{2C} \tag{3.2}$$

where D_2 and D_3 are the outside sheave diameters.

The angles of wrap for the crossed-belt drive are equal and are given by:

$$\theta_2 = \theta_3 = \pi + 2 \sin^{-1} \frac{D_3 + D_2}{2C} \tag{3.3}$$

The belt length for an open drive is approximated by:

$$L = 2C + \frac{\pi}{2}\left(D_3 + D_2\right) + \frac{\left(D_3 - D_2\right)^2}{4C} \tag{3.4}$$

and for the crossed belt drive the length is:

$$L = 2C + \frac{\pi}{2}\left(D_3 + D_2\right) + \frac{\left(D_3 + D_2\right)^2}{4C} \tag{3.5}$$

Kinematics of V-belt drives. As a belt bends to conform to the sheave curvature, the outer section stretches and the inner section is compressed. The location of the neutral axis, which establishes the

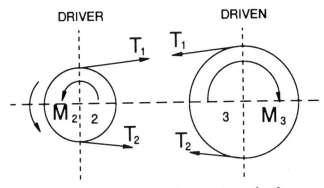

Figure 3.2–Belt tensions and moments on the sheaves.

pitch diameter of the sheave, is determined by the position of the load-carrying cords within the belt cross-section. Differences between sheave effective outside diameters and pitch diameters are included in table 3.1. Pitch diameters, rather than outside diameters, should always be used in calculating speed ratios and belt speeds.

The belt speed (m/s) is calculated as:

$$v = \pi n_2 D_{p2} = \pi n_3 D_{p3} \qquad (3.6)$$

where
n_2, n_3 = angular speeds of rotation of sheaves 2 and 3, respectively (rev/s)

D_{p2}, D_{p3} = pitch diameters of sheaves 2 and 3, respectively (m)

From the above equation we get the following relationship:

$$\frac{n_2}{n_3} = \frac{D_{p3}}{D_{p2}} \qquad (3.7)$$

Mechanics of V-belt drives. A V-belt transmits power by virtue of the difference in belt tensions between the point at which it enters a sheave and the point at which it leaves (fig. 3.2). This difference in tension is developed through friction between the belt sidewalls and the sides of the sheave groove. The wedging effect as the belt is pulled into the groove because of belt tension greatly increases the potential driving force.

Figure 3.3 shows the forces acting on a segment of the belt as it wraps around the sheave. In a belt drive there is a tight side and a slack side of the belt. In the free body diagram as shown in figure 3.3, T + dT represents the tight side tension, T represents the slack side

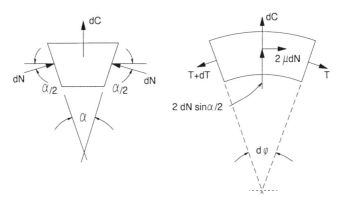

Figure 3.3–Forces acting on an element of V-belt.

tension, dC is the centrifugal force, dN is the normal sheave reaction force, and μdN is the frictional force.

The centrifugal force (dC) is given by:

$$dC = \frac{dmv^2}{R}$$

(3.8)

where
    dm = mass of the belt element (kg)
    R   = pitch radius (m)
    v   = belt speed (m/s)

Elemental belt mass (dm) can be obtained by multiplying the density of the belt material by its volume as follows,

$$dm = \rho_b aRd\phi$$

(3.9)

where
    ρ_b = density of the belt material (kg/m^3)
    a = belt cross-section area (m^2)
    dϕ= elemental wrap angle (rad)

Substituting equation 3.9 into equation 3.8 we obtain:

$$dC = \rho_b av^2 d\phi$$

(3.10)

Summing forces in the radial direction we get:

$$dC + 2dN\sin\left(\alpha/2\right) - T\sin\left(d\phi/2\right) - \left(T + dT\right)\sin\left(d\phi/2\right) = 0 \quad (3.11)$$

Let $dN = p_N\,R\,d\phi$, where p_N is the normal reaction force per unit belt length. Substituting the expressions for dC and dN in equation 3.11 and taking the limit we get:

$$\rho_b a v^2 + 2\,p_N R\sin\left(\alpha/2\right) - T = 0 \quad (3.12)$$

If the belt is not transmitting any power, the tension in the belt would only be due to the centrifugal force, i.e., $T_c = \rho a v^2$. Substituting T_c in equation 3.12 and solving for p_N we get:

$$p_N = \frac{T - T_c}{2R\sin\left(\alpha/2\right)} \quad (3.13)$$

Summing forces in the tangential direction we get:

$$\left(T + dT\right)\cos\left(d\phi/2\right) - T\cos\left(d\phi/2\right) - 2\mu p_N R\,d\phi = 0 \quad (3.14)$$

which in the limit becomes:

$$dT - 2\mu p_N R\,d\phi = 0 \quad (3.15)$$

Substituting for p_N, letting $k = \mu/\sin\left(\alpha/2\right)$, and rearranging we get:

$$\frac{dT}{T - T_c} = \frac{\mu}{\sin\alpha/2}\,d\phi \quad (3.16)$$

Integrating we get:

$$\int_{T_2}^{T_1} \frac{dT}{T - T_c} = k\int_0^\theta d\phi \quad (3.17)$$

Carrying out the integration, applying the limits, and rearranging we get:

TABLE 3.2. DIAMETERS OF ASAE STANDARD
ADJUSTABLE-SPEED SHEAVES*

Belt Cross Section	Recommended Minimum OD		Maximum PD with Min. OD		Maximum Belt Diam. Change	
	(mm)	(in.)	(mm)	(in.)	(mm)	(in.)
HI	177.8	7.00	170.2	6.70	72.1	2.84
HJ	222.2	8.75	212.8	8.38	94.7	3.73
HK	266.7	10.50	255.3	10.05	117.3	4.62
HL	311.2	12.25	298.0	11.73	140.2	5.52
HM	355.6	14.00	340.4	13.40	162.8	6.41

* ASAE Standard S211.3.

$$\frac{T_1 - T_c}{T_2 - T_c} = e^{k\theta} \tag{3.18}$$

If the belt speed is low, T_c may be eliminated in the above equation.

Power transmitted by a V-belt drive is determined by the effective pull and the belt speed as given by the following equation.

$$P = \frac{(T_1 - T_2)\,v}{1000} \tag{3.19}$$

where

T_1　　　= tight-side tension (N)
T_2　　　= slack-side tension (N)
P　　　　= power transmitted (kW)
v　　　　= belt speed (m/s)
$T_1 - T_2$ = effective pull (N)

It is customary to calculate tensions on the basis of a design power load that is somewhat greater than the average load to be transmitted, thus allowing for the effects of overloads or fluctuating loads. The design power for each driven wheel in a drive system is determined by multiplying the actual power by an appropriate service factor. Recommended values for service factors in agricultural machinery applications are included in table 3.3 and range mostly from 1.2 to 1.5.

If the ratio between the tight-side and slack-side tensions is too great, belt slippage will be excessive. Slippage in a properly designed drive should not exceed 1 to 2%. If the ratio is smaller than it needs to be, unnecessarily high tensions will be needed for a given effective pull, thereby reducing belt life. The maximum allowable tension ratio is:

TABLE 3.3. SERVICE FACTOR AND SERVICE LIFE FOR SOME
AGRICULTURAL MACHINES (GATES RUBBER CO.)

Machine or Operating Unit	Service Factor	Service Life (h)
Combine cylinder	1.5	1000-2000
Sickle bar	1.5	1000-2000
Straw walker	1.0	1000-2000
Cleaning shoe	1.0	1000-2000
Stack shredder	1.5	400-1000
Hay rake	1.2	600-1200
Ensilage cutter	1.5	500-1000
Ensilage blower	1.5	500-1000
Hay conditioner	1.5	800-2000
Delivery auger	1.3	400-1000
Tree shaker harvester	1.5	400-1000
Peanut digger	1.3	800-1600
Orchard sprayer	1.3	800-2000

$$R_{a\theta} = \frac{T_1}{T_2} = e^{k\theta} \qquad (3.20)$$

In designing a drive with a V-belt in a V-sheave, a tension ratio of $R_{a\pi} = 5$ (allowable tension ratio for 180° arc of contact) is commonly assumed. This gives a value of k = 0.512. A somewhat higher tension ratio is permissible if automatic tensioning is provided. For a V-belt running on a flat pulley, a value of $R_{a\pi} = 2.5$ is satisfactory (k = 0.292).

When the arc of contact is less than 180°, the allowable tension ratio is less, as indicated by equation 3.20, thus requiring higher values of T_1 and T_2 for a given effective pull and power. For example, if an effective pull of 360 N is required for the design power, values of T_1 and T_2 would be 450 N and 90 N, respectively, if the arc of contact on a grooved sheave is 180° ($R_{a\pi} = 5$). But if the arc of contact is only 120°, the maximum allowable tension ratio is 2.9, requiring tensions of 549 and 189 N. Flat, backside idlers are often employed to effect tensioning and, at the same time, increase the arcs of contact on the loaded sheaves.

In a two-sheave drive without an idler, the smaller sheave is the critical one in regard to tension ratio (slippage) because it has the smaller arc of contact. In a V-flat, two-wheel drive without an idler, the sheave and the flat pulley have equal maximum allowable tension ratios when the arc of contact is about 130° on the sheave and 230° on the flat pulley. When a drive has more than one driven sheave or pulley, tensions must be determined in a cumulative manner. All tensions in the system must be adjusted so that no wheel has a tension ratio greater than its allowable value. In a multi-wheel drive, the driver is usually the one most likely to slip.

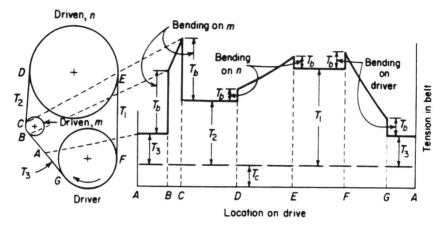

Figure 3.4–Belt tensions in relation to position on a three-sheave drive (Gates Rubber Co.; Reprinted from _Principles of Farm Machinery_, Kepner et al., 1978).

Stresses and service life. Stresses in a V-belt drive arise from the effective pull needed for the power load, slack-side tension needed to prevent slippage, bending around each wheel, and centrifugal forces acting on the belt. The bending tension, T_b, in the outer fibers of a belt with a given cross-section is inversely proportional to the wheel diameter. The tension due to centrifugal force may be expressed as:

$$T_c = wv^2 \qquad (3.21)$$

where
$\quad T_c$ = centrifugal tension (N)
$\quad w$ = belt mass (kg/meter of belt length)

The tensions in a three-sheave drive are illustrated in figure 3.4. The slack-side tension is T_3 and the differences, $T_2 - T_3$, $T_1 - T_2$, and $T_1 - T_3$, represent the effective pulls needed to transmit the power. Note that there is one peak tension at each wheel. It has been determined experimentally that a V-belt usually fails from fatigue caused by repetition of peak tensions and that the average fatigue life of a belt is predictable if loads are accurately known or can be estimated.

The Gates Rubber Co. has developed a design method for predicting the service life of a V-belt that includes the effects of the following factors.

1. The number of wheels on the drive.

2. The design power for each wheel (including an appropriate service factor for each driven wheel).
3. Belt speed.
4. The arc of contact for each wheel.
5 The sequence of loaded wheels and idlers on the drive.
6. The pitch diameter of each wheel.
7. The stress-fatigue characteristics and cross-sectional dimensions of the particular type and cross-section of belt being considered.
8. Belt length.

The Gates system is based on the determination (from an empirical equation or nomographs) of a "fatigue rate" corresponding to the peak tension for each wheel at a given belt speed. The units of the fatigue rate are millimeters of belt length per 100 h of life. The fatigue rates for the individual wheels are added together to obtain the total fatigue rate for the particular size and type of belt being considered for the drive. The calculated average service life of the belt at a given speed is:

$$\text{Belt Service Life (h)} = \frac{\text{Belt Length (mm)} \times 100}{\text{Total Fatigue Rate}} \qquad (3.22)$$

For a given tight-side tension and wheel pitch diameter, increasing the belt speed increases the fatigue rate, primarily because of the greater frequency of stress cycles but also because of increased centrifugal tension at high speeds. (The transmitted power would be increased also.)

The relation of fatigue rate to tension and speed for each type or quality of belt and each cross section is determined experimentally by means of durability tests in the laboratory, from which constants in a generalized equation are evaluated. A typical curve for one speed is shown in figure 3.5. Essentially, a tension-fatigue-rate curve is the inverse of the usual S-N curve (fatigue cycles vs. stress).

In designing a drive, the sequence of the driven sheaves or pulleys affects the magnitudes of the peak tensions and hence the service life. If a multiple sheave drive can be arranged so the belt leaving the driver comes to the driven sheaves in order of increasing power requirements, the magnitudes of tension peaks for the low-power sheaves will be minimized. Exceptionally small-diameter sheaves should be in belt spans of lesser tension to avoid the combination of a high tight-side tension and a high bending tension. An idler, if used, should be in the span with the least tension.

Increasing the sheave diameters on a particular drive, if feasible, reduces both the bending stresses and the required effective

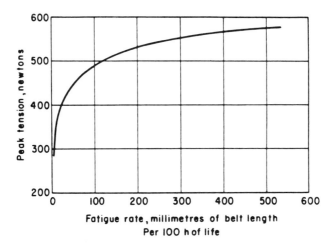

Figure 3.5–Typical relation between tension and fatigue rate for one V-belt cross-section and one speed (Gates Rubber Co.; Reprinted from *Principles of Farm Machinery*, Kepner et al., 1978).

pull and may even permit the use of a smaller belt cross-section. Centrifugal tension is seldom a limiting factor at speeds encountered in agricultural machinery drives.

Variable-speed V-belt drives. An adjustable-pitch V-belt sheave has provision for moving one face axially with respect to the other, thus changing the radius at which the belt operates. Some adjustable-pitch sheaves can be changed only when stopped, but others can be changed while in motion (fig. 3.6). In this textbook, the term "variable-speed drive" implies the ability to change the speed ratio over the entire range of control while the drive is in operation and under load.

Belts designed specifically for variable-speed drives are wider than conventional V-belts in relation to their thickness. The extra width is necessary to obtain reasonable ranges of speed ratio as well as increased load capacities. Relatively thin belts are needed because minimum operating diameters are generally small in this type of drive.

With adjustable-speed sheaves and V-belts as shown in tables 3.1 and 3.2, maximum speed-range ratios ranging from 1.75 for HI belts to 1.9 for HM belts are obtainable when one adjustable pitch sheave of the minimum allowable diameter is used in conjunction with a fixed-diameter sheave. The range for a given belt size varies inversely with the sheave diameter, since the maximum change in pitch diameter is fixed by the 26° groove angle and the belt top width (fig. 3.6a).

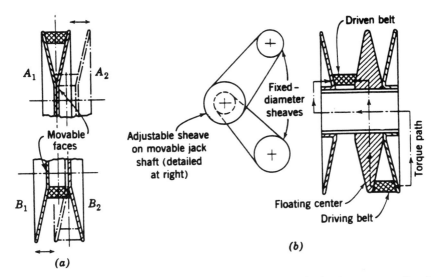

Figure 3.6–(a) Arrangement with two adjustable-pitch sheaves on fixed centers. (b) Double adjustable-pitch sheave with floating center (Reprinted from *Principles of Farm Machinery*, Kepner et al., 1978).

The speed range for a combination of two adjustable-pitch sheaves is the product of the two individual ranges. When both sheaves have the minimum recommended diameter, the maximum speed ratio varies from 3.0 for HI belts to 3.7 for HM belts. The most common arrangement is with the two sheaves on fixed centers, as shown in figure 3.6a. If the faces A_1 and B_2 are fixed axially while A_2 and B_1 are moved simultaneously, proper belt alignment is maintained at all speed ratios because the entire belt moves axially.

A third arrangement has two adjustable-speed belts in tandem and a double adjustable-pitch sheave with floating center section, as shown in figure 3.6b. The speed ratio is changed by moving the adjustable-pitch sheave along a path that keeps the sum of the required belt lengths constant as the floating center changes its lateral position. This system is subject to belt misalignment as discussed above for arrangements employing a single adjustable pitch sheave.

V-belt drive design. The Gates design procedure is summarized below:

- Determine the design power of the drive by multiplying the actual power demand by the service factors. Table 3.3 shows examples of service factors as recommended by the Gates Rubber Co.
- Determine belt type and cross section based on the design power. The selection of belt type and cross-section is based on the pitch diameter of the driver and the drive sheaves and

their speeds. Graphs used to select appropriate belt sections based on the speed of faster shaft and the design power are given by Gates Rubber Co., (1976). As the design power increases for a constant shaft speed larger belt sections are required. Also, if the shaft speed decreases, bigger belts would be necessary to transmit the same power.

- Layout the drive and determine pitch diameters of the driver and all driven sheaves, and calculate approximate belt length. Also, find arc of contact for each sheave.
- The next step is to determine belt tension ratios, effective pull and span tensions. These are computed using the equations given above.
- Determine total fatigue rate and service life by peak tension at a given belt speed. The nomograms to determine the fatigue rate are given in the Gates manual.
- The estimated belt life should be compared with the recommended values as given in table 3.3. If the calculated belt life is not acceptable then one or more of the following steps should be taken to change it.
  1. Increase number of belts.
  2. Increase smallest diameter.
  3. Change belt cross section.
  4. Increase belt length or reduce speed.
  5. Reduce torque.

3.1.2 Chain Drives

Perhaps the first use of chain was made in a reaper by Cyrus McCormick in 1837. Today chains play an important part in many agricultural machines such as hay balers, corn pickers, combines, cotton pickers, and beet harvesters. As opposed to the V-belt drives, chain drives are used where it is important to maintain exact speed ratio. Chain drives are capable of transmitting a large amount of power at slower speeds. Chain drives require better shaft alignment and more maintenance than V-belt drives.

Types of chains and standardization. Chains can be divided in the following categories:
- Roller Chains
  - Standard Pitch Roller Chains
  - Standard Double Pitch Roller Chain
- Other Types
  - Detachable Chains
  - Cast Roller Chains
  - Pintle Chains

The pitch of a chain is the effective length of one link. Standard-pitch roller chain, double-pitch roller chain, and detachable-link

Standard-pitch roller chain

Double-pitch roller chain

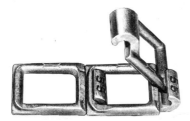

**Malleable-cast-iron,
detachable-link chain**

**Pressed-steel,
detachable-link chain**

Figure 3.7–Four types of drive chain common on farm machines (Reprinted from *Principles of Farm Machinery*, Kepner et al., 1978).

chain (fig. 3.7) are all common on agricultural machines. All roller chains are so constructed that the rollers rotate when contacting the teeth of the sprocket. Roller chains may be used in a single or multiple strand arrangement. Standardized dimensions for each of these types have been adopted by the American Standards Association (ASA). The standard dimensions of roller chains are given in table 3.4.

Standard pitch roller chain drives are satisfactory at linear speeds from less than 0.5 m/s up to 20 m/s and are well-suited for heavy loads requiring a compact drive. The maximum permissible speed decreases as the pitch is increased. Multiple width chains of short pitch can be used for extremely compact drives at high speeds. Roller chains are precision-built and under favorable conditions may have efficiencies as high as 98 to 99%.

Sprockets may be driven from either the inside or the outside of a roller chain. Although oil-bath lubrication is recommended for high-speed drives, this system often is not practical on agricultural machines. Standard-pitch roller chain is several times as expensive as steel detachable chain.

Double pitch roller chain employs the same pins, bushings, and rollers as standard-pitch roller chain, but the side plates have twice

TABLE 3.4. GENERAL CHAIN DIMENSIONS mm (INCHES)(REPRODUCED FROM *IDENTIFICATION*, *INSTALLATION*, *LUBRICATION AND MAINTENANCE OF POWER TRANSMISSION ROLLER CHAINS IN ANSI B29.1 AND ANSI B29.3*, BY PERMISSION OF THE AMERICAN CHAIN ASSOCIATION, ROCKVILLE, MD)

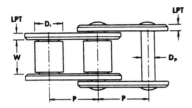
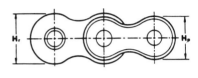

Standard Chain No.	Pitch P	Max. Roller Diam. D_r	Nominal Width W	Nominal Pin Diam. D_p	Link Plate Thickness LPT Standard Series	Heavy Series
25	6.35 (0.250)	3.30 (0.130)*	3.18 (0.125)	2.30 (0.090)	0.76 (0.030)	– –
35	9.52 (0.375)	5.08 (0.200)*	4.78 (0.188)	3.58 (0.141)	1.27 (0.050)	– –
41	12.70 (0.500)	7.77 (0.306)	6.35 (0.250)	3.58 (0.141)	1.27 (0.050)	– –
40	12.70 (0.500)	7.92 (0.312)	7.92 (0.312)	3.96 (0.156)	1.52 (0.060)	– –
50	15.88 (0.625)	10.16 (0.400)	9.52 (0.375)	5.08 (0.200)	2.03 (0.080)	– –
60	19.05 (0.750)	11.91 (0.469)	12.70 (0.500)	5.94 (0.234)	2.39 (0.094)	3.18 (0.125)
80	25.40 (1.000)	15.87 (0.625)	15.87 (0.625)	7.92 (0.312)	3.18 (0.125)	3.96 (0.156)
100	31.75 (1.250)	19.05 (0.750)	19.05 (0.750)	9.52 (0.375)	3.96 (0.156)	4.75 (0.187)
120	38.10 (1.500)	22.22 (0.875)	25.40 (1.000)	11.10 (0.437	4.75 (0.187)	5.56 (0.219)
140	44.45 (1.750)	25.40 (1.000)	25.40 (1.000)	12.70 (0.500)	5.56 (0.219)	6.35 (0.250)
160	50.80 (2.000)	28.57 (1.125)	31.75 (1.250)	14.27 (0.562)	6.35 (0.250)	7.14 (0.281)
180	57.15 (2.250)	35.71 (1.406)	35.71 (1.406)	17.45 (0.687)	7.14 (0.281)	7.92 (0.312)
200	63.50 (2.500)	39.67 (1.562)	38.10 (1.500)	19.84 (0.781)	7.92 (0.312)	9.52 (0.375)
240	76.20 (3.000)	47.62 (1.875)	47.62 (1.875)	23.80 (0.937)	9.52 (0.375)	12.70 (0.500)

*Bushing diameter, these chains have no rollers.

the pitch. Thus, double-pitch chains have the same strength and precision as corresponding standard-pitch chains but less mass. They are less expensive than standard-pitch roller chains, but considerably more expensive than steel detachable chain. Double-pitch chains are suitable for slow and moderate-speed drives. Because the roller diameter is only 5/16 of the pitch, there is ample space for sprocket teeth, and precision, cast-tooth sprockets are satisfactory (more economical than machine-cut teeth).

During the 1950s several companies developed chains that are physically interchangeable with standard-pitch and double-pitch roller chains but which are self-lubricating. This type of chain has oil-impregnated, sintered-steel bushings at the joints, replacing the bushings and rollers of conventional roller chain. It was designed for applications where external lubrication is impossible or impractical.

Many farm machinery applications fall into this category. Because this chain does not have rollers, it is not recommended for high speeds or extremely heavy loads.

The cost of standard-pitch or double-pitch self-lubricating chain is the same as that of the corresponding size of conventional roller chain. Ultimate strengths are perhaps 5 to 20% lower. Laboratory tests and field experience have indicated that, for a given load and a given allowable percentage elongation due to wear, the service life of a self-lubricating chain is several times as great as that of nonlubricated conventional roller chain. But, where a conventional chain can be adequately lubricated, it will out-perform the self-lubricating chain.

To further reduce the cost of this type of chain, an agricultural double-pitch chain has been developed that is dimensionally the same as the regular double-pitch chain but has a lower cost because of different materials and because the joints have more clearance, thus permitting greater manufacturing tolerances. Performance is said to be somewhat inferior to that of regular double-pitch chain. Steel detachable-link chains are used extensively on agricultural implements, both for transmitting power and in conveyors and elevators. This is the least expensive type of chain and it is well-suited for moderate loads at speeds not exceeding 2 to 2.5 m/s. Under dirty conditions, detachable chains are subject to greater wear than roller chains because of the loose-fitting, open hooks. Detachable chains usually are not lubricated, because the lubricant would tend to retain grit particles in the joint.

An improved type of steel detachable-link chain, developed in the early 1950s, is said to have one-third more tensile strength than conventional steel detachable chain, and more than twice the fatigue strength. The hook is rolled up from material in front of the link rather than from the material punched out from the center. This "high-fatigue" steel detachable chain is more expensive than the conventional type.

Pintle chain is composed of identical links with hollow cored cylinders cast or forged integrally with two offset sides bars. The links are jointed by pins inserted in holes in the ends of the side bars in through the cored cylinders.

Geometry of chain drives. The pitch diameter is a function of the chain pitch and the number of teeth in the sprocket. Referring to figure 3.8 the pitch diameter is given by:

$$PD = \frac{P}{\sin(180/N)} \qquad (3.23)$$

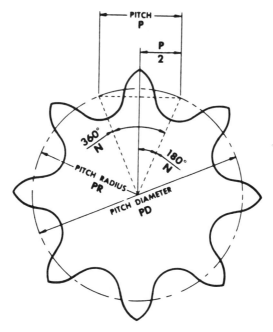

Figure 3.8–Computation of sprocket pitch diameter (Reproduced from *Chains for Power Transmission and Material Handling*, by permission of the American Chain Association, Rockville, MD).

where
  P = the chain pitch
  N = the number of teeth in the sprocket

The length (L) is determined in pitches and is approximated by the following formula:

$$\frac{L}{P} = \frac{2C}{P} + \frac{N_1 + N_2}{2P} + \frac{(N_2 - N_1)^2}{4\pi^2 (C/P)} \qquad (3.24)$$

where C is the center distance between the sprockets and N_1 and N_2 are the number of teeth on the two sprockets.

Kinematics of chain drives. Since a sprocket is essentially a polygon with as many sides as there are teeth or pitches, either the chain speed or the angular velocity of the sprocket must vary as the chain engages or leaves the sprocket due to the chordal action as shown in figure 3.9. The fewer teeth there are on the sprocket, the greater is the speed variation. Theoretically, a 10-tooth sprocket

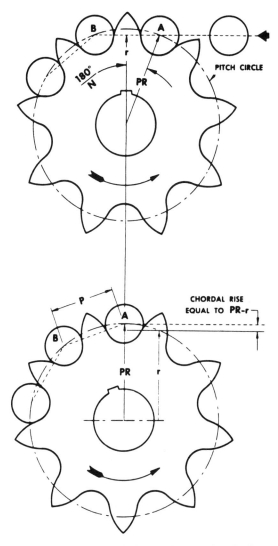

Figure 3.9–Chordal action of chain
(Reproduced from *Chains for Power
Transmission and Material Handling*, by
permission of the American Chain
Association, Rockville, MD).

would give a variation of about 5%. Practically, however, small speed
variations as well as sudden load shocks tend to be absorbed or
cushioned by the natural elasticity of the chain and the catenary
effect of the driving side. Although sprockets with as few as six teeth
are available, sizes with less than 17 or 18 teeth are not
recommended for high-speed drives. The chordal speed variation is
given by:

TABLE 3.5. SERVICE FACTORS ROLLER CHAINS
(REPRODUCED FROM *CHAINS FOR POWER TRANSMISSION AND*
***MATERIAL HANDLING*, BY PERMISSION OF THE AMERICAN CHAIN**
ASSOCIATION, ROCKVILLE, MD)

Type of Driven Load	Type of Input Power		
	Internal Combustion Engine with Hydraulic Drive	Electric Motor or Turbine	Internal Combustion Engine with Mechanical Drive
Smooth	1.0	1.0	1.2
Moderate shock	1.2	1.3	1.4
Heavy shock	1.4	1.5	1.7

$$\frac{\Delta v}{v} = \frac{\pi}{N}\left(\frac{1}{\sin(180/N)} - \frac{1}{\tan(180/N)}\right) \qquad (3.25)$$

whereas the chain velocity is $v = NPn$ and n = angular speed in rev/s.

Design of chain drives. In general, the load capacity of a chain is based upon the rate of wear rather than the ultimate strength. Because wear is mainly due to the hinge action as the chain engages or leaves a sprocket, the rate of wear is greater with small sprockets than with large ones. The rate of wear is also directly related to chain speed and inversely related to chain length. As a chain wears, the pitch length increases and the chain rides farther out on the sprocket teeth. The more teeth a sprocket has, the sooner the chain will ride out too far and have to be replaced. For this reason, speed ratios should not exceed ten to one for standard-pitch roller chain or six to one for other chains.

Power ratings published in chain catalogs are for the relatively long life expected in industrial applications. As in designing V-belt drives, actual power requirements are multiplied by appropriate service factors to obtain design power. Because of the shorter life requirements on agricultural machines in comparison with industrial applications, somewhat greater loadings are often acceptable. However, unfavorable environmental conditions may tend to shorten the life.

Chain selection for extremely slow drives is sometimes based on ultimate strength rather than wear rate. With roller chains, the recommended maximum ratios of working load to ultimate strength range from 0.2 at 0.13 m/s to 0.1 at 1.3 m/s. Conventional, steel detachable chain has inherent stress concentration points that promote early fatigue failures if the chain is loaded to more than 10%

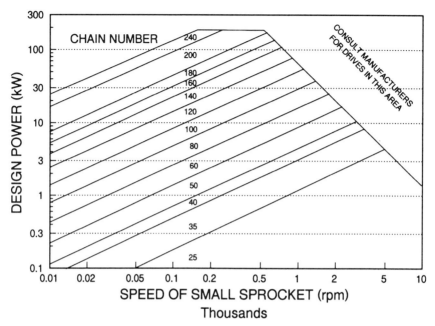

Figure 3.10–Roller chain pitch selection chart (Redrawn from *Chains for Power Transmission and Material Handling*, by permission of the American Chain Association, Rockville, MD).

of its ultimate strength. The pull required for a given power and speed can be determined from equation 3.19. T_2 is assumed to be zero, since a chain should run with essentially no slack-side tension. Chain speed in meter per second = (chain pitch, mm/1000) × (number of teeth on sprocket) × (sprocket r/min ÷ 60).

The chain drive design procedure, in general, includes the following steps:

- **Design power.** A service factor based on the type of power source and the nature of load is selected to determine the design power. Table 3.5 gives the recommended values for service factors. Design power is determined by multiplying transmitted power by the service factor.
- **Tentative chain selection.** Once the design power is determined chain pitch is selected based on figure 3.10.
- **Selection of small sprocket.** The sprocket selected must be large enough to accommodate the shaft. For a given chain speed and power the effect of increasing the number of teeth on the sprocket is to increase the linear speed of chain and to decrease the pull and to decrease the chordal action. This results in a quieter drive with less impact.
- **Selection of large sprocket.** After selecting the small sprocket the desired speed ratio is used to determine the

Figure 3.11–A tractor pto drive.

number of teeth on the large sprocket. It is recommended that the
speed ratios greater than 10:1 should not be attempted in a single
drive.

  • **Determine chain length and center distance.** The chain
    length is a function of number of teeth on both sprockets and
    the center distance. It is preferred that the chain consist of
    an even number of pitches in order to avoid an offset link.
    The center distance is based on the physical requirements of
    the application. The chain length is calculated by using the
    equation given above.

3.1.3 Power-Take-Off Drives

A power-take-off (pto) drive provides a means for transmitting
rotary power to machines that are coupled to a tractor. The most
common location for the pto shaft is at the rear of the tractor (see
fig. 3.11), but some tractors have auxiliary pto shafts at other
locations. The direction of rotation, rotational speed, approximate
location and exact dimensions of the pto shaft were standardized by
the ASAE in 1926 to provide ability to interchange between
equipment of different manufacturers. With growth in tractor size, it
became necessary to develop faster and larger pto shafts to transmit
the increased available power. There are now three standard pto
shafts. Illustrated in figure 3.12 are the 35 mm (diameter) shafts
with standard rotation speeds of 540 rev/min and 1000 rev/min. The

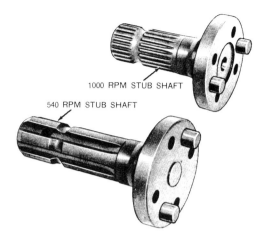

Figure 3.12–Splines for 540 and 1000 rev/min pto shafts (Courtesy of Deere and Co.).

shaft with standard speed of 540 rev/min is used on tractors with up to 65 kW pto power. The 35 mm shaft with standard speed of 1000 rev/min is used on tractors with 45 to 120 kW of pto power. Note the power overlap, i.e., tractors in the 45 to 65 kW power range could be equipped with either of the shafts in figure 3.12. The 45 mm shaft with standard speed of 1000 rev/min is not shown in figure 3.12; it is similar in appearance to the other 1000 rev/min shaft, except that it is larger in diameter and has 20 splines instead of 21. It is used on tractors of 110 to 190 kW of pto power. Some large, four-wheel drive tractors do not have a pto drive.

Early pto drives were driven from the tractor transmission and stopped rotating whenever the traction clutch was disengaged. Present standard practice is to provide an independent pto which is controlled by its own separate clutch. Figure 3.13 illustrates the most common type of universal joint drive that is used for transmitting power from the pto shaft to an implement. Two Cardan universal

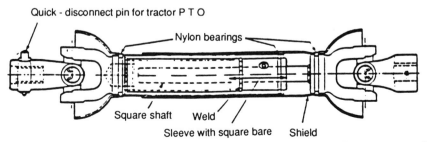

Figure 3.13–A telescoping pto shaft with integral safety shield (Courtesy of Neapco Products, Inc.).

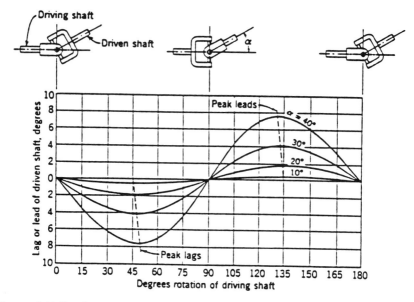

Figure 3.14–Lead or lag of shaft driven by a cardan-type universal joint, in relation to rotational position of the driving shaft (Reprinted from *Principles of Farm Machinery*, Kepner et al., 1978).

joints are included and the connecting shaft is telescoping to accommodate changes in angularity and distance between the implement and tractor. An integral shield surrounds the shaft and partially surrounds each joint. The shield normally rotates with the shaft but can stop if it contacts a person or other object. A single Cardan joint creates fluctuations in drive line rotation when operating at an angle, as shown in figure 3.14. The curves in figure 3.14 are based on the following equation:

$$\tan\left(\phi_{jo}\right) = \cos\,(\alpha)\tan\left(\phi_{ji}\right) \qquad (3.26)$$

where

ϕ_{ji} = angular displacement of joint input shaft (radian)
ϕ_{jo} = angular displacement of joint output shaft (radian)
α = joint angle (see fig. 3.14)

The relationship between shaft velocities is:

$$\frac{n_{jo}}{n_{ji}} = \frac{\cos\,(\alpha)}{1 - \sin^2(\alpha)\sin^2(\phi_{ji})} \qquad (3.27)$$

where n_{ji}, n_{jo} = speeds, respectively, of joint input and output shafts (rev/min). When two Cardan joints are connected in series, as in figure 3.13, the velocity fluctuations will cancel if the two joint angles are equal and the joints are 90° out of phase. Proper phasing is accomplished when the yokes connected to the two ends of the intermediate shaft are in line with each other. Then the velocity fluctuations are canceled in the output shaft but not in the intermediate shaft. Constant speed universal joints, such as the Bendix-Weiss joint, can transmit power through an angle without introducing the speed fluctuations of the Cardan joint. Although the Bendix-Weiss joints transmit torque more smoothly, they are not well suited for the high torque levels often encountered in agricultural equipment.

Experimental tests have shown that peak torques in a pto driveline far exceed average torques. Thus, drive lines are designed on the basis of fatigue stresses imposed by repeated peak torques. One technique for reducing fatigue stresses is to limit the joint angles encountered during normal operations when the tractor and implement are not in a turn.

3.1.4 Overload Safety Devices

In many types of farm machinery, a single power source drives various components that have widely differing power requirements and are subject to varying degrees of possible overload. In such a system some overload protection is almost mandatory, especially for the lower-powered components. Three general types of safety devices commonly used in rotary drives are:

- Those that depend upon shearing of a replaceable connecting member in the drive.
- Units in which spring force holds two corrugated members together, utilizing the principle of the inclined plane.
- Devices depending entirely upon friction.

Shear devices. This type of device is simple and relatively inexpensive, but the sheared element must be replaced after each overload. Thus, it is most suitable where overloads are rather infrequent. Shear devices can be designed for almost any desired load rating, although pin or key sizes become rather small for low torque ratings unless a material with low shear strength is selected. Typical arrangements for shear devices are:

- Shear key between shaft and hub (usually brass key, with tapered shaft and bore).
- Diametral shear pin through hub and shaft (gives double shear).
- Flange-mounted shear pin parallel to shaft, as illustrated in figure 3.15.

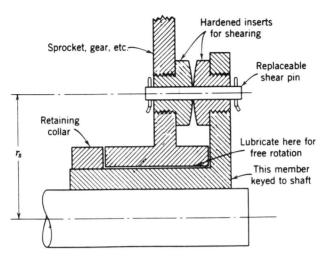

Figure 3.15–An arrangement with a flange-mounted shear pin. The hardened shearing inserts could be omitted, particularly if overloads are expected only infrequently or if necked-down shear pins are used (Reprinted from *Principles of Farm Machinery***, Kepner et al., 1978).**

Regardless of the arrangement, the driving and driven members must rotate freely with respect to each other after the shear element has failed. With either of the first two types, the shaft or bore is likely to be scored by the sheared element. Removal of the hub from the shaft may be necessary in the first type to replace a sheared key.

The flange-mounted shear pin is the most easily replaced, but the unit is more costly than a diametral pin and not as well-adapted to low torques because of the greater radius to the shear section. For experimental testing, interchangeable pins necked down to different diameters can be used to vary the load at which failure occurs. In production units, a full-sized pin of an ordinary material (such as hot-rolled steel) is desirable for convenience of replacement by the operator.

The torque at which a flange-mounted shear pin will fail and the power are given by the following equations:

$$T = r_s \left(\frac{\pi}{4} d_1^2 S_s \right) 10^{-3} \qquad (3.28)$$

$$kW = \frac{2\pi NT}{60,000} = 8.225 \, N r_s \, d_1^2 \, S_s \, 10^{-8} \qquad (3.29)$$

where
T = torque $(N \cdot m)$

**Figure 3.16–Typical arrange-
ment of a jump clutch (Reprinted from *Principles of
Farm Machinery*, Kepner
et al., 1978).**

N = shaft speed (rev/min)

r_s = distance between shaft center and shear-pin center (fig. 3.15) (mm)

d_1= diameter of shear pin at shear section (mm)

S_s= ultimate shear strength of shear pin (MPa)

Similarly, a diametral shear pin (double shear) will fail when:

$$kW = 8.225 \ NDd_1^2 \ S_s \ 10^{-8} \qquad (3.30)$$

where D = shaft diameter (diameter at which shear occurs) (mm)

Jump clutch. A jump clutch has rounded, mating jaws or corrugations that are held together by an adjustable spring. In figure 3.16, part A is keyed to the shaft and part B, the driving member, is free to rotate on the shaft when an overload occurs. The overload torque required to rotate B with respect to A and cause jumping is a function of the slope of the inclined corrugation faces, the coefficient of friction between the faces, the effective radius from the shaft centerline to the contact area, and the force required to compress the spring and permit axial movement of B with respect to A.

The spring must have sufficient deflection available so it is not compressed solid before the relative displacement of the two corrugated faces is sufficient to permit jumping. Although friction between the corrugated faces influences the magnitude of the torque required for jumping, the unit would function (at a lower torque) even if the coefficient of friction were zero.

Because of its automatic resetting feature, the jump clutch is more suitable than shear devices where overloads may occur rather frequently. There is no slippage until the load exceeds the setting of the unit, and then the operator is warned audibly that an overload has occurred. Jump clutches are more expensive than shear devices and are not well-suited to large loads because of the excessive physical size required. When they are jumping, they impose high shock loads upon the drive system.

The magnitude and variability of the friction force required to slide the movable member axially can have an important effect upon the torque required to cause jumping. To minimize the axial friction force, the torque should be transmitted to or from the movable member at a relatively large radius, as with a sprocket or sheave, rather than through splines or a key in the shaft.

Friction devices. A properly designed belt drive can serve as a friction safety device, although its performance is affected by variations in belt tension and by the increase in coefficient of friction as the percentage of belt slip increases. The performance is more consistent with a spring-loaded idler than with a fixed adjustment.

Single-plate clutches with two friction surfaces, similar to tractor or automotive clutches, are often used for overload protection. The spring pressure is adjusted to drive normal loads but slip under abnormal loads. In comparison with jump clutches, friction safety clutches have the advantages of more consistent breakaway torque and no damaging peaks during slippage. However, tests have shown that the momentary dynamic torque capacity under sudden load application may be two to three times the static value.

Friction clutches are very effective in protecting a drive from high-frequency peak torques. But under some conditions it is possible to have a friction clutch slipping sufficiently to become overheated without the operator being aware of the overload.

3.2 Fluid Power

3.2.1 Basic Principles and Elements of Fluid Power

When fluid power systems gained widespread use on agricultural equipment in the 1940s, physical strength was no longer a necessary qualification for equipment operators. Fluid power permits the raising and lowering of heavy implements with a minimum of physical effort. Also, fluid power can be transmitted to remote locations much more conveniently than mechanical power. There are five principles that are important to an understanding of fluid power circuits. They are (a) liquids have no shape of their own but will flow to acquire the shape of their container, (b) liquids can be considered incompressible at the pressures used in fluid power systems, (c) liquids transmit pressure equally in all directions, (d) the

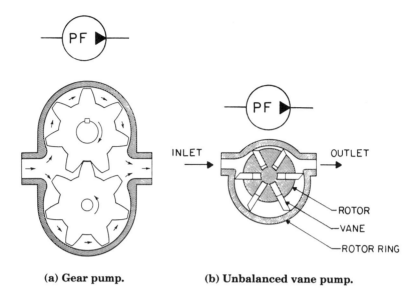

(a) Gear pump.   (b) Unbalanced vane pump.

Figure 3.17–Fixed displacement pumps.

rate of flow from a positive displacement pump depends proportionally with pump speed but is virtually independent of system pressure, and (e) any flow of liquid through a pipe or orifice is accompanied by a reduction in liquid pressure.

Fluid power systems include, at a minimum, a reservoir, one or more pumps to convert mechanical power into fluid power, one or more control valves, one or more actuators to convert the fluid power back into mechanical power, lines to join the various components, and filters to remove contaminants from the oil. Each of these components will be discussed, as well as the types of circuits in which the components can be used.

Making physical drawings of the many components in fluid power systems would be very time consuming and such drawings would not necessarily convey the system logic. Thus, a Joint Industry Conference (JIC) of the fluid power industry was convened to devise symbols for fluid power components. The resulting JIC symbols are summarized in Appendix B. The JIC symbols are analogous to electrical symbols and they simplify the drawing of fluid power circuits in the same way that electrical symbols simplify the drawing of electrical circuits. The shape of every JIC symbol was chosen to be as self explanatory as possible and you should be able to recognize and use the symbols very quickly. Physical drawings may be used to explain some fluid power components in this chapter, but the corresponding JIC symbol will also be shown.

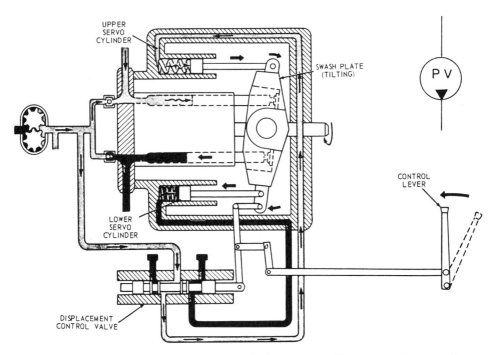

Figure 3.18–Variable-displacement, axial-piston pump (Courtesy of Deere and Co.).

3.2.2 Pumps

A pump is the heart of any fluid power system; it converts mechanical power into fluid power. Only positive displacement pumps are used in fluid power systems; thus the pump delivery is nearly independent of the pressure at the outlet port of the pump. The three basic types of pumps used in fluid power systems include gear pumps, vane pumps, and piston pumps.

Diagrams of gear and vane pumps are shown in figure 3.17. The displacement of these pumps is the theoretical amount of liquid that would be moved from the inlet port to the outlet port in one revolution of the pump shaft. Liquid is carried in the tooth spaces of the gear pump but meshing of the gears prevents oil from making a full circle; thus the oil is forced out of the outlet port. Likewise, oil is carried in the spaces between the sliding vanes in the vane pump. Both the gear pump and the vane pump have fixed displacement, i.e., the displacement cannot be changed after the pump is manufactured.

Both axial piston pumps (fig. 3.18) and radial piston pumps (fig. 3.19) are available. The former have pistons parallel to the pump shaft, while the latter have pistons arranged radially to the shaft. The piston pumps in figures 3.18 and 3.19 both have variable

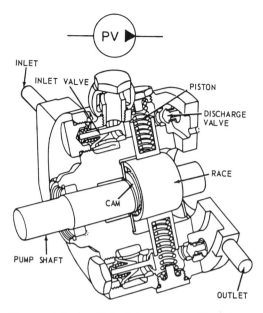

Figure 3.19–Radial-piston pump (Courtesy of Deere and Co.).

displacement, but piston pumps can also be designed with fixed displacement.

The delivery of oil from a pump can be calculated using equation 3.31:

$$Q_p = \frac{V_p \, n_p \, \eta_{vp}}{1000} \tag{3.31}$$

where

Q_p = pump delivery (L/min)
V_p = pump displacement (cm^3/rev)
n_p = pump speed (rev/min)
η_{vp} = volumetric efficiency of the pump (decimal)

Because of internal leakage within a pump, the volumetric efficiency is always less than one, i.e., the pump always delivers less than its theoretical delivery. Generally, internal leakage in a hydraulic component is directly proportional to the area of the leakage path and the pressure drop across the leakage path and inversely proportional to viscosity. The leakage flow is given by the following equation:

$$Q_L = \frac{(6 \times 10^7) C_L \, A \, \Delta p}{\mu} \tag{3.32}$$

where
Q_L = leakage flow (L/min)
C_L = leakage length constant (cm)
A   = cross-sectional area of the leakage path (cm^2)
μ = dynamic viscosity of the fluid (mPa·s)
Δp = pressure drop (MPa)

Therefore, the volumetric efficiency can be calculated as:

$$\eta_{vp} = \frac{Q_{tp} - Q_L}{Q_{tp}} = 1 - \frac{Q_L}{Q_{tp}} \qquad (3.33)$$

where Q_{tp} is the theoretical pump delivery and can be completed from equation 3.31 by equating $\eta_{vp} = 1$.

The torque requirement of a pump can be calculated from equation 3.34:

$$T_p = \frac{\Delta p V_p}{2 \pi \eta_{tp}} \qquad (3.34)$$

where
T_p = torque required to drive the pump (N·m)
Δp = pressure rise across the pump (MPa)
η_{tp} = torque efficiency of the pump (decimal)

Because of friction within the pump, the torque efficiency is always less than one and more than the theoretical amount of torque required to drive the pump. The frictional torque (T_{fp}) is the amount of torque require to overcome friction within the pump. The frictional torque is given by:

$$T_{fp} = \frac{2\pi \, C_f \, \mu \, n_p}{6 \cdot 10^{10}} \qquad (3.35)$$

where C_f = constant (cm^3). The friction torque is called the damping torque since it is proportional to the shaft speed. There is an additional frictional torque due to shaft seals. The torque efficiency can be calculated as:

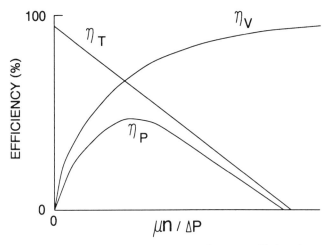

Figure 3.20–Torque, volumetric, and power efficiencies.

$$\eta_{tp} = \frac{T_{tp}}{T_{tp} + T_{fp}} = \left(1 + \frac{T_{fp}}{T_{tp}}\right)^{-1} \tag{3.36}$$

where T_{tp} is the theoretical torque and it can be calculated from equation 3.34 by letting $\eta_{tp} = 1$.

The fluid power produced by a pump can be calculated using equation 3.37:

$$P_{fl} = \frac{Q_p \, \Delta p}{60} \tag{3.37}$$

where P_{fl} = fluid power, kW. The shaft power required to drive a pump can be calculated from equation 3.38.

$$P_{sp} = \frac{P_{fl}}{\eta_{pp}} \tag{3.38}$$

where
P_{sp} = shaft power required to drive the pump (kW)
$\eta_{pp} = \eta_{vp} \cdot \eta_{tp}$ = power efficiency of the pump

Since both η_{vp} and η_{tp} are less than one, η_{pp} is also less than one and more than the theoretical amount of power is required to drive the pump.

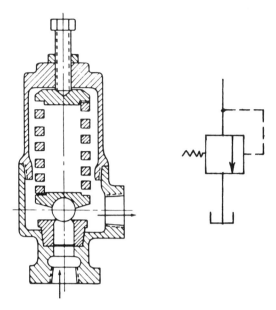

Figure 3.21–A direct-acting relief valve.

The efficiencies of a pump vary with operating conditions, as illustrated in figure 3.20. The internal leakage in a pump increases with Dp; as pump speed approaches zero, the entire theoretical delivery can leak back to the inlet and η_{vp} goes to zero. As pump speed increases, however, the internal leakage becomes small relative to the theoretical delivery and η_{vp} approaches its maximum. Some shaft torque is used to overcome the friction which is always present in a pump; at high Δp, that friction torque is relatively small compared to the theoretical torque required and η_{tp} is at a maximum. Conversely, at low Δp, the friction torque is dominant and η_{tp} reaches zero. Since η_{pp} is the product of η_{vp} and η_{tp}, the shape of its curve on figure 3.20 is defined by the shape of the torque and volumetric efficiency curves. Figure 3.20 implies that a pump must be operated within proper limits of speed and pressure or its power efficiency will drop to unacceptable levels.

3.2.3 Valves

Valves are used in fluid power systems to control pressure, volume and direction of flow. Valves are classified, accordingly, as pressure control valves (PCV), volume control valves (VCV), and directional control valves (DCV).

Pressure control valves. Liquid passes through orifices in control valves, resulting in pressure drops. equation 3.39 relates the pressure drop across an orifice to the flow through it:

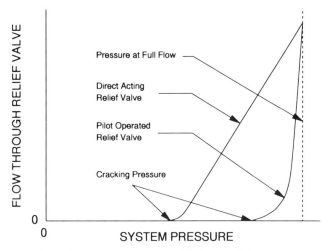

Figure 3.22–Pressure over-ride in a relief valve.

$$Q = 60 \ C_0 \ A_0 \ \sqrt{\frac{2 \ \Delta p}{\rho_f}} \qquad (3.39)$$

where
  Q = flow through orifice (L/min)
  C_0 = orifice coefficient (dimensionless)
  A_0 = orifice area (mm^2)
  Δp = pressure drop across the orifice (MPa)
  ρ_f = mass density of the fluid (kg/m^3)

   In the usual case where A_0 is much smaller than the upstream channel and flow is turbulent, $C_0 = 0.60$ for a sharp-edged orifice, but

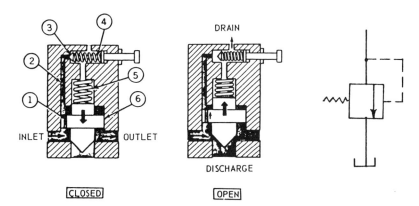

Figure 3.23–A pilot-operated relief valve.

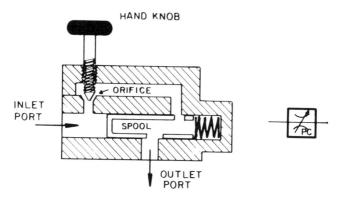

Figure 3.24–A pressure-compensated throttling valve.

can rise to more than 0.80 if the orifice edges are rounded. The orifice shape has little effect, i.e., C_0 will be nearly the same for a long narrow orifice as for a circular one. For typical, petroleum-based fluids used in fluid power systems, $\rho_f = 850\text{-}950 \text{ kg/m}^3$.

The most common PCV is the relief valve. Relief valves are closed during normal operation, but open at a set pressure to discharge liquid to the reservoir. Thus, relief valves are intended to limit the pressure in a circuit to a safe level. Because direct-acting relief valves (fig. 3.21) have a large pressure override (fig. 3.22), pilot-operated relief valves are sometimes used (fig. 3.23). Pilot-operated relief valves have a light spring which allows a pilot relief valve (see nos. 3 and 4 in fig. 3.23) to open at the desired cracking pressure. The resulting flow passing through an orifice in the valve piston causes a pressure drop (see equation 3.39) which raises the piston, thus opening the main relief valve. The pressure override, which is the full-flow pressure minus the cracking pressure, is thus much smaller

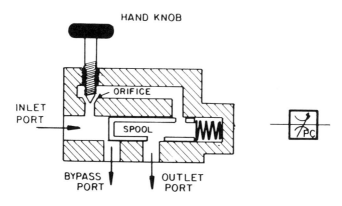

Figure 3.25–A bypass-type flow-divider valve.

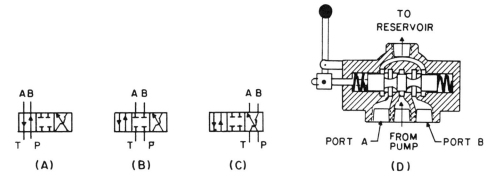

Figure 3.26–A closed-center directional control valve.

in a pilot-operated relief valve than in a direct acting relief valve. Note that the direct-acting relief valve is classified as a two-way valve, meaning that it has two ports for connection to the fluid power circuits. The pilot-operated relief valve would be classified as a three-way valve unless the drain was internally connected to the discharge port.

Volume control valves. The two most common VCVs are the throttling valve (fig. 3.24) and the flow-divider valve (fig. 3.25). The purpose of both valves is to regulate the flow to the outlet port regardless of downstream pressure. Both valves have a spring-loaded spool valve whose purpose is to maintain a constant pressure across an orifice and thus, in accordance with equation 3.39, maintain constant flow to the outlet port. If the flow through the orifice increases, the pressure drop across the orifice will also increase in accordance with equation 3.39 and the pressure within the spool will fall. The resulting pressure imbalance across the head of the spool will move the spool to the right to partially block the outlet port, thus reducing the flow to the outlet port. Conversely, if the flow through the orifice declines, the spool will move to the left to create a larger opening to the outlet port. Both the throttling valve and the flow-divider valve are pressure compensated, because they automatically compensate for changes in downstream pressure. Both of the valves that are illustrated have adjustable flow rates, i.e., the operator can use the hand knob to set the desired flow level. Nonadjustable valves are also available.

The primary difference between the throttling valve and the flow-divider valve is that the latter has a third port for bypass flow. The throttling valve can only be used in systems in which the pump flow reduces automatically when the flow is throttled. In systems with fixed-displacement pumps, any surplus flow must be bypassed and thus only the flow-divider valve is suitable. The flow-divider valve can also be used as a priority valve, i.e., circuits with top

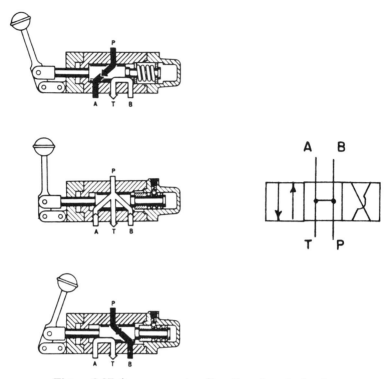

Figure 3.27–An open-center directional control valve.

priority (for example, steering circuits) are connected to the outlet port. Any excess flow passes to through the bypass port to circuits with lower priority.

Directional control valves. A directional control valve (DCV) is illustrated in figure 3.26. It has four ports and is thus classified as a four-way valve. It is also classified as a three-position valve because the valve spool has three possible positions, right, centered or left. In figure 3.26a, the spool is to the right to connect port P (for pump) to B and port T (for tank, or reservoir) to A. These connections are reversed when the spool is to the left as in figure 3.26c. An actuator can be connected to ports A and B and, by moving the DCV spool left or right, the direction of movement of the actuator can be reversed. With the spool centered, as in figure 3.26b, all ports are blocked and thus the valve is also classified as a closed-center valve, in circuits in which pump flow changes automatically to meet demand. In drawings of fluid power circuits, DCVs are always shown with the spool centered for simplicity and it is left to the reader to imagine the other spool positions.

The valve illustrated in figure 3.27 is a four-way, three-position, open centered DCV. It could be used with a fixed-displacement pump

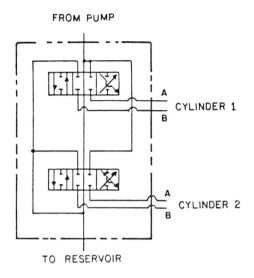

FROM PUMP

A
CYLINDER 1
B

A
CYLINDER 2
B

TO RESERVOIR

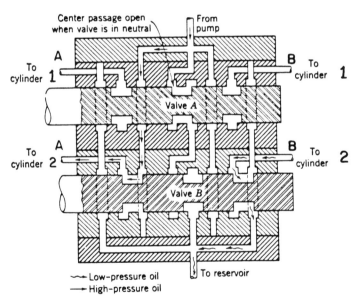

Figure 3.28–A dual tandem-center directional control valve (Reprinted from *Principles of Farm Machinery*, Kepner et al., 1978).

because, with the spool centered, pump flow can pass through the DCV to the reservoir. Note, however, that any actuator connected to the DCV would be free to move when the spool was centered. If the actuator was a hydraulic cylinder used to raise an implement, for

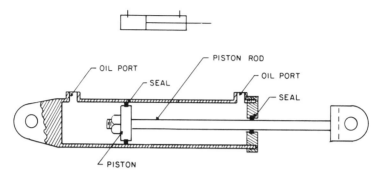

Figure 3.29–A double-acting hydraulic cylinder.

example, the implement would lower as soon as the spool was centered. For that reason, open-centered DCVs are seldom used on agricultural equipment. Instead, if the fluid power system has a fixed-displacement pump, a tandem-centered DCV is used. A dual tandem-centered DCV is illustrated in figure 3.28. With both spools centered, all actuator ports are blocked but the pump port is connected to the reservoir port. Moving either spool left or right blocks the pump connection to the reservoir and oil is forced to flow to an actuator.

Although the JIC symbols do not reveal it, all DCVs also provide some degree of flow control. By partial movement of the spool to either the left or right, the orifice within the valve can be partially opened and, in accordance with equation 3.39, can provide partial flow delivery to the actuator.

3.2.4 Actuators

Actuators include hydraulic motors to provide rotary mechanical power and hydraulic cylinders to provide linear mechanical power.

Hydraulic motors. Motors are similar to pumps and, with suitable precautions, the pumps shown in figure 3.17 could also be used as motors. To prevent seal damage, the shaft seals of most pumps and motors are internally vented to the low pressure port. Low pressure exits at the inlet of a pump but at the outlet of a motor and thus, to use a gear or vane pump as a motor, the direction of rotation must be reversed. Axial piston motors of either fixed or variable displacement are also available.

Equations 3.40 to 3.42 are for the speed, torque, and power output, respectively, of a hydraulic motor:

$$n_m = \frac{1000 \, Q \, \eta_{vm}}{V_m} \qquad\qquad (3.40)$$

$$T_m = \frac{\Delta p \ V_m \ \eta_{tm}}{2 \pi} \qquad (3.41)$$

$$P_{sm} = \frac{Q \ \Delta p \ \eta_{pm}}{60} \qquad (3.42)$$

where
n_m = motor speed (rev/min)
η_{vm} = volumetric efficiency of motor
V_m = motor displacement (cm^3/rev)
T_m = motor torque (N·m)
η_{tm} = torque efficiency of motor
P_{sm} = motor shaft power (kW)
$\eta_{pm} = \eta_{vm} \cdot \eta_{tm}$ = power efficiency of motor
Q = fluid flow through motor (L/min)
Δp = pressure drop across motor (MPa)

The volumetric, torque and power efficiencies for a motor are analogous to those for a pump and vary as illustrated in figure 3.20.

Hydraulic cylinders. Both single-acting and double-acting hydraulic cylinders are available. A cutaway of a double acting cylinder is shown in figure 3.29. Oil is forced into the port on the left to extend the cylinder and the piston movement forces oil out of the port on the right. Conversely, by reversing the port connections, the cylinder can be made to retract. The double-acting cylinder of figure 3.29 could be converted into a single-acting cylinder by emptying the oil to the right of the piston and installing an air breather in the port to the right. A single-acting cylinder is used in those situations where an external load is available to make the cylinder retract. Dimensions for hydraulic cylinders to control implements have been specified in ASAE Standard S201.4.

The load capacity of a cylinder can be calculated using equation 3.43:

$$F = \frac{p_1 A_1 - p_2 A_2}{10} \qquad (3.43)$$

where
F = force capacity of the cylinder (kN)
A_1 = area of piston (cm^2)
A_2 = area of piston minus area of piston rod (cm^2)
p_1 = pressure (gage) acting on area A_1 (MPa)
p_2 = pressure (gage) acting on area A_2 (MPa)

The factor of 10 is simply a units conversion factor. A negative answer indicates the cylinder is retracting. In many situations, one of the ports will be connected to the reservoir and the corresponding pressure will be zero gage pressure.

The speed at which a cylinder extends or retracts can be calculated using equation 3.44:

$$v = \frac{Q}{6\,A_i} \qquad (3.44)$$

where
   v = speed of movement of rod (m/s)
   Q = flow into cylinder (L/min)
   $A_i = A_1$ if cylinder is extending or A_2 if retracting

Note that, for a given Q, the cylinder extends slower than it retracts, since $A_1 > A_2$. The return flow from a double-acting cylinder is calculated from the following equation:

$$Q_{cr} = 6\,A_j\,v \qquad (3.45)$$

where
   Q_{cr} = cylinder return flow (L/min)
   A_j = A_2 if cylinder is extending or A_1 if retracting

Equations 3.44 and 3.45 will show that a cylinder returns less oil than it receives while extending and more oil than it receives while retracting. The reservoir must supply the flow deficit or absorb the excess flow.

3.2.5 Reservoirs, Fluids, Filters, and Lines

A reservoir supplies oil to the pump and provides a place for oil to return from the circuit. The reservoir must be large enough to allow the oil to cool; i.e., a larger reservoir will allows more resident time for the oil to cool in the reservoir. If the reservoir cannot provide sufficient cooling, an oil cooler can be used to provide supplementary cooling. A properly designed reservoir has internal baffles to reduce oil splashing and has its inlet and outlet ports arranged to prevent oil returning from the hydraulic circuit from immediately re-entering the pump. The return port should be below the oil surface to reduce air entrainment and foaming as the oil returns to the reservoir. Finally, the reservoir must be vented to the atmosphere to accommodate changing oil levels and the vent should have a filter to prevent dust entry. As the oil passes through lines, valves and other devices that do no mechanical work, any pressure drops result in conversion of fluid power to heat. The power loss and heat generation rate can be calculated from equation 3.46:

$$P_L = \frac{\Delta p \, Q}{60} \qquad (3.46)$$

where
  P_L = power loss in a nonworking device (kW)
  Δp = pressure drop across the device (MPa)
  Q = flow through the device (L/min)

Viscosity is the most important property of a hydraulic fluid. Manufacturers generally recommend fluid viscosities between 12 and 49 mPa·s at the operating temperature of the pump. Fluid viscosities fall markedly with increased temperatures, but the viscosity dependence on temperature is less if the fluid has a high viscosity index. A high viscosity index is highly desirable for hydraulic fluids, since the fluid is subject to wide variations in temperature and pumps and motors become very inefficient when the viscosity is either too low or too high (see fig. 3.20). Petroleum-based hydraulic fluids are subject to oxidation. The oxidation rate doubles for every 10° C increase in temperature but is very low when the temperature is below 60° C. Additives are used in the fluid to reduce oxidation, foaming and wear. A rust inhibitor is also generally used. The transmission case on tractors and self-propelled machinery is often used as the reservoir for the hydraulic system. Then the same fluid that serves as the hydraulic fluid must also lubricate the gears in the transmission.

Metal particles and other solid contaminants can be very damaging to hydraulic components. Clearances between mating parts are 10 μm or less in some hydraulic components and, if particles of that size pass between the mating parts, rapid failure can result. Thus filters are used to remove contaminants in fluid power systems. Three possible alternatives for locating a filter in a fluid power circuit include (a) between the reservoir and the pump inlet port, (b) immediately after the pump outlet port, and (c) just before the return inlet to the reservoir. Location (a) is seldom used because the pressure drop across the filter can cause subatmospheric pressures to be generated within the pump, leading to cavitation and pump damage. Location (b) is seldom used because the filter would have to withstand very high pressures in that location. Thus, location (c) is usually chosen for filters that can remove particles as small as 10 μm. In addition, a strainer or porous filter may be used in location

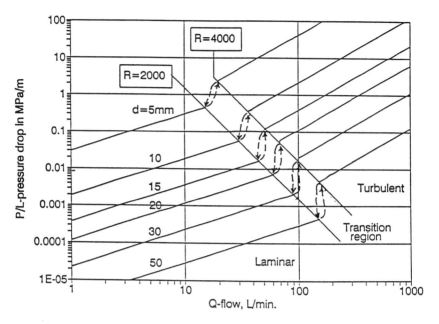

Figure 3.30–Pressure drop in hydraulic conduits for ρ = 850 kg/m³ **and** μ = 27.6 mPa·s.

(a) to prevent the largest particles (typically larger than 150 µm) from reaching the pump.

Lines consist of hydraulic tubing and/or hydraulic hoses to convey fluid between the various devices in a fluid power circuit. Both the tubing and the hoses are treated as smooth conduits for which the correct diameter must be selected to avoid excessive pressure drops in the lines. The Reynold's number is used to determine whether flow in the lines is laminar or turbulent. Reynold's number is defined as:

$$N_{Re} = \frac{4\,C\,\rho_f\,Q}{\pi\,\mu\,d} \qquad (3.47)$$

where
N_{Re} = Reynold's number (dimensionless)
ρ_f = fluid density (kg/m³)
C = 16.67 = units constant
Q = flow through conduit (L/min)
μ = dynamic viscosity of oil (mPa·s)
d = inside diameter of conduit (mm)

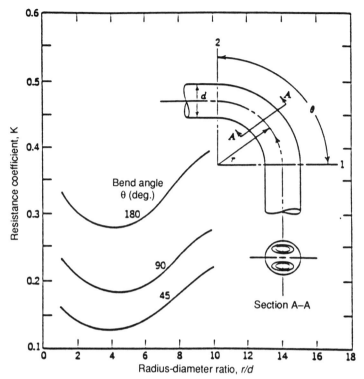

Figure 3.31–Resistance coefficients of pipe bends (Reprinted from J. J. Taborek, "Fundamentals of Line Flow", *Machine Design Magazine*, 16 April 1959).

Flow is laminar for Reynold's numbers less than 2000 and fully turbulent for Reynold's numbers above 4000. Between these limits, flow is in a transition region. The Hagen-Poiseuille law is used to compute pressure losses for laminar flow in conduits, i.e.:

$$\frac{\Delta p}{L} = \frac{2.13\,\mu\,Q}{\pi\,d^4} \tag{3.48}$$

where
Δp = pressure drop (MPa)
L = length of conduit over which pressure drop occurs (m)

For fully-turbulent flow, the pressure drop can be calculated from the following equation:

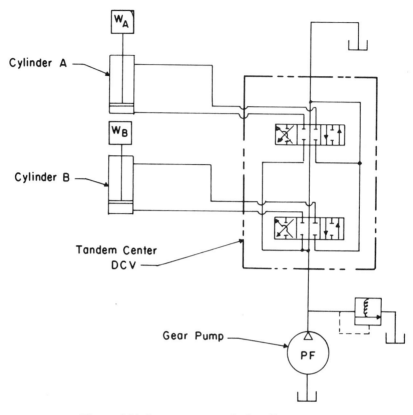

Figure 3.32–An open-center hydraulic system.

$$\frac{\Delta p}{L} = \frac{0.0333 \, \mu^{0.25} \, \rho^{0.75} \, Q^{1.75}}{d^{4.25}} \tag{3.49}$$

where terms are defined as in equation 3.48. For convenience, equations 3.48 and 3.49 have been plotted in figure 3.30.

The term, minor losses, refers to pressure drops that result from fittings, bends and sudden changes in cross-section. The pressure drop associated with bends can be calculated from the following equation:

$$\Delta p = \left(1.39 \times 10^{-4}\right) K \, \rho_f \frac{Q^2}{A^2} \tag{3.50}$$

where
   Δp = pressure drop (MPa)
   Q = flow in conduit (L/min)
   ρ_f = fluid density (kg/m^3)

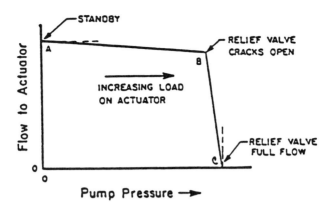

Figure 3.33–A pressure-flow diagram of an open-center hydraulic system.

A = cross-sectional area of the conduit (mm$_2$)
K = dimensionless factor taken from figure 3.31

The numerical constants in equations 3.48 through 3.50 are unit conversion factors. The pressure drop calculated from equation 3.50 is added to the pressure drop that would be calculated for a straight conduit of equal length. Pressure drops occur in the various elbows, valves and other fittings that are used in connecting fluid power circuits. Data on these pressure drops can be obtained from component manufacturers or by experimental measurement.

3.2.6 Types of Fluid Power Systems

On most modern agricultural equipment, the hydraulic pump is driven directly by the engine so that fluid power will be available whenever the engine is running. The fluid power system is said to be in standby when the pump is running but no fluid power is needed. Any power delivered to the pump during standby is converted into heat, so it is necessary to minimize shaft power to the pump during standby. As equations 3.37 and 3.38 show, there are three ways to minimize standby power. They are to minimize (a) pump pressure, (b) pump delivery, or (c) pump delivery and pressure. These approaches have led, respectively, to the open-center (OC), pressure-compensated (PC), and pressure-flow-compensated (PFC) fluid power systems that are now available for use on agricultural equipment.

Open-center systems. An open-center fluid power system (fig. 3.32) was the first system used on agricultural equipment and is still used on some smaller tractors. It includes a fixed-displacement gear pump, a relief valve, a tandem center DCV with one or more spools, and one or more actuators. A pressure-flow diagram for an OC system is shown in figure 3.33. During standby, the system operates

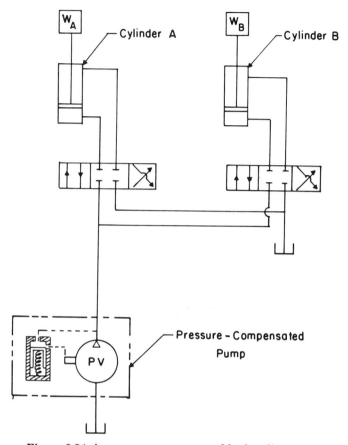

Figure 3.34–A pressure-compensated hydraulic system.

at full flow but very low pressure because the pump can discharge freely to the reservoir through the tandem-center DCV. When a DCV spool is displaced to send oil to an actuator, pressure rises only enough to move the load; flow declines slightly as η_{vp} falls with increasing pressure (see fig. 3.20). If the actuator load is too large, the relief valve cracks open and flow to the actuator declines as oil is diverted to the reservoir through the relief valve. Maximum fluid power is produced just to the left of point B in figure 3.33, i.e., just before the relief valve opens. When two or more spools in the DCV are displaced at the same time, oil flows to the actuator which requires the least pressure; the remaining actuators are stalled until the pressure can rise. If cylinder load W_A in figure 3.32 was larger than cylinder load W_B, for example, cylinder B would move first and cylinder A would be stalled until cylinder B reached the end of its stroke. Such action is called sequencing and is a major disadvantage of OC systems.

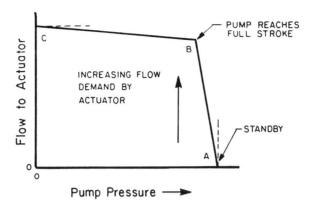

Figure 3.35–A pressure-flow diagram of a pressure-compensated hydraulic system.

Pressure-compensated systems. The pressure-compensated system (fig. 3.34) was developed to overcome some of the limitations of the OC system. The heart of the system is a pressure-compensated pump (see fig. 3.19) that automatically adjusts its delivery to stroke-control valve opens to admit oil to the pump crankcase, holds the radial pistons away from the cam and causes delivery to cease. If pressure falls, for example, when a DCV spool is displaced, the pressure in the crankcase drops and the pump again begins delivering oil. The stroke-control valve eliminates the need for a relief valve. Notice that the PC system includes a closed-center DCV; thus the pump flow is zero at standby, as shown in figure 3.35. Any number of actuators can be connected simultaneously; since the pump automatically adjusts its stroke to maintain full pressure, no sequencing will occur unless the pump reaches full stroke. If oil demand is more than the pump can supply at full stroke, the system moves to the left of point B in figure 3.35 and behaves like the OC system of figure 3.33. Thus, sequencing can occur in the PC system if one of the connected actuators has a high flow demand and a low pressure demand.

Pressure-flow-compensated systems. The most recent innovation in fluid power systems is the pressure-flow-compensated system illustrated in figure 3.36, alternatively called a load-sensing system. It includes a closed-center DCV, so that flow is near zero at standby. Unlike the PC system, however, pressure is also low at standby and rises only high enough to meet the highest pressure demand in the system. Thus, sequencing is eliminated. The heart of the PFC system is a pressure-compensated, axial-piston pump whose stroke is controlled by a differential-pressure compensating valve (DPCV). With port B of the DPCV blocked, the system would behave like a PC system with very low standby pressure, since a weak spring

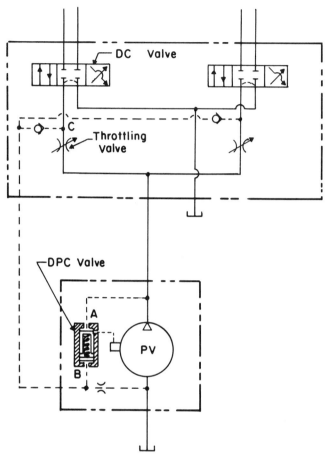

Figure 3.36–A pressure-flow-compensated hydraulic system.

is used in the DPCV. Thus, standby pressure is low, typically about 1.4 MPa. When a DCV spool is displaced, the pressure demand of the load is transmitted to port B of the DPCV via a sensing line, thus assisting the spring and allowing the pump outlet pressure to rise to 1.4 MPa above the actuator demand. The same differential pressure of 1.4 MPA appears across the throttling valve (see fig. 3.24) which regulates flow to the actuator. When two or more actuators with differing pressure demands are engaged simultaneously, the highest pressure is transmitted to port B of the DPCV. A pressure drop larger than 1.4 MPa appears across those throttling valves controlling the actuators with smaller pressure demands. Each throttling valve has a manual adjustment to allow the operator to control the speed of the associated actuator. The pressure-flow diagram for the PFC system is similar to that of figure 3.35. except

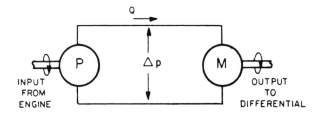

Figure 3.37–A hydrostatic drive.

that the system can operate at any point under the curves. Pressure is controlled by actuator demand and flow is controlled by the throttling valves. Standby for the PFC system is near the origin in figure 3.35, not at point A.

3.2.7 Pressure Transients

The equations that have been presented in section 3.2 are for the steady-state behavior of fluid power systems. They are generally sufficient for analyzing and designing manually-controlled fluid power systems. Pressure transients must be considered in automatically-controlled systems which incorporate feedback, or the systems may exhibit unstable behavior. The equations which describe transient behavior are beyond the scope of this textbook. However, software packages are available which enable the use of computers to simulate transient behavior of fluid power systems.

3.2.8 Hydrostatic Transmission

A hydrostatic transmission consists of a pump connected to a hydraulic motor, as illustrated in figures 3.37 and 3.38. The output speed of the transmission can be calculated from:

$$n_m = \eta_{vp}\, \eta_{vm}\, \frac{V_p}{V_m}\, n_p \qquad (3.51)$$

Two equations are available for calculating output torque:

$$T_m = \eta_{tp}\, \eta_{tm}\, \frac{V_m}{V_p}\, T_p \qquad (3.52)$$

$$T_m = \frac{V_m\, \eta_{tm}}{2\,\pi}\, \Delta p \qquad (3.53)$$

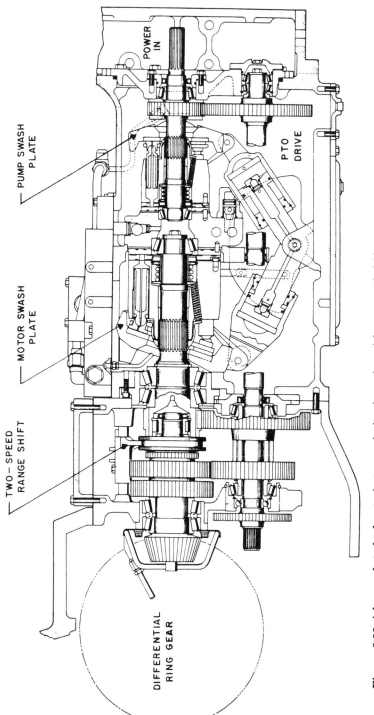

Figure 3.38-A heavy-duty hydrostatic transmission in series with a manual shift transmission (Courtesy of Case-IH).

Equation 3.52 calculates the output torque, subject to maximum pressure limit expressed by equation 3.53. Variables in equation 3.51 through 3.53 are as defined previously. To provide a variable speed ratio, the pump or the motor or both must have variable displacement. Equations 3.51 and 3.53 show that a transmission with a variable V_p and fixed V_m is a constant-torque transmission; decreasing V_p reduces the output speed but the output torque is limited by the pressure rating of the transmission and cannot be increased. Thus, power capability declines with decreasing output speed. Constant-torque hydrostatic transmissions are used in some lighter-duty vehicles which require only limited output torque.

A transmission with constant V_p and variable V_m is a constant-power transmission because, as V_m is increased to reduce the output speed, the output torque is automatically increased with no increase in system pressure. All gear-type transmissions have the constant-power feature, which is desirable in a transmission. However, the constant-power hydrostatic transmission is seldom used because of its limited range; V_m cannot reach the infinite value that would be needed to bring the output speed to zero. Also, V_m cannot reach zero without blocking the pump flow, so the tilt of the motor swash plate (see fig. 3.38) cannot be reversed and the transmission cannot reverse the direction of travel of the vehicle.

As figure 3.38 illustrates, hydrostatic transmissions for heavy-duty tractors include a variable-displacement pump and a variable-displacement motor. The variable V_p allows linear control of output speed and full reversing capability. The variable V_m allows some increase in output torque as the output speed declines. Theoretically the hydrostatic transmission can provide full-range speed control but, as figure 3.20 illustrates, the transmission efficiency would be very low at either low or high speed ratios. To improve efficiency, a mechanical transmission is often used in series with the hydrostatic transmission, as shown in figure 3.38. The mechanical transmission allows the hydrostatic transmission to work over a much narrower speed range and thus better maintain its efficiency.

Problems

3.1   An HB-section V-belt is to transmit 5 kW at a belt speed of 17 m/s. The included angle between the sides of the belt cross-section is 38° and the belt density is 1.25 g/cm^3. The arc of contact of the smaller sheave is 150°. Tensioning is accomplished by changing the position of an adjustable idler (not automatic). Calculate T_1 and T_2.

3.2   A V-belt drive has two sheaves with effective outside diameter 125 mm and 348 mm. One shaft is to be movable for take-up and the desired center distance is about 460 mm. (a) Using the ASAE Standard S211 and the example therein, select the best normally available effective belt length for an HA belt and determine the maximum and minimum center distances needed for installation and take-up. (b) Calculate the speed of the larger sheave if the smaller sheave runs at 1250 rev/min.

3.3   (a) Compute the theoretical percentage variation in speed of a chain as it leaves an 8-tooth sprocket rotating at a uniform speed. (b) Repeat for an 18-tooth sprocket.

3.4   A 9-tooth sprocket operating at 200 rev/min drives a 23-tooth sprocket through No. 45 steel detachable-link chain. The pitch of this chain is 41.4 mm and the ultimate strength is 9.34 kN. Calculate (a) average linear speed of chain in m/s; (b) recommended maximum power in kW; (c) average torque applied to the drive shaft at recommended power.

3.5   The two universal joints of a pair are operating at joint angles of 30° and 22°, respectively. The input shaft, intermediate shaft, output shaft are all in the same plane and the yokes on the two ends of the intermediate shaft are in line. (a) Calculate the lead or lag in each joint for each 15° increment of the input shaft from 0-90°. (b) Plot lead or lag versus degree rotation of the input shaft, showing a curve for each joint and one for the system. On each joint indicate where the peak occurs. (c) What changes might be made in this drive system to provide uniform rotation of the output shaft?

3.6   Two shafts are connected by a universal joint which is operating at a joint angle of 30°. The speed of the input shaft is 1000 rev/min. (a) Calculate and plot the speed of the output shaft through one full revolution of the input shaft. (b) Determine the angle of the input shaft at which acceleration of the output shaft is at a maximum.

3.7   A hydrostatic drive includes a pump with $C_f = 9.9 \times 10^6$ cm^3 and $A \cdot C_L = 4.53 \times 10^{-8}$ cm^3; equations for pump efficiencies are given in problem 3.11. The pump is hydraulically coupled to a motor whose efficiency equations are given in problem 3.14 and with $C_f = 2.5 \times 10^6$ cm^3 and $A \cdot C_L =$

4.0×10^{-8} cm^3. The viscosity of the oil in the hydrostatic drive is 27 mPa·s. Assume the pump speed is held constant at 2200 rev/min. The pump displacement (V_p) can be changed from 120 cm^3/rev for forward travel to 120 cm^3/rev for reverse travel. Motor displacement (V_m) is 120 cm^3/rev when $V_p = 0$ and changes linearly with V_p to a minimum of 60 cm^3/rev when $V_p = 120$ cm^3/rev. Assuming the torque load on the transmission is such that $\Delta p = 39$ MPa, calculate the following variables at 10 increments of V_p from 0 to 120 cm^3/rev: (a) η_{vp}, (b) η_{tp}, (c) η_{pp}, (d) torque, and (e) power required to drive the pump, (f) oil flow rate in the pump-motor circuit (g) η_{vm}, (h) η_{tm}, and (i) η_{pm}, (j) motor output speed, (k) torque, and (l) power and (m) overall power efficiency of the hydrostatic drive. Note that this is a good spread sheet problem. Also, with pump delivery known, n_m depends on η_{vm} and vice versa so iteration is required.

3.8   Same as problem 3.7, except $\Delta p = 15$ MPa because of reduced torque load on the hydrostatic drive.

3.9   A hydraulic piston pump with a displacement of 10.54 cm^3/rev has a rated speed of 1800 rev/min and rated pressure of 10.3 MPa. The leakage flow is given by:

$$Q_{Lp} = 0.00368 \, \Delta p$$

Using the equation in this problem and in the text, (a) calculate the speed (in terms of Δp) at which $\eta_{vp} = 0$. (b) Starting at this minimum speed and ending at rated speed, plot η_{vp} versus pump speed for Δp values of 5 and 10 MPa, i.e., plot two curves on the graph. (c) Specify the speed and pressure ranges in which this pump can be operated if η_{vp} is to be 0.95 or greater.

3.10   For the pump of problem 3.9, the friction torque can be calculated using the following equation:

$$T_{fp} = 0.0014 \, n_p$$

where T_{fp} = friction torque in N·m and n_p = pump speed in rev/min. Calculate the (a) friction torque when the pump is running at rated speed, (b) theoretical, and (c) actual shaft torque, and (d) torque efficiency when the pump is working at rated pressure. (e) Also plot η_{tp} versus pump pressure for pressures ranging from 0.1 MPa to rated pressure and for pump speeds of 900 and 1800 rev/min, i.e., plot two curves on the graph. (f) Specify the speed and pressure ranges in which this pump can be operated if η_{tp} is to be 0.85 or greater.

3.11   (a) Using equations from the text and from problem 3.9, derive the following equation for the volumetric efficiency of a pump:

$$\eta_{vp} = 1 - \left(\frac{2\pi\, A\, C_L}{V_p}\right)\left(\frac{\mu\, n_p}{C_u\, \Delta p}\right)^{-1}$$

where
μ = viscosity (mPa·s)
n_p = pump speed (rev/min)
Δp = pressure rise (MPa)
$C_u = (3 \times 10^{10})/\pi$ = constant inserted to make a dimensionless variable

Note that, for normal values of μ, n_p, and Δp, the magnitude of the dimensionless variable is very small. The quantity $(2\pi\cdot A\cdot C_L/V_p)$ is also dimensionless when V_p = pump displacement in cm^3/rev, A = leakage area in cm^2, and C_L = leakage constant in cm. (b) Using equations from the text and from problem 3.10, derive the following equation for the torque efficiency of a pump:

$$\eta_{tp} = \left[1 + \left(\frac{2\pi C_f}{V_p}\right)\left(\frac{\mu\, n_p}{C_u\, \Delta p}\right)\right]^{-1}$$

The quantity, $(2\pi\cdot C_f/V_p)$ will be dimensionless when C_f = friction constant in cm^3. (c) Assume that $\mu = 25$ mPa·s, $\Delta p = 30$ MPa, $V_p = 120$ cm^3/rev, $A \cdot C_L = 4.53 \times 10^{-8}$ cm^3 and $C_f = 9.91 \times 10^8$ cm^3. Letting n_p range from 200 to 2500 rev/min, plot η_{vp}, η_{tp}, and η_{pp} all versus the dimensionless variable $(\mu\cdot n_p/C_u\, \Delta p)$. Compare your results with the curves plotted in figure 3.20.

3.12 A pump with characteristics as given in problems 3.9 and 3.10 is operated at rated speed and pressure. Calculate the (a) pump delivery in L/min (b) required torque to drive the pump, and (c) the shaft power.

3.13 In a throttling valve as illustrated in figure 3.24, let the pressure be p_i at the inlet port, p_o at the outlet port and p_x in the passage between the hand-controlled orifice and the spool-controlled orifice. Let the flow area of the hand-controlled orifice be A_m (for manually controlled) and the area through the spool be A_a (for automatically controlled). (a) Starting with equation 3.39, derive an equation for p_x in terms of p_i, p_o, A_m, and A_a. (b) Calculate the value of p_x when $p_i = 14$ MPa, $p_o = 6$ MPa, and $A_m = A_a$. (c) Also calculate the value of A_m and A_a required to deliver 70 L/min of flow through the valve. (d) Assuming the pressure at outlet port rises to 8 MPa with no change in A_m, to what value must A_a automatically change to maintain 70 L/min of flow through the valve. (e) repeat part (d) except let the pressure at the outlet port fall to 4 MPa.

3.14 The leakage and friction equations for a motor are the same as those for a pump as given in problems 3.9 and 3.10, respectively. (a) Derive the following equation for volumetric efficiency of a motor:

$$\eta_{vm} = \left[1 + \left(\frac{2\pi C_L A}{V_m}\right)\left(\frac{\mu n_m}{C_u \Delta p}\right)^{-1}\right]^{-1}$$

(b) Derive the following equation for torque efficiency of a motor:

$$\eta_{Tm} = 1 - \left(\frac{2\pi C_f}{V_m}\right)\left(\frac{\mu n_m}{C_u \Delta p}\right)$$

where, in both of the above equations, symbols are as defined in problem 3.11 except that subscript m denotes a hydraulic motor. (c) Assume that $\mu = 25$ mPa·s, $\Delta p = 25$ MPa, $V_m = 60$ cm³/rev, $A \cdot C_L = 0.4 \times 10^{-7}$ cm³, $C_f = 0.025 \times 10^8$ cm³. Letting n_m vary from 200 to 2000 rev/min, plot η_{vm}, η_{tm}, and η_{pm} all versus the dimensionless variable and compare your results with figure 3.20.

3.15   On the double-acting cylinder of figure 3.29, let port 2 be the port on the right (the rod-end of the cylinder) and port 1 be the port on the left. The piston and rod have diameters of 75 mm and 25 mm, respectively, and the maximum stroke length of the cylinder is 200 mm. One port of the cylinder is to be connected to a hydraulic system which has a rated pressure of 10 MPa and produces a maximum flow of 50 L/min; the other cylinder port is to be connected to the reservoir, which is at zero gage pressure. When the cylinder is extending with port 2 connected to the reservoir, calculate (a) the maximum force that can be exerted, (b) the rod speed, and (c) the length of time required to fully extend the cylinder. (d) Also calculate the flow rate of oil delivered from port 2 to the reservoir. Next, with port 1 connected to the reservoir while retracting the cylinder, calculate (e) the maximum force, (f) rod speed, and (g) length of time to fully retract the cylinder. (h) Also calculate the flow rate of oil from port 1 to the reservoir.

3.16   Rework problem 3.15, but use dimensions of a cylinder assigned by the instructor.

3.17   The flow through the throttling valve of figure 3.24 is 50 L/min while the pressure drop across the valve is 10 MPa. (a) Compute the rate of heat generation (in kW) due to the power loss in the valve. (b) If the throttling valve discharges into a reservoir whose capacity is 20 L, how much time would be required to completely displace all of the oil in the reservoir? (c) During the time calculated in part b, how much heat energy would be delivered from the valve to the reservoir? (d) If no energy was dissipated from the reservoir during that time, how much would the oil temperature increase in the reservoir? Assume the oil density is 900 kg/m^3 and the specific heat of the oil is 2.3 kJ/kg-° C. (Note that the true temperature rise would be less than that of part d because heat is dissipated from the reservoir).

3.18   A hydraulic fluid with dynamic viscosity of 27.6 mPa·s and density of 850 kg/m^3 is to be conveyed through hydraulic tubing at the rate of 75 L/min. Calculate (a) the smallest diameter tubing which would permit laminar flow, (b) the pressure drop per meter of tubing, and (c) the power loss per meter of tubing. (d) Use figure 3.30 to do an approximate check on the calculated pressure drop.

3.19   Same as problem 3.18, except use the smallest diameter tubing which would give fully turbulent flow.

3.20   A 90° bend of radius 40 mm is to be formed in the hydraulic tubing of problem 3.18. Calculate the additional pressure drop that would occur in the tubing due to the bend.

3.21   Same as problem 3.20, except use the hydraulic tubing of problem 3.19.

3.22   Assume both hydraulic cylinders of figure 3.32 have a bore of 60 mm, a rod diameter of 25 mm and a maximum stroke of 200 mm. The relief valve cracks open at a pressure of 15 MPa. A load of 30 kN rests on cylinder A while a load of 40 kN rests on cylinder B. The pump delivers a flow rate of 60 L/min at rated speed. Note that the pump pressure is zero when both DCVs are in the neutral position. If the operator moves the handles on both DCVs simultaneously to try to raise both loads and continues to hold the handles in the raise position, the pump pressure will increase from zero to one level, later to a second level and still later to a third level., i.e., there will be three phases of operation. Neglecting line losses, (a) calculate the pressure level during the first phase, (b) calculate the duration of the phase, and (c) describe the oil flow, i.e., where would the system be operating on figure 3.33 and to where would the pump be delivering the oil? For answers (d), (e), and (f), repeat steps (a), (b), and (c) for phase 2. For answers (g), (h), and (i), repeat steps (a), (b), and (c) for phase 3.

3.23   Repeat problem 3.22, except the relief valve cracks open at 10 MPa. Also, the number of phases may not be equal to three, as in problem 3.22; you are to determine how many phases will occur.

3.24   In the PC system of figure 3.34, the cylinders have the same dimensions as in problem 3.22. On figure 3.35, the pressures are 15.5 MPa at point A and 15 MPa at point B; the pump deliveries are 60 L/min at point B and 63 L/min at point C. The loads on the cylinders are the same as those in problem 3.22. Neglecting line losses, predict the behavior of the system if the operator holds both DCV handles to try to extend both cylinder loads simultaneously, i.e., calculate system pressures, flows and durations of those conditions as in problem 3.22.

3.25   Assume that cylinder A of figure 3.36 is connected to the left DCV of figure 3.36 and the flow is controlled by throttling valve A. Cylinder B is connected to the right DCV and the flow is controlled by throttling valve B. The cylinders have the same dimensions as given in problem 3.22. A weight of 30 kN rests on cylinder A while 40 kN of weight is on cylinder B. The pressure drop across the DPCV is 1.4 MPa. The pump is capable of delivering 60 L/min and both throttling valves are set to transmit 25 L/min. Now assume that the operator hold both DCV handles to attempt to raise both cylinder loads simultaneously. Neglecting line losses, calculate (a) the pump outlet pressure, the pressure on the piston of (b) cylinder A, and (c) cylinder B, the pressure drop across (d) throttling valve A, and (e) throttling valve B, and the power loss in (f) throttling valve A,, and (g) throttling valve B.

3.26   Repeat problem 3.25 except that the weight is 40 kN on both cylinders.

4

Tractor Hitching, Traction, and Testing

Introduction

Tractors frequently serve as the power source for field machines. A hitch connects the implement to the tractor. The tractor provides the tractive force to move the implement through the field. Thus, this chapter deals with tractor hitching and traction. Standard testing procedures have been developed for tractors and tractor testing is also discussed in this chapter.

4.1 Hitching Systems

4.1.1 Principles of Hitching

Most agricultural operations involve hitching some type of implement to a tractor. The forces transmitted through a hitch can affect the performance of both the tractor and the implement. Modern hitches include feedback for automatic control of pull and/or depth of tillage implements. In addition to transmitting forces, the hitch may also be required to carry the implement for transport.

Figure 4.1–A tractor with a pto drive and three-point hitch.

4.1.2 Types of Hitches

Early tractors included only a drawbar hitch, which permitted pulling but not carrying an attached implement. The three-point hitch has now become standard equipment on most tractors. The tractor of figure 4.1 is equipped with both a drawbar and a three-point hitch. Terminology of a three-point hitch is illustrated in figures 4.2 and 4.3. The points of attachment of the hitch links to the tractor are called link points, while the links are attached to the implement at the hitch points. Quick-attaching couplers (fig. 4.4) have been developed to allow faster attachment of three-point hitches to implements. Dimensions of three-point hitches have been standardized by ASAE since 1959. Table 4.1 shows four of the hitch categories that have been standardized for different sized tractors; in addition, there is a category zero hitch standard for garden tractors. The hitch dimensions that are standardized include hitch pin diameters, mast height and lower hitch point spread. Exact dimensions can be found by referring to ASAE Standard S217. There are also ASAE standards relating to the drawbar; Standard S207 specifies minimum vertical loads which drawbars must withstand, while Standard S203 specifies the location of the drawbar hitch point relative to the pto shaft.

An implement with a mast (fig. 4.3) can be carried entirely by the tractor and such implements are said to be fully mounted. Semi-mounted implements are attached to the tractor by only the two

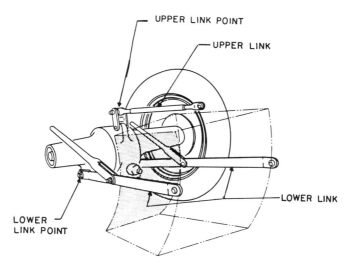

UPPER LINK POINT

UPPER LINK

LOWER LINK

LOWER
LINK POINT

Figure 4.2–A three-point hitch for a tractor (Reprinted from ASAE
Standard S217.10, Three-point free-link attachment for hitching
implements to agricultural wheeled tractors, reconfirmed December,
1989. NOTE: ASAE Standards, Engineering Practices, and Data are
informational and advisory only. Their use by anyone engaged in
industry or trade is entirely voluntary. The ASAE assumes no
responsibility for results attributable to the application of these ASAE
Standards, Engineering Practices, and Data. Conformity does not ensure
compliance with applicable ordinances, laws and regulations. Prospective
users are responsible for protecting themselves against liability for
infringement of patents.).

lower links and the ground must provide part of the implement
support. Semi-mounted moldboard plows are the best known
example of this type of hitch. Thus, the three types of hitching
include towed (for implements hitched to the drawbar), semi-
mounted and fully mounted implements.

4.1.3 Hitching and Weight Transfer

Hitching affects both vertical and horizontal force relations
between tractor and implement. Vertical effects on the tractor are of
special interest because of their effect on the tractive performance of
the tractor. The force imposed on the tractor by the implement
(fig. 4.5) could be transmitted through a drawbar or through a semi-
mounted or fully mounted hitch. The following equations can be
obtained by taking moments about points C_2 and C_1, respectively:

$$R_r = \frac{m_t g(x_1 - x_2)}{x_1} + \frac{F_{hx}z}{x_1} + F_{hz} \qquad (4.1a)$$

$$R_f = \frac{m_t g x_2}{x_1} - \frac{F_{hx}z}{x_1} \qquad (4.2a)$$

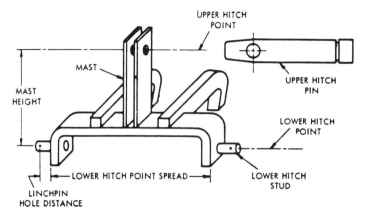

Figure 4.3–Three-point hitch connections on an implement (Reprinted from ASAE Standard S217.10, Three-point free-link attachment for hitching implements to agricultural wheeled tractors, reconfirmed December, 1989. NOTE: ASAE Standards, Engineering Practices, and Data are informational and advisory only. Their use by anyone engaged in industry or trade is entirely voluntary. The ASAE assumes no responsibility for results attributable to the application of these ASAE Standards, Engineering Practices, and Data. Conformity does not ensure compliance with applicable ordinances, laws and regulations. Prospective users are responsible for protecting themselves against liability for infringement of patents.).

where

R_r = total vertical soil reaction on rear wheels (kN)

R_f = total vertical soil reaction on front wheels (kN)

Figure 4.4–Three-point hitch with quick-attaching coupler (Courtesy of Deere and Co.).

TABLE 4.1. THREE-POINT HITCH CATEGORIES*

Category	Maximum Drawbar Power kW (hp)	
I	15 - 35	(20 - 45 hp)
II	30 - 75	(40 - 100 hp)
III and III-N	60 - 168	(80 - 225 hp)
IV and IV-N	135 - 300	(180 - 400 hp)

* Reprinted from ASAE Standard S217.10, Three-point free-link attachment for hitching implements to agricultural wheeled tractors, reconfirmed December, 1989.

NOTE: ASAE Standards, Engineering Practices and Data are informational and advisory only. Their use by anyone engaged in industry or trade is entirely voluntary. The ASAE assumes no responsibility for results attributable to the application of these ASAE Standards, Engineering Practices, and Data Conformity does not ensure compliance with applicable ordinances, laws and regulations. Prospective users are responsible for protecting themselves against liablity for infringement of patents.

m_t = tractor mass (Mg)

g = acceleration of gravity = 9.801 m/s^2

F_{hz} = z-component of hitch force (kN)

F_{hx} = x-component of hitch force (kN)

x_1 = wheelbase of tractor (mm)

x_2 = distance from rear axle center to tractor center of gravity (mm)

z = distance from ground to intersection of R_r with line of pull (mm)

Points C_1 and C_2 are directly under the axle centers when a tractor is sitting on level ground with $F_{hx}=0$, but move forward somewhat due to rolling resistance when the tractor is moving. The vertical wheel forces calculated from equations 4.1a and 4.2a when $F_{hx}=F_{hz}=0$ are

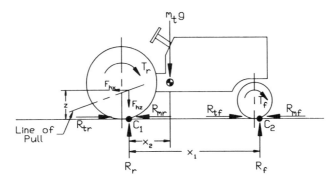

Figure 4.5–Force and moment relations for a tractor when pulling an implement at a uniform velocity on level ground.

called the static wheel reactions. The quantity, $(F_{hx} \cdot z / x_1)$, is called weight transfer because it is removed from the front wheel reaction and added to the rear wheel reaction due to the moment of the pull transmitted through the hitch. If the line of pull is inclined as shown in figure 4.5, an additional term, F_{hz}, is also added to the rear wheel reaction. Some weight transfer is helpful on 2WD (two-wheel-drive, typically rear-wheel-drive) tractors because the tractive ability of the drive wheels is limited by the vertical soil reaction. However, too much weight transfer will bring R_f to zero, upon which the front wheels will raise off the ground. For 4WD (four-wheel-drive) tractors, weight transfer is not helpful because tractive effort gained at the rear wheels is lost at the front wheels.

While equations 4.1a and 4.2a give exact values for wheel reactions, they are difficult to use in practice. The distances, x_2 and z, are not easily measured and are constantly changing during agricultural operations. Thus, an approximate method has been developed for computing wheel reactions. The approximate equations are:

$$R_r = R_{ro} + C_{dw} F_{hx} \qquad (4.1b)$$

$$R_f = R_{fo} - C_{dw} F_{hx} \qquad (4.2b)$$

where

R_{ro} = $m_t g (x_1 - x_2)/x_1$ = static rear wheel reaction (kN)
R_{fo} = $m_t g x_2 / x_1$ = static front wheel reaction (kN)
C_{dw} = dynamic weight coefficient (dimensionless)

Experimental studies have shown that the approximate values for C_{dw} are 0.20, 0.45, and 0.65 for towed, semimounted, and fully mounted hitching, respectively. The C_{dw} values were chosen to incorporate the effect of force F_{hz} on the rear wheels; thus, equation 4.2b somewhat overestimates the weight transfer from the front wheels.

4.1.4 Control of Hitches

A single-acting hydraulic cylinder is usually provided to raise the lower links of a three-point hitch and lowering is accomplished by the weight of the attached implement. In the system illustrated in figure 4.6, the cylinder rotates a rockshaft; arms attached to the ends of the rockshaft lift the lower links to raise the hitch. A feedback control system is provided as a standard feature of three-point hitches so that the hitch movement will mimic the movement of the hitch control lever. In the system shown in figure 4.6, moving the position-control handle leftward pulls on the spool of the main control

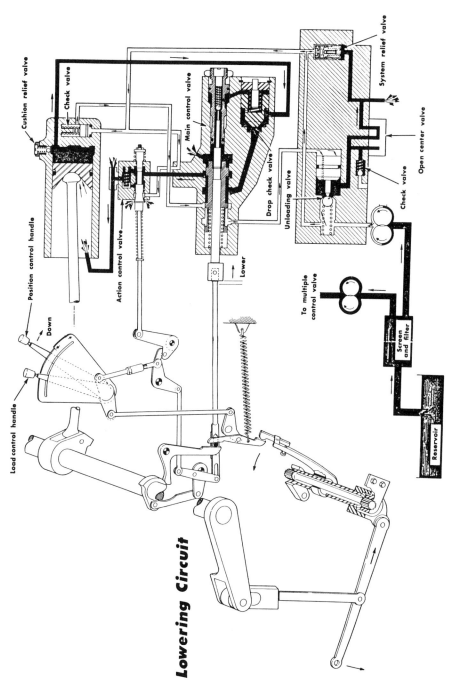

Figure 4.6–A combination draft and position control system for a tractor hitch (Courtesy of Case-IH).

valve, initiating oil flow to the cylinder to raise the hitch. As the hitch raises, a cam on the rockshaft pushes on the spool of the main control valve so that hitch movement stops at a position corresponding to that of the position control handle. Conversely, when the position control handle is moved to the right, the hitch mimics that movement in lowering as the control valve releases oil from the cylinder.

With the first three-point hitches, when a tractor was pulling a heavy-duty tillage implement under varying field conditions, the operator would raise the hitch slightly when the pull became excessive in heavy soils and would again lower the hitch when the pull subsided in lighter soils. Engineers soon modified the three-point hitch controls to accomplish such raising and lowering automatically. In figure 4.6, a torsion bar is used to sense force in the lower links; as the force increases, twisting of the torsion bar moves a linkage to pull out on the spool of the main control valve and causes the lower links to be lifted. Conversely, declining force in the lower links causes them to be lowered. Just as the position control handle is used to set the desired position of the lower links, the load (draft) control handle is used to set the desired amount of force in them. On some small tractors, draft sensing is accomplished by sensing compressive force in the top link. In recent larger tractors, the torsion bar and mechanical linkage are eliminated. Lower link sensing is accomplished by use of instrumented link pins that sense shear at the lower link points. Through circuitry that is provided, the voltage from the link pins is used to control an electrically-actuated hydraulic valve which, in turn, controls raising and lowering of the hitch.

4.2 Tires and Traction

The power of a tractor engine may be transmitted through the pto shaft, the hydraulic system or through a hitch. The latter is the most common means of transmitting tractor power and the efficiency of transmission is limited by tractive efficiency. Thus, traction mechanics which supports the design of efficient tractive devices is of great interest. Wheels are the tractive devices considered in this textbook. When a wheel works on soil, the soil must compress in order to acquire sufficient strength to provide a high tractive force to the wheel. The compression is provided by relative movement between the wheel and the soil. Consequently, some wheel slip must occur to provide traction but excessive slip is inefficient. Traction mechanics provides a means for determining optimum wheel slip.

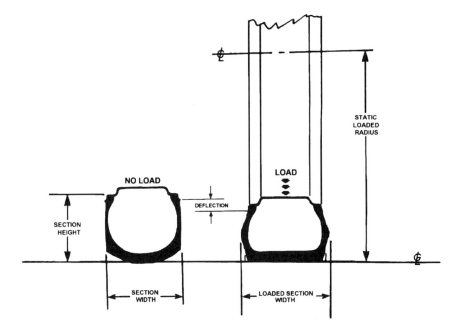

Figure 4.7–Tire and rim dimensions.

The soil strength is an important factor in traction mechanics, and is represented by the cone index.

4.2.1 Basic Tire Design

Dimensions associated with tires are illustrated in figure 4.7. The aspect ratio of a tire is the section height divided by the section width. Typical aspect ratios range from 0.75 or less for low-profile tires to 1.0 or higher for high molded tires. Agricultural tires typically deflect about 19% of their section height at rated inflation pressure when the rated vertical load is applied, and thus the loaded radius (fig. 4.7) is less than half of the outside diameter of the tire. As the tire deforms under load, the section height decreases and the width increases. The dimensions for the loaded tire in figure 4.7 are for a motionless tire. The stress distribution in a moving tire causes a slight lifting action and thus the rolling radius is slightly larger than the static loaded radius. Agricultural tractors have not yet been converted to metric sizes. Thus, the tire size gives dimensions in inches. Consider the following tire, for example:

20.8-32, 8

The first number is the section width in inches, the second number is the rim diameter in inches, and the third number is the

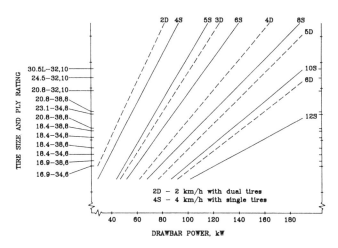

Figure 4.8–Tangential-pull limited drawbar power.

ply rating. The tire in the above example has a section width of 20.8 in., a rim diameter of 32 in. and it is an 8-ply tire.

Tire manufacturers specify the load-carrying capacity of their tires. The load-carrying capacity increases with tire size, ply rating, and inflation pressure. Travel speed affects the load rating and thus manufacturers of agricultural tires publish two sets of load rating tables. One table is for speeds up to 32 km/h and the other for speeds below 8 km/h. Considerably higher loading is permitted for the slower speeds. Lugged tires are used to convert axle torque to pull and, on such tires, the maximum tangential pull on the tire must be kept within allowable limits. Thus, the drawbar power must be limited to keep the tire bead from slipping on the rim and/or the tire sidewall from buckling. Figure 4.8 illustrates the use of dual tires to increase the tangential-pull-limited drawbar power. The figure is for bias-ply tires on a 2WD tractor. For example, if 20.8-34, 8 ply tires are on the rear axle, the maximum allowable drawbar power is 55 kW when the tractor is pulling at 4 km/h with a single tire on each rear axle. Pulling with duals (two 20.8-34, 8 ply tires on each rear axle) at 4 km/h would increase the allowable drawbar power to 96 kW. Notice that, at a given speed, the allowable power with duals is not double the power with singles; tire manufacturers derate the tangential pull on each tire by 12% when used in the dual configuration and by 18% when triples are used. Allowable drawbar power can also be increased by increasing the travel speed. When 20.8-34, 8-ply singles are used, for example, figure 4.8 shows that the allowable drawbar power increases from 55 kW to 110 kW when the travel speed is increased from 4 to 8 km/h.

The previous discussion has been on agricultural tires with bias-ply construction, but radial tires are also available. Figure 4.9

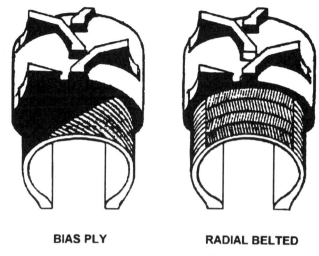

BIAS PLY   **RADIAL BELTED**

Figure 4.9–Bias and radial-ply agricultural tires.

illustrates differences between these two types of construction. With
bias-ply construction, the reinforcing cords in the tire are arranged
diagonally across the tire from bead to bead. With radial
construction, the cords are arranged perpendicular to the tire beads.
An inextensible belt is positioned between the plies and the tread to
restrict the flexing action of the radial tire. Radial construction
permits increased radial deflection and increased bulging of the
sidewall compared to biased-ply tires. Radial tires thus have a larger
footprint, resulting in approximately 10% higher pull for a given slip
or 15 to 25% reduced slip at a given pull compared to biased-ply tires.

The tires in figure 4.9 have rubber lugs on the outer tread to
provide better traction on soft soil. Agricultural tires without lugs are
available for implements and for unpowered tractor wheels. The tire
industry has established the codes listed in table 4.2 to indicate the
various types of tires. Only those with prefix R have lugs or knobs, to
indicate that they are the *rear* tires on a 2WD tractor. The R-type
tires are also used on the front wheels of 4WD tractors. The terms
lugged and *nonlugged* would be more descriptive of the tires, but the
R-designation is still used by the tire industry to indicate lugged
tires. R-2 tires have much taller lugs than R-1 tires to provide
traction in the wet conditions encountered in rice production. The
letter F in table 4.2 is used to indicate front tires, that is, tires which
are used on the front wheels of 2WD tractors. Implement tires have
the prefix I and off-road industrial tires have the prefix E.

In selecting tires for a tractor or implement that is being
designed, only a rough estimate of the tire loading may be available
initially. It is good practice to base the tire selection on the lowest ply

TABLE 4.2. STANDARD INDUSTRY CODES
FOR TIRE TYPES*

Type of Tire	Code
FRONT TRACTOR	
Rice tread	F-1
Single rib tread	F-2
Dual rib tread	F-2D
Triple rib tread	F-2T
Industrial tread	F-3
DRIVE WHEEL TRACTOR (REAR)	
Rear wheel, regular tread	R-1
Cane and rice, deep tread	R-2†
Shallow, non-directional tread	R-3
Industrial, intermediate tread	R-4
IMPLEMENT	
Rib tread	I-1
Traction tread	I-3
Plow tailwheel	I-4
Smooth tread	I-6
OFF-THE-ROAD TIRES (INDUSTRIAL)	
Rib	E-1
Traction	E-2
Rock	E-3
Rock deep tread	E-4
Rock intermediate	E-5
Rock maximum	E-6
Flotation	E-7

* Source: Reprinted with permission © 1970 Deere and Co., *Fundatmentals of service — Tires and tracks*, 4.
† Also includes similar treads for "G", "L", and "ML" series codes.

rating available when selecting a tire that can fit within available space and carry the estimated load. Also, the tires must provide a large enough contact area to carry the vertical load without excessive sinkage into soft soils. Tires on driving wheels must be able to transmit the required amount of power without exceeding the tangential pull limits. Thus many factors influence the initial tire selection. If refinement of the design shows increased tire loading, a larger ply rating can be selected to provide increased load-carrying capacity without increasing the tire size.

4.2.2 Traction Models

The equations which govern traction were developed for individual wheels but the same equations can be assembled into a traction model for an entire vehicle. The gross traction ratio relates torques and forces on a wheel (see fig. 4.5) to wheel and soil parameters, i.e.:

$$\frac{T_i}{r_{Li} \cdot R_i} = C_{gi} = 0.88 \left(1 - e^{-0.1 \cdot B_{ni}}\right) \left(1 - e^{-k_1 \cdot S}\right) + k_2 \qquad (4.3)$$

where

B_{ni} = wheel numeric (see eq. 4.4)
T_i = Traction-limited torque on wheel i (N·m)
i   = f for a front wheel or r for a rear wheel
r_{Li} = static loaded radius of wheel i (mm)
R_i = dynamic vertical load on wheel i (kN)
C_{gi} = gross traction ratio for wheel i (dimensionless)
k_1 = constant = 7.5 for bias-ply tires or 8.5 to 10.5 for radial tires
k_2 = constant = 0.04 for bias-ply tires or 0.03 to 0.035 for radial tires
S   = wheel slip (decimal)

The torque calculated using equation 4.3 is the maximum torque that can be supported by traction. If the engine and power train attempts to deliver higher torque, wheel torque will increase somewhat until maximum wheel slip is reached but will not increase further. Note that, for a given C_{gi}, the maximum torque increases in direct proportion with the dynamic load on the wheel. Also, C_{gi} increases with wheel slip and with B_{ni}. The wheel numeric (B_{ni}) is defined as:

$$B_{ni} = \frac{CI_i b_i d_i}{1000 R_i} \cdot \frac{1+5\delta_i/h_i}{1+3r_A} \qquad (4.4)$$

where

B_{ni} = dimensionless wheel numeric for *ith* wheel
CI_i = effective cone index for *ith* wheel (N/mm^2)
b_i = section width of *ith* wheel (mm)
d_i = outside diameter of *ith* wheel (mm)
δ_i = deflection of *ith* tire due to vertical loading (mm)
h_i = section height of *ith* wheel (mm)
r_A = aspect ratio = section height / section width

The wheel numeric is the product of two dimensionless terms. The numerator of the first term is a measure of the load carrying capacity of the soil, while the denominator gives the actual loading. The second dimensionless term is a correction term to account for deformation of the tire under load. As equation 4.4 indicates, B_{ni} increases with soil strength, wheel diameter, tire width and tire deflection. The quantities, b_i, d_i, and r_{Li}, can be found in ASAE Standard S220 for specific tires. If the standard is not available or for tires not listed in the standard, d_i and r_{Li} can be calculated from the tire size specifications by using the following equations:

$$d_i = 25.4\left(d_{nri} + 2\, r_A\, b_{ni}\right) \tag{4.5}$$

$$r_{Li} = 25.4\left(\frac{d_{nri}}{2} + 0.81\, r_A\, b_{ni}\right) \tag{4.6}$$

where

d_{nri} = nominal rim diameter for the ith wheel (in.)
b_{ni} = nominal section width, inches

Note the inclusion of a factor (25.4) in the above equations to convert to mm from the tire size specifications in inches. Equation 4.6 is based on an assumed tire deflection of 19% of the section height. The following aspect ratios should be used in equations 4.5 and 4.6: For low-profile, R-1 and R-2 type tires (indicated by an L in the tire size designation), use 0.70; for other R-1 and R-2 type tires, use an aspect ratio of 0.85. For low-profile F- or I-code tires (indicated by an L after the width in the size specification), use an aspect ratio of 0.78. For other F- or I-code tires, use an aspect ratio of 1.01. These choices for aspect ratio and tire deflection generally allow calculation of d_i and r_{Li} with less than 10% error.

Two other tire parameters can be calculated using the following equations:

$$\delta_i = \frac{d_i}{2} - r_{Li} \tag{4.7}$$

$$h_i = \frac{d_i - 25.4\, d_{nri}}{2} \tag{4.8}$$

The motion resistance ratio (ρ_i) is defined as follows:

$$\left(\frac{F}{W}\right)\frac{R_{mi}}{R_i} = \rho_i = k_2 + \frac{k_3}{B_{ni}} + 0.5\, SB_{ni}^{-0.5} \tag{4.9}$$

where

R_{mi} = motion resistance force on ith wheel (kN) (see fig. 4.5)
k_3 = constant = 1.0 for bias-ply tires or 0.9 for radial tires
ρ_i = motion resistance coefficient for ith wheel

    S   = slip of powered wheels or zero for unpowered wheels
Motion resistance is subtracted from the gross traction ratio to obtain
the net traction ratio (C_{ni}) for the *ith* wheel, i.e.:

$$C_{ni} = C_{gi} - \rho_i \qquad (4.10)$$

Wheel slip, S, is defined as:

where
    V_a = actual travel speed of vehicle (m/s)
    V_{ti} = theoretical travel speed of *ith* wheel (m/s)

$$S = 1 - \frac{V_a}{V_{ti}} \qquad (4.11)$$

The theoretical travel speed can be calculated from the engine speed,
tire radius and drive train speed ratio, i.e.:

$$V_{ti} = \frac{\pi \; n_e r_{Li}}{30000 \; N_{pti}} \qquad (4.12)$$

where
    n_e = engine speed (rev/min)
    N_{pti} = power train speed ratio for *ith* wheel

The tractive efficiency, η_{ti}, is the ratio of the tractive power out of the
ith wheel divided by the rotational power in, i.e.:

$$\frac{\left(R_{ti} - R_{mi}\right) V_i}{T_i \, \omega_i} = \eta_{ti} = \frac{\left(1 - S_i\right) C_{ni}}{C_{gi}} \qquad (4.13)$$

where
    R_{ti} = tractive force on *ith* wheel (kN) (see fig. 2.48)
    η_{ti} = tractive efficiency of *ith* wheel (dimensionless)
    ω_i = rotational speed of *ith* wheel (rad/s)

    The preceding equations can be used to calculate the tractive
performance of an entire vehicle. By summing forces in the
x-direction of figure 4.5:

$$F_{hx} = C_{nr} R_r + C_{nf} R_f \qquad (4.14)$$

In applying equation 4.14, R_r is the combined dynamic load on all wheels on the rear axle, while R_f is the combined load on all front wheels. The value for b_i in equation 4.4 must be the combined width of all tires on axle i. Equation 4.13 is valid for vehicles with two or four-wheel drive. For two-wheel drive, $C_{gi}=0$ for all nondriving wheels while v_{ti} is calculated only for the driving wheels.

Note that, for a specified S, F_{hx} must be calculated iteratively because B_{ni} for each axle depends on the dynamic weight on that axle, the dynamic weight depends on the weight transfer, and the weight transfer depends on F_{hx}. A suitable procedure is to assume zero weight transfer in the first iteration, which allows calculation of an initial value of F_{hx}. That value can be used in equations 4.1b and 4.2b to find new dynamic weights, after which a new value of F_{hx} can be calculated. After a few iterations, the value of F_{hx} will converge to some constant. If the dynamic reaction on the front axle reaches zero during the iterations, the entire tractor weight is supported on the rear axle and no further iteration is necessary.

What value of slip should be used in the calculations? The form of equation 4.3 is such that C_{gi} and, consequently, F_{hx} increase with slip. The draft of most soil-engaging implements increases with speed but, since slip reduces forward speed, greater slip reduces implement draft. Thus, when an equation for implement draft (see ASAE Data D497 for such equations) is added to the traction model presented above and the model is solved iteratively, the solution for the tractor-implement combination will converge to some equilibrium slip (S_e). The calculated S_e may not produce maximum tractive efficiency, so it may be desirable to change it until maximum η_t is achieved. The S_e can be increased by removing ballast to reduce the vertical loads on the powered wheels or by increasing implement draft, i.e., by use of a larger implement. The S_e can be reduced by the converse measures. The goal of traction is to transmit drawbar power, which can be calculated using equation 4.15:

$$P_{db} = V_a F_{hx} \qquad (4.15)$$

where P_{db} = drawbar power in kW. Increasing v_a reduces the F_{hx} and thus the ballast needed to transmit a given amount of drawbar power. To prevent overloading the tractor and excessively compacting the soil, it is recommended that v_a be at least 2 m/s or 7.2 km/h.

The effective cone index is measured by pushing a cone penetrometer into the soil. Dimensions of the standard penetrometer and directions for using it are given in ASAE Standard S313. The cone index varies with depth but, by averaging the cone index values over the first 150 mm of depth, an effective cone index is obtained for use in equation 4.4 for wheels that run in undisturbed soil. Typically, effective cone indexes range from 0.33 N/mm² for soft soil to 1.0 N/mm² for firm soil. If the rear wheels run in the track of the front wheels, the effective cone index for the rear wheels is increased due to the compaction provided by the front wheels. The following equation can then be used to estimate the effective cone index for the rear wheels:

$$\frac{CI_a}{CI_b} = 1 + 1.8 \, e^{-0.11 \cdot B_{ni}} \qquad (4.16)$$

where
CI_b = effective cone index before wheel passage (N/mm²)
CI_a = effective cone index after wheel passage (N/mm²)

4.3 Soil Compaction

The passage of wheels over agricultural soils results in soil compaction, that is, an increase in soil cone index as indicated by equation 4.16 and an accompanying increase in soil density. The cone index is a composite measure of soil strength which is a function of soil texture, density, and moisture. A proven relationship for field soils is not yet available, but Ayers and Perumpheral (1982) developed an equation to relate soil density to cone index and soil moisture for several artificial soils. The artificial soils consisted of mixtures of zircon sand, fire clay and water. The following equation is equivalent to the one presented by Ayers and Perumpheral:

$$\frac{\rho_d}{\rho_{do}} = \left\{ \frac{CI}{CI_o} \left[1 + C_o \left(\frac{m_s}{m_{so}} - 1 \right)^2 \right] \right\}^n \qquad (4.17)$$

where
ρ_d = dry density of soil (Mg/m³)
ρ_{do} = reference density of soil (a constant, Mg/m³)
CI = soil cone index (kPa)
CI_o = reference cone index (a constant, kPa)
m_s = soil moisture content (percent) dry basis
m_{so} = reference moisture content (a constant, percent)
C_o, n = dimensionless constants

The five constants in equation 4.17 depend upon soil type. Although values are not yet available for field soils, one of the homework problems provides data for illustrating the use of the equation with artificial soils.

Compaction results in an increase in soil density, but the effect of soil density on crop growth and yield is complex. In a relatively dry growing season, increased soil density may help to keep plant roots in contact with moisture and provide increased crop yields. Conversely, in a wet season, internal drainage is retarded by dense soil and crop yields may be reduced. Even within a given growing season, there is an optimum soil density for maximum crop production. Vomicil (1958) proposed a relationship between crop yield and soil density which can be expressed as follows:

$$\frac{Y}{Y_i} = 1 - C_y \left(\frac{\rho_d}{\rho_{di}} - 1 \right)^2 \qquad (4.18)$$

where
$\quad$ Y $\quad$ = actual crop yield
$\quad$ Y_i $\quad$ = crop yield with ideal soil density
$\quad$ ρ_d $\quad$ = actual dry density of soil (Mg/m^3)
$\quad$ ρ_{di} $\quad$ = ideal dry density of soil (Mg/m^3)
$\quad$ C_y $\quad$ = a soil-crop-climate constant

Notice from equation 4.18 that $Y=Y_i$ when $\rho_d=\rho_{do}$ and that the yield decreases with either smaller or larger values of ρ_d. A limited amount of data are provided with one of the homework problems for illustrating the use of equation 4.18.

4.4 Traction Aids

A number of techniques are available for increasing the tractive performance of a tractor. One of the earliest techniques was to use dual or triple tires on each rear axle of a 2WD tractor. Careful studies have shown that such use of duals or triples provides little increase in C_{ni} or in η_t. However, the duals or triples increase the load-carrying capacity as discussed in section 4.3.1, thus permitting much higher dynamic loads on the drive axles and, consequently, higher drawbar pull. In soft ground, duals or triples also reduce the sinkage of the tires into the soil. Whether single, dual or triple tires are used, use of increased axle loads leads to increased soil compaction. Soil compaction can be avoided and axle stress can be reduced by use of travel speeds of 7.2 km/h or higher. As equation 4.15 shows, use of higher travel speeds reduces the amount of pull needed to achieve a given drawbar power level.

Only the rear wheels of early 2WD tractors were powered; the front wheels produced motion resistance and thus only a negative contribution to tractor pull. Two methods have been used to power both front and rear wheels. Tractors designated as 4WD have all wheels powered. All of the wheels are of equal size and the rear wheels run in the tracks of the front wheels. Thus, in addition to the pulling contribution of the front wheels, the soil strengthening they provide (see eq. 4.14) increases the pulling capacity of the rear wheels. More recently, FWA (an alternate name is MFWD for Mechanical Front Wheel Drive) tractors have been designed as 2WD tractors with a front wheel assist option. The peripheral speeds of the front and rear wheels are closely matched with a slightly higher peripheral speed for the front wheels. The front wheels of FWA tractors are intermediate in size between conventional, unpowered front wheels and powered rear wheels; the front wheels on FWA tractors are also equipped with lugs to aid pulling. Since the rear tires of 2WD and FWA tractors are always wider than the front tires, the rear tires must form part of their own rut and equation 4.14 somewhat overestimates the effective cone index for the rear tires.

Optimum weight distribution varies according to type of tractor. For 2WD tractors, only enough dynamic weight is needed on the front axle to provide reliable steering. With typical weight transfer, reliable steering is achieved if approximately 25 to 30% of the static weight is carried on the front axle. For 4WD tractors, approximately 55 to 60% of the static weight is carried on the front axle; weight transfer then generates approximately equal dynamic loads on the front and rear axles. Ballasting of FWA tractors depends upon their use. When the optional FWA is disengaged, the tractor should be ballasted the same as a 2WD tractor. Conversely, when the FWA is engaged, ballasting should be that of a 4WD tractor.

To allow use of more ballast and to reduce sinkage in soft soils, some FWA tractors are equipped with dual or triple wheels on the rear axles, but steering considerations generally require use of a single tire on each front axle. Most 4WD tractors have articulated steering, i.e., the tractor has a vertical hinge between the front and rear axles which allows those axles to move out of their parallel orientation for a turn. Such tractors may be equipped with dual or triple tires on both the front and rear axles, i.e., there may be 8 or 12 tires on the tractor. As before, the benefit of the dual or triple tires is to reduce sinkage in soft soils and to allow the use of more ballast to increase traction.

The design of individual tires affects traction. Studies have been made of the effect of lug height, lug angle, and number of lugs on a tire, but few consistently clear trends have been observed from such studies. Biased-ply construction was used on all early tires, but tires with radial plies are now gaining wider use on farm equipment. Some studies have shown that radial tires provide a significant improvement in net coefficient of traction. Note that, in traction mechanics theory, traction parameters k_1, k_2, and k_3 for radial tires differ from those for bias ply tires. The reader can thus use the traction mechanics equations to assess performance differences between radial and bias ply tires under various conditions of tractor loading and soil strength.

In countries where rice is grown in flooded paddies, effective soil cone indexes will typically be less than 0.5 N/mm^2. The performance of conventional tires becomes unacceptable in such conditions because of high wheel slippage and adhesion of sticky soil to the tires. One solution has been the use of tires with very high lugs. Another solution is to attach an auxiliary wheel with steel lugs to the side of each tire. The steel lugs improve the traction coefficient and, for road transport, may be folded to avoid contact with the road surface.

4.5 Tractor Testing

4.5.1 Basic Principles of Tractor Testing

Tractor testing provides data which may be used in comparing performance of various makes and models of tractors. When comparative tests are done by agencies independent of the tractor manufacturers, the resulting competition among the manufacturers also tends to promote improvements in tractor design. The original independent agency to do tractor testing was the University of Nebraska Tractor Testing Laboratory (NTTL). It was authorized by the 1919 session of the Nebraska legislature, which passed a bill requiring testing and maintenance of service stations for all models of tractors sold within the state. The bill was prompted by the presence of inferior tractors on the market at that time. The provisions of the current law do not apply to tractors whose engines develop less than 30 kW (40 hp) nor to tractors manufactured or sold as nonagricultural tractors. Standard tests conducted at the NTTL were developed and are periodically updated by SAE (Society for Automotive Engineers) working in cooperation with ASAE. The SAE/ASAE tractor tests are also in good agreement with International Standards Organization (ISO) test standards. Thus, these tests will be referred to as SAE/ASAE/ISO tests.

The NTTL served as a uniquely independent tractor testing agency for many years. As tractor manufacturing and marketing became global in the 1980s, the Organization for Economic Cooperation and Development (OECD) test codes became the commonly accepted official test procedure for world-wide marketing. These test codes were developed in Europe. The US was not a full participant during the development of the OECD test codes, but the Farm and Industrial Equipment Institute (FIEI) (recently renamed to EMI, the Equipment Manufacturer's Institute) attended as a US observer; the OECD codes were in existence by about 1960. In 1986, the Nebraska legislature changed their tractor test law to accept OECD tests as well as those conducted by the NTTL as a prerequisite to selling tractors in the state. By 1988, the NTTL had been designated as an official OECD testing station for the United States. In addition, the NTTL has begun producing summaries of OECD tests conducted elsewhere if the tractor requires a Nebraska sales permit. The summaries are similar in format to the reports of the SAE/ASAE/ISO tests and are distributed to Nebraska farmers and other interested parties.

There are now three widely-recognized standard test procedures for testing tractors. They include the standard ASAE/SAE/ISO test, the OECD restricted test and the OECD long test. The OECD tests are described by code designations, as follows:

Code I: OECD Standard Code for the official testing of agricultural tractor performance.

Compulsory tests:
   1. Main pto
   2. Hydraulic power and lifting force
   3. Drawbar power, ballasted tractor
   4. Turning area and turning circle
   5. Position of center of gravity
   6. Braking (wheeled tractors only)
   7. External (bystander) noise (wheeled tractors only)

Tests performed and reported at manu-facturer's option:
   8. Engine
   9. Performance at the belt or belt pulley shaft
   10. Performance in a hot atmosphere
   11. Low temperature starting
   12. Drawbar power and fuel consumption for unballasted tractor

Code II: OECD Restricted Standard Code for the Official
                   Testing of Agricultural Tractor Performance.

               Compulsory tests:
               1. Main pto
               2. Hydraulic power and lifting force
               3. Drawbar power and fuel consumption for
                  unballasted tractor

               In addition, tests 3 through 11 above from the
               Standard Code may be performed and reported at the
               manufacturer's option.

Code III: OECD Standard Code for the Official Testing of
                   Protective Structures on Agricultural Tractors
                   (Dynamic Test).

Code IV: OECD Standard Code for the Official Testing of
                   Protective Structures on Agricultural Tractors (Static
                   Test).

Code V: OECD Standard Code for the Official Measurement of
                   Noise in Protective Structures on Agricultural
                   Tractors.

The SAE/ASAE/ISO test and the OECD restricted test are similar;
the ASAE/SAE/ISO procedure includes a 10-h drawbar test at 75%
load, whereas the OECD test requires only a 5-h test. The OCED test
report requires more detailed tractor specifications, including more
design data on the engine, power train, brakes, etc. In some
countries, either of the OECD tests can be conducted using the
manufacturer's test facilities provided an OECD-authorized
supervisor monitors the tests. Conversely, the SAE/ASAE/ISO tests
are all performed at the NTTL by NTTL personnel. An OECD test
can be carried out at more than one facility. For example, an
SAE/ASAE/ISO test conducted at the NTTL can be supplemented by
tests carried out in other countries to obtain an OECD test. NTTL is
not equipped to conduct OECD Code III or Code IV tests, but
NTTL personnel witness such tests conducted at the manufacturer's
facility.

   Manufacturing tolerances are an inherent part of mass
production of tractors but, because of such tolerances, there is
variation between tractors produced on the same assembly line. Thus
some procedure must be used to select the specific tractor used for
testing. The procedure used for the SAE/ASAE/ISO test or either of

the OECD tests is to permit the manufacturer to select a tractor from the assembly line and pre-test it before submitting it for an official test. In addition to pre-testing tractors prior to an official test, manufacturers routinely test tractors and their components for durability and to gain other useful information. For example, an engine may be tested to reveal which combinations of speed and torque produce the highest fuel economy.

4.5.2 Official Tractor Tests

Official OECD reports are too lengthy for distribution to the public. For every tractor model which is sold in the state of Nebraska and has an OECD test, however, the NTTL publishes a summary of the test in a format similar to that of the earlier Nebraska Tractor Test reports. An example of such a report is shown in figure 4.10. The purpose of the summary reports is to allow prospective tractor buyers to compare tractors. Performance at the pto is directly comparable by using either the OECD summaries or reports of SAE/ASAE/ISO tests. Care must be used in comparing drawbar performance because of differences in test procedures. For example, SAE/ASAE/ISO tests are run at rated engine speed, while OECD tests are run at the maximum power point.

If the tractor has a pto shaft, a two-hour pto test is run at the speed which produces maximum power. Short tests are also run at rated engine speed and at standard pto speed if these speeds differ from the speed at maximum power. In the report of figure 4.10, for example, rated engine speed was 2200 rev/min but maximum power was at 2050 rev/min. A series of short, part-load pto tests are run in the governor-controlled range. The engine is also loaded into the load-controlled range so that the torque reserve can be reported. In addition to power and speed, fuel consumption is measured during each pto test. By neglecting power losses between the engine and pto shaft, the approximate engine torque for each test can be calculated from power and speed by using equation 2.13. As indicated by equations 2.23 and 2.24, the ambient temperature and barometric pressure affect the mass air consumption of an engine and thus the atmospheric conditions prevailing during the pto tests are reported. In SAE/ASAE/ISO testing, ambient conditions are recorded for every pto test. As shown in figure 4.10, however, the average ambient conditions during all pto tests are recorded in OECD tests. Note that, in the Varying Power tests of figure 4.10, the SFC (in kg/kW·h) increases substantially as engine load decreases, as could be predicted from the discussion in section 2.2.5.

In OECD tests, the tractor is tested in each gear provided that slip and speed limits are not exceeded. The first drawbar test reported in the NTTL summary (fig. 4.10) is for the best pulling gear,

NEBRASKA OECD TRACTOR TEST 1621—SUMMARY 059
JOHN DEERE 4755 POWERSHIFT DIESEL
15 SPEED

POWER TAKE-OFF PERFORMANCE

Power HP (kW)	Crank shaft speed rpm	Gal/hr (l/h)	lb/hp.hr (kg/kW.h)	Hp.hr/gal (kW.h/l)	Mean Atmospheric Conditions
MAXIMUM POWER AND FUEL CONSUMPTION					
Rated Engine Speed—(PTO speed—998 rpm)					
177.06 (132.04)	2200	9.73 (36.82)	0.380 (0.231)	18.20 (3.59)	
Maximum Power (2 Hours)					
178.96 (133.45)	2050	9.61 (36.39)	0.371 (0.226)	18.62 (3.67)	Air temperature
VARYING POWER AND FUEL CONSUMPTION					
177.06 (132.04)	2200	9.73 (36.82)	0.380 (0.231)	18.20 (3.59)	78°F (25°C)
155.14 (115.69)	2263	8.85 (33.52)	0.394 (0.240)	17.52 (3.45)	Relative humidity
117.70 (87.77)	2292	7.16 (27.11)	0.421 (0.256)	16.44 (3.24)	39%
79.51 (59.29)	2323	5.51 (20.87)	0.479 (0.291)	14.42 (2.84)	Barometer
40.16 (29.95)	2353	3.86 (14.62)	0.665 (0.404)	10.40 (2.05)	28.74" Hg (97.33 kPa)
2.08 (1.55)	2375	2.30 (8.71)	7.651 (4.654)	0.90 (0.18)	

Maximum Torque 569 lb.-ft (771 Nm) at 1450 rpm
Maximum Torque Rise 34.5%
Torque Rise at 1000 engine rpm 12%

DRAWBAR PERFORMANCE
FUEL CONSUMPTION CHARACTERISTICS

Power Hp (kW)	Drawbar pull lbs (kN)	Speed mph (km/h)	Crank-shaft speed rpm	Slip %	Fuel Consumption lb/hp.hr (kg/kW.h)	Hp.hr/gal (kW.h/l)	Temp.°F (°C) cool-ing med	Air dry bulb	Barom. inch Hg (kPa)
Maximum Power—12th Gear									
147.76 (110.19)	6267 (27.88)	8.84 (14.23)	2201	2.43	0.455 (0.277)	15.19 (2.99)	186 (86)	58 (14)	29.07 (98.44)
75% of Pull at Maximum Power—12th Gear									
115.26 (85.95)	4697 (20.89)	9.20 (14.81)	2282	1.98	0.489 (0.297)	14.14 (2.78)	184 (84)	61 (16)	29.04 (98.34)
50% of Pull at Maximum Power—12th Gear									
78.04 (58.20)	3132 (13.93)	9.34 (15.04)	2305	1.52	0.569 (0.346)	12.15 (2.39)	181 (83)	58 (14)	29.04 (98.34)
75% of Pull at Reduced Engine Speed—13th Gear									
115.49 (86.12)	4707 (20.94)	9.20 (14.81)	1842	1.98	0.459 (0.279)	15.07 (2.97)	183 (84)	59 (15)	29.04 (98.34)
50% of Pull at Reduced Engine Speed—13th Gear									
78.12 (58.25)	3131 (13.93)	9.36 (15.06)	1865	1.52	0.519 (0.315)	13.33 (2.63)	181 (83)	58 (14)	29.04 (98.34)

Location of Test: Center for Agricultural Equipment, Lincoln Nebraska 68583-0832, U.S.A.

Dates of Test: April-May, 1989

Manufacturer: John Deere Waterloo Works, P.O. Box 3500, Waterloo, Iowa 50704

FUEL OIL and TIME: Fuel No. 2 Diesel **Cetane No.** 51.1 **Specific gravity converted to 60°/60°F** *(15°/15°C)* 0.8301 **Fuel weight** 6.912 lbs/gal *(0.828 kg/l)* **Oil SAE** 15W40 **API service classification** CD/SD **To motor** 4.915 gal *(18.606 l)* **Drained from motor** 4.667 gal *(17.666 l)* **Transmission and hydraulic lubricant** John Deere HyGard fluid **Front axle lubricant** John Deere GL-5 Gear Lubricant 85W-140 **Total time engine was operated** 28.0 hours.

ENGINE: Make John Deere Diesel **Type** six cylinder vertical with turbocharger and intercooler **Serial No.** *RG6076A102454* **Crankshaft** lengthwise **Rated engine speed** 2200 **Bore and stroke** (as specified) 4.56" × 4.75" *(115.8 mm × 120.7 mm)* **Compression ratio** 16.0 to 1 **Displacement** 466 cu in *(7634 ml)* **Starting system** 12 volt **Lubrication** pressure **Air cleaner** two paper elements **Oil filter** one full flow cartridge **Oil cooler** engine coolant heat exchanger for crankcase oil, radiator for hydraulic and transmission oil **Fuel filter** one paper element and prefilter **Muffler** vertical **Cooling medium temperature control** 2 thermostats and variable speed fan.

ENGINE OPERATING PARAMETERS: Fuel rate 66.6-72.8 lb/hr *(30.2-33.0 kg/hr)* **High idle** 2350-2400 rpm **Turbo boost** nominal 16-19 psi *(110-131 kPa)* as measured 16.5 psi *(114 kPa)*.

CHASSIS: Type front wheel assist **Serial No.** *RW4755P001033* **Tread width** rear 64.6" *(1642 mm)* to 115.7" *(2938 mm)* front 66.6" *(1691 mm)* to 87.8" *(2230 mm)* **Wheel base** 117.1" *(2974 mm)* **Hydraulic control system** direct engine drive **Transmission** selective gear fixed ratio with full range operator controlled powershift **Nominal travel speeds mph (km/h)** first 1.42 *(2.28)* second 2.03 *(3.27)* third 2.45 *(3.95)* fourth 3.08 *(4.96)* fifth 3.55 *(5.71)* sixth 4.03 *(6.49)* seventh 4.64 *(7.47)* eighth 5.33 *(8.58)* ninth 6.14 *(9.89)* tenth 6.97 *(11.22)* eleventh 8.03 *(12.93)* twelfth 8.99 *(14.46)* thirteenth 11.12 *(17.90)* fourteenth 15.56 *(25.04)* fifteenth 19.25 *(30.98)* reverse 1.96 *(3.16)*, 2.81 *(4.52)*, 4.27 *(6.87)*, 6.43 *(10.34)* **Clutch** multiple wet disc hydraulically power actuated by foot pedal **Brakes** multiple wet disc hydraulically power actuated by two foot pedals which can be locked together **Steering** hydrostatic **Power take-off** 998 rpm at 2200 engine rpm **Unladen tractor mass** 18165 lb *(8239 kg)*.

Figure 4.10–Nebraska OECD tractor test 1621 — Summary 059 (Courtesy of the University of Nebraska Tractor Testing Laboratory).

DRAWBAR PERFORMANCE AT 2050 RPM
MAXIMUM POWER IN SELECTED GEARS

Power Hp (kW)	Drawbar pull lbs (kN)	Speed mph (km/h)	Crank-shaft speed rpm	Slip %	Fuel Consumption lb/hp.hr (kg/kW.h)	Hp.hr/gal (kW.h/l)	Temp.°F (°C) cool-ing med	Air dry bulb	Barom. inch Hg (kPa)
					5th Gear				
133.33 (99.42)	16452 (73.18)	3.04 (4.89)	2192	14.78	0.502 (0.305)	13.77 (2.71)	184 (84)	55 (13)	29.13 (98.65)
					6th Gear				
145.68 (108.64)	14852 (66.06)	3.68 (5.92)	2175	8.23	0.461 (0.281)	14.98 (2.95)	184 (84)	56 (13)	29.11 (98.58)
					7th Gear				
149.31 (111.34)	13767 (61.24)	4.07 (6.55)	2051	6.59	0.444 (0.270)	15.55 (3.06)	184 (84)	56 (13)	29.10 (98.54)
					8th Gear				
147.50 (109.99)	11613 (51.66)	4.76 (7.67)	2050	4.82	0.448 (0.273)	15.41 (3.04)	187 (86)	57 (14)	29.09 (98.51)
					9th Gear				
148.21 (110.52)	10021 (44.58)	5.55 (8.93)	2052	4.04	0.447 (0.272)	15.48 (3.05)	187 (86)	58 (14)	29.08 (98.48)
					10th Gear				
150.57 (112.28)	8929 (39.72)	6.32 (10.18)	2053	3.42	0.444 (0.270)	15.58 (3.07)	186 (86)	58 (14)	29.08 (98.48)
					11th Gear				
148.54 (110.76)	7597 (33.79)	7.33 (11.80)	2053	2.88	0.446 (0.271)	15.51 (3.06)	186 (86)	58 (14)	29.07 (98.44)
					12th Gear				
151.39 (112.89)	6901 (30.70)	8.23 (13.24)	2053	2.61	0.436 (0.265)	15.85 (3.12)	186 (86)	60 (16)	29.06 (98.41)
					13th Gear				
146.82 (109.48)	5386 (23.96)	10.22 (16.45)	2053	2.16	0.449 (0.273)	15.41 (3.04)	186 (86)	61 (16)	29.05 (98.37)

DRAWBAR PERFORMANCE AT 2050 RPM
MAXIMUM POWER IN SELECTED GEARS—BALLASTED TRACTOR

Power Hp (kW)	Drawbar pull lbs (kN)	Speed mph (km/h)	Crank-shaft speed rpm	Slip %	Fuel Consumption lb/hp.hr (kg/kW.h)	Hp.hr/gal (kW.h/l)	Temp.°F (°C) cool-ing med	Air dry bulb	Barom. inch Hg (kPa)
					3rd Gear				
131.75 (98.25)	21481 (95.55)	2.30 (3.70)	2262	9.38	0.491 (0.299)	14.07 (2.77)	185 (85)	55 (13)	29.02 (98.27)
					4th Gear				
143.08 (106.70)	18882 (83.99)	2.84 (4.57)	2164	6.81	0.467 (0.284)	14.81 (2.92)	187 (86)	57 (14)	29.00 (98.21)
					5th Gear				
145.44 (108.45)	16667 (74.14)	3.27 (5.27)	2125	5.13	0.461 (0.280)	15.00 (2.95)	186 (85)	60 (16)	28.99 (98.17)
					6th Gear				
151.62 (113.06)	15727 (69.96)	3.62 (5.82)	2051	4.26	0.437 (0.266)	15.82 (3.12)	187 (86)	62 (17)	28.95 (98.04)
					7th Gear				
149.61 (111.56)	13376 (59.50)	4.19 (6.75)	2051	3.65	0.443 (0.269)	15.62 (3.08)	187 (86)	63 (17)	28.93 (97.97)
					8th Gear				
145.51 (108.50)	11246 (50.02)	4.85 (7.81)	2050	2.94	0.454 (0.276)	15.22 (3.00)	186 (86)	62 (17)	28.97 (98.10)
					9th Gear				
146.62 (109.33)	9776 (43.49)	5.62 (9.05)	2053	2.49	0.454 (0.276)	15.24 (3.00)	187 (86)	61 (16)	28.98 (98.14)
					10th Gear				
146.96 (109.59)	8607 (38.29)	6.40 (10.30)	2053	2.22	0.451 (0.274)	15.33 (3.02)	186 (86)	63 (17)	28.91 (97.90)
					11th Gear				
145.44 (108.45)	7379 (32.82)	7.39 (11.90)	2051	1.94	0.459 (0.279)	15.06 (2.97)	187 (86)	65 (18)	28.88 (97.80)
					12th Gear				
150.69 (112.37)	6817 (30.32)	8.29 (13.34)	2053	1.76	0.439 (0.267)	15.76 (3.10)	186 (86)	65 (18)	28.87 (97.77)
					13th Gear				
145.63 (108.59)	5305 (23.60)	10.30 (16.57)	2054	1.39	0.455 (0.277)	15.18 (2.99)	189 (87)	65 (18)	28.87 (97.77)

REPAIRS AND ADJUSTMENTS: No repairs or adjustments.

REMARKS: All test results were determined from observed data obtained in accordance with official OECD, SAE and Nebraska test procedures. For the maximum power tests, the fuel temperature at the injection pump return was maintained at 125° F (52° C). This tractor is equipped with a variable speed cooling fan. Since engine power is influenced by fan speed, all power tests were conducted at approximately the same ambient air temperatures. This tractor did not meet manufacturers 3 point lift capacity claim of 8870 lb (4023 kg) or 9710 lb (4404 kg) with lift assist cylinder. The pull in 3rd gear (ballasted tractor) was limited to avoid tractor bouncing. The performance figures on this summary were taken from a test conducted under the OECD restricted standard test code procedure.

We, the undersigned, certify that this is a true and correct report of official Tractor Test No. **1621,** Summary 059, December 22, 1989.

LOUIS I. LEVITICUS
Engineer-in-Charge

K. VON BARGEN
R. D. GRISSO
G. J. HOFFMAN
Board of Tractor Test Engineers

Figure 4.10–(Continued).

DRAWBAR PERFORMANCE AT 2200 RPM
MAXIMUM POWER IN SELECTED GEARS—BALLASTED TRACTOR

Power Hp (kW)	Drawbar pull lbs (kN)	Speed mph (km/h)	Crank-shaft speed rpm	Slip %	Fuel Consumption lb/hp.hr (kg/kW.h)	Fuel Consumption Hp.hr/gal (kW.h/l)	Temp.°F (°C) cool-ing med	Temp.°F (°C) Air dry bulb	Barom. inch Hg (kPa)
				3rd Gear					
128.71 (95.98)	21192 (94.27)	2.28 (3.67)	2261	10.23	0.499 (0.303)	13.85 (2.73)	186 (85)	55 (13)	29.01 (98.24)
				4th Gear					
144.03 (107.40)	18563 (82.57)	2.91 (4.68)	2202	6.23	0.467 (0.284)	14.79 (2.91)	186 (85)	55 (13)	29.00 (98.21)
				5th Gear					
143.97 (107.36)	15867 (70.58)	3.40 (5.48)	2200	4.70	0.468 (0.285)	14.77 (2.91)	186 (86)	58 (14)	28.99 (98.17)
				6th Gear					
149.72 (111.65)	14393 (64.02)	3.90 (6.28)	2202	3.91	0.448 (0.273)	15.41 (3.04)	186 (86)	62 (17)	28.96 (98.07)
				7th Gear					
147.48 (109.98)	12265 (54.56)	4.51 (7.26)	2196	3.39	0.454 (0.276)	15.24 (3.00)	186 (85)	62 (17)	28.94 (98.00)
				8th Gear					
143.79 (107.23)	10330 (45.95)	5.22 (8.40)	2199	2.58	0.466 (0.283)	14.84 (2.92)	186 (85)	62 (17)	28.97 (98.10)
				9th Gear					
143.75 (107.19)	8917 (39.66)	6.05 (9.73)	2203	2.31	0.469 (0.285)	14.75 (2.91)	186 (86)	60 (16)	28.98 (98.14)
				10th Gear					
143.85 (107.27)	7861 (34.97)	6.86 (11.04)	2196	1.94	0.466 (0.283)	14.83 (2.92)	186 (85)	63 (17)	28.91 (97.90)
				11th Gear					
141.98 (105.87)	6700 (29.80)	7.95 (12.79)	2201	1.76	0.470 (0.286)	14.71 (2.90)	185 (85)	65 (18)	28.89 (97.83)
				12th Gear					
145.55 (108.54)	6136 (27.29)	8.90 (14.32)	2199	1.58	0.461 (0.281)	14.98 (2.95)	186 (85)	65 (18)	28.89 (97.83)

TRACTOR SOUND LEVEL WITH CAB

	dB(A)
Gear closest to 4.7 mph (7.5 km/h)—7th Gear	76.5
Maximum sound level	77.0
Transport speed—no load—15th Gear	77.0
Bystander in 15th Gear	85.5

LUGGING ABILITY IN 10th GEAR

Crankshaft Speed rpm	2196	1978	1762	1537	1321	1097
Pull—lbs (kN)	7861 (34.97)	8972 (39.91)	10056 (44.73)	10775 (47.93)	10785 (47.97)	9948 (44.25)
Increase in Pull %	0	14	28	37	37	27
Power—Hp (kW)	143.85 (107.27)	147.48 (109.97)	146.73 (109.42)	136.79 (102.00)	117.81 (87.85)	90.38 (67.39)
Speed—Mph (km/h)	6.86 (11.04)	6.16 (9.92)	5.47 (8.81)	4.76 (7.66)	4.10 (6.59)	3.41 (5.48)
Slip %	1.94	2.22	2.58	2.76	2.76	2.58

THREE POINT HITCH PERFORMANCE (SAE Static Test)

Observed Maximum Pressure psi. (bar)	2530 (174)
Location	remote outlet
Hydraulic oil temperature °F(°C)	137 (58)
Location	transmission sump
Category	III
Quick attach	Yes

Hitch point distance to ground level in. (mm)	9.0 (229)	16.0 (406)	25.0 (635)	33.0 (838)	40.0 (1016)
Lift force on frame lb. " " " " " " (kN)	8700 (38.7)	9228 (41.0)	9432 (42.0)	8944 (39.8)	8283 (36.8)

with 1-44 mm. lift assist cylinder

Hitch point distance to ground level in. (mm)	9.0 (229)	16.0 (406)	25.0 (635)	33.0 (838)	40.0 (1016)
Lift force on frame lb. " " " " " " (kN)	9860 (43.9)	10570 (47.0)	10854 (48.3)	10224 (45.5)	9411 (41.9)

with 1-55 mm. lift assist cylinder

Hitch point distance to ground level in. (mm)	9.0 (229)	16.0 (406)	25.0 (635)	33.0 (838)	40.0 (1016)
Lift force on frame lb. " " " " " " (kN)	10518 (46.8)	11434 (50.9)	11576 (51.5)	10737 (47.8)	10041 (44.7)

Figure 4.10–(Continued).

TIRES AND WEIGHT

	With Ballast	Without Ballast
Rear Tires—No., size, ply & psi (kPa)	Four 20.8R42; **; 12 *(85)*	Two 20.8R42; **; 16 *(110)*
Ballast—Duals (total)	1950 lb *(885 kg)*	None
—Cast Iron (total)	1000 lb *(454 kg)*	None
Front Tires—No., size, ply & psi *(kPa)*	Two 16.9R30; ***; 24 *(165)*	Two 16.9R30; ***; 24 *(165)*
Ballast—Test Equip (total)	230 lb *(104 kg)*	None
—Cast Iron (total)	1500 lb *(680 kg)*	None
Height of Drawbar	20.5 in *(520 mm)*	19 in *(485 mm)*
Static Weight—Rear	14245 lb *(6461 kg)*	11590 lb *(5257 kg)*
—Front	8600 lb *(3901 kg)*	6575 lb *(2982 kg)*
—Total	22845 lb *(10362 kg)*	18165 lb *(8239 kg)*

THREE POINT HITCH PERFORMANCE
(OECD Static Test)

CATEGORY: III
Quick Attach: Yes

Maximum Force Exerted Through Whole Range:	5821 lbs	*(25.9 kN)*
	*6614 lbs	*(29.4 kN)*
	**7057 lbs	*(31.4 kN)*
i) Opening pressure of relief valve:	NA	
Sustained pressure with pump stalled	2530 psi	*(174 Bar)*
ii) Pump delivery rate at minimum pressure:	31.6 GPM	*(119.6 l/min)*
iii) Pump delivery rate at maximum hydraulic power:	30.6 GPM	*(115.8 l/min)*
Delivery pressure:	1750 psi	*(121 Bar)*
Power:	31.2 Hp	*(23.3 kW)*

*with 44 mm lift assist cylinder
**with 55 mm lift assist cylinder

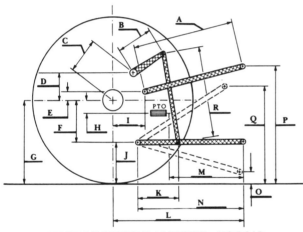

	inch	mm
A	28.1	714
B	18.4	468
C	12.9	327
D	12.9	327
E	6.8	172
F	13.0	330
G	36.1	918
H	7.0	177
I	15.1	384
J	23.1	588
K	28.2	716
L	44.3	1124
L'	49.3	1251
M	22.3	565
N	38.1	968
O	10.1	257
P	45.1	1146
Q	42.5	1080
R	37.3	946

L" to end of Quick attach

HITCH DIMENSIONS AS TESTED—NO LOAD

John Deere 4755 Powershift Diesel

Agricultural Research Division
Institute of Agriculture and Natural Resources
University of Nebraska–Lincoln
Darrell Nelson, Dean and Director

Figure 4.10–(Continued).

i.e., the gear which produces the most drawbar power. Next, the NTTL reports results of a 5-h test at 75% of the pull that produces maximum power. Listed next in the report are results of a short test at 50% of the pull that produces maximum power. The next two tests listed are again at 75% and 50% of pull, but at reduced engine speed. In the latter two tests, the tractor is shifted to a higher gear (from 12th to 13th gear in this case) and the engine speed is reduced to give approximately the same travel speed as in the earlier tests. The next three sections of the report are on series of drawbar tests in selected gears. The first series is drawbar performance of the unballasted tractor at maximum power. Note that, for the engine to produce maximum power, the drawbar load must be increased as the tractor is shifted to lower gears. Also note the increase in reported wheel slip as the drawbar pull was increased. First through fourth gears were not tested because the pull would have produced excessive wheel slip. The engine was running at 2050 rev/min to produce maximum power in the pto test and, since that same engine speed prevailed, the engine was at maximum power during the tests in gears 5th through 13th. In gears 5th and 6th, however, the drawbar load was reduced to prevent excessive slip and the engine produced less than maximum power. Gears 14 and 15 were not tested to avoid use of excessive speeds. In the second series of tests of various gears, the engine was again operated at 2050 rev/min (for peak power) but the tractor was fully ballasted. In the third series of drawbar tests of various gears, the ballasted tractor was operated at rated engine speed rather than at maximum power. Atmospheric conditions, fuel consumption and other performance parameters were reported for each of the drawbar tests mentioned above. The final series of drawbar tests show the lugging ability of the tractor. Most of the increase in pull during the lugging tests is provided by the torque reserve of the engine. The engine torque increased 34.5% and peaked at 1450 rev/min in the pto tests (see fig. 4.10). In the drawbar lugging tests, the pull increase was 37% at engine speeds of both 1537 and 1321 rev/min; a drawbar lugging test at 1450 rev/min would probably have shown a pull increase slightly above 37%.

The test report contains details as to the fuel and lubricating oil used, engine specifications and operating parameters and information about the chassis. The latter includes the gear selections available and advertised speeds in each gear. Data are given on the center of gravity location, axle loads, drawbar height and tires used which would be useful in calculating tractive performance as described in section 2.6. The lifting performance of the three-point hitch is measured and reported. Finally, sound levels inside the cab and at a bystander location are measured and reported.

Problems

4.1 Use data from Nebraska test No. 1621 (fig. 4.10) to calculate (a) the governor regulation, (b) the peak-torque speed as a percent of rated speed. (c) What is the engine torque reserve as reported on the Nebraska test? You can assume that governor's maximum speed is the same as rated speed in the Nebraska test.

4.2 Rework problem 4.1, except use data from a Nebraska Test specified by the instructor.

4.3 Using data from the maximum power test in fifth gear of Nebraska Test No. 1621 (fig. 4.10), calculate (a) the ambient air density, (b) the theoretical air consumption rate of the turbocharged, intercooled engine, (c) the pressure, and (d) the temperature of the air in the intake manifold,, (e) the estimated volumetric efficiency of the engine, (f) air consumption by the engine, (g) air/fuel ratio, and (h) equivalence ratio of the engine. What would the (i) air consumption, and (j) air/fuel ratio be if the intercooler was removed from the engine? In working part (c) of the engine, note that the measured boost at maximum power is given in the report. In working part (d), assume that the efficiency of the turbocharger compressor is 0.7.

4.4 Rework problem 4.3, except use data from a Nebraska Test specified by the instructor.

4.5 Using data from Nebraska OECD Test 1621 (fig. 4.10), calculate (a) the distance x_2, i.e., the horizontal distance from the rear axle center to the tractor center of gravity (Note: the unballasted weight distribution in figure 4.10 was obtained with the tractor unballasted except for full tanks and with 75 kg of mass on the tractor seat). (b) Then, assuming that a level drawbar load is attached to the drawbar, calculate the dynamic weight coefficient, C_{dw}. (c) For each of the gears used in the drawbar tests of MAXIMUM POWER IN SELECTED GEARS, calculate R_r and R_f and plot these soil reactions versus drawbar pull.

4.6 Assume that the tractor of problem 4.5 is operating on a soil with a soil cone index of 1.5 N/mm^2 (a very firm soil). (a) Making use of equations 4.3 through 4.15 as needed, calculate the maximum drawbar pull that can be produced by the tractor at 10% wheel slip while pulling a semimounted plow.

To simplify the problem, assume that the front wheel assist is disengaged. Note that ASAE Standard S220 can be used to obtain needed dimensions for the tires, or the dimensions can be calculated from the tire size as indicated in the text. Also note that an iterative solution is necessary, since the pull depends on the value of the wheel numerics, the wheel numerics depend on the tire loading and, because of weight transfer, the tire loading depends on pull. Thus, you may save time by preparing a computer program to calculate the traction-limited pull. If, during the iterations, the pull becomes large enough to reduce the front wheel vertical reaction to zero, no further iteration is necessary since the entire tractor weight is then carried on the rear axle. (b) Repeat part (a) but use wheel slip of 15%. (c) Repeat part (a) but use wheel slips of 10, 15, 20, 25, and 30%; then plot maximum pull versus wheel slip.

4.7   Same as problem 4.6, except that the soil cone index is 0.5 N/mm^2 (a medium soil).

4.8   Same as problem 4.7, except that the soil cone index is 0.25 N/mm^2 (a soft soil).

4.9   (a) Using data from problem 4.6 and equation 4.16, determine the cone index before and after passage of the rear wheels of the tractor (ignore any compaction due to passage of the front wheels). (b) Then use equation 4.17 to estimate the dry density of the soil before and after wheel passage assuming $m_s=17\%$. Use the following constants in equation 4.17:

$$\rho_{do} = 1.0 \text{ Mg/m}^3$$
$$CI_0 = 1000 \text{ kPa or } 1.0 \text{ N/mm}^2$$
$$C_o = 5.1 \text{ (dimensionless)}$$
$$m_{so} = 5\%$$
$$n = 0.1333$$

(c) Finally, use equation 4.18 to assess the change in crop yield due to the passage of the rear wheels. Constants for use in equation 4.18 are given in the table below. Assume conditions are similar to those for 1981 in the table. (Note: Equation 4.17 is very sensitive to m_s and equation 4.18 is very sensitive to ρ_d. Thus the equations are useful for illustrating trends but not for reliable prediction of actual yields).

Year	Soil Type	Y_i (Mg / ha)	ρ_{di} (Mg / m^3)	C_y
1976	Clay	16.0	0.99	5.74
1977, 80	Clay	12.3	1.13	17.96
1981	Sandy-loam	11.4	1.375	9.46

Crop Corn silage.
Data source.

4.10 Same as problem 4.9, except m_s=20%.

5

Soil Tillage

Introduction

Tillage may be defined as the mechanical manipulation of soil for any purpose, but usually for nurturing crops. In agriculture, the objectives of soil tillage are:

1. To develop a desirable soil structure for a seedbed or a rootbed. A granular structure is desirable to allow rapid infiltration and good retention of rainfall, to provide adequate air capacity and exchange within the soil, and to minimize resistance to root penetration. A good seedbed, on the other hand, is generally considered to imply finer particles and greater firmness in the vicinity of the seeds to enhance moisture absorption by the seeds needed for germination.

2. To control weeds or remove unwanted crop plants (thinning).

3. To manage plant residues. Thorough mixing of residue is desirable from the tilth and decomposition standpoints, whereas retention of residue on the soil surface or in the top layers reduces erosion. On the other

hand, complete coverage is sometimes necessary to control over-wintering insects or to prevent interference with precision operations such as planting and cultivating certain crops.

4.   To minimize soil erosion by following such practices as contour tillage, listing, and proper placement of plant residue.

5.   To establish specific surface configurations for planting, irrigating, drainage, or harvesting operations.

6.   To incorporate and mix fertilizers, manure, pesticides, or soil amendments into the soil.

7.   To accomplish segregation. This may involve moving soil from one layer to another, removal of rocks and other foreign objects, or root harvesting.

5.1 Methods and Equipment

A tillage tool is defined in this textbook as an individual soil-engaging element, such as a plow bottom or a disk blade. A tillage implement consists of a single tool or a group of tools, together with the associated frame, wheels, hitch, control and protection devices, and any power transmission components. For tillage implements, the process system consists of the tillage tools, while the other components form the support systems.

Throughout the world farmers choose from a variety of implements for soil tillage. The set of implements which an individual farmer chooses depends on local customs, crop type, soil moisture level, soil type, and the amount of plant residue from the previous crop. Tillage implement selection is also affected by the availability of implements, power units, labor, and capital.

Erosion of soil by wind or moving water is a problem which plagues agriculture in many parts of the world. The erosion process removes nutrients and other chemicals from land as well as soil. Some farmers in North America have begun to use conservation tillage, a practice which leaves plant residue on the soil surface to reduce erosion. Practicing *conservation tillage* can reduce the time and energy required for tillage, although this practice frequently requires better management than *conventional tillage*.

5.1.1 Conventional Tillage System

Tillage operations for seedbed preparation are often classified as *primary* or *secondary*, although the distinction is not always clear-cut. A primary tillage operation constitutes the initial, major soil-working operation after harvest of the previous crop; it is normally designed to reduce soil strength, cover plant materials, and rearrange aggregates. Secondary tillage operations are intended to create refined soil conditions following primary tillage. The final tillage operation prior to planting a crop is usually secondary tillage, but farmers may use more than one secondary tillage operation. In some situations, a tillage operation may fit the definition of both secondary and primary tillage. For example, a farmer may prepare a field for planting winter wheat with a single disking operation after harvesting soybeans. This single disking operation is both the initial tillage operation after harvest and the final tillage operation before planting.

Primary tillage. Most farmers use only one primary tillage operation after harvesting a crop. An exception is when a farmer uses a subsoiler in the fall shortly after harvest followed by another primary tillage in the spring. Implements used for primary tillage are moldboard plows, disk plows and tillers, chisel plows, subsoilers, stubble-mulch plows and tillers, rotary tillers, listers, and bedders.

Moldboard plows. All moldboard plows are equipped with one or more tillage tools called plow bottoms (fig. 5.1). Each plow bottom is a three-sided wedge with the landside and the horizontal plane of the share's cutting edge acting as flat sides and the top of the share and the moldboard together acting as a curved side. The primary functions of the plow bottom are to cut the furrow slice, shatter the soil, and invert the furrow slice to cover plant residue. Most moldboard plows are also equipped with tillage tools called rolling coulters (fig. 5.2) to help cut the furrow slice and to cut through plant residue which might otherwise collect on the shin or plow frame and cause clogging. The vertical edge of the furrow slice left uncut by the rolling coulter is cut by the shin. The bottoms along with the rolling coulters are responsible for the process function of the moldboard plow.

Moldboard plows are the most common implement used for primary tillage, but they are never used for secondary tillage. They are usually equipped with adjustments to ensure that the plow is level in the longitudinal and lateral directions and that the plow bottom is oriented with the landside parallel to the direction of travel. A five-bottom moldboard plow is shown in figure 5.3.

The three hitching configurations available for moldboard plows are integral (mounted), semi-integral (semi-mounted), and drawn (pull-type). Integral and semi-integral plows are attached to the three-point hitch of a tractor, but a drawn plow is attached to the drawbar of the tractor.

An integral moldboard plow, in the transport position, is fully supported by the tractor. The rear furrow wheel of an integral plow provides vertical and lateral support along with the hitch when the plow is in its operating position. Plowing depth for an integral plow is usually controlled by changing the vertical position of the tractor's

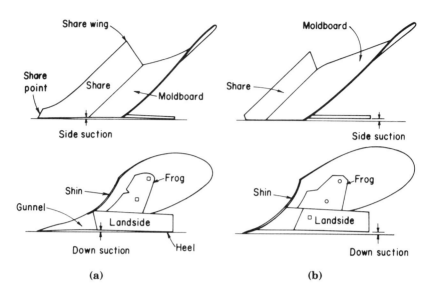

Figure 5.1–Typical moldboard plow bottoms, (a) with gunnel-type share, showing method of measuring suction when no rear furrow wheel or depth control devices are used, (b) with throw-away share, indicating clearances when a rear furrow wheel is used (Reprinted from *Principles of Farm Machinery*, Kepner et al., 1978).

hitch. A semi-integral plow is supported at the front by the tractor's hitch and at the rear by the plow's furrow transport wheel in both the transport and operating positions. The front of the plow is raised and lowered by the tractor's hitch while the rear of the plow is raised and lowered by a remote hydraulic cylinder. The drawn moldboard plow is fully supported by its own transport wheels and is raised and lowered by a remote hydraulic cylinder.

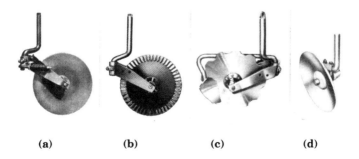

Figure 5.2–(a) Plain coulter with spring, (b) ripple-edge coulter, (c) notched coulter with jointer attachment, (d) concave coulter or disk jointer (Reprinted from *Principles of Farm Machinery*, Kepner et al., 1978).

Figure 5.3–A semi-mounted five bottom moldboard plow bottom (ASAE).

Integral moldboard plows have the lowest purchase price and the best maneuverability for small and irregular fields. However, they are limited in size due to tractor stability and the lift capacity of the hitch. The furrow transport wheel of a semi-integral plow is automatically steered to provide more maneuverability than for a drawn plow. Both integral and semi-integral plows improve a tractor's traction by applying a downward force on the hitch. Drawn plows provide the most uniform plowing depth, but have the highest purchase price.

Some agricultural soils contain rocks which are hidden below the soil surface. Impacting a rock at high speed can damage a tillage tool or the frame of a tillage implement. Moldboard plows are frequently equipped with automatic reset standards which allow a plow bottom to move rearward and upward to pass over an obstacle without damage. A hydraulic cylinder or a spring mechanism

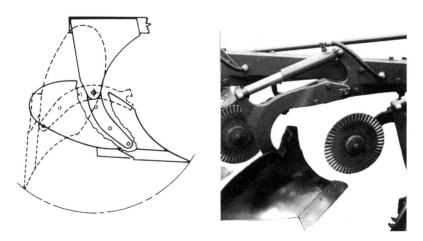

Figure 5.4–Spring-trip (left) and hydraulic reset mechanisms (right) used as overload protection devices for moldboard plows (Left-reprinted from *Principles of Farm Machinery*, Kepner et al., 1978; right-courtesy of Deere and Co.).

Figure 5.5–A rear-mounted two-way plow (ASAE).

automatically moves the bottom to its original position after it passes over the obstacle (fig. 5.4).

Most moldboard plows are designed to turn the furrow slices only to the right. Two-way plows, however, have two sets of opposed bottoms that can be used selectively. With this arrangement, all the furrows can be turned toward the same side of the field by using the right-hand bottoms for one direction of travel and the left-hand bottom on the return trip. The two sets of bottoms are mounted on a common frame that is rotated 180° about a longitudinal axis to change from one set to the other as shown in figure 5.5. In most cases, rotation is accomplished with a hydraulic cylinder that is part of the plow. A two-way plow eliminates the back furrows and dead furrows, leaving the field more nearly level for irrigation or drainage.

Figure 5.6–A mounted three bottom disk plow (ASAE).

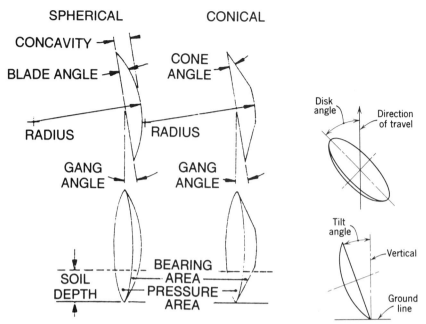

Figure 5.7–(a) Disk blade geometry, Sommer et al., 1983, (b) disk and tilt angles (Reprinted from *Principles of Farm Machinery*, Kepner et al., 1978).

Two-way plows are also advantageous for terraced fields or contour plowing and for small fields of irregular shape.

Disk plows. A *standard disk* plow consists of a series of disk blades mounted individually on a frame as shown in figure 5.6. The disk blades are set at an angle from the forward line of travel called the *disk angle* and also from the vertical called the *tilt angle* as shown in figure 5.7. Standard disk plows usually have three to six blades, spaced to cut 18 to 30 cm/disk. The disk angles vary from 42 to 45° and the tilt angles vary from 15 to 25°. The disk diameter are commonly between 60 to 70 cm. A disk tiller is similar to a disk plow with the exception that the blades are mounted on one axle and there is no tilt angle. The disk diameter is slightly smaller (50 to 60 cm) and the disk angle is commonly between 35 and 55°.

The disks used in the disk implements are either conical or spherical (sections of hollow spheres). Both blades have a *spherical radius* associated with the *concavity* of the blades as shown in figure 5.7. A conical blade has its outside surface flattened to a specific *cone angle*. The *blade* angle of a spherical blade is defined as the tangent at the edge surface area of the blade.

Disk plows are used for primary tillage and are available in integral, semi-integral, and drawn hitching configurations. They are most suitable for conditions under which moldboard plows do not work satisfactorily, such as in hard, dry soils, and in sticky soils where a moldboard plow will not scour. Scrapers, furnished as standard equipment on most disk plows, assist in covering plant residue and inverting the soil and prevent soil buildup in sticky soils. Reversible disk plows have an arrangement whereby the disk angle can be reversed at each end of the field to permit one-way plowing.

Under most conditions, and particularly in hard, dry soils, any disk tool must be forced into the ground by its weight rather than depending upon suction as does a moldboard plow. Consequently, standard disk plows are built with heavy frames and wheels (total masses of 180 to 540 kg/disk blade), and even then additional mass must sometimes be added to obtain a desired depth. The soil penetration ability of disk plow depends upon disk diameter, tilt angle and disk angle. Whereas the moldboard plow absorbs side forces mainly through the landsides, a disk plow must depend upon its wheels for this purpose.

A standard disk plow does not have special attachments to protect its disk blades from damage due to impact with rocks buried in the soil. Usually, the disk plow is able to withstand impact forces because of its heavy frame and its lower operating speed.

Disk tillers. The disk tiller is also known as one-way disk plow, vertical-disk plow, harrow plow, and wheatland plow. It is similar to a standard disk plow in regard to the frame, wheels and depth control, but the disk blades are uniformly spaced along a common axle or gang bolt and clamped together through spacer spools so the entire gang rotates as a unit. This implement is used in dryland grain-growing regions for shallow tillage (often only 8 to 13 cm) and mixing plant residue with the soil. The soil surface is left rough with visible plant residue to reduce soil erosion. Disk tillers are used for primary tillage and are frequently used in subsequent operations for summer fallowing. Some disk tillers are equipped with seed and fertilizer attachments to accomplish seedbed preparation, seeding, and fertilizing in a single operation.

The blades of a disk tiller are somewhat smaller than those of a standard disk plow, the most common diameters being between 51 and 61 cm. They are generally spaced 20 to 25 cm apart along the gang bolt. The width of cut per blade depends upon the spacing and upon the gang angle (adjustable) between the gang axis and the direction of travel. Gang angles range from 35 to 55°, with 40 to 45° being most common. A disk tiller is shown in figure 5.8.

Since disk tillers are primarily for relatively shallow tillage, they are built much lighter than standard disk plows (usually 45 to 90 kg/blade). They are available with integral and drawn hitching configurations. Most disk tillers move the soil only to the right, but reversible models are available which can move the soil in either direction.

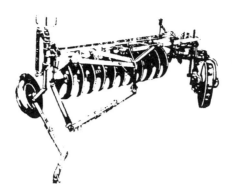

**Figure 5.8–A pull-type one-way
(wheatland) plow (ASAE).**

Chisel plows and subsoilers. A chisel plow is an implement
designed for primary tillage at depths from 15 to 46 cm. The soil
engaging tools are shanks (fig. 5.9) which are equipped with
replaceable points or shovels. They shatter, mix, and aerate the soil
with little soil inversion and little coverage of plant residue. Chisel
plows function most effectively when the soil is dry and firm because
the tools can pass through wet soil with almost no shattering action.
They leave a rough soil surface with most of the plant residue
remaining uncovered. This condition helps prevent wind and water
erosion while improving water penetration into the soil.

A chisel plow requires approximately one-half of the draft of a
moldboard plow with the same working width and operating at the
same tillage depth. However, farmers usually operate a chisel plow
at a greater depth than a moldboard plow to break up the plow sole

**Figure 5.9–A pull-type chisel plow with
rigidly mounted shanks (ASAE).**

Figure 5.10–A pull-type V-frame subsoiler (ASAE).

for improved water and root penetration. Under the conditions the draft requirement of a chisel plow increases.

The plant residue on the soil surface acts as an insulator and slows soil warm-up and soil drying in the spring compared with bare soil from moldboard plowing. Some researchers have found a need for increased chemical application rates because chisel plowing does not bury weed seeds and because plant residue may absorb some of the chemicals. At harvest time the plant residue on the soil surface improves traction for harvesting equipment during wet soil conditions.

Chisel plowing is usually completed in late summer or early fall and is followed by one or more secondary tillage operations during the following spring. Both the surface roughness and required draft increase with increased operating speed. Chisel plows are available with integral and drawn hitching configurations. The shanks are designed with spring-cushion, spring-reset, or spring-trip mountings to protect the tool and frame from impacts with buried rocks.

Subsoilers are used to break through and shatter compacted or otherwise impermeable soil layers and to improve rainfall penetration. They have heavy standards that can be operated at depths of 45 to 75 cm or more. Subsoilers do very little soil mixing and no soil inversion. They are most effective under dry and firm soil conditions. A subsoiling operation is usually followed by another primary tillage operation before secondary tillage is begun. Most subsoilers use the integral hitching configuration, but a few are available with the drawn hitching configuration. Subsoilers frequently rely on the heavy design of the frame and standards for protection during impact with buried rocks. Figure 5.10 shows a pull type V-frame subsoiler.

Stubble-mulch plows and tillers. Stubble mulch plows are made of wide V-shape sweeps that operate at shallow depth of 10 cm or less. The purpose is to cut weed roots just below the surface and leave the stubbles of the previously harvested crops on the surface to act as mulch (cover) to retain moisture and reduce soil erosion. The width of each sweep is in the range of 1.5 m. There may be several

Figure 5.11–A rear-mounted moldboard lister bottoms with wheels for
depth control (ASAE).

sweeps on a plow. Very wide plows have folding wings that fold
during transport. These plows may be used as primary tillage tools
right after the harvest or as a secondary tillage tools before planting.
When used for primary tillage it may be necessary to mix some
surface residue into the soil using a disk tiller or a disk harrow before
planting.

Stubble-mulch tillers are a combination of chisel plows and disk
harrows. The disk section is in the front to cut stubbles such as corn
stalks while the rear section is the chisel plow that accomplished
deep tillage. They are used where it is essential to till deep to break
old plow pan and it is not necessary to leave all of the crop residue for
erosion control. Mixing some of the crop residue helps to improve
organic matter in the soil.

Listers and bedders. Listers look like double moldboard plows
as shown in figure 5.11. Listers are used to create furrows for
planting. Sometimes it is desirable to plant in beds as opposed to a
flat surface to protect the plants from wind and to place seed down
near the moisture. These ridges are flattened due to the cultivation
performed during the growing season so at the time of harvest the
field is level. Often planters are attached to listers to accomplish
planting in the same operation. Bedders are used to make ridges or
beds when it is desirable to plant on the bed in the areas of high rain
fall. Bedders are made of disk implements that work in pairs to form
the ridges as shown in figure 5.12.

Rotary tillers. Rotary tillers are also called power tillers
because the power is transferred to the tiller from the tractor via the
power-take-off drive. A shaft containing blades is located at 90° to the
line of travel and rotates in the same direction as the forward travel
of the tractor. Since the shaft turns at a rate that is considerably

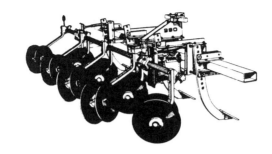

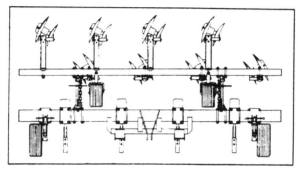

Figure 5.12–A rear-mounted bedder-ridger with disk
staggered gangs. Shown with a subsoiler (ASAE).

faster than the corresponding tractor speed, soil pulverization is
accomplished. Also, the tiller pushes the tractor forward and
generates a negative draft. Consequently, lighter tractors can be
used for rotary tillage operation. Total power requirements for rotary
tillers are generally higher than the conventional plows. However,
one rotary tillage operation may be equivalent to several
conventional tillage operation as far as the quality of the seed bed is
concerned. Figure 5.13 shows a rotary tiller.

    Secondary tillage. Any tillage operations performed after the
primary tillage are called secondary tillage. Generally, several
secondary tillage operations are performed before the field is ready
for planting. The main objective of secondary tillage is to break down
large clods and to prepare an ideal seedbed for planting. An ideal
seedbed is the one that allows for good seed-to-soil contact, conserves
moisture needed for germination, and allows for vigorous and
uninhibited root and shoot growth. The equipment used for
secondary tillage are generally called harrows. The most common is
the disk harrow with spring tine and spike tooth harrows being some
other types. Often in dry climates, culti-packers are used as the final
tillage operation before planting. The purpose of a culti-packer is to
increase the density of the top few centimeters of the soil depth. This

Figure 5.13–A rear-mounted full width rotary tiller (ASAE).

tends to break the capillaries in this soil zone and prevent moisture from escaping.

Disk harrows. Disk harrows differ from disk plows in that there is no tilt angle and several blades are mounted on a common axis called the gang. The gang may be arranged in different configurations as shown in figure 5.14. The arrangements may be single action, offset, or tandem. It should be noted that the gangs are always in pairs with opposite disk orientation to balance the side draft produced by each disk. The disk harrows may be either mounted or pull type. Smaller units tend to be mounted while larger units tend to be pull type with wheels for transportation. Remote hydraulic cylinders are used to raise or lower the implement from the drivers' seat. Some very large units are designed to fold over for transportation. Pull type units with wheels allow for better depth control.

The size and spacing of the disk is determined by the field conditions and the purpose of disking. Narrow spacing of about 18 cm is used for final seedbed preparation when the ground is not hard with little surface residue. About 23 cm spacing is used when mixing of chemicals or when cutting of surface trash is desirable. Disk spacing of about 28 cm and higher is needed for harder soils or when

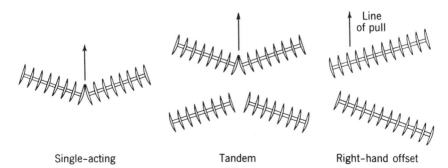

Figure 5.14–Gang arrangements for three general types of disk harrows (Reprinted from Kepner et al., 1978).

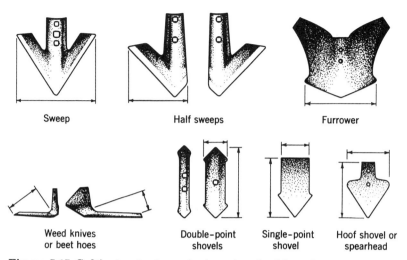

Sweep   Half sweeps   Furrower

Weed knives   Double-point   Single-point   Hoof shovel or
or beet hoes   shovels   shovel   spearhead

Figure 5.15–Cultivator tools — single point, double point, and spear point shovels; a full sweep and right and left half-sweeps (Reprinted from Kepner et al., 1978).

heavy surface residue is present. Disking with larger disks should be followed by lighter disks for final seedbed preparation. The operating depth is determined by the soil conditions and the weight per unit disk of the plow. The weight ranges from 20 to 200 kg/disk. The disk diameters range from 40 to 80 cm. The disk spacing increases with disk diameter and so does the weight. The gang angle varies from 15 to 35° as measured from a line perpendicular to the line of travel. Gang angles may be changed to meet the field conditions. Increasing the gang angle makes the disks more aggressive, increasing their depth and power requirement.

Cultivators. There are basically two types of cultivators. These are field cultivator and row crop cultivator. Field cultivators are often used as secondary tillage tools for seedbed preparation. Field cultivators are similar to the chisel plows in appearance but they operate at much shallower depths. Figure 5.15 shows the different types of tools that can be attached to a cultivator shank for different applications. Field cultivators may be either mounted or pull type with wheels for depth control. Some very large units are designed to be folded while transporting. The lateral tine spacing may vary from 15 to 30 cm. Usually two or three rows of tines are used with fore and aft spacing ranging from 50 to 80 cm. Row crop cultivators are used for cultivation and weed control operation during the active growth period of crops planted in rows.

Spike, tine, and spring tooth harrows. These tillage tools are used in the final seedbed preparation. They are also used for post planting operations to breakup soil crust and remove weeds. In a

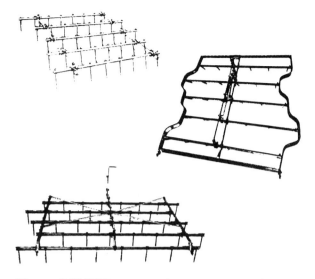

Figure 5.16–Different sections used in spike-tooth harrows (ASAE).

spike tooth harrow, the spikes are rigidly mounted on a frame, however, the mounting bars may be spring-loaded (fig. 5.16). The angle of the spikes may be altered to change the aggressiveness. Vertical orientation being the most aggressive. Tine tooth harrow as shown in figure 5.17 uses spring tines that create additional action for soil breakup. The tines are more closely spaced than the spikes, about 3.8-5 cm apart. Spring tooth harrow (fig. 5.18) uses round wire teeth made of spring steel. Due to the spring action, these harrows are more suited for stony ground. However, their lack of depth penetration limits their use to less than hard soils. All of these harrows may be used as attachments to other tillage tools such as moldboard plows and disk harrows because of their low draft

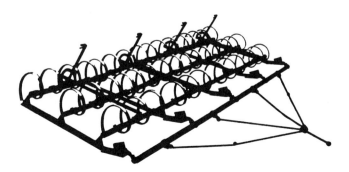

Figure 5.17–A rear mounted tine-tooth harrow (ASAE).

Figure 5.18–A spring-tooth harrow section (ASAE).

requirements. Some units may be up to 16 m wide with fold-up frames for road transport.

Rotary hoes and cultivators. Rotary hoes and cultivators, unlike rotary tillers, are not powered. They are designed to operate at shallow depth and are used for weed control in row crops, breaking soil crests for better seedling emergence, and mixing of fertilizer. Rotary hoes are made of several star wheels, often called spiders, mounted on a shaft at a spacing of about 15 cm to form a gang. Each spider has 10 to 16 teeth and the tip diameter ranges from 45 to 50 cm. Two staggered parallel gangs make a section and provide a working width of about 8 to 10 cm. Several sections are used in a given implement. The section width is such that they fit between the rows for row crop cultivation. The teeth in a rotary hoe have forward curvature for more aggressive cultivation. A rotary hoe is shown in figure 5.19.

Rotary cultivators have spiders similar to rotary hoes but the teeth have a twist and the ends are shaped like a chisel. This creates a sideways movement of the soil. Only two spiders are mounted on a shaft that is located at an angle from the forward line of travel. The spider wheels turn backward as the implement is pulled forward creating the necessary tilling action. The cultivator may be arranged

Figure 5.19–A rear mounted rotary hoe with in-line sections on spring-loaded arms (ASAE).

Figure 5.20–A rear-mounted, row crop rotary cultivator with ground-driven finger wheels (ASAE).

to cultivate row crops or the entire field. A rotary cultivator is shown in figure 5.20.

Culti-packers, rollers, and finishing boards. Often in dry conditions or when the soil has many clods, culti-packers, rollers or finishing board are used to breakup soil clods and to conserve moisture for better seed germination. These tools are used almost always as attachment to harrows (fig. 5.21).

5.1.2 Conservation Tillage System

Conservation tillage systems are designed to conserve soil, water, and/or energy. In areas prone to wind soil erosion, it is advisable to leave surface cover on the soil to prevent or minimize soil erosion. Primary tillage operation that turns the soil over and buries the surface residue under the soil is eliminated. In heavy soils subjected to compaction due to wheel traffic, it is recommended that primary tillage performed during wet spring season be eliminated. In this situation weed control is accomplished by use of herbicides. Generally, conservation tillage systems require some other changes to be made in the method and equipment. For example, planter changes are needed to cut through the surface residue in order to plant seeds. This is accomplished by adding a fluted coulter ahead of the furrow openers. There are different levels of conservation tillage. These are minimum tillage, strip tillage, and zero tillage systems. Zero tillage system consists of no primary or secondary tillage operation. A small band or strip of soil is tilled and the crop is planted in this strip in a strip tillage system. Elimination of any primary or secondary tillage operation results in the minimum tillage system.

5.2 Mechanics of Tillage Tools

5.2.1 Soil Classification

Soil classification consists of dividing soils into groups, each with distinctive properties. Soil classification makes it possible to describe a soil by its properties. There are different soil classification

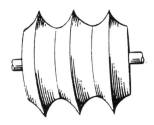 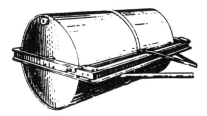

Figure 5.21–Rollers and culti-packer.

systems. Some have been established by U.S. Dept. of Agriculture, M.I.T., and Bureau of Soil. These classification systems are based on the size of soil particles. On the basis of the particle size soils are called gravel, sand, silt, and clay. Figure 5.22 illustrates the different soil classification systems.

Natural soils generally consist of mixtures of several size groups. A soil is named after its principal constituents. For example, a soil containing predominantly clay but also containing some silt would be called *silt clay*. One convenient method of naming mixed soils is the Public Roads Administration System as shown in figure 5.23. The sides of the triangle are axes, each representing percentages of clay, silt and sand that constitute the soil. Special names are assigned to various combinations as designated by the areas within the triangle. Thus, if a soil is composed of 40% sand, 35% silt and 25% clay, it is called a clay loam. This is shown as point A in figure 5.23.

U.S. Dept. of Agriculture

CLAY	SILT	SAND	GRAVEL

M.I.T.

CLAY	SILT	SAND	GRAVEL

U.S. Bur. of Soils

CLAY	SILT	SAND	GRAVEL

0.0001   0.001   0.01   0.1   1   10   100
PARTICLE SIZE (mm)

Figure 5.22–Soil classification by size.

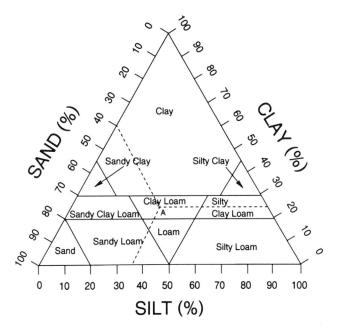

Figure 5.23–Public Roads Administration System of soil classification.

5.2.2 Physical Properties of Soils

Porosity (n) is a measure of the relative amount of voids in the soil. It is the ratio of the void volume (V_v) to the total volume (V) of the soil sample (fig. 5.24), or:

$$n = \frac{V_v}{V} \tag{5.1}$$

where
    V_v = void volume
    V = total volume

The *void ratio* (e) is the ratio of the void volume to the volume of the solids in a soil sample, or:

$$e = \frac{V_v}{V_s} \tag{5.2}$$

where V_s = volume of solids.

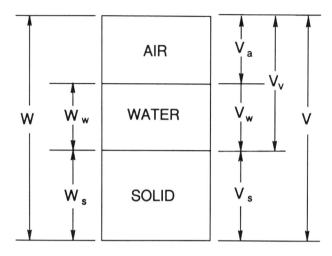

Figure 5.24–Soil weight and volume fractions.

The *water content* of the soil (w) is the ratio of the weight of water (W_w) to that of the solids (W_s) expressed as a percentage, or:

$$w = \frac{W_w}{W_s} \cdot 100 \tag{5.3}$$

where
    W_w = weight of water
    W_s = weight of solids

The *degree of saturation* (S_r) is the percentage of void space that is occupied by water, or:

$$S_r = \frac{V_w}{V_v} \cdot 100 \tag{5.4}$$

where V_w = volume of water.

The *unit weight* or *density* (γ) is defined as the weight divided by the volume. For soils:

$$\gamma = \frac{W}{V} = \frac{W_s + W_w}{V_s + V_w + V_a} \tag{5.5}$$

The *dry density* (γ_d) is the weight of solids divided by the total volume, or:

$$\gamma_d = \frac{W_s}{V} \qquad (5.6)$$

Finally, the density of the solid particles in the soil (γ_s) is expressed as follows:

$$\gamma_s = \frac{W_s}{V_s} \qquad (5.7)$$

The density of the solids in soils is found to be somewhat constant. It generally remains between 2.6 and 2.8 g/cc. The average value is 2.65 g/cc for sand and silt and 2.75 g/cc for clay.

Example 5.1

A 100 cc soil sample weighs 165 g and its water content was found to be 49%. If the specific gravity of the solids is assumed to be 2.6, find the void ratio, porosity, degree of saturation, and dry density.

Solution. First, find the weights and volumes of all fractions of soil specimen.

w	$= \dfrac{W_w}{W_s} = 0.49$; or
W_w	$= 0.49 W_s$
$W_s + W_w$	$= 165$ g; or
$W_s + 0.49 W_s$	$= 165$ g
W_s	$= \dfrac{165}{1.49} = 110.74$ g; and
W_w	$= 165 - 110.74 = 54.26$ g
V_s	$= \dfrac{W_s}{\gamma_s} = \dfrac{110.7}{2.6} = 42.59$ cc
V_w	$= \dfrac{W_w}{\gamma_w} = \dfrac{54.26}{1.0} = 54.26$ cc; and
V_a	$= V - V_s - V_w = 100 - 42.59 - 54.26 = 3.15$ cc

Now find the required ratios from the weight and volume values as computed above.

Void ratio, e
$$= \frac{V_v}{V_s} = \frac{V_w - V_a}{V_s}$$

$$= \frac{54.26 + 3.15}{42.59} = 1.35$$

Porosity, η
$$= \frac{V_v}{V} = \frac{54.26 + 3.15}{100} = 0.57$$

Degree of saturation, S_r
$$= \frac{V_w}{V_v} \cdot 100$$

$$= \frac{(54.26)\,100}{57.41} = 0.95\%$$

Dry density, γ_d
$$= \frac{W_s}{V} = \frac{110.74}{100} = 1.107 \text{ g/cc}$$

5.2.3 Mechanical Properties of Soils

Shear strength. If a soil specimen is subjected to shear stress the shear stress-strain diagram may look like one of the curves in figure 5.25 depending upon the soil condition. A highly cemented soil will result in a well defined failure point as shown by curve A. Loose soil may not show any definite failure point and the stress may increase exponentially with strain reaching some maximum value as shown by curve B. Curve C is for a soil that is well compacted but not cemented. The soil strength refers to the value of the shear stress on a plane within the soil sample where soil failure has taken place either by rupture or breakage. For curves A and C this point is clearly defined but for curve B soil failure is not distinct. In the case of curve C the failure is considered to have taken place by yielding or plastic flow and the asymtotic value of shear stress is taken as the shear strength for this case. The shear stress-strain curves shown in figure 5.25 are for a given normal stress on the sample. If the normal stress is changed the shear stress-strain diagram will change and consequently the value of the maximum shear stress will also change. An increase in the normal stress would cause an increase in maximum shear. Therefore, the shear strength is a function of the normal stress on the failure plane.

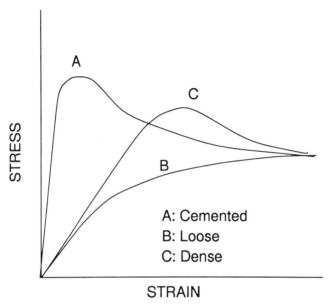

Figure 5.25–Typical shear stress-strain diagrams for soils in three conditions: A: cemented, B: loose, and C: dense.

Mohr-Coulomb failure theory states that failure in a material occurs if the shear stress on any plane equals the shear strength of the material. Furthermore, the shear strength (s) along any plane is a function of the normal stress (σ) on the plane, as shown below:

$$s = f(\sigma) \tag{5.8}$$

Coulomb, in 1776, conducted experiments to determine the maximum shear stress that could be applied on a plane within a sample of soil at varying levels of normal stress. He plotted the maximum shear stress values at failure against the corresponding normal stress on the failure plane and suggested the following linear relationship:

$$s = c + \sigma \tan\phi \tag{5.9}$$

The Coulomb criterion is shown as a straight line in figure 5.26, with an intercept on the shear stress (τ) axis equal to c and a slope equal to $\tan\phi$. The quantities c and ϕ are material properties frequently called cohesion and angle of internal friction, respectively. The shear strength as defined by equation 5.9 represents the

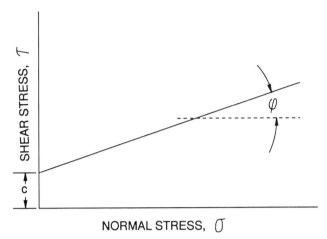

Figure 5.26–Soil failure envelopes.

maximum shear stress that may be sustained on any plane in a given material. The strength function is called the failure envelope since it defines the limiting stress.

Determination of shear strength. *Direct shear test* and the *triaxial test* are the two most widely used methods for determining soil shear strength. The purpose of these tests is to determine the value of c and needed in equation 5.9 to define soil shear failure envelope.

The direct shear test. The direct shear test is performed using an apparatus as illustrated in figure 5.27. The box consisting of an upper and a lower half contains the soil sample to be tested. Drainage of water from the specimen is permitted using a porous stone at the bottom. The soil sample fails at the interface of the two halves. A normal stress is applied through a loading head, and the shear stress is increased until the specimen fails. A stress-strain curve is obtained by plotting the shear stress against the shear displacement.

To obtain the failure envelope, several tests utilizing different normal stresses are performed on specimens of the same soil. The specimens are then sheared at a slow rate to allow time for volume changes. If the shear strength is plotted against the normal stress, we obtain the solid line in figure 5.28. The linear relationship between s and σ is the failure envelope.

The triaxial test. Consider a cylindrical soil sample subjected to a hydrostatic stress σ_3 as shown in figure 5.29a and then an additional normal stress called the deviator stress (σ') as shown in figure 5.29b. The deviator stress is increased until soil fails. Figure 5.30a shows a two dimensional representation of stresses on

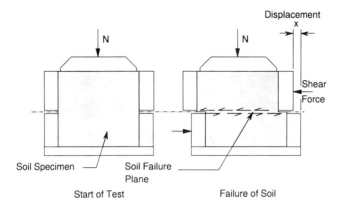

Figure 5.27–Direct shear test apparatus.

the soil specimen. The soil failure plane orientation is shown by an angle (θ) from the horizontal. Figure 5.30b shows the shear and the normal stresses on the failure plane. Since the specimen failed the shear stress on this plane is equal to the shear strength. We now have to determine the values of the shear stress (τ) and the normal stress (σ) on this plane. These stresses can be determined by means of Mohr's circles as shown in figure 5.31. Point 'A' on the circle represents the failure plane. It should be noted that the angle or orientation of the failure plane is doubled in the Mohr's diagram. The coordinates of this point are the shear and the normal stresses on the

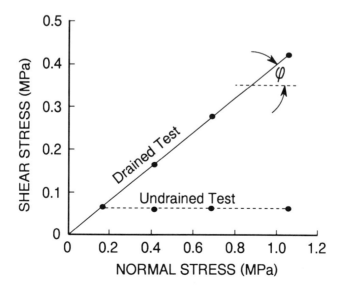

Figure 5.28–Typical result of direct shear test.

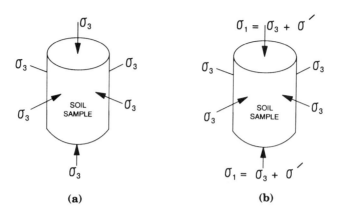

Figure 5.29–(a) Application of hydrostatic stresses during consolidation, (b) application of the normal deviatoric stress to cause shear failure.

failure plane. Using this diagram the following relationships can be written for these stresses:

$$\sigma = \frac{\sigma_1 + \sigma_3}{2} + \frac{\sigma_1 - \sigma_3}{2} \cos 2\theta \qquad (5.10)$$

$$\tau = \frac{\sigma_1 - \sigma_3}{2} \sin 2\theta \qquad (5.11)$$

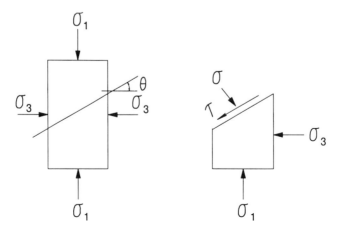

Figure 5.30–Two-dimensional representation of the stresses on a soil sample during tri-axial shear test showing the shear and normal stress on the failure plane.

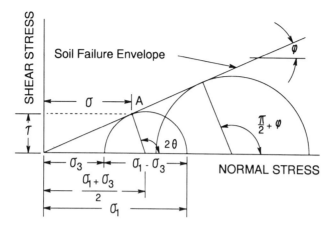

Figure 5.31–Mohr's circle representation of principal stresses.

Figure 5.32 is a schematic diagram describing the triaxial apparatus and the application of stresses. The cylindrical soil specimen is enclosed within a thin rubber membrane and is placed inside a triaxial cell. The cell is then filled with a fluid. The specimen is subjected to a hydrostatic compressive stress (σ_3) by pressurizing the cell. This causes the soil sample to consolidate. An additional vertical stress (σ') is applied through the piston as shown in the figure. This deviator stress is steadily increased until failure of the specimen occurs. The specimen fails under a set of principal stresses $\sigma_3 + \sigma'$, and σ_3.

Drainage of water from the specimen is measured by the burette and valve A is closed to prevent drainage from the specimen. Another line from the base leads to a pressure sensor to measure porewater pressure.

To obtain the failure envelope, several triaxial tests are performed on specimens of the same soil at different values of cell pressure (σ_3). A Mohr's circle is drawn for the principal stresses at failure for each specimen. These are shown in figure 5.31 and the line tangent to these circles constitutes the failure envelope. The stress on the failure surface is represented by the point of tangency. From the geometry of Mohr's circle this plane makes an angle of $(\pi/2+\phi)/2$ with the major principal stress plane.

The triaxial test may be performed as drained (d), consolidated-undrained (c-u), or undrained test (u). In the drained test, water is allowed to seep out of the sample during the application of the hydrostatic and deviator stresses, and the pore water pressure is equal to zero. During the c-u test drainage is permitted during the application of the hydrostatic stress and the corresponding pore water pressure, $u_a = 0$. When the deviator stress is applied, drainage

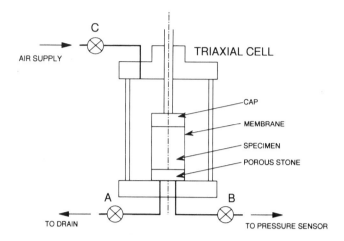

Figure 5.32–A tri-axial shear test apparatus.

is not permitted and the pore water pressure, $u_b > 0$. In an undrained test, no drainage is permitted and the total pore water pressure is equal to u. The effective stress $\bar{\sigma}$ for the three drainage conditions may be calculated using the following equations:

Drained: $\qquad\qquad\qquad \bar{\sigma}_1 = \sigma_1 \qquad\qquad \bar{\sigma}_3 = \sigma_3 \qquad\qquad (5.12)$

Consolidated-undrained: $\quad \bar{\sigma}_1 = \sigma_1 - u_b \qquad \bar{\sigma}_3 = \sigma_3 - u_b \qquad (5.13)$

Undrained: $\qquad\qquad\qquad \bar{\sigma}_1 = \sigma_1 - u \qquad \bar{\sigma}_3 = \sigma_3 - u \qquad (5.14)$

Figure 5.33 illustrates typical Mohr's envelopes obtained from undrained, drained, and consolidated-undrained triaxial tests; the envelopes are constructed from the principal stresses at failure. The failure envelope corresponding to the drained test, called effective failure envelope, may be determined from equations 5.13 and 5.14 depending on the drainage condition of the test. Regardless of the type of the test performed, there exists an effective failure envelope unique to the soil being tested.

The effective-stress failure envelope is written as:

$$s = \bar{c} + \bar{\sigma} \tan\phi \qquad\qquad (5.15)$$

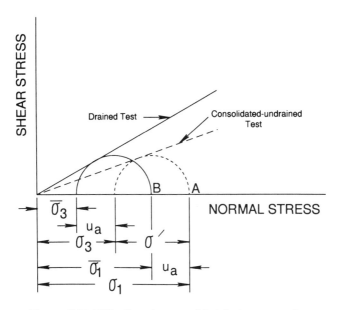

Figure 5.33–Effective-stress and total-stress envelopes.

Example 5.2

A consolidated-undrained triaxial test was performed on a specimen of saturated clay. The value of the hydrostatic pressure (σ_3) was 200 kPa. The specimen failed when σ' was 280 kPa, u = 180 kPa. If the failure plane in this test makes an angle of 57° with the horizontal, calculate the normal and shear stresses on the failure surface.

Solution. The principal stresses at failure are calculated as:

$$\sigma_3 = 200 \text{ kPa}; \sigma_1 - \sigma_3 = 280 \text{ kPa}; \sigma_1 = 280 + 200 = 480 \text{ kPa}$$

On the 57° plane the normal and the shear stresses are calculated as follows:

$$\sigma = \frac{\sigma_1 + \sigma_3}{2} + \frac{\sigma_1 - \sigma_3}{2} \cos 2\theta$$

$$= \frac{480 + 200}{2} + \frac{480 + 200}{2} \cos 114 = 283 \text{ kPa}$$

$$\tau = \frac{\sigma_1 - \sigma_3}{2} \sin 2\theta = \frac{480 - 200}{2} \sin 114 = 127 \text{ kPa}$$

The effective normal stress on the failure plane was:

$$\bar{\sigma} = \sigma - u = 283 - 180 = 103 \text{ kPa}$$

Example 5.3

If the value of cohesion for the sample in the above example was 80 kPa and the angle of internal friction was 24°. Show why failure occurred on the plane $\theta = 57°$ instead of the plane of maximum shear stress. What was the maximum shear stress within the sample?

Solution. The effective normal stress on the failure plane is 103 kPa. The corresponding shear strength on this plane is computed as:

$$s = c + \bar{\sigma} \tan \phi = 80 + 103 \tan 24 = 127 \text{ kPa}$$

The shear strength is equal to the shear stress on this plane and consequently failure occurs. The maximum shear stress occurs at a 45° plane and the normal effective stress on this plane is computed as:

$$\sigma = \frac{480 + 200}{2} + \frac{480 - 200}{2} \cos 2(45) = 340 \text{ kPa}$$

$$\bar{\sigma} = 340 - 180 \text{ kPa} = 160 \text{ kPa}$$

$$s = 80 + 160 \tan 24 = 151 \text{ kPa}$$

The maximum shear stress occurs on a plane oriented at 45° from the horizontal:

$$\tau_{max} = \frac{\sigma_1 - \sigma_3}{2} = 140 \text{ kPa}$$

Failure does not occur at 45° plane because the strength is higher than the stress.

Shear strength of cohesionless soils. Sand and silt are cohesionless soils. Figure 5.34 shows a typical failure envelope of a cohesionless soil. The envelope passes through the origin. Thus, only one Mohr's circle is needed to establish the failure envelope. The following equations are used to determine the drained (effective) failure envelope for cohesionless soils.

$$s_{cu} = \sigma \tan \phi_{cu} \tag{5.16}$$

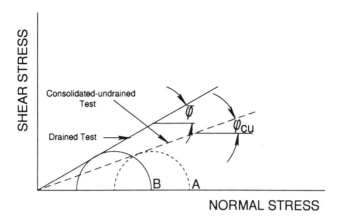

Figure 5.34–Failure envelopes of cohesionless soils.

$$s = \overline{\sigma} \tan\overline{\phi} = (\sigma - u) \tan\overline{\phi} \qquad (5.17)$$

The value of $\overline{\phi}$ for cohesionless soils ranges from about 28 to 42°. Generally the value of $\overline{\phi}$ increases with increasing density. Extremely loose sands with an unstable structure may have a $\overline{\phi}$ as low as 10°.

Field measurement of soil shear strength. The previously described direct shear test and triaxial shear test are laboratory procedures to measure the shear strength. Soil samples must be taken from field to perform these tests. The samples may get disturbed and their shear strengths may be altered in the process. To avoid this some methods for shear strength measurement in field have been developed. The first method is a round shear box which is rotated after it is inserted into the soil as shown in figure 5.35. The box is driven into the soil until the top of the box is in contact with the soil surface. The soil is excavated carefully outside the box before applying the torque to shear the soil. The soil at the bottom of the box is sheared. The shear strength is calculated using the following equation:

$$s = \frac{3M}{2\pi r^3} \qquad (5.18)$$

where
    s = soil shear strength
    M = moment at failure
    r = radius of the shear box

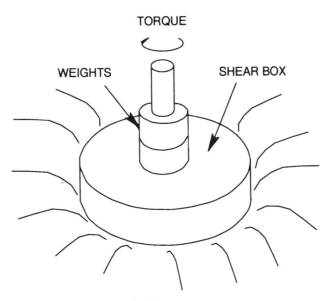

Figure 5.35–A field soil shear apparatus.

Markers are placed on the soil inside the box that are visible through small holes in the top of the box. The markers are used to ensure that the soil shears uniformly.

To overcome the problem that the soil located near the outer edge of the shear box must move considerably farther than that near the center, a narrow annulus has been designed as a shear box. Shear strength for the narrow annulus shaped box is calculated from the following equation:

$$ s = \frac{3M}{2\pi(r_1^3 - r_2^3)} \qquad (5.19) $$

where r_1 and r_2 are the inner and the outer radii of the annulus, respectively.

The field apparatus described above requires excavating the soil at the outside after inserting it into the ground. A vane type apparatus as shown in figure 5.36 does not require excavation. Once driven into the soil the rotation causes shear of soil along the surface of the cylinder which is generated by the vanes. This device may be used at greater depths. Measurements can be made at increasing depths without extracting the shear device so that a rather complete strength profile of natural soil conditions can be obtained. The vanes have a height-to-radius ratio of 4:1. The vane shear apparatus

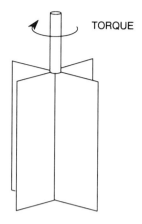

TORQUE

**Figure 5.36–A vane
shear apparatus.**

provides no means of varying normal load. Shear strength is
computed as:

$$s = \frac{3M}{28\pi r^3} \tag{5.20}$$

where r is the radius of the circle inscribed by the vane tips.

Friction. There are three types of frictional parameters in
problems involving soil dynamics. These are soil metal-friction (μ'),
soil-soil friction (μ) and soil internal friction (tan ϕ). Soil internal
friction has been discussed above in reference to soil shear strength.
To determine soil-soil friction and soil-metal friction, we make use of
Coulomb's concept of friction coefficient, or

$$\mu \text{ or } \mu' = \frac{F}{N} = \tan\psi \tag{5.21}$$

where
    F = frictional force tangent to the sliding surface
    N = normal force to the sliding surface
    ψ = friction angle

An apparatus to measure soil-metal friction is shown in
figure 5.37. Frictional force corresponding to different normal loads is
measured and plotted against the normal loads. The slope of the line
is the coefficient of friction. It must be pointed out that there is a

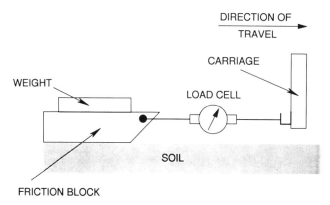

Figure 5.37–Measuring soil-metal friction.

difference between the soil-soil friction and the internal friction angle. In soil-soil friction phenomenon, the soil moves as a rigid body against another soil surface. Whereas the internal friction of soil comes into play when soil fails under shear loading. Therefore, if we continue to apply shearing load in a shear test after failure then we will measure soil-soil frictional behavior.

Adhesion. Adhesion is defined as the force of attraction between two unlike bodies. In the case of soils, adhesion is due to the film of moisture between the soil particles and the contacting surface in the soil. The force of adhesion is due to the surface tension of water and consequently it depends upon the value of surface tension and moisture content of the soil. In mechanics applications it is virtually impossible to differentiate between friction and adhesion. An apparent coefficient of friction is often used to include both friction and adhesion. Figure 5.38 shows the effect of moisture content on the apparent coefficient of friction. It can be seen that initially at low moisture content the friction is due to pure sliding action. As the moisture content increases, the friction value increases due to increased adhesion. As the moisture content is increased even further the friction reduces due to the lubricating effect created by the moisture film. The following model has been proposed to include adhesion:

$$F = a \cdot C_\alpha + N \tan\psi \qquad (5.22)$$

where
$\quad C_\alpha \quad$ = adhesion
$\quad a \quad$ = surface area

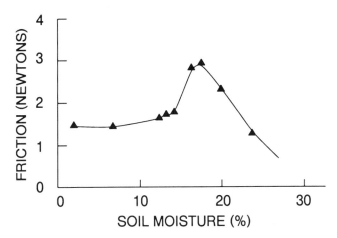

Figure 5.38–Effect of soil moisture content on apparent coefficient of friction (Gill and Vandenberg, 1968).

5.2.4 Mechanics of a Simple Tillage Tool

A discussion of soil-tool interaction as the tool travels through the soil is presented. Consider a tillage tool in the shape of an inclined blade travelling through soil as shown in figure 5.39. As the tool moves forward, the soil in front of the tool undergoes loading similar to that of an unconfined compression test. As the tool continues to move forward the loading increases until the soil fails in shear. Successive shear planes are formed and the soil mass between the shear planes travels along the surface of the tillage tool. W. Soehne (1956) analyzed the forces acting on the tillage tool and the soil to develop an expression for the total draft force needed to overcome the various soil reactions. Gill and Vandenberg (1968) have presented the work by Soehne.

Soehne (1956) concluded that soil-metal friction, shear failure, acceleration force for each block of soil, and cutting resistance act on the tillage tool as it moves through the soil. Figure 5.40a shows a free

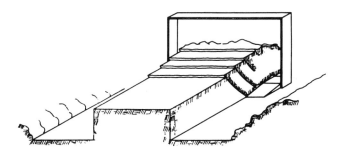

Figure 5.39–An inclined plane tillage tool (Soehne, 1956, cited in Gill and Vandenberg, 1968).

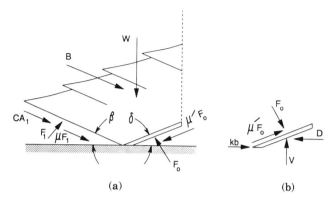

Figure 5.40–Soil and tool reaction forces (Soehne, 1956, cited in Gill and Vandenberg, 1968).

body diagram of a segment of soil as it reacts to the advancing tool. Forces CA_1 and μF_1 are due to soil shear and are those present at the instant incipient shear failure occurs. Forces due to soil-metal friction ($\mu' F_0$) and acceleration (B) are also present. The soil cutting resistance, defined as the cutting force per unit length of the cutting edge, is given by (k). The forces acting on the tillage tool are shown in figure 5.40b. These forces are soil cutting resistance (kb) obtained by multiplying the unit cutting resistance (k) by the cutting width (b); soil normal reaction (F_0); soil frictional reaction ($\mu' F_0$); and the tool support forces (V) and draft (D).

Summing forces in the horizontal direction and equating them to zero the following equation is obtained:

$$D = F_0 \sin\delta + \mu' F_0 \cos\delta + kb \qquad (5.23)$$

where
    D = horizontal draft force
    μ' = coefficient of soil-metal friction
    F_0 = normal load on the inclined plane
    k = soil cutting resistance
    δ = tool lift angle

The specific draft of the soil (D^*) is defined as:

$$D^* = D - kb$$

or

$$D^* = F_0 \sin\delta + F_0 \mu' \cos\delta \qquad (5.24)$$

Summing all the vertical components of forces acting on the soil mass and equating them to zero for equilibrium results in the following equation:

$$W - F_0 (\cos \delta - \mu' \sin \delta) - F_1 (\cos \beta - \mu \sin \beta) + (CA_1 + B) \sin \cos \beta = 0 \qquad (5.25)$$

where
$\quad W =$ soil weight (N)
$\quad F_1 =$ normal force on the forward failure surface (N)
$\quad \beta \; =$ angle of the forward failure surface (rad)
$\quad \mu \; =$ coefficient of internal soil friction (–)
$\quad A_1 =$ area of forward shear failure surface (m^2)
$\quad C \; =$ soil cohesion (Pa)
$\quad B \; =$ soil acceleration force (N)

The horizontal forces on the soil segment can be summed and placed in equilibrium from the relations shown in figure 5.40 to give:

$$F_0 (\sin \delta + \mu' \cos \delta) - F_1 (\sin \beta + \mu \cos \beta) - (CA_1 + B) \cos \beta = 0 \quad (5.26)$$

Equation 5.24 can be used to solve for F_0. Substituting F_0 in equation 5.26 to solve for F_1 we get:

$$F_1 = \frac{D^* - (CA_1 + B)\cos \beta}{\sin \beta + \mu \cos \beta} \qquad (5.27)$$

Substituting for F_0 and F_1 in equation 5.25 gives:

$$W - \left(D^* \frac{\cos \delta - \mu' \sin \delta}{\sin \delta + \mu' \cos \delta} \right) - \left[D^* - (CA_1 - B) \cos \beta \right] \left(\frac{\cos \beta - \mu \sin \beta}{\sin \beta + \mu \cos \beta} \right)$$
$$+ (CA_1 + B) \sin \beta = 0$$

Expanding and rearranging terms gives:

$$D^* \left(\frac{\cos \delta - \mu' \sin \delta}{\sin \delta + \mu' \cos \delta} + \frac{\cos \beta - \mu \sin \beta}{\sin \beta + \mu \cos \beta} \right) = W + \frac{CA_1 + B}{\sin \beta + \mu \cos \beta}$$

and by letting:

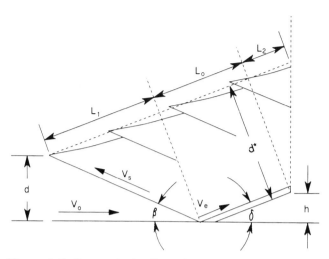

Figure 5.41–Segment of soil on the inclined tillage plane tillage tool (Soehne, 1956, cited in Gill and Vandenberg, 1968).

$$z = \left(\frac{\cos\delta - \mu' \sin\delta}{\sin\delta + \mu' \cos\delta} + \frac{\cos\beta - \mu \sin\beta}{\sin\beta + \mu \cos\beta} \right)$$

$$D^* = \frac{W}{z} + \frac{CA_1 + B}{z\left(\sin\beta + \mu \cos\beta\right)} \tag{5.28}$$

Equation 5.28 relates the forces acting in the soil-tool system. The weight of soil may be calculated from the volume of the soil supported by the inclined tool. Figure 5.41 shows a trapezoidal area that may be assumed to be supported by the tool. The area of the trapezoid multiplied by the depth of the area (width of tool) and the density of the soil gives the weight. By using the relationships in figure 5.41, the weight of soil is:

$$W = \gamma bd^* \left(L_0 + \frac{L_1 + L_2}{2} \right) \tag{5.29}$$

where

γ = wet bulk density of soil (kg/m^3)
b = tool width (m)
d = tool depth (m)
d^* = d {[sin($\delta+\beta$)]/sin β} (m)
L_1 = d {[cos($\delta+\beta$)]/sin β} (m)

$L_2 = d^* \tan\delta$ (m)

The shear plane area (A_1) can be determined easily from either figure 5.40 or 5.41 and it is given by:

$$A_1 = \frac{bd}{\sin\beta} \qquad (5.30)$$

The acceleration force (B) is the only item in equation 5.27 that remains to be specified. Using Newton's Second Law of Motion:

$$B = m\frac{dv}{dt} \qquad (5.31)$$

where
  m = accelerated soil mass (m/s^2)
  v = soil velocity (uniform within the mass) (m/s)
  t = time (s)

The mass of the soil being accelerated or disturbed by the tool at time (t) is given by:

$$m = \frac{\gamma}{g} d b t_0 v_0 \qquad (5.32)$$

where
  v_0 = tool velocity (m/s)
  t_0 = average time a particle of soil is engaged by the tool (s)
  g = acceleration due to gravity (m/s^2)

After having developed an expression for the accelerated soil mass (m) in equation 5.31 we must now develop an expression for the acceleration (dv/dt). Referring to figure 5.41, v_s is the absolute velocity of the soil mass and v_e is the velocity of the soil mass relative to the tool. The direction of v_s is along the failure plane of the soil oriented at an angle β from the horizontal as shown in figure 5.41. The relative velocity v_e is the sliding velocity along the surface of the tool oriented at an angle δ from the horizontal (fig. 5.41). The tool velocity (v_0) is directed horizontally as shown in the figure. The three velocity vectors make a closed triangle as indicated by the following vector equation:

$$v_s = v_0 + v_e$$

Soehne assumed that:

$$\frac{dv}{dt} \approx \frac{\Delta v}{\Delta t} = \frac{v_s - 0}{t_0 - 0} = \frac{v_s}{t_0} \tag{5.33}$$

$v(0) = 0$ since the soil was initially at rest at time $t = 0$. In addition, since the velocity vectors (v_0, v_s, and v_e) form a closed triangle, we can write the following relationship:

$$v_0 = v_s \cos \beta + v_e \cos \delta$$

and

$$v_s \sin \beta = v_e \sin \delta$$

so that v_e can be eliminated to give:

$$v_s = v_0 \frac{\sin \delta}{\sin(\delta + \beta)} \tag{5.34}$$

Substituting equations 5.32, 5.33, and 5.34 into 5.31 and simplifying gives:

$$B = \frac{\gamma}{g} bd v_0^2 \frac{\sin \delta}{\sin(\delta + \beta)} \tag{5.35}$$

Equations 5.28, 5.30, and 5.35 may be substituted into equation 5.28 to provide a single equation in which parameters of the tool, soil, and mode of operation are related to the horizontal force to move the tool. Soil friction may be calculated from:

$$\mu = \tan \phi$$

where ϕ is the angle of internal friction. The angle β can be evaluated from the equation (see fig. 5.31):

$$\beta = (90° - \phi)/2$$

Vertical forces on the tool can be placed in equilibrium to provide a relation similar to equation 5.23. Equations 5.25 and 5.26

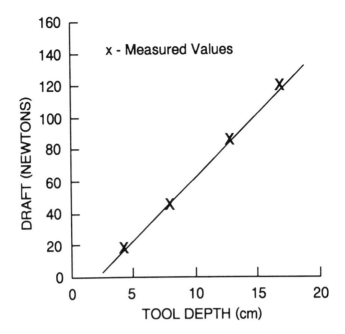

Figure 5.42–Predicted and measured draft forces on a simple tillage tool in a sandy soil (Soehne, 1956, cited in Gill and Vandenberg, 1968).

again can be used to calculate an equation similar to equation 5.28. Equation 5.28 and its implied vertical counterpart thus constitute a simple mechanics for inclined tools. Soehne (1956) attempted to verify equation 5.28 experimentally. He used an inclined tool supported in the center. Figure 5.42 compares the measured and the calculated values.

There is a general agreement in the measured and the predicted data that indicates that the mechanics are correct. Several factors might have contributed to the prediction error. Edge and supporting standard effects were present for the tool, but not for the mathematical model. Experimental determination of the dynamic soil parameters may have been in error. The shear failure may be a progressive failure rather than a simultaneous failing of the entire surface. Refinement in any one of these limiting factors could greatly improve the accuracy of the mechanics.

Example 5.4

An inclined blade tillage tool 25 cm wide and 10 cm long is operating at 25 cm depth in cohesionless soil with density equal to 1.2 g/cc, and the angle of internal friction of 37°. The tool speed is 5 km/h and the soil metal friction is to be taken as 0.3. Assuming a negligible cutting resistance determine the horizontal force acting on the tillage tool.

Solution. The following parameters are given by the problem statement:

$$\delta = 45°; d = 25 \text{ cm}; \phi = 37°; b = 25 \text{ cm}; L_0 = 10 \text{ cm}; \mu' = 0.3;$$
$$\rho = 1200 \text{ kg/m}^3; \text{ and } v_0 = 1.389 \text{ m/s}.$$

Using equation 5.34 the acceleration force can be computed. Note that $\rho = \gamma/g$ and $\beta = 1/2(90 - \phi) = 26.5°$. Substituting these values in the equation we get:

$$B \approx 1200 \left(\frac{25}{100}\right)\left(\frac{25}{100}\right)(1.389)^2 \frac{\sin 45}{\sin(45 + 26.5)} = 108 \text{ N}$$

The area of shear plane (A_1) ahead of the tool is calculated from equation 5.30 as follows:

$$A_1 = \frac{(25)^2}{(100)^2 \sin(26.5)} = 0.14 \text{ m}^2$$

The soil weight is calculated next from equation 5.29 as follows:

$$d^* = \frac{25}{100} \frac{\sin(45 + 26.5)}{\sin(26.5)} = 0.53 \text{ m}$$

$$L_1 = \frac{25}{100} \frac{\cos(45 + 26.5)}{\sin(26.5)} = 0.178 \text{ m}$$

$$L_2 = 0.53 \tan(45) = 0.53$$

$$W = 9.81(1200)\frac{25}{100}0.53\left(0.10 + \frac{0.178 + 0.53}{2}\right) = 708 \text{ N}$$

The geometric factor (Z) is calculated as follows:

$$Z = \left(\frac{\cos 45 - \mu' \sin 45}{\sin 45 + \mu' \cos 45} + \frac{\cos 26.5 - \mu \sin 26.5}{\sin 26.5 + \mu \cos 26.5}\right)$$

$$= 1.062$$

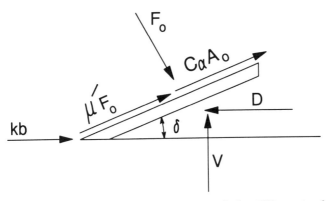

Figure 5.43–A free body diagram of the tillage tool showing soil adhesion force (Rowe and Barnes, 1961, cited in Gill and Vandenberg, 1968).

Finally, the draft force (D^*) is calculated from equation 5.28 as follows:

$$D^* \approx \frac{942}{1.062} + \frac{108}{1.062\left(\sin 26.5 + 0.75\cos 26.5\right)}$$

$$= 978\,\text{N. Ans.}$$

Rowe and Barnes (1961) attempted to overcome some of the inherent limitations in the mechanics. They used the physical arrangement shown in figure 5.39 to eliminate the influence of extraneous forces along the sides of the soil block and the standard holding the tool. They also incorporated into the mechanics the influence of adhesion on the soil-metal sliding surface. The adhesion parameter (C_α) requires a change in the forces as shown in figure 5.43. Incorporating the adhesion parameter changes equation 5.28 to give:

$$D^* = \frac{W}{z} + \frac{CA_1 + B}{z\left(\sin\beta + \mu\cos\beta\right)} + \frac{C_\alpha + A_0}{z\left(\sin\delta + \mu'\cos\delta\right)} \qquad (5.36)$$

where
A_0 = area of the inclined tool
C_α = soil-metal adhesion

Rowe and Barnes (1961) were primarily concerned with the influence of speed on the magnitude of the soil shear parameters,

TABLE 5.1 SOIL SHEAR STRENGTHS AT DIFFERENT RATES
(ROWE AND BARNES, 1961, CITED IN
GILL AND VANDENBERG, 1968)

Rate of Shear (in. / sec)	Sand (psi)	Ida (psi)	Colo (psi)	Luton (psi)
0.76	1.15	1.67	------	3.14
8.27	1.27	1.96	2.72	3.69
15.76	1.45	2.31	3.28	4.39
22.95	1.46	2.24	3.28	------
26.97	------	------	3.33	------

which would, in turn, influence the draft. Consequently, they measured the soil shear parameters at various speeds and assumed that the soil sheared at velocity (v_s) which can be calculated by equation 5.34. The results of performing shear tests at different speeds are given in table 5.1. The results of their measurements and calculations are shown in figure 5.44. A reasonable agreement was obtained between calculated and measured values.

5.3 Performance of Tillage Implements

The performance of tillage tools is determined by their draft and power requirements and the quality of work. The definition of quality of work depends upon the type of tillage tool. For a plow it is the degree of soil inversion and pulverization while for a harrow it is the level of clod break-up. However, no universally accepted method has been developed to quantify the quality of work. Therefore, in this section only the draft force acting on the tillage tools and their power requirements are presented. The effects of soil and tool parameters as well as the operating conditions on the draft force and power requirements are discussed.

5.3.1 Moldboard Plows

The draft is defined as the component of tractor pull acting on the plow that is parallel to the line of travel. The specific draft is the draft divided by the cross-sectional area of the furrow. Soil type and condition are by far the most important factors contributing to variations in specific draft. Values of specific draft range from 1.4 to 2 N/cm² (2 to 3 lbf/in.²) for sandy soils and up to 10 to 14 N/cm² (15 to 20 lbf/in.²) for heavy gumbo soils. Sandy or silt loams may have specific drafts from 2 to 5 N/cm² (3 to 7 lbf/in.²), whereas 4 to 8 N/cm² (6 to 12 lbf/in.²) would be typical for clay loams and heavy clay soils.

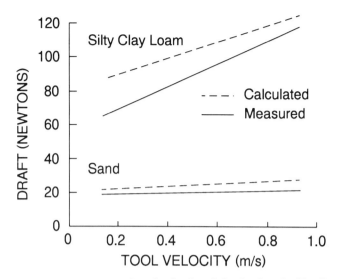

Figure 5.44–Measured and calculated draft of an inclined tillage tool at various tool velocities (Rowe and Barnes, 1961, cited in Gill and Vandenberg, 1968).

Soil moisture content is an important factor in regard to both draft and quality of work. A dry soil requires excessive power and also accelerates wear of the cutting edges. An increase of moisture content from 9.1 to 11.7% may reduce the specific draft in a fine sandy loam by 15 to 35%. Other pertinent soil factors include the degree of compaction and the type or absence of cover crop. The draft may increase 15 to 35% when the apparent specific gravity of a fine sandy loam changes from 1.68 to 1.83.

Most available evidence indicates that the specific draft of a plow generally decreases as the depth is increased to some optimum depth/width ratio and then increases as the depth is increased further. It has been reported that the minimum specific draft for a number of 36-cm (14-in.) bottoms was at depths of 13 to 18 cm (5 to 7 in.). It has been found that the specific draft was increased as the width of cut was reduced below 26 cm. Results from several sources indicate that the draft of a rolling coulter may be 10 to 17% of the total for the plow-coulter combination. Comparative test in loam soils indicate about 5 to 7% reduction in draft by taking most of the side thrust on the rear furrow wheel rather than all on the landside.

McKibben and Reed (1952) consolidated the many speed-versus-draft test results. They plotted the percent increase in draft as a function of speed, taking the draft at 4.83 km/h (3 mph) as 100% in each case. This data includes several runs with moldboard plows, mostly at speeds from 1.6 to 13 km/h (1 to 8 mph). The data for moldboard plows can be represented reasonably well by the relation:

$$\frac{D_s}{D_r} = 0.83 + 0.00730 \, S^2 \qquad\qquad (5.37)$$

where
> D_r = draft at reference speed (4.83 km/h)
> D_s = draft at speed S (in same units as D_r)
> S = speed (km/h)

Hendrick (CRC, 1988) gave the following equations for the specific draft (N/cm^2) for different soil types:

Silty Clay (South Texas)	$7 + 0.049 \, S^2$
Decatur Clay Loam	$6 + 0.053 \, S^2$
Silt Clay (N. Illinois)	$4.8 + 0.024 \, S^2$
Davidson Loam	$3 + 0.020 \, S^2$
Sandy Silt	$3 + 0.032 \, S^2$
Sandy Loam	$2.8 + 0.013 \, S^2$
Sand	$2 + 0.013 \, S^2$

Once the specific draft is determined, the value of total draft can be calculated by multiplying the specific draft by the total cross-sectional area of the plow. The power requirement can then be determined by multiplying the the total draft by the implement speed.

5.3.2 Disk Implements

The performance of disk implements is measured in terms of draft, specific draft, power requirements, and depth. Unlike moldboard plows, the depth of penetration of disk implements is determined by the implement weight and soil condition. Thus, the ability to maintain a uniform desired depth becomes an important performance criterion.

Disk plows. Hendrick (CRC, 1988) developed equations for the draft per unit cross section area of a furrow slice for a 66 cm disk, 22° tilt and 45° disk angles. Specific draft in N/cm^2 is given by the following equations:

Decatur Clay:	Specific draft (N/cm^2) = $5.2 + 0.039 \, S^2$	(5.38)
Davidson Loam:	Specific draft (N/cm^2) = $2.4 + 0.045 \, S^2$	(5.39)

where s = speed (km/h).

Disk harrows. For disk harrows the draft is a function of mass M (kg) for any speed as follows:

Clay Draft (N) = 14.7 M
Silt Loam Draft (N) = 11.7 M
Sandy Loams Draft (N) = 7.8 M   (5.40)

The typical weights for disk harrows ranges from 160 to 210 kg/m of width for mounted tandem type with 41 to 51 cm diameter disks. The mass for wheel type is 240 to 510 kg/m with 41 to 66 cm diameter disks. For offset pull harrows with wheels the mass is 390 to 890 kg/m with 56 to 81 cm diameter disks. The numbers also apply for harrows with no wheels and 61 to 81 cm disks.

Disk tillers. Sommer et al. (1983) summarized results of a five-year study for a primary tillage disk with a 610 mm diameter blade in a range of 55 to 120 kg/blade. The tests focused on the effects of gang angle, mass per blade, blade type, blade spacing, and speed on the performance parameters such as concave specific draft, depth, and draft. Concave specific draft is calculated by dividing the total draft by the concave pressure area. The concave and the projected areas are given in figure 5.45. They developed prediction equations using a base disk with 610-mm blade diameter and a 648-mm spherical radius. The disk spacing was 228 mm with 55 kg per disk. There were a total of 40 blades on the tandem double offset disk implement. Figure 5.46 shows the effect of gang angle. The draft and the depth increase with an increase in the gang angle but the concave specific draft reduces. The following prediction equations were developed:

$$\text{Depth (mm)} = -0.15 \, (\alpha^2 - 67.3\alpha + 104) \qquad (5.41)$$

$$\text{Draft (kN)} = -0.013 \, (\alpha^2 - 181\alpha + 808) \qquad (5.42)$$

where α = gang angle (°)

Figure 5.47 shows the effect of mass per blade for a gang angle of 18°. As the mass per blade increases, concave specific draft, depth and draft increase. The increase in the concave specific draft indicates that the draft increases faster that the tilled area. The following equations were developed:
18° gang angle:

$$\text{Depth (mm)} = K_d \, (-4.93\beta - 509) \qquad (5.43)$$

$$\text{Draft (kN)} = K_f \, (-39.2\beta + 42) \qquad (5.44)$$

22° gang angle:

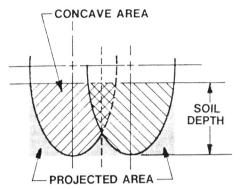

Figure 5.45–Concave and projected pressure areas (Sommer et al., 1983).

$$\text{Depth (mm)} = K_d \, (- 2.9\beta - 733) \qquad (5.45)$$
$$\text{Draft (kN)} = K_f \, (- 36.2\beta + 700) \qquad (5.46)$$

where β = mass per blade (kg).

The values of K_d and K_f have been found to be $- 0.15$ and $- 0.013$, respectively.

5.3.3 Cultivators

Gullacher and Coates (1980) studied the effect of cultivator sweep pitch on tillage forces. They measured both the draft and suction forces. Suction is defined as the vertical force that the soil exerts on the sweep. Figure 5.48 shows three typical shank

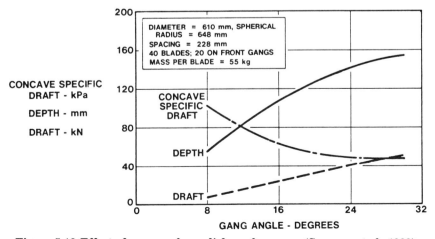

Figure 5.46–Effect of gang angle on disk performance (Sommer et al., 1983).

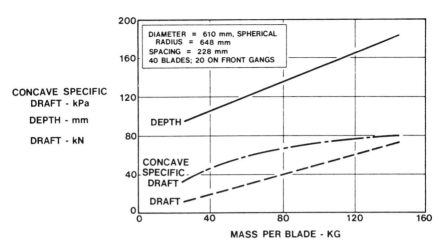

Figure 5.47–Effect of mass per blade on disk performance (Sommer et al., 1983).

assemblies used for mounting cultivator sweeps. The angle that the bottom of the sweep makes with the horizontal is known as the sweep pitch. A positive pitch angle is defined when the sweep tip is lower than its heel. During tillage, soil forces on the sweep causes the pitch to increase as shown in figure 5.49. The increase in pitch at low to moderate forces is due to the flexing of the shank. But as the forces exceed spring preload, the shank begins to rotate upward and the pitch angle increases more rapidly.

Figure 5.50 shows the geometry and dimension of the sweep used in their study. They found that during the primary tillage operation, the draft per unit width increased 31% from 1.7 kN/m at 2.5° pitch to 2.3 kN/m at 18.5°. These results were obtained at a depth of 40 mm and at a speed of 8 km/h. This represents an increase of about 2% per degree change in the pitch angle. In secondary tillage operation in Oxbow loam under similar operating

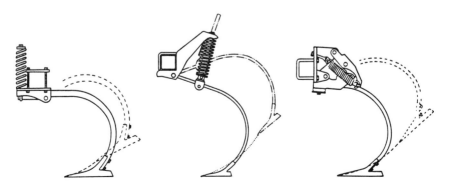

Figure 5.48–Typical shank assemblies (Gullacher and Coates, 1980).

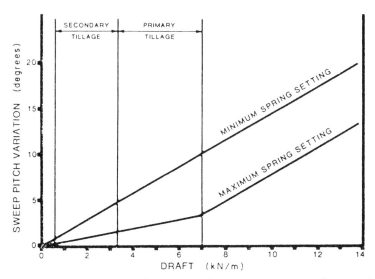

Figure 5.49–Variation in sweep pitch over a range of normal tillage forces for one shank assembly (Gullacher and Coates, 1980).

conditions the draft increased from 0.8 kN/m to 1.7 kN/m, an increase of 106%. At 60 mm depth the increase was 78%. These data are shown in figures 5.51 and 5.52.

Hendrick (CRC, 1988) reported the draft for chisel plows and field cultivators in firm soil spaced at 30 cm apart and operating at a depth of 8.26 cm and travelling at 5.5 to 10.5 km/h as follows:

Loam (Saskatchewan):   Draft (N) = 520 + 49.2 S
Clay Loam (Saskatchewan):   Draft (N) = 480 + 48.1 S
Clay (Saskatchewan):   Draft (N) = 527 + 36.1 S   (5.47)

Draft at depth (d) is given by:

$$D = D_{8.26} \left(\frac{d}{8.26} \right)^2 \tag{5.48}$$

where $D_{8.26}$ is the draft at a depth of 8.26 cm and d is depth (cm).

5.3.4 Rotary Tillers

Rotary tillers are primarily L-shaped blades mounted on a shaft which is driven by the tractor pto shaft. The width of the tillers range up to 4 m. Tillers are very common in rice fields primarily for

Test Sweep Specifications

Make: Mackay

Model: 101-10

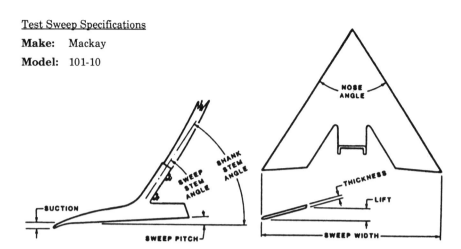

Dimensions:

- sweep width   258 mm
- lift   20 mm
- thickness   4.9 mm
- nose suction   6 mm
- nose angle   60.5°
- sweep stem angle   48°

Figure 5.50–Specifications of the test sweep (Gullacher and Coats, 1980).

puddling operation. Rotary tillers produce high degree of soil pulverization but have high power requirements.

Figure 5.53 shows an L-shape blade for a conventional rotary tiller and the cutting path as followed by the blade. The rotor rotates in the same direction as the forward travel. The tiller make two to three cuts per revolution of the blade. The bite length is defined as the amount of forward travel per cut. The bite length is affected by the speed of rotation and the forward travel speed.

The rotor develops a forward and an upward soil reaction. The forward reaction generates a negative pull on the tractor while the upward pull reduces the implement weight. Under hard soil conditions the tiller may 'walk out' of the ground due to excessive upward soil reaction. Both force reactions increase with operating depth. The forward reaction represents negative power requirements which is generally less than 7% of the pto shaft power but can be as high as 20% depending on the bite length. Increasing bite length reduces specific energy requirements. Specific energy is defined as

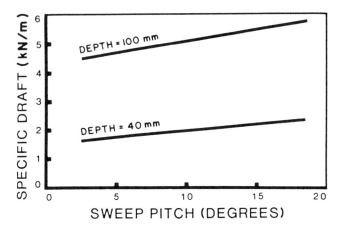

Figure 5.51–Variation in specific draft with sweep pitch for primary tillage in Oxbow loam at 8 km/h (Gullacher and Coates, 1980).

the total energy required divided by the volume of soil disturbed by the tiller. Energy requirements are influenced by the ratio of the depth to the rotor diameter. As shown in figure 5.54, even the lowest rotor specific energy is about three times higher than that for a moldboard plow in the same soil. However, a rotary tiller may produce the same degree of soil pulverization as obtained by one pass with a moldboard plow, two passes with a disk harrow, and one pass with a spike tooth harrow. These factors must be kept in mind while comparing rotary tillers with other tillage tools.

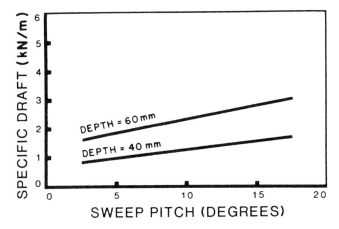

Figure 5.52–Variation in specific draft with sweep pitch for secondary tillage in Oxbow loam at 8 km/h (Gullacher and Coates, 1980).

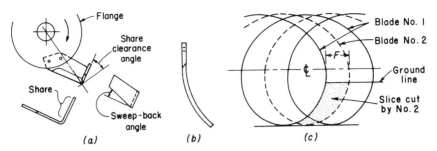

Figure 5.53–(a) Three views of an L-shaped blade for a rotary tillage, (b) curved blade, (c) paths of cutting edges or tips for two blades 180° apart, in relation to forward speed (Reprinted from *Principles of Farm Machinery*, Kepner et al., 1978).

5.4 Hitching of Tillage Implements

The material presented in this section has been taken from Kepner (1978) and reorganized.

5.4.1 Force Representation for a Tillage Tool

A tillage tool moving through the soil is subjected to the following forces:

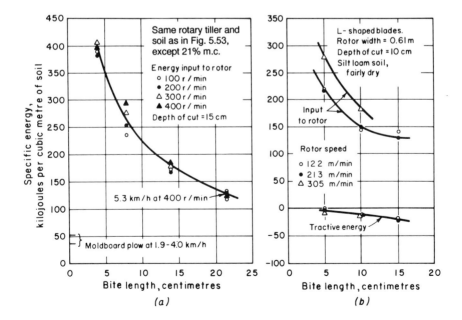

Figure 5.54–Effect of bite length upon specific energy requirements for a conventional rotary tiller (Reprinted from *Principles of Farm Machinery*, Kepner et al., 1978).

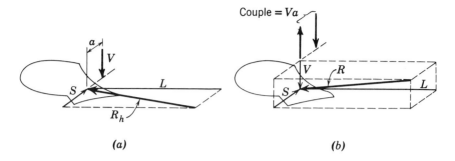

1. Implement weight
2. Soil reaction forces
3. Forces exerted by the prime mover

Implement weight determines the operating depth in case of the disk implements. Often weight is added to improve penetration in hard soils. The soil reaction forces are divided into *useful* and *parasitic* forces. Useful soil forces are those needed to cut, break up, and move soil. Parasitic forces are due to friction and rolling resistance and act on the stabilizing surfaces such as the landside and the furrow wheel. The useful forces are determined by soil condition and the parasitic forces are affected by tool design and adjustments. The resultant of forces exerted by the prime mover is the pull of the power unit upon the implement.

When the tool is not symmetric, rotational effects are produced by the useful soil forces. There are several ways to represent these forces on a tillage tool. The method shown in figure 5.55 consists of three mutually perpendicular force vectors and a moment. On tillage equipment with multiple soil engaging tools, resultants of forces acting on individual bottoms is computed. The resultant forces acting on the entire implement are used in hitching. The objective of proper hitching is to minimize parasitic forces and to obtain a stable operation.

The following notations are used while analyzing hitching of tillage implements:

R = resultant of all useful forces acting on the plow
L = longitudinal component of R
S = lateral component of R
V = vertical component of R
Q = resultant of all parasitic forces acting on the plow
P = resultant pull exerted by the tractor
W = implement weight

subscripts
h = horizontal component of a force
v = vertical component of a force

The useful soil force components L, S, and V (or resultants R_h and R_v) and the implement gravitational force (W) are the independent force variables involved in analyzing either a simple drawbar hitch arrangement or an integral hitch system. The parasitic soil forces (Q) and the pull (P) are dependent variables that may be influenced by the hitch arrangement. The analysis procedures in this section assume that W and the components of the useful soil force are known or can be estimated. Another approach for determining the force relations between the implement and the tractor is to actually measure the magnitude and direction of the pull (or its components).

Forces representation for a moldboard plow. Figure 5.56 shows a typical representation of the useful soil force component (R_h) parasitic force component (Q_h) and the horizontal component of the pull (P_x) as suggested by Clyde (1944). Force (R_h) consists of a lateral component (S) and a longitudinal component (L). Generally, the S/L ratios varies from 0.35-0.45 for sand (Randolph and Reed, 1938); 0.25-0.45 for sandy loams (Getzlaff, 1953; Nichols et al, 1958; Randolf and Reed, 1938); and 0.2-0.3 for clay loams (Cooper and McCreery, 1961); all with the coulter removed (Clyde, 1944). From these ratios the orientation of R_h can be determined. The component Q_h of the parasitic force consists of a landside reaction force equal to S but in the opposite direction and the frictional force that acts on the surface of the landside opposite to the direction of travel. The friction force is determined by multiplying the reaction force by the coefficient of soil metal friction. The soil metal friction determines the orientation of Q_h. Having established the parasitic and the useful force vectors, the magnitude of the draft force (P_x) along the line of pull may be determined by summing these force vectors. The point of convergence of the vectors is called the center of resistance and is located midway along the length of the landside and about one-third of the width from the landside shown as point H in the figure. As shown in figure 5.56c, increasing the landside length moves the center of resistance towards the rear of the plow bottom. It should also be noted that H moves closer to the landside since the line of R_h does not change. Figure 5.56b shows the effect of an angled pull on the draft (P_x) and the parasitic force (Q_h). Because the line of pull is not the same as the direction of travel, the plow pulls harder against the furrow wall. This causes a larger reaction force (the lateral component of Q_h) and

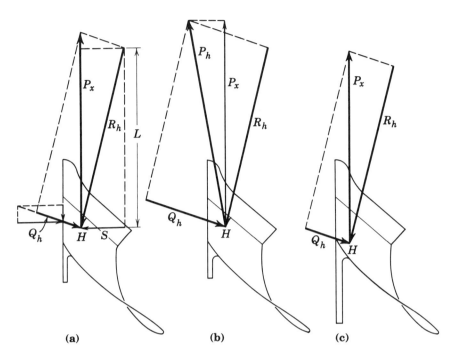

Figure 5.56–Typical location of R_h and its relation to the landside force and pull: (a) straight pull, (b) angled pull, (c) long landside (Reprinted from *Principles of Farm Machinery,* Kepner et al., 1978).

consequently a larger frictional force. The net result is an increase in the draft force.

Force representation for a disk blade. The net effect of all soil forces acting on a disk blade as a result of soil cutting, pulverizing, elevating, and inverting the furrow slice, plus any parasitic forces acting on the disk, can be expressed in many ways. In figure 5.57a, the resultant effect is expressed by two non-intersecting forces, one being a thrust force (T) parallel to the disk axis, and the other being a radial force (U). This method is particularly advantageous in calculating loads on disk support bearings. The thrust force is always below the disk centerline because the soil acts against the lower part of the disk face. The radial force, which includes the vertical support force on the disk blade, must pass slightly to the rear of the disk centerline to provide the torque necessary to overcome the bearing friction and cause rotation of the disk.

The resultant effect can also be represented in terms of the longitudinal, lateral, and vertical components (L, S, and V), and resultants of these components as shown in figure 5.57b. This

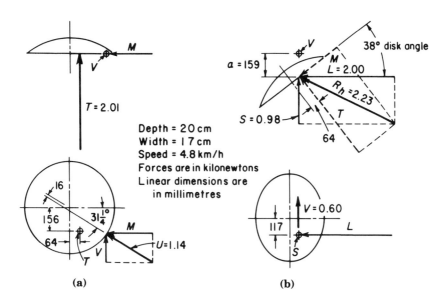

Figure 5.57–Example of resultant soil forces acting upon a vertical disk blade. The total effect is represented by two non-intersecting forces: (a) a thrust force T and a radial force U, (b) a horizontal force V (Reprinted from *Principles of Farm Machinery,* Kepner et al., 1978).

representation is more useful when considering the soil forces on the whole implement. In figure 5.57b, S and L are combined into R_h so that the entire effect is represented by two non-intersecting forces. Because the forces don't intersect, they constitute a couple V_a that causes the disk to rotate.

Forces on a disk harrow. Figure 5.58b shows forces on an offset disk harrow without wheels when it is operating with no side draft. The location of the horizontal center of resistance H is determined by the intersection of R_{hf} and R_{hr}. For no side draft the hitch linkage of the disk harrow must be adjusted so the hitch point F_0 is directly in front of H.

If the hitch linkage is changed to move the implement either to the right or to the left from the no-side-draft position, side draft is introduced and the operating conditions of the harrow are changed. For example, if the hitch point in figure 5.58a is moved from F_0 to F_2, the force equilibrium is momentarily destroyed and the side component of the new pull, acting at point H, rotates the implement counter clockwise about F_2. Rotation continues until the disk angle of the two gangs have readjusted themselves so that the difference between their lateral force components S_f and S_r become equal to the side draft P_y. Note that the magnitude of L_f and L_r and the position of H also change during this readjustment.

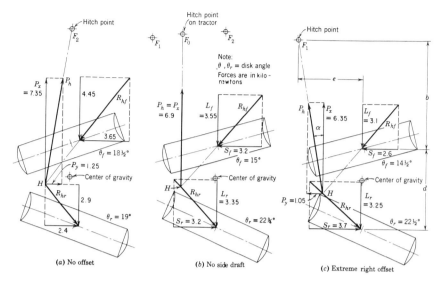

(a) No offset   (b) No side draft   (c) Extreme right offset

Figure 5.58–Horizontal force relations for a pull-type, right-hand offset disk harrow without wheels (Reprinted from *Principles of Farm Machinery*, Kepner et al., 1978).

The force relations for a tandem disk harrow are symmetrical about the implement centerline because both front gangs are operating under the same soil condition (untilled), with the side components equal and opposite to each other, and both rear gangs are in tilled soil.

Amount of offset available. Let e be the amount of offset from the hitch point to the center of cut, α = the horizontal angle of pull, d = the longitudinal distance between the centers of the two gangs, and b = the longitudinal distance from the center of the front gang to the hitch point (fig. 5.58c). Taking moments about F_1 yields the following relationship assuming that the R_{hf} and R_{hr} pass through the centers of the gangs:

$$eL_f + eL_r + bS_f - (b + d) S_r = 0$$

from which:

$$e = \frac{b(S_r - S_f) + dS_f}{L_f + L_r} = b \tan\alpha + \frac{dS_r}{L_f + L_r} \qquad (5.49)$$

For the condition of no side draft ($S_f = S_r = S$ and $\alpha = 0$). Then, from equation 5.49, the offset with no side draft is:

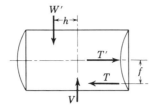

Figure 5.59–Vertical and thrust forces acting
upon a disk-harrow gang (Reprinted from
Principles of Farm Machinery, Kepner et al.,
1978).

$$e_0 = \frac{dS}{L_f + L_r} \qquad (5.50)$$

Equation 5.50 states that the amount of offset obtainable
without side draft is a function only of the distance between gangs
and of the relative magnitudes of the lateral and longitudinal soil
reactions. The soil force relations, however, are affected by soil
condition, disk angle, disk blade size and concavity, and other
factors. S/L increases as the disk angle is increased and, according to
Clyde (1944), is greater in firm soils than in soft soils.

Couples acting on disk harrow gangs. It is a well known fact
that the concave end of a disk-harrow gang tends to penetrate more
deeply than the convex end. This condition exists because the soil-
force component (T), perpendicular to the disk blade, is applied well
below the axle (fig. 5.59) while the balancing force (T') is applied at
axle height, thus forming a couple (T·f).

With uniform penetration, V will act approximately at the
center of the gang. To obtain uniform penetration with a single gang,
the resultant downward force (W' – the implement weight minus the
upward component of pull) must act at a distance h from the center
of the gang (toward the convex end) such that:

$$W'h = T \cdot f \qquad (5.51)$$

It is a relatively simple matter with single acting and tandem
disk harrows to obtain uniform penetration by having the couples of
the laterally opposed gangs counteract each other through the frame.
The design problem is more complex in the case of an offset disk
harrow because the opposing couples subject the frame between the
gang to torsion. Adequate torsional stiffness and appropriate
adjustments for lateral leveling of one gang with respect to the other
are important.

It is a common practice in analyzing force relations for hitching tillage implements to give separate consideration to horizontal components of R, Q, and P, and to W and the components of these forces in a vertical plane (or planes) parallel to the line of motion. These considerations are referred to as horizontal hitching and vertical hitching.

The following sections considers force relations involved in hitching pull-type and mounted implements.

5.4.2 Pull-Type Implements

It is necessary to establish the locations and/or magnitudes of the resultant parasitic support force (Q_h or Q_v) and the pull (P_h or P_v) that are the most desirable from the standpoints of their effects on the pulling force upon the tractor and the magnitude and distribution of parasitic forces acting upon the implement.

Vertical hitching. Pull-type tillage implements generally fall into one of the following three categories in regard to vertical-hitching arrangements and the effects of hitching upon the force system.

(a) Implements with hinged pull members that have support wheels or support runners to gage the depth. The pull member acts as a free link in the vertical plane. Examples are moldboard plows, disk plows, and drag-type spring-tooth harrows.

(b) Implements with hinged pull members that do not have gage wheels or runners. The only support is through the soil-working units, and parasitic forces cannot be separated from the useful soil forces. Examples are disk harrows without wheels, spike-tooth harrows, and tandem-gang rotary hoes.

(c) Single-axle implements with rigid pull members. Examples are field cultivators and chisels, subsoilers, and disk harrows that have wheels for transport and depth gaging.

Force relations are shown in the following sections for one example of each type, and hitch adjustment recommendations are included for some other types. One must remember that in all the force analyses, the direction and magnitude of R_v may vary widely from those shown, even within one field.

Implements having hinged pull members and support wheels or runner. Figure 5.60 shows the vertical force relations for a pull-type moldboard plow. For uniform motion, W, R_v, and Q_v must be in equilibrium. Knowing the magnitudes and locations of the implement gravitational force W and the useful soil force Rv under the particular operating conditions involved, the first step in

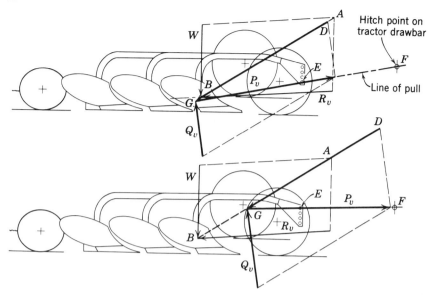

Figure 5.60–Vertical force relation for a pull type implement having support wheels and a hinged pull member (Reprinted from *Principles of Farm Machinery*, Kepner et al., 1978).

analyzing the hitch is to combine these forces graphically into the resultant AB.

The line of pull is established next. It must pass through the hitch point F on the tractor and the hitch hinge axis selected at E, since the pull member acts as a free link in the vertical plane. The line of pull and the resultant AB intersect at G. The line of action of the support force Q_v is now drawn through G, although its magnitude is not yet known. In figure 5.60, Q_v is shown with some backward slant to include the rolling resistance of the wheels furnishing the vertical support. If the support were mostly on sliding surfaces, more slant would be needed to include the friction force. Since P_v must be in equilibrium with AB and Q_v, the magnitudes of Q_v and P_v can be determined by moving AB along its line of action to DG and then completing the force parallelogram as indicated.

The top example in figure 5.60 represents a desirable hitch adjustment for a moldboard plow, with Q_v located well behind the front wheels so there is enough load on the rear wheel for stable operation. The lower example illustrates an extreme condition in which the hitch point E is so high on the plow that Q_v is about under the front wheels, with practically no load being carried on the rear wheel. The rear of the plow will be very unstable, particularly when momentary variations in the direction and magnitude of R_v are considered.

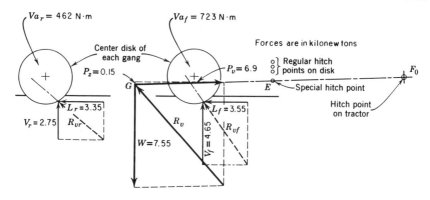

Figure 5.61–Vertical force relation for a pull type offset or tandem disk harrow without wheels and no hinge axis between the front and the rear gangs (Reprinted from *Principles of Farm Machinery*, Kepner et al., 1978).

Hitching at too low a point on the implement has the opposite effect. The resultant support force (Q_v) is moved toward the rear, thus reducing the load on the front wheels. Increasing or decreasing the slope of P_v without changing the location of G decreases or increases Q_v but does not change its location. Having too great a slope for P_v can cause difficulty in maintaining the desired depth, particularly with a relatively high implement that has little or no suction, such as a spring- tooth harrow.

Clyde (1944) recommended that for moldboard plows the preliminary adjustment of the hitch height on the plow frame be such that P_v passed through a point slightly below the ground surface and directly above the average location of all share points. For disk plows the suggested trial point for establishing the line of pull is at the ground surface midway between the centers of the front and rear disks. If the rear furrow wheel of a disk plow has the proper amount of lead toward the plowed ground and still tends to climb out of the furrow, the hitch point on the plow frame should be lowered, thus putting more of Q_v on the rear wheel.

Implements with hinged pull members but without gage wheels or runners. Vertical force relations for an offset or tandem disk harrow without wheels are shown in figure 5.61. The only support from the soil is through the disk blades. the position of point G is established by the intersection of W and the line of pull (P_v). The soil forces R_{vf} and R_{vr} automatically adjust themselves, by means of depth changes, so their resultant R_v passes through point G and is in equilibrium with W and P_v.

Raising the hitch on the implement frame raises G and moves R_v closer to the front gang, thus increasing R_{vf} and decreasing R_{vr}. The result would be increased depth of penetration for the front gang and decreased depth for the rear gang. In the example shown, R_{vf} is

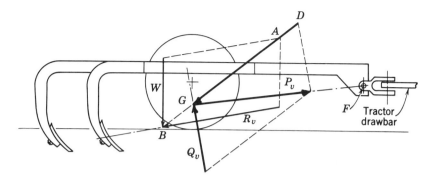

Figure 5.62–Vertical force relations for a single axle, pull implement receiving vertical support only through its wheels (Reprinted from *Principles of Farm Machinery*, Kepner et al., 1978).

greater than R_{vr} because the front gang is operating in firm soil and the rear gang is in loosened soil.

Single-axle implements with rigid pull members. When a single-axle implement receives vertical support only through its wheels, the location of Q_v is fixed. The line of Q_v must pass slightly behind the axle centerline (fig. 5.62) in order to supply torque to overcome wheel-bearing friction and cause rotation of the wheels. Point G is fixed by the intersection of AB and Q_v, and the line of pull is through G and the vertical hitch point F at the tractor drawbar. The only possible hitch adjustment is changing the height of the drawbar at F, which would change the slope of P_v. In the example shown, with R_v having a downward slope, moving the wheels rearward with respect to the soil-engaging tools would increase the slope of P_v and reduce the magnitude of Q_v.

The force relations for a disk harrow having wheels to gage the depth would be basically the same as the relations shown in figure 5.62, but R_v would have a steep upward slope as shown in figure 5.61. The fore-and-aft location of R_v would be determined by the relative depths and soil resistances of the front and rear gangs. The relative depths would be related to the attitude of the frame, as established by the vertical adjustment of the rigid pull member.

Horizontal hitching. Most tillage implements, with the exception of moldboard plows, disk plows and offset disk harrows, are symmetrical about their longitudinal centerline. The side components of the soil forces are balanced, the horizontal center of resistance is at the center of the tilled width, and the horizontal line of pull is in the direction of travel.

Plows and offset disk harrows can withstand substantial amounts of side draft (lateral component of pull), and proper hitching is necessary to minimize adverse effects on the tractor and the implement. Moldboard plows absorb side forces through the landsides, disk plows through the furrow wheels, and offset disk harrows by automatically changing the disk angles to create a difference between the soil-force side components for the front and rear gangs. Pull-type disk plows have essentially free-link pull members, whereas moldboard plows and disk harrows have laterally rigid pull members. Horizontal hitching for moldboard plows and disk plows is discussed in the following sections.

It is not always possible to have the horizontal center of resistance of an implement directly behind the center of pull of the tractor, particularly for narrow implements and wide-tread tractors. If the implement can withstand side forces, the alternatives are a *central angled pull*, or an *offset angled pull*. If the implement cannot withstand side draft, the only alternative is an offset straight pull. The center of pull of the tractor is generally considered to be midway between the rear wheels and slightly ahead of the axle.

A central angled pull does not affect tractor steering, whereas the offset pulls do. An angled pull (either central or offset) introduces a side force on the tractor rear wheels which is sometimes of sufficient magnitude to be objectionable. An angled pull is undesirable with some implements, even though the implement can resist the side forces. Usually, some compromise in hitching is best, with part of the adverse effect being absorbed by the tractor and part by the implement.

Horizontal hitching of pull-type moldboard plows. The location of the horizontal center of resistance H for a moldboard plow bottom is determined by the point of intersection of the parasitic force (Q_h) acting upon the landside, and R_h. The lateral location of H varies somewhat, depending upon soil conditions, length of landside, amount of side force taken by the rear furrow wheel, etc. For hitching purposes the location is often assumed to be about one-fourth of the width of cut over from the landside and a little behind the rear edge of the share. The line of pull is determined by the location of H and the location of the drawbar hitch point F (fig. 5.63) since the pull member is laterally rigid.

The ideal hitch is obtained when the tractor tread can be adjusted so the center of pull is directly ahead of the horizontal center of resistance. In some cases, however, a sufficiently narrow wheel tread cannot be obtained or is not practical, even with one rear wheel in the furrow. With large plows, the tractor is sometimes operated with both wheels on unplowed ground, primarily to reduce soil compaction from the wheel in the furrow. When a central straight pull cannot be obtained, it is common practice to divide the effects of the offset, as indicated in figure 5.63, so that the line of pull passes a little to the right of the center of pull but not enough to

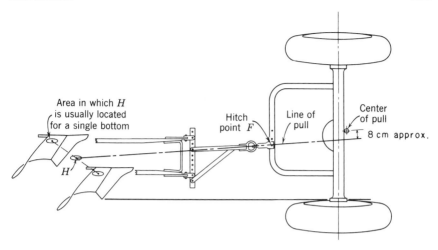

Figure 5.63–Recommended horizontal hitching for a moldboard plow pulled by a wide tractor (Reprinted from *Principles of Farm Machinery*, Kepner et al., 1978).

cause steering troubles. Fortunately, a moldboard plow will operate satisfactory even when the line of pull is at a considerable angle from the line of travel.

Horizontal hitching of pull-type disk plows. The horizontal force relations (fig. 5.64) are somewhat different for a disk plow than for a moldboard plow, because all the side thrust must be taken through the wheels and because the pull member on a disk plow (DF in fig. 5.64) is essentially a free link in regard to horizontal forces. Whereas the horizontal line of pull on a moldboard plow must pass through the hitch point on the tractor and through a center of resistance established primarily by the plow and soil characteristics. The horizontal line of pull for a disk plow is determined by the

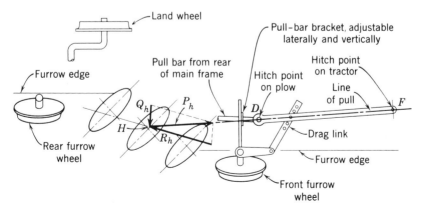

Figure 5.64–Horizontal force relation and hitching for pull-type disk plow (Reprinted from *Principles of Farm Machinery*, Kepner et al., 1978).

location of hitch points D and F. The position of the horizontal center of resistance H and the location of the resultant side force Q_h and R_h.

For the side force to be divided equally between the front and rear furrow wheels, the line of Q_h must pass midway between them. With most pull-type disk plows, this condition will be approximated if the hitch is adjusted so the line of pull passes through a point slightly to the left of the average position of all disk centers (thus establishing H in the desired location). If hitch point D in figure 5.64 is moved to the left on the plow frame, H and Q_h will be moved toward the rear of the plow, and the rear furrow wheel will carry a greater proportion of the side thrust. Moving D to the right (or F to the left) puts more of the side thrust on the front wheel.

5.4.3 Mounted Implements

Two types of hitch linkages are common on modern tractors. Practically all rear-mounted hitches are of the three-point, converging-link type, and parallel-link hitches are employed extensively for front-mounted cultivators. Single-axis hitches have been superseded by three-point hitches in new designs. Any of these three types can be operated with the hitch members acting as free links in vertical planes or with the implement supported through the lift mechanism of the tractor (restrained links).

Free-link operation of three-point hitches. With free-link operation, depth is controlled by gage wheels or other supporting surfaces on the implement. Although depth control for mounted moldboard plows can be obtained through vertical support from the rear furrow wheel and the heel of the rear landside, gage wheels running on the unplowed ground are more common when free-link operation is desired.

The vertical force relations for free-link operation with a moldboard plow having a gage wheel are shown in figure 5.65. In free-link operation, the convergence of the links in a vertical plane provides a vertical hitch point or instantaneous center of rotation as shown at F_v. The location of F_v can readily be changed by modifying the arrangement of the links and it shifts automatically as the implement is raised or lowered. The broken-line position of the links in figure 5.65 illustrates how F'_v is lower than F_v and farther to the rear when the tool is entering the ground. This shift promotes more rapid entry of tools that have appreciable bottom support surfaces (such as a moldboard plow).

The force analysis is basically the same as for a single-axle, pull-type implement except that the line of pull P_v must pass through the virtual hitch point F_v rather than through a real hitch point. All the vertical support in this example is assumed to be on the gage wheel, thus establishing the line of action of Q_v. The slope represents

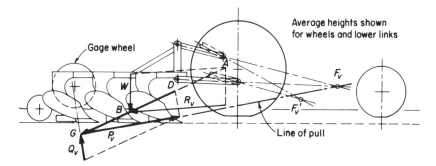

Figure 5.65–Vertical force relations for a three-point hitch when operated as a free-link system (Reprinted from *Principles of Farm Machinery*, Kepner et al., 1978).

the coefficient of rolling resistance. W and R_v are first combined into the resultant AB, and the location of G is established by the intersection of AB and Q_v. P_v then passes through G and F_v.

Raising F_v, by modifying the linkage, would reduce Q_v and increase the load on the tractor rear wheels. However, Q_v must not be reduced to the point where the implement becomes unstable due to momentary variations in R_v. Increasing the plow length by adding more bottoms would move W, R_v, Q_v, and G farther to the rear. P_v would then have less slope but would be higher above the ground at the tractor wheels.

Gaged, free-link operation gives more uniform depth than either automatic position control or automatic draft control when the field surface is irregular and the soil resistance varies substantially, particularly with the larger sizes of mounted moldboard plows. Gage wheels are sometimes used in preference to the other systems in light soils where the draft is relatively low. Wide field cultivators and chisels often have gage wheels to minimize depth variations across the width of the implement.

Restrained-link operation of three-point hitches. In restrained-link operation, the implement gets all or most of its vertical support from the tractor, the hitch links being free only when the tool is entering the ground. As soon as a moldboard plow, for example, reaches its working depth, it is held by the hydraulic system. Its landside and rear furrow wheel must have clearance above the furrow bottom so the plow can go deeper when the controls call for greater depth.

Since the implement obtains no support from the soil, P_v is merely the vector sum of W and R_v as indicated in figure 5.66. The lift links are in tension and the implement exerts downward bending moments on the portions of the lower links behind the lift links.

With restrained-link operation, the effect of the implement upon the tractor when the implement is at its operating depth is

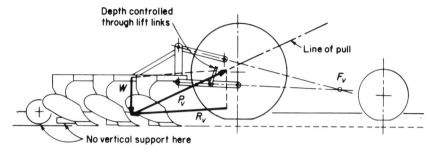

Figure 5.66–Vertical force relations for a mounted implement when supported by restrained links (Reprinted from *Principles of Farm Machinery*, Kepner et al., 1978).

independent of the hitch linkage arrangement. The only significance of the virtual center of rotation (F_v) is that, with single-acting lift mechanisms (the usual arrangement for integral systems), the line of pull cannot pass below this point. However, when the tool is entering the ground, the location of the virtual center of rotation affects the pitch of the tool, just as it does with full free-link operation.

Operating with restrained links rather than free links increases the vertical load on the tractor rear wheels and thereby provides greater tractive ability. This is because the support forces that would act upon the gaging units in a free-link system are transferred to the tractor rear wheels when the links are restrained and because the higher location of P_v at the rear wheels increases the load transfer from the front wheels to the rear wheels.

Problems

5.1   A specimen of soil has a water content of 30%, a unit weight of 1.8 g/cc and a specific gravity (of solids) of 2.70. Find the void ratio and the degree of saturation.

5.2   A compacted soil sample weighs 1903 g and its volume is 930 cc. The water content of the specimen is 10%. The specific gravity of solids is 2.7. Determine the wet density, dry density, void ratio, and the degree of saturation.

5.3   A soil sample has water content of 25%, dry density of 1.1 g/cc. (a) Find the void ratio and wet density. (b) The compaction does not change but the water content changes from 25% to 50%; find the void ratio and the wet density. Assume $\gamma_s = 2.7$.

5.4   A specimen of cohesionless sand was subjected to the direct
        shear test under a normal stress of 100 kPa. The specimen
        failed when the shear stress reached 60 kPa. Plot the stresses
        and find the value of internal friction. At what value would
        the soil fail if the normal stress is 250 kPa?

5.5   In the consolidated-undrained triaxial test, two specimens
        were loaded to failure after consolidation under all around
        pressures of 200 and 400 kPa, and the results are shown
        below:

Sample No.	σ_3 (kPa)	σ' (kPa)	u (kPa)
1	200	150	140
2	400	300	280

Calculate (a) the values of c and ϕ for total stress, (b) the
values c and ϕ for effective stress, (c) maximum shear
stresses for both specimens, and (d) the shear and the normal
stress on the failure planes for both cases.

5.6   A cohesionless soil with a 30° angle of internal friction is
        subjected to a consolidation pressure of 150 kPa. At what
        value of the major principal stress will the specimen fail?

5.7   Consolidated-undrained triaxial tests were performed on two
        clay soil samples. The following are the stresses and pore
        water pressures at failure:

Sample No.	σ' (kPa)	σ_3 (kPa)	u_a (kPa)
1	40	100	30
2	80	200	60

Find the expression for the effective soil shear strength.

5.8   Derive an expression for the total vertical force (V) acting on
        an inclined blade tillage tool. Follow a procedure similar to
        that used in the text to develop the horizontal force
        expression.

5.9   Determine the draft on a plane tillage tool inclined at 45°, operating at 25 cm depth in a cohesionless soil. The tool forward speed is 5 kph. The soil density is 1.2 g/cc and the angle of internal friction (ϕ) is 37°. The tool is 10 cm long and 25 cm wide and the soil-metal friction is 0.3. Neglect adhesion, the cutting resistance, and the effects of the tool supports.

5.10   Repeat problem 5.9 but vary the tool depth from 10 cm to 25 cm in intervals of 5 cm. Plot the draft force against the tool depth. (Hint: Use of a spreadsheet is recommended.)

5.11   Repeat problem 5.9 but vary the tool speed from 1 to 10 kph in 1 k/h intervals. Plot the draft force against the tool speed. (Hint: Use of a spreadsheet is recommended.)

5.12   Repeat problem 5.9 but vary the soil-metal friction from 0.1 to 0.5 in 0.05 intervals. Plot the draft force against soil metal friction. (Hint: Use of a spreadsheet is recommended.)

5.13   The line of pull on an implement is 15° above the horizontal and is in a vertical plane which is at an angle of 10° with the direction of travel. (a) Calculate the draft and side-draft forces for a pull of 11 kN. (b) What drawbar power would be required at 5.5 km/h?

5.14   Referring to figure 5.56 of the text, determine (a) the percent increase in the draft of a plow bottom if the pull is at 10° to the left from the direction of travel. Assume that R_h is at 15° to the right and the soil-metal friction is 0.3. (b) The percent increase in the perpendicular force on the landside. (Hint: A graphical solution is recommended.)

5.15   The total draft of a four-bottom 41 cm moldboard plow when plowing 18 cm deep at 6 km/h was 15 kN. (a) Calculate the specific draft. (b) What is the actual power requirements?

5.16   Each gang of an offset disk harrow without wheels has thirteen 61-cm blades spaced 24 cm apart. The total mass is 1400 kg. In operation, V_f = 8.7 kN and V_r = 5.3 kN. The disk angles are 16° for the front gang and 22° for the rear gang. Based on figures 5.58 and 5.61, the estimated L/V is 0.9 for the front gang and 1.2 for the rear gang, and the estimated

S/V 0.7 for the front gang and 1.1 for the rear gang. Calculate (a) draft, (b) side draft, and (c) draft per unit mass (N/kg).

5.17   A right hand offset disk harrow is operating with disk angle of 15° and 21°, respectively, for the front and rear gangs. The centers of the two gangs are 2.45 m and 4.25 m behind a transverse line through the hitch point on the tractor drawbar. The horizontal soil force components are: L_f = 3.1 kN, S_f = 2.65 kN, L_r = 3.35 kN, S_r = 3.8 kN. Calculate (a) the horizontal angle of pull, (b) the horizontal pull, and (c) the amount of offset of the center of cut with respect to the hitch point.

5.18   Assume that P_v = 9.9 kN in figure 5.65. Determine the force in the top link and the total force in the bottom two links, indicating whether tension or compression. Scale the dimensions and angles from the text and solve by graphical methods. Also, determine the draft.

6

Crop Planting

Introduction

The growth of a new crop begins with the planting of seed or transplanting of seedlings. After planting, seeds must survive on energy stored within the seed until germination occurs and a seedling emerges through the soil surface. Usually not all of the seeds are able to survive through *germination* and *emergence*; thus the number of seeds planted per unit area must be greater than the final desired *plant population*. The most important factors affecting germination and emergence include seed viability (percent germination under controlled laboratory conditions), soil temperature, availability of moisture and air to the seeds, and soil strength and resistance to seedling emergence. While transplanted seedlings are already emerged, their survival and initial rate of growth are also dependent upon soil moisture and temperature. A planter can exert a strong influence on the rate of germination and emergence of seeds through control of planting depth and firming of soil around the seeds or roots of seedlings. In

Figure 6.1—A centrifugal broadcast seeder (Courtesy of Vicon Corporation).

addition, the planter must meter seeds at the proper rate and, in some cases, must control the horizontal placement of seeds in a desired pattern.

6.1 Methods and Equipment

Three different planting methods can be distinguished by the horizontal pattern of seed placement. *Broadcasting* refers to random scattering of seeds on the soil surface. *Drilling* is the random placement of seeds in furrows which are then covered; the seeds thus emerge in rows. In *precision planting*, the seeds are planted in rows and the spacing of seeds within the rows is uniform. A fourth method of planting is the *transplanting* of plant seedlings into a field. Mechanisms and machines have been developed to permit each of these planting methods.

6.1.1 Broadcast Seeding

A *centrifugal broadcast seeder* is shown in figure 6.1. The seed is metered from a hopper through a *variable orifice*. An *agitator* is provided above the orifice to prevent bridging of the seed over the

Figure 6.2–A drill seeder (Courtesy of Deere and Co.).

gate and to assure continuous feeding. Sometimes a fluted wheel is used to meter the seed. The metered seed drops onto a *spinning disk* which accelerates and throws it, usually horizontally. The width of coverage depends upon the size, shape, and density of the seeds. Two counter-rotating spinning disks may be used to increase the width of coverage. The seeding rate is controlled by the size of the gate opening, the speed of travel and the width of coverage. Centrifugal broadcasters are flexible in that they can be used for broadcasting seed, dry fertilizer or pesticides, or other granular materials. After broadcast seeding, a secondary tillage operation may be performed to cover the seeds with soil.

6.1.2 Drilling

A drill seeder is illustrated in figure 6.2. Typically, for each row, the seeds are metered from a *hopper* by a ground-driven *fluted wheel* past an *adjustable gate* which controls the seeding rate. The seeds then enter a tube and fall by gravity to a furrow which has been opened by a disk. Typical row spacings range from 150 to 400 mm. A common method of covering the seeds is to pull a small *drag chain* behind each *furrow opener*. Figure 6.2 is an example of a wheel drill, in which the weight of the machine is carried on transport wheels. In the press drill illustrated in figure 6.3, much of the weight of the drill is carried on *press wheels* which follow each row. Press drills thus provided firmer soil around the seeds compared to wheel drills. The term, *fluid drilling*, has been used to describe a planting technique in which germinated seeds are sown using a protective gel. The gel and seed mixture can be pumped through a hose for transport to the furrow if seed spacing is not critical. For more uniform seed placement, Shaw (1985) was issued a patent for a device to singulate and meter seeds from a liquid gel or suspension.

Figure 6.3–A press drill (Courtesy of Deere and Co.).

6.1.3 Precision Planting

Precision planters provide accurate placement of single seeds at equal intervals within rows; the rows are usually spaced widely enough to allow cultivation (fig. 6.4). Precision planters are available in many variations, but four functions are always included. These are opening a furrow of controlled depth, metering seeds into the furrow at uniform intervals, covering the furrow, and firming the soil against the seeds. On some planters, a pair of inclined wheels accomplish both the covering and the soil firming. Until the mid-1960s, most precision planters included seed plates for metering seeds. Pockets along the periphery of the plates were sized to match the seed dimensions, so that only one seed could fit in each pocket. As each pocket passed the seed tube, a spring-loaded knockout device would push the seed into the tube. Plates were easily replaceable, and farmers kept sets of plates to match each size of seed that was to be planted. *"Plateless" planters* were developed in the late 1960s and now there is a wide variety of mechanisms available for metering seed. The term, punch planting, is used to describe planting in *dibbles* created by a spaded wheel rather than planting in furrows.

Figure 6.4–A precision planter (Courtesy of Deere and Co.).

Figure 6.5–A seedling transplanter (Courtesy of Deere and Co.).

When vegetable crops are to be grown in soil covered by a plastic sheet, punch planting is especially useful in planting through the plastic cover.

6.1.4 Transplanting

A number of crops, including cabbage, lettuce, rice, strawberries, sweet potatoes, tobacco, and tomatoes, may be grown from seed in special beds and then transplanted into fields. Trees grown for commercial purposes are nearly always transplanted. The transplanting operation has not been fully mechanized, but a *transplanter* machine (fig. 6.5) can greatly increase the rate at which workers can do the transplanting. One or more seats are included on transplanters to position the workers conveniently for doing the transplanting. The transplanter also includes a hopper for the seedlings, provision for opening a furrow, means for accepting seedlings from a worker (see fig. 6.6) and placing them in the furrow, and means for closing the furrow and firming the soil around the seedlings. Runner-type furrow openers are usually employed, while a pair of press wheels tilted outward at the top accomplish furrow closing and soil firming. A water supply tank and suitable plumbing is often included to water the newly-planted seedlings, and some signaling device may be provided to help the workers achieve correct spacing of the seedlings along the furrow.

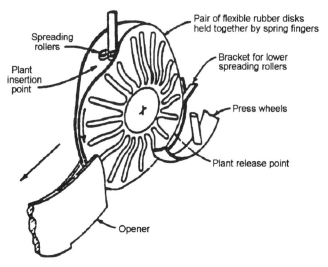

Figure 6.6–Key elements of a seedling transplanter (Courtesy of Deere and Co.).

6.2 Functional Processes

6.2.1 Seed Metering

Seed metering has two aspects. The first, *metering rate*, refers to the number of seeds that are released from the hopper per unit of time. Metering rate is important in any planter to ensure that the desired final plant population will be achieved. In addition, seeds must be singulated in precision planters to allow placement of seeds at uniform spacing in each row.

Seed metering mechanisms. The oldest principle for metering seeds is the variable orifice and this simple principle is still in use. The volumetric flow rate of seeds is regulated by changing the orifice size. An agitator is used above the orifice to prevent bridging of the seeds (fig. 6.7).

The most popular system for seed metering in a drill is the fluted wheel (fig. 6.8). The fluted-wheel assemblies are positioned at the bottom of the seed hopper so that seed can flow into the openings by gravity. The fluted wheel provides quasi-positive-displacement metering, i.e., seeds in the flute openings are carried toward an adjustable gate as the fluted wheel rotates. The gate opening is set to match the seed size. The fluted wheel can be moved endwise to control the volumetric flow rate of seeds. Maximum flow rate occurs when the fluted wheel covers the entire width of the gate, while zero flow rate occurs when the nonrotating cutoff covers the full gate width. The flow rate also varies with the rotational speed of the fluted wheel.

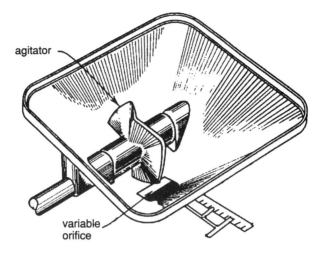

Figure 6.7–Metering seeds with a variable orifice.

The internal double-run seed metering mechanism is used on some drills (fig. 6.9). As with the fluted wheel, the internal run is a quasi-positive-displacement metering device but the seed spaces are formed by fins on the inside of the wheel. It is called a double run because two wheels are positioned back-to-back. One has much smaller seed spaces and is used for small seeds, while the side with large spaces is used for large seeds. The internal double-run units are positioned at the bottom of the seed hopper so that seeds can flow in

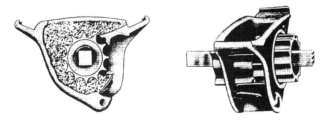

Figure 6.8–Metering seeds with a fluted wheel.

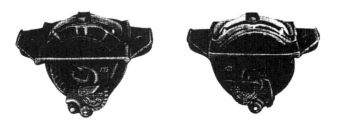

Figure 6.9–Internal double-run metering.

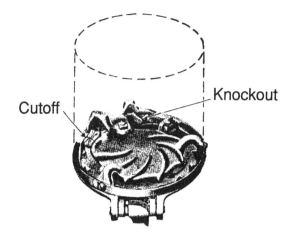

Figure 6.10–Metering with gravity-fed seed plates.

by gravity. Only one side of the internal double-run is used at a time; a removable feed cover is used to block off the side that is not being used. An adjustable feed gate is provided for each side of the unit. The distance between the gate edge and the internal fins can be regulated to control the feed rate.

Mechanisms previously mentioned in this section have metered seeds by volume. The remaining mechanisms to be discussed all meter individual seeds for precision planting.

Until the mid-1960s, the horizontal *seed plate planter* (fig. 6.10) was by far the most popular precision planter. The periphery of the seed plates contained cells designed to accept single seeds. Seeds entered the cells as the plate rotated in the bottom of the seed hopper. Any excess seeds were removed by a stationary *cutoff* and, as each cell passed over the seed tube, a spring-loaded *knockout* forced the seed into the drop tube. The cutoff was either a brush or a spring-loaded scraper. Uniformity of seeds was necessary to ensure that only one seed would fit into each cell. Seeds that were naturally nonuniform, such as corn kernels, had to be graded into uniform lots prior to planting. A wide variety of replaceable seed plates were available to match the various sizes and shapes of seeds. Plate planters are still commercially available, but they no longer dominate the market.

Introduction of the *finger pickup planter* in 1968 started a movement toward plateless planters (Anonymous, 1968). The finger pickup planter is best suited for planting corn kernels. In the metering unit shown in figure 6.11, twelve spring-loaded fingers are mounted on a vertical disk which rotates in a seed hopper. As they travel on their circular path, the fingers ride on a stationary disk

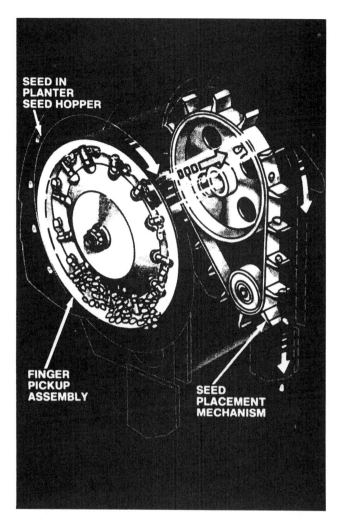

Figure 6.11–Seed metering by finger pickup (Courtesy of Deere and Co.).

which is concentric with the rotating disk. As each finger passes through the bottom of the hopper, it picks up one or more seeds. With continued movement, the finger passes over an indentation in the stationary disk, causing it to grip one seed while any others fall back into the seed hopper. With further movement, the finger passes across an opening in the stationary disk and the seed is ejected into the seed placement belt for transport to the seed tube. The entire seed-metering unit is ground driven to provide controlled spacing of the seeds along the rows.

The next innovation in plateless planting was the *air planter* (Anonymous, 1971). A ground-driven *seed drum* (fig. 6.12) is

Figure 6.12–Seed drum in an air planter (Courtesy of Case-IH).

pressurized to about 4 kPa by a pto-driven fan. Maximum practical drum speed is approximately 35 rev/min. Seeds flow by gravity from a central hopper to maintain a shallow reservoir of seed in the bottom of the drum. Each drum can be designed to serve four, six, or eight rows, depending upon the number of rows of perforated holes that are provided. The drum shown in figure 6.12 has eight rows of holes and thus meters seeds to eight rows in the field. Each hole terminates in a seed pocket at the inner face of the drum. As the drum rotates, air escapes through the holes and, when seeds enter the seed pockets, differential pressure holds each seed in its pocket until drum rotation brings the seed close to a seed tube. A row of external wheels near the seed tubes block the holes momentarily, thus removing the differential pressure and allowing the seeds to fall into the seed tubes. Air escaping through the seed tubes carries the seeds to the planting units and deposits them in the rows. Crops that can be planted with the air planter include beans, corn, delinted cotton seed and sorghum. The seed drums are easily replaceable and are changed to suit the seed being planted. A key advantage of the air planter is that it has only one seed hopper to be refilled, thus permitting faster refilling.

The *pressure-disk planter* (fig. 6.13) is similar to the air planter in that positive pressure in the seed reservoir is used to hold seeds in the pockets of the rotating seed plate. Unlike the air planter, however, the pressure-disk planter has a separate seed reservoir and plate for each row. Gravity moves the seeds from the hopper to the metering unit, where differential pressure holds a seed in each cell. As each cell nears the drop tube, a soft brush cuts off the air supply to the cell and the seed falls into the seed tube by gravity. Unlike the

Figure 6.13–Pressure-disk metering of seeds (Courtesy of White Farm Equipment Co.).

air planter, the seed tubes are not a conduit for escaping air. As with all precision metering units, the seed plate must be ground driven. Seed disks are replaceable and disks are available for corn, soybeans, edible beans, delinted cotton seed, pelleted or segmented sugar beet seeds, sunflowers, and sorghum.

Vacuum-disk metering (fig. 6.14) is similar to pressure-disk metering, except that the pressure differential is supplied by creating a vacuum on the side of the seed disk opposite the seeds. Seed from the hopper enters the seed reservoir, where vacuum created by a pump holds the seeds in the seed cells on the rotating seed disk. The vacuum is blocked as the cells reach a point above the seed tube and the seeds fall into the tube by gravity. A vacuum of 15 kPa was used for holding seeds in a vacuum-disk planter designed by Giannini, et al. (1967). In commercially-available vacuum-disk planters, seed disks are available for metering edible beans, soybeans, corn, delinted cotton seed, edible peas, peanuts, sorghum, sugar beets, and sunflowers.

Figure 6.14–Vacuum-disk metering of seeds (Courtesy of Deere and Co.).

Seed metering theory. The two classes of seed metering mechanisms are those that meter by volume and those that meter individual seeds. When planting with metering by volume, the application rate can be expressed in number of seeds per hectare or in kilograms of seed planted per hectare. The application rate can be calculated by using the following equation:

$$R_s = \frac{10000 \, Q \, \rho_b}{w \, v} \qquad (6.1)$$

where
R_s = seeding rate (kg/ha [seeds/ha])
Q = flow rate of seeds from the metering unit (L/s)
ρ_b = bulk density (kg/L [number of seeds/L])
w = width of coverage of the planter (m)
v = travel speed of planter (m/s)

It is impractical to count the number of very small seeds per unit volume and seeding rates are thus given in kilograms per hectare. For larger seeds, the seeding rate can be given either in kilograms per hectare or in seeds per hectare. If the planter plants in rows and has a separate metering device for each row, Q is the flow rate from one device and W is the row spacing. The method of controlling Q varies with type of metering device.

The variable orifice is the simplest and oldest method for volume metering of seeds. In studying the flow of grain through orifices, Moysey et al. (1988) reported that the flow rate is independent of the depth of grain above an orifice in the bottom of a hopper. The following equation was adapted from their data:

$$Q = -0.0342 + 770 A_n \sqrt{g D_e} \qquad (6.2)$$

where
    Q = volume flow rate (L/s)
    g = acceleration of gravity = 9.801 m/s^2
    D_e = hydraulic diameter of orifice (m)
    A_n = net effective area of orifice (m^2)

The equation is valid for circular or rectangular orifices which are centered at the bottom of the hopper. The volume flow rate is about 15% greater for a given orifice when the orifice is at the edge of the hopper. Both the effective diameter and the effective net area are smaller than the physical opening because seeds overhanging the edge reduce the effective opening size. To account for this effect, each linear dimension of the orifice should be reduced by k times the seed size. For a circular orifice of diameter D, the hydraulic diameter is $D_e = D - k d$, where d = seed size and k is a constant. For a rectangular orifice with physical length "a" and width "b", the effective opening is $a' = a - k d$ and $b' = b - k d$. The area is $A_n = 0.25 \pi D_e^2$ for the circular orifice or $A_n = a' b'$ for the rectangular orifice. The hydraulic diameter for a rectangular orifice is $D_e = (0.5 a' b')/(a' + b')$. Moysey et al. (1988) reported kd values of common seeds as 7.5 mm for barley, 5 mm for wheat, 3.3 mm for flax and 1.8 mm for rapeseed, where k = 1.4. The flow through the orifice became irregular when D_e was less than 6d and was independent of grain size when D_e was more than 20d. The hopper shape had little effect on flow rate when D_e was greater than 12d. Equation 6.2 was developed for stationary hoppers without agitation. In a seeder, an agitator is used to prevent bridging and the vibration of the hopper due to rough terrain could influence the flow rate. Thus, equation 6.2 only provides a starting point for design and accurate flow rates must be determined through calibration of a prototype. Example problem 6.1 illustrates the use of equation 6.2.

Example Problem 6.1

Calculate the flow rate of sweetclover seed from a seed hopper on a centrifugal spreader. The rectangular orifice with dimensions of 30 mm by 80 mm is located at the edge of the hopper.

Solution. In the problems section at the end of the chapter, a table of seed properties indicates the diameter of sweetclover seeds is 1.41 mm. The effective orifice dimensions are:

$$a' = a - kd = 0.03 - 1.4(0.00141) = 0.0280 \text{ m}$$

$$b' = b - kd = 0.08 - 1.4(0.00141) = 0.0780 \text{ m}$$

$$A_n = a' \cdot b' = (0.0280)(0.0780) = 0.00218 \text{ m}^2$$

$$D_e = 0.5 \cdot a' \cdot b'/(a'+b') = 0.5(0.028)(0.078)/(0.028+0.078)$$
$$= 0.0103 \text{ m}$$

Then, from Equation 6.2, the flow rate for a centered orifice would be:

$$Q = -0.0342 + 770(0.0218)(9.801 \cdot 0.0103)^{0.5} = 0.499 \text{ L/s}$$

The flow rate for an orifice on the edge is 15% greater, that is:

$$Q = 0.499(1.15) = 0.574 \text{ L/s}$$

Both the fluted wheel and the internal run metering mechanisms are quasi-positive-displacement devices. For such devices, the following equation is useful for estimating the volume flow rate of seeds:

$$Q = \frac{V_c \lambda_c n}{60 \cdot 10^6} \qquad (6.3)$$

where
   Q = volumetric flow rate (L/s)
   V_c = cell volume = volume of each cell (mm^3)
   λ_c = number of cells on periphery of fluted wheel or internal run
   n = rotational speed of fluted wheel or internal run (rev/min)

The flow rate is controlled by changing of the speed ratio between the ground drive wheels and the metering device and/or by changing V_c.

As noted in the section on seed metering, V_c is changed by sliding the fluted section endwise (fig. 6.8) or by changing the gate setting on a double internal run device (fig. 6.9). The term, quasi-positive was used to describe the displacement of the fluted wheel or the internal double run because the void space between seeds means that not all of the cell volume is occupied by seeds. Also, some seeds will typically project beyond the edge of the cells. Thus, the volume of seeds delivered each time a cell passes the seed tube is not precisely equal to the cell volume. Equation 6.3 can be used for design purposes, but accurate determination of the flow rate for any given type of seed requires calibration using a prototype machine.

For any of the planters that meter individual seeds, the theoretical seeding rate can be calculated by using the following equation:

$$R_{st} = \frac{10,000}{w\, x_s} \qquad (6.4)$$

where
   R_{st} = theoretical seeding rate (seeds/ha)
   w = row width (m)
   x_s = seed spacing along the row (m)

The seed spacing along the row can be calculated by using the following equation:

$$x_s = \frac{60\, v}{\lambda_c\, n} \qquad (6.5)$$

where
   λ_c = number of seeds delivered per revolution of the metering device
   n = rotational speed of metering device (rev/min)
   v = travel speed of planter (m/s)

Note that, for a given row spacing, the theoretical seeding rate can be changed only by changing the seed spacing in the rows. The seed spacing is changed by changing the speed ratio between the ground drive wheels and the metering device.

Performance of seed metering mechanisms. Of the various types of planters discussed in this chapter, the broadcast seeder is least accurate in holding to a desired rate for three reasons. The first is that the variable orifice is not a positive-displacement metering device. The second is that, since the metering unit does not have positive displacement, the metering rate is not linked to the travel speed of the seeder; rather, operator skill is required to coordinate the travel speed with the metering rate. The third is that the swath width of the broadcast seeder is not as precisely determined as the swath width of the other seeders mentioned in the chapter. Thus, the broadcast seeder is best suited to situations in which precise control of the seeding rate is not important. Broadcast seeders are capable of fast application, with spreading widths up to 15 m and travel speeds of 5 m/s or more.

Drilling provides more precise control of seeding rates because the swath width can be controlled precisely and the metering rate is automatically linked to the travel speed. Through calibration, the volumetric flow rate of any given seed from the metering device can be determined with good accuracy. Seed spacing within the row is not uniform because the seeds are delivered to the seed tube in cells. Seeds began to trickle into the seed tube as a cell approaches the tube and, after the cell empties into the tube, seeds again began to trickle in as the next cell approaches the tube. Thus, although the average seeding rate may be accurate, the seed tends to be deposited in bunches along the row. Field slope may affect the flow rate from fluted wheel metering. The tendency is for flow rates to increase as the drill travels downslope; in one case, flow rate increased 44% on a 15% downslope. Since the metering device is ground driven, the inflation pressure of the ground drive wheels can affect seeding rate; if the tires are under-inflated, the wheel radius will be reduced, thereby causing more rotations of the wheels per distance travelled and increasing the seeding rate. Slippage of the drive wheels reduces the seeding rate, so wheel slippage must be considered in calculating the seeding rate. Typical travel speeds for drills are in the range from 1 to 3 m/s. Power requirements for pulling a drill are typically in the range from 1.0 to 1.4 kW per row.

Planters that meter individual seeds provide the most precise control of seeding rates. The actual seeding rate will equal the theoretical rate if and only if every finger pickup or seed cell carries exactly one seed. Some cells may fail to fill for various reasons, and then the actual seeding rate will be less than the theoretical rate. Conversely, if some cells contain more than one seed due to a poor fit between seed size and cell size, the actual rate can be higher than the theoretical rate. The metering device on precision planters is ground driven and, as with drills, drive-wheel slippage, and/or inflation pressure therefore affect the seeding rate. Electronic seed monitors have been developed for precision planters. A sensor in each seed tube senses the passage of seeds. Some monitors can be programmed to sound an alarm if the seed passage rate is too high or too low. Travel speeds for precision planters are typically in the range from 1 to 3 m/s. Power requirements for pulling a row-crop planter are typically in the range from 1 to 2.4 kW per row.

Monitoring and control of seed metering. For crops which require metering of individual seeds, malfunctioning of the metering system can result in unacceptable planting performance. Monitors have been developed to warn the operator when the metering system is malfunctioning. Early monitors included mechanical switches which were tripped by passage of seeds in the seed delivery tubes, but the mechanical devices disrupted the natural trajectory of the seeds. Current monitoring devices are noncontacting. For example seeds can be made to interrupt the light-transmission path between a light source and a photocell, resulting in an electrical pulse each time a seed passes. Simple monitors use each electrical pulse to flash a light on the operator console (there is a separate light for each row) each time a seed passes. Operation is satisfactory as long as the light for each row continues to flash. In more advanced systems, the amount of forward travel between the electrical pulses is measured. The seeding rate (in seeds/ha) is computed and displayed for the operator. Feedback control permits automatic control of metering rates. With feedback control systems, the operator sets the desired seeding rate. The seeding rate detected by the counters is compared with the desired rate and, if the desired and actual rates differ, an actuator is signaled to readjust the variable-speed drive of the metering device to correct the seeding rate.

6.2.2 Seed Transport
Seed transport mechanisms. After the seeds are metered, they must be transported to the soil surface or into a furrow. Most transport systems rely primarily on gravity for vertical movement of seeds. Horizontal movement, if it is needed, must be generated by the transport device. Friction is always present in seed transport and may have an effect on the path travelled by the seeds.

Seed transport theory. For broadcast seeders, typically one or more spinning disks (fig. 6.15) are used to transport the seed. Seeds traveling down through a central seed tube enter the spinner through gates. Only one gate is shown on figure 6.15. The following equations governing seed movement on the disk assume that the seeds slide along the disk and vane surfaces rather than rolling (Cunningham 1963). The angle (θ) through which the disk turns while a seed is in contract with a vane can be calculated by solving the following equation:

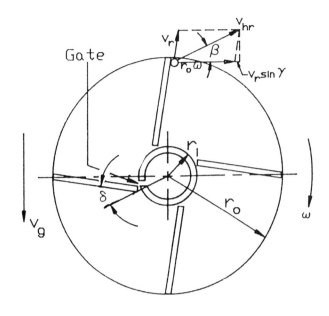

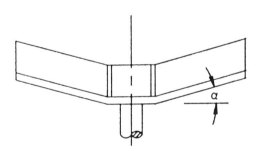

Figure 6.15–A centrifugal spreader.

$$\frac{(C_1+f)e^{C_2(C_1-f)\,\theta} + (C_1-f)e^{-C_2(C_1+f)\theta}}{2C_1} = \frac{r_o - \dfrac{C_3\,g}{C_4\,\omega^2}}{C_5\,r_i - \dfrac{C_3\,g}{C_4\,\omega^2}} \qquad (6.6)$$

After θ is calculated, the following equation can be used to calculate the velocity of seeds relative to a blade:

$$v_r = \frac{\omega}{2C_1}\left(C_5\,r_i - \frac{f\,g}{\omega^2}\right)\left(e^{C_2(C_1-f)\theta} - e^{-C_2(C_1+f)\theta}\right) \qquad (6.7)$$

where

v_r = velocity of seeds relative to a blade

f = coefficient of friction between spinner and seeds

g = acceleration of gravity = 9.801 m/s^2

C_1= $(f^2 + C_4/C_2)^{0.5}$

C_2= cos α

C_3= sin α + f cos α

C_4= cos α − f sin α

C_5= cos δ − f sin δ

r_i = radius to inner ends of blades (m)

r_o = outer radius of disk (m)

ω = rotational speed of disk (rad/s)

angles θ, δ, and α are all in radians; δ is positive for forward slanted blades (as shown in figure 6.15) and negative for rearward-slanted blades.

Angles α and δ are shown on figure 6.15. The spinning disk is a flat disk when α = 0 and a cone-shaped disk when α > 0. The cone-shaped disk increases the range of the seed trajectory by giving the seeds an upward component of velocity, $v_v = v_r \cdot \sin α$. Angle δ is positive when the blades are forward pitched as shown in figure 6.15, zero when the blades are radial and negative when the blades have backward pitch.

Equation 6.6 cannot be solved explicitly for θ, so an iterative solution is required. As an alternative, figure 6.16 has been prepared to solve equation 6.6 graphically. The three variables on the left side of equation 6.6 are f, α, and θ. In figure 6.16, the value of the left side of equation 6.6 has been plotted on the y-axis versus values of θ on the x-axis; curves are shown for three values of α. Although f = 0.33 was used in plotting the graph, the solution is only weakly dependent on f and would be useable for any 0.2 < f < 0.45. The coefficient of sliding friction falls within that range for virtually all seeds sliding on steel. To use figure 6.16, the value of the right side of equation 6.6 is calculated for the specific situation and entered on the y-axis of figure 6.16. A line is drawn to the right to the curve for the appropriate α, and then a vertical line is drawn to the x-axis to find the corresponding value of θ. Then, as previously mentioned, equation 6.7 can be used to calculate the sliding velocity of the seed relative to the blade at the outer end of the blade.

The magnitude and direction of the horizontal component of velocity as the seeds leave the disk can be calculated by using the following respective equations:

$$v_{hr} = \sqrt{(v_r \cos α \, \cos γ)^2 + (r_o \, ω + v_r \cos α \cdot \sin γ)^2} \qquad (6.8)$$

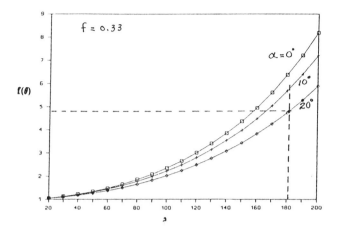

Figure 6.16–Graph for graphical solution of equation 6.6.

$$\beta = \arctan \frac{v_r \cos\alpha \cdot \cos\gamma}{r_o\,\omega + v_r \cos\alpha \cdot \sin\gamma} \qquad (6.9)$$

where $\gamma = \arctan(r_i \cdot \tan\delta/(r_o - r_i))$. The velocity at which the spreader moves over the ground, v_g, is shown in figure 6.15. By adjusting the parameters in equation 6.6, the direction of the seed trajectory relative to the direction of travel can be adjusted. Usually, several gates must be provided in the central seed tube to generate good coverage of seeds over the swath. Example problem 6.2 illustrates the calculations.

Example Problem 6.2

A centrifugal spreader is to be used to seed sweetclover seed. The following data are available:

Blade inner radius ($r_i = 0.05$ m)
Blade outer radius ($r_o = 0.20$ m)
Dish angle ($\alpha = 10°$)
Blade direction angle ($\delta = 20°$)
Rotational speed ($\omega = 78.5$ rad/s [750 rev/min])
Coefficient of friction ($f = 0.28$)

Determine (a) the angle θ through which the spinner turns while the seed is in contact with the blade, (b) the velocity of each seed relative to the blade at the outer end of the blade, (c) the magnitude and direction of the horizontal component of velocity as the seeds leave the spinner and (d) the vertical component of velocity as the seeds leave the spinner.

Solution. The first step is to calculate values for constants in equation 6.6.

$C_2 = \cos(10°) = 0.985$

$C_3 = \sin(10°) + (0.28) \cos(10°) = 0.449$

$C_4 = \cos(10°) - (0.28) \sin(10°) = 0.936$

$C_5 = \cos(20°) - (0.28) \sin(20°) = 0.844$

$C_1 = (0.28^2 + 0.936/0.985)^{0.5} = 1.014$

$C_3 \cdot g/(C_4 \cdot \omega^2) = (0.449 \cdot 9.801)/(0.936 \cdot 78.5^2) = 0.000763$

(a)   The value of θ can now be determined. The value of the right side of equation 6.6, $f(\theta)$, is:

$f(\theta) = (0.20 - 0.000763)/(1.035 \cdot 0.05 - 0.000763) = 3.908$

As shown by the dashed lines on figure 6.16, a value of $f(\theta)$ corresponds to $\theta = 181°$ or 3.157 radians when $\alpha = 10°$.
(b)   Next, equation 6.7 can be used to calculate V_r. The lengthy equation will not be re-written but, when the values are inserted, the result is:

$V_r = 15.83$ m/s

(c)   Next, γ angle must be calculated for use in equations 6.8 and 6.9:

$\gamma = \arctan[(0.05 \tan(20°)/(0.20 - 0.05)] = 6.92°$ or 0.121 radians

Then, from equation 6.8, the seeds leave the disk with a horizontal velocity of:

$v_{hr} = [(15.83 \cos(10°) \cos(6.92°))^2$
$+ (0.20 \cdot 78.5 + 15.83 \cos(10°) \sin(6.92°))^2]^{0.5} = 23.4$ m/s

From equation 6.9, the departure angle is:

$\beta = \arctan[15.83 \cos(10°) \cos(6.92°)/(0.2 * 78.5$
$+ 15.83 \cos(10°) \sin(6.92°))] = 41.4°$

(d)   Finally, the vertical component of velocity of the seeds is:

$v_v = 15.83 \sin(10°) = 2.75$ m/s (upward)

Upon leaving the spinner, the seeds enter ballistic trajectories with absolute velocity V_v and velocity v_{hr} relative to the moving spreader. While the absolute horizontal velocity is the vector sum of v_{hr} and v_g, the contribution of v_g is usually negligible and v_{hr} can be used as the absolute initial horizontal velocity of the seeds. The following equations can be used to calculate the trajectory of a particle in still air (Goering et al., 1972; Pitt et al., 1982):

$$\ddot{h} = -C_6\,\dot{h}\sqrt{\dot{h}^2 + \dot{z}^2} \qquad (6.10)$$

$$\ddot{z} = g - C_6\,\dot{z}\sqrt{\dot{h}^2 + \dot{z}^2} \qquad (6.11)$$

where
  h = horizontal direction (m)
  z = vertical direction, m, positive downward
  C_6 = 0.5 $C_D\,\rho_a\,A_p/m$
  g = acceleration of gravity (m/s²)
  A_p = projected frontal area of particle (m)
  m = mass of particle (kg)
  ρ_a = mass density of air (kg/m³ = $29 \cdot p_b/(8.314 \cdot \Theta_a)$)
  p_b = barometric pressure (kPa)
  Θ_a = ambient air temperature (°K = °C + 273)

The single dot over h or z indicates the first derivative with respect to time (velocity) while two dots represents the second derivative (acceleration). The drag coefficient, C_D varies with the Reynold's number. The following equations give a good approximation to drag coefficients first measured by Eisner (1930):

$$C_D = \frac{24}{N_{re}} \qquad \text{for } N_{re} \leq 1 \qquad (6.12)$$

$$C_D = \left(26.38\,N_{re}^{-0.845} + 0.49\right) \qquad \text{for } N_{re} > 1 \qquad (6.13)$$

where the Reynold's number is given by the following equation:

$$N_{re} = \frac{\rho_a v_p d_p}{\mu_a} \qquad (6.14)$$

where

N_{Re} = dimensionless Reynold's number
v_p = velocity of particle (m/s = $(\dot{h}^2 + \dot{z}^2)^{0.5}$)
d_p = effective diameter of particle (m)
μ_a = dynamic viscosity of air (N·s/m²)

Over a wide range of barometric pressures, the air viscosity is a function only of air temperature, i.e.:

$$\mu_a = 4.79 \; 10^{-6} \; e^{0.678 + 0.00227 \, \theta_a} \qquad (6.15)$$

Equations 6.10 through 6.15 do not have a general closed solution but, by use of a computer, they can be solved iteratively to calculate the trajectory of a seed. The required parameters are the seed mass, effective diameter and frontal area, the air temperature and barometric pressure, and the initial velocity of the seed as it leaves the spinner. For a cone-shaped disk, the initial velocity in the z-direction is $-v_v$. The initial velocity in the h-direction is v_{hr}. The trajectory equations are based on the assumption of wind-still conditions.

Pitt et al. (1982) made further simplifying assumptions to enable calculation of trajectories without iteration. The first assumption is that the particle is launched horizontally, that is, the initial vertical velocity is zero. Also, the vertical velocity was set equal to zero in equation 6.10 while the horizontal velocity was set equal to zero in equation 6.11. Also, the drag coefficient was assumed to be constant. Under those simplifying assumptions, the time required for the particle to fall distance z can be calculated by using the following equation:

$$t = \frac{\ln\left(Arg + \sqrt{Arg^2 - 1}\right)}{2 C_6 C_7} \qquad (6.16)$$

where

Arg = $2 e^{(2 C_6 \cdot Z)} - 1$
C_7 = $(g/C_6)^{0.5}$

The horizontal distance travelled during that fall time can be calculated from:

$$h = \frac{\ln\left(C_6 \dot{h}_o t + 1\right)}{C_6} \qquad (6.17)$$

where
  t = time for particle to fall distance z
  h_o = initial velocity in h-direction (m/s)

Equations 6.6 through 6.17 provide a means for evaluating the various transport factors that influence the uniformity of the pattern created by a broadcast seeder. Example problem 6.3 illustrates the use of equations 6.16 and 6.17 to calculate the end point of a seed trajectory.

Example Problem 6.3
  Alfalfa seeds leave a centrifugal spreader horizontally with an initial velocity of 20 m/s. If the spreader disk is 2 m above the land surface, calculate the horizontal distance travelled by each seed before it reaches the ground. The barometric pressure is 100 kPa and the air temperature is 20° C.
  Solution. Before equation 6.16 can be used, values must be calculated for constants C_6 and C_7. For a spherical particle, it can be shown that:

$$C_6 = 0.75 \ C_D \ \rho_a/(\rho_p \ d_p)$$

where ρ_p is the particle density in kg/m3. From the table in the homework problems at the end of the chapter, d = 0.00153 m and ρ_p = 1184 kg/m3. The Reynolds number must be calculated for use in calculating a drag coefficient. The air density is:

$$\rho_a = 29 \cdot 100/(8.314 \cdot 20 + 273) = 1.19 \ kg/m3$$

  From equation 6.15, at 20° C, the air viscosity is 1.835×10^{-5} N·s/m2. Although the particle velocity changes throughout the trajectory, we will use the initial velocity of 20 m/s in computing the Reynolds number, that is:

$$N_{re} = 1.19 \cdot 20 \cdot 0.00153/(1.835 \times 10^{-5}) = 1984$$

Then, from equation 6.13, the drag coefficient is:

$$C_D = 26.38 \cdot 1984^{-0.834} + 0.49 = 0.533$$

Now, values for C_6 and C_7 can be calculated, that is:

$C_6 = 0.75 \cdot 0.533 \cdot 1.19/(1184 \cdot 0.00153) = 0.263$

$C_7 = (9.801/0.263)^{0.5} = 6.10$

For a seed fall distance of 2 m, the value for Arg is 4.727 and, from equation 6.16, the fall time is 0.697 s. Finally, from equation 6.17, the horizontal distance travelled by the seed in 0.697 s is 5.86 m. By comparison, a computer simulation of the same trajectory using Equations 6.10 through 6.15 indicated that the time for a 2 m fall would be 0.82 s and the horizontal travel in that time would be 6.05 m. Thus, the simplified approach using equation 6.16 underpredicted the fall time by 15% but equation 6.17 underpredicted the horizontal distance by only 3%. A plot of the entire trajectory showed that the seed was moving almost vertically near the end of the trajectory and thus the underprediction of fall time had only a small effect on horizontal distance travelled. Using typical parameters for broadcasting of seeds, equations 6.16 and 6.17 can generally predict the horizontal distance within 10% of the value calculated by equations 6.10 through 6.15. If equations 6.16 and 6.17 are used to calculate and plot a complete trajectory, inserting a factor in equation 6.16 to increase each fall time by approximately 10% would improve the accuracy of the calculated trajectory.

Drills and precision planters include drop tubes for transporting seed from the metering device to the furrow. The drop tubes are nearly vertical and, if friction between the seed and the tube walls is neglected, equation 6.11 can be used to calculate the time required for the seed to pass through the drop tube and the vertical velocity at the exit point. Since the tube is nearly vertical, at least at the seed entry point, the velocity in the x-direction can be set equal to zero in equation 6.11. If C_D is variable, as in equations 6.12 and 6.13, a computer is required to solve equation 6.11. If C_D is assumed to be constant, the approximate transit time in the seed tube can be calculated using equation 6.16 with z equal to the length of the tube. Also, by solving equation 6.16 for z and differentiating with respect to time, the following equation can be obtained for seed velocity in the drop tube:

$$\dot{z} = \frac{C_7 \sinh\left(2C_6 C_7 t\right)}{1 + \cosh\left(2C_6 C_7 t\right)} \tag{6.18}$$

When t is taken as the transit time in the drop tube, then equation 6.18 gives the z-direction velocity at the exit. Often the tube is curved toward the rear near the exit (see fig. 6.14) to give the seed a rearward velocity component near the exit. If the exit velocity is at an angle θ_e from the vertical, then the x-component of velocity at the exit, relative to the planter, is:

$$\dot{x}_r = \dot{z}\tan\theta_e \qquad\qquad (6.19)$$

Seed bounce in the furrow disrupts the spacing of uniformly metered seeds. Seed bounce can be minimized or eliminated if the x-component of seed velocity relative to the planter is equal to the forward velocity of the planter. Then the seed will drop with zero horizontal velocity relative to the ground.

In the air planter, seeds are pneumatically conveyed from the metering point to the furrow through flexible hoses. It can be shown that the seeds must quickly attain the velocity of the air flowing through the hoses. Thus, the transit time in a hose can be calculated if the length of hose and the air velocity in the hose are known. v_a is the velocity of the air in the hose and if the exit velocity is at an angle θ_e from the vertical, then the horizontal component of the exit velocity relative to the planter will be:

$$\dot{x}_r = v_a\sin\theta_e \qquad\qquad (6.20)$$

Again, seed bounce can be eliminated by ensuring that the horizontal component of exit velocity relative to the planter is equal to the forward speed of the planter. Example problem 6.4 illustrates the calculation of velocities in drop tubes.

Example Problem 6.4

A precision planter is to plant soybean seeds. The seeds leave the metering device with zero velocity relative to the planter and fall through a vertical distance of 0.5 m through a drop tube to reach the furrow. The barometric pressure is 100 kPa and the air temperature is 20° C. Calculate (a) the vertical velocity of the seed at the exit, and (b) the exit angle required if the seed is to have zero horizontal velocity relative to the furrow when the planter speed is 1.8 m/s.

Solution. (a) As in example problem 6.3, values are needed for C_6 and C_7 before the fall time can be calculated. The air density is 1.19 kg/m^3 and the air viscosity is 1.835×10^{-5} N·s/m^2. From the table of seed properties in the homework problems, the soybean seed diameter is 0.006 76 m and the seed density is 1176 kg/m^3. However, values are needed for the Reynolds number and drag coefficient before C_6 can be calculated. The fall velocity increases from zero to some as yet unknown value. To permit a solution, we will use the terminal velocity of 13.11 m/s for soybeans (see seed properties table). Then the values for Reynolds number and drag coefficient are:

$$N_{re} = 1.19 \cdot 13.11 \cdot 0.00676/(1.835 \times 10^{-5}) = 5747$$

$$C_D = 26.38 \cdot 5747^{-0.845} + 0.49 = 0.507$$

The resulting values for C_6 and C_7 are:

$$C_6 = 0.75 \cdot 0.507 \cdot 1.19/(1176 \cdot 0.00676) = 0.057$$

$$C_7 = (9.801/0.057)^{0.5} = 13.11$$

The value for Arg is 1.117 and, from equation 6.16, the calculated fall time is 0.321 s. Then, from equation 6.18, the vertical velocity at the exit is 3.09 m/s. For comparison, a computer simulation using equations 6.10 through 6.15 gave an exit velocity of 3.0 m/s. Note that this exit velocity is much less than the 13.11 m/s terminal velocity that was used in calculating the Reynolds number. The solution could be repeated while using a velocity of 3.09 m/s to calculate the Reynolds number. At high Reynolds numbers, however, the drag coefficient is so weakly dependent on Reynolds number that a second iteration would change the drag coefficient very little.

(b) From equation 6.19, the required exit angle to give the seed zero horizontal velocity relative to the furrow is:

$$\theta_e = \arctan(1.8/3.09) = 30° \text{ from vertical}$$

Performance of seed transport mechanisms. Of the seed transport mechanisms discussed in the previous section, the spinning disk provides the least accurate control of seed transport. Since the seeds travel on ballistic paths, wind can disrupt the pattern of coverage. As can be seen from equations 6.6 and 6.7, both the swath width and the uniformity of the pattern are affected by the rotational speed of the spinning disk. Pattern is affected because the disk speed influences the angle at which the seed departs from the spinner (eq. 6.6); swath width is affected because the disk speed controls the launch speed of the seeds. Spinner speeds typically are in the range from 500 to 600 rev/min. Some typical distribution patterns from centrifugal spreaders are shown in figure 6.17. By proper overlapping of adjacent swaths, it is theoretically possible to achieve uniform distribution using either the pyramid or flat-topped patterns.

Seeds are transported through drop tubes when drilling or precision planting. Since drilling does not require precise placement

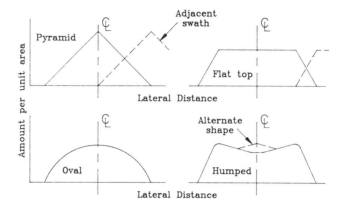

Figure 6.17–Typical lateral distribution patterns from centrifugal spreaders.

of seeds, drop tubes have only to remain open for acceptable performance. In the usual case in which the furrow openers can move vertically relative to the seed hopper, the drop tubes must accommodate the vertical movement. In precision planting, precise metering is of little value unless the transport process also distributes the seeds uniformly in the rows. Horizontal bounce of the seeds can be eliminated if the seeds are released with zero horizontal velocity relative to the ground (eqs. 6.19 and 6.20). Vertical bounce can be reduced by releasing the seeds close to the bottom of a narrow furrow. It is also important that each seed should have the same transit time in the drop tube. Thus, all seeds should have the same initial velocity upon entering the drop tube and random bouncing within the tube must be minimized. A tube with smooth interior will minimize seed-to-wall friction forces and a tube of small diameter will minimize bouncing within the tube.

6.2.3 Furrow Opening and Covering

Furrow opening and covering mechanisms. Hoes, runners, single and double disks can be used to open furrows for planting seeds (fig. 6.18). Drills (figs. 6.2 and 6.3) normally employ the single-disk opener to open a furrow. Runner openers were widely used with plate-type planters and are still used on some precision planters. The double-disk opener is now used on many precision planters, either alone or in combination with a runner-type opener. For precision planting, the seeds must be placed at the proper spacing and also at the proper depth. Thus gage wheels (fig. 6.19) are located in close proximity to the furrow opener and seed release point to ensure controlled, uniform planting depth. Use of a V-shaped tool to further shape the furrow provides a furrow cross-section that minimizes seed bounce (fig. 6.20a and figure 6.20b). After the seeds are deposited,

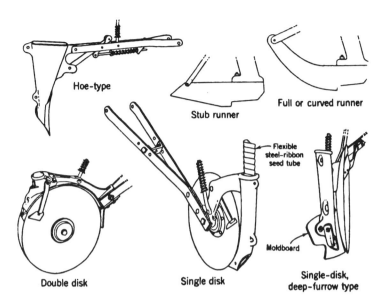

Figure 6.18–Some common types of furrow openers.

covering disks (fig. 6.20c) or a scraper may be used to close the furrow. A press wheel (fig. 6.20d) may be used to firm the soil to assure good moisture transfer to the seeds. Alternatively, both covering and soil firming can be accomplished by a set of soil firming wheels (fig. 6.19) which move and firm the soil horizontally and without vertical pressure. A continuous furrow is not opened when the punch planter is used. Rather, spade-shaped wedges on the wheel (fig. 6.21) open holes or "dibbles" in the soil into which the seeds are

Figure 6.19–A complete precision planter unit (Courtesy of Deere and Co.).

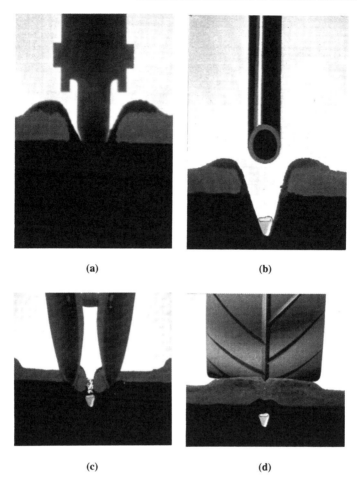

(a)   (b)

(c)   (d)

Figure 6.20–Furrow-shaping and closing techniques (Courtesy of
Case-IH).

dropped. Then the press wheel closes the soil over the seeds. The
punch planter eliminates the nonuniform seed spacing that results
from seed bouncing in a furrow. The spade wheel can roll over and
punch through surface residue or other cover. It is the only type of
planter that can plant through the plastic covers that are sometimes
used in growing high-value crops.

Theory of furrow opening and covering. In a tilled soil that
is devoid of vegetation, drying occurs through moisture transfer to
the surface and thus the soil moisture content increases with depth.
Seeds require moisture for germination and growth; moisture
transfer from soil to seed is promoted by placing the seeds in firm
contact with moist soil. Increased depth of planting thus promotes
better moisture transfer to the seeds. Choice of an optimum seed

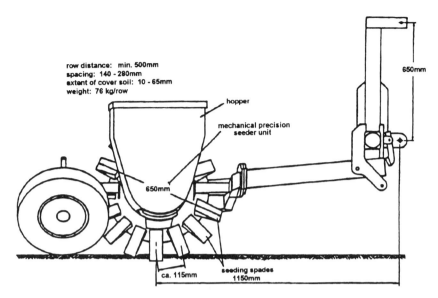

row distance: min. 500mm
spacing: 140 - 280mm
extent of cover soil: 10 - 65mm
weight: 76 kg/row

650mm

hopper

mechanical precision
seeder unit

650mm

ca. 115mm

seeding spades
1150mm

Figure 6.21–A punch planter (Courtesy of L. N. Shaw, University of Florida, Gainesville).

depth is a compromise, however, because two factors favor shallower planting. The first is that soil is normally warmer near the surface at planting time and warmer soil promotes seed germination. The second is that a seedling may not have sufficient strength to emerge if the seed is planted too deep in firm soil. Thus, there is an optimum depth of planting which varies with type of crop and other factors (Morrison and Gerik, 1985). Typical planting depths, are: corn, 40 to 65 mm, cotton, 25 to 50 mm; grass seeds, 5 to 10 mm; sorghum, 19 to 25 mm; soybeans, 25 to 50 mm; and wheat, 25 to 50 mm. Theory relating to soil-seedling relationships is beyond the scope of this book, but the reader is referred to publications of a number of researchers who have investigated these relationships (Stapleton and Meyers, 1971; Vaughn and Bowen, 1977; Phene et al., 1978; and Goyal et al., 1980).

Performance of furrow opening and covering mechanisms. The most important criterion for judging the success of a furrow opening and covering mechanism is the percent emergence of the seeds that are planted in the furrow. Since percent emergence varies with soil and weather factors that vary from year to year, it is not possible to judge the effect of any given mechanism on emergence based on data from only one season. However, there are other performance criteria which can be judged based on more limited testing. Many farmers are now using tillage techniques which leave crop residues on the soil surface in order to reduce soil erosion. The furrow openers must be able to cut through these crop residues.

Disk-type openers are much better than runner-type openers (fig. 6.18) in cutting through surface residues. In addition, special notched disks may be attached ahead of the furrow opener to clear a path through the residue. The ability of the planter to maintain the desired, uniform depth of planting is an important criterion that may be evaluated using short-term tests.

6.2.4 Transplanting

Mechanisms for transplanting seedlings. A successful transplanting system includes the following elements:
1. Planting the seeds in a seedbed or greenhouse trays.
2. Removing the seedlings from the seed bed with or without retaining soil on the roots.
3. Storage of singulated seedlings in a carrier on the transplanter.
4. Feeding the seedlings to the planting mechanism one at a time.
5. Opening a furrow or hole for insertion of the seedlings.
6. Firming the soil around the roots of the seedlings.
Elements 1 and 2 are not part of the transplanter machine, can be labor intensive and, if the system is to be successful, must be coordinated with the design of the transplanter. The transplanter itself includes elements 3 through 6 and can also include provision for watering and fertilizing the newly planted seedlings.

On early transplanters (figs. 6.5 and 6.6), only elements 5 and 6 were mechanized; one or more seats were provided on the transplanter for human workers to accomplish item 4. Automated transplanting refers to a system in which element 4 is also accomplished mechanically (Brewer, 1988). One promising method is to grow the seedlings in paper pockets attached to Z-folded strands which, when the seedlings are ready, are loaded into a carrier on the transplanter. Figure 6.22 shows a "Ferris-Wheel" transplanter in which wheel-mounted grippers grasp each cell (segment of the strand containing one seedling), tear it from the strand and carry it to the release point in the furrow. A strand restrainer holds the strand so that only one cell is torn away by each set of grippers. The "roll-feed" transplanter of figure 6.23 also uses Z-folded strands for seedling storage. A pair of feed rolls feeds the strand into a pair of high-speed acceleration rolls which tear away the cells one by one and drop them into a drop chute. The seedlings fall though the chute to the furrow. A pair of firming wheels (see fig. 6.19) can be used to push soil laterally in closing the furrow and firming the soil around the seedlings. The paper cells are biodegradable, leaving only the transplanted seedlings. Transplanters based on the principles

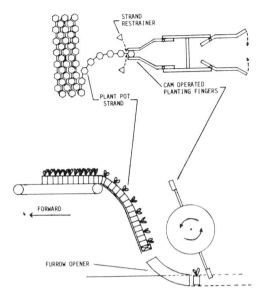

Figure 6.22–A ferris-wheel type feeding mechanism for automatic transplanting (Suggs et al., 1987).

illustrated in figures 6.22 and 6.23 are in commercial production (Suggs et al., 1987).

The experimental transplanter (Munilla and Shaw, 1987) illustrated in figure 6.24 is similar to the spade planter in that it does not require a furrow. Rather, a seedling bucket dibbles holes in the soil and places a seedling in each hole. Each bucket is pivotally connected to a pair of arms such that the top of each bucket must remain horizontal. At their midpoints, the arms are pivotally connected to rotating disks so that the midpoints of the arms travel on circular paths. The remaining end of each arm follows a cam which is specially shaped to control the movement of the buckets. The rotating disks should be ground driven so that the movement of the buckets is automatically coordinated to the forward motion of the transplanter. The cams are shaped to cause the buckets to descend with zero horizontal velocity relative to the ground. Seedlings released from a carrier fall vertically into the descending buckets. As the dibbles enter the soil, the cams cause the dibbles to continue zero horizontal movement relative to the ground. Just before a dibble is raised from the soil, the bucket opens at the bottom to release the seedling into the hole. The bucket closes as it rises to accept the next seedling, thus completing the cycle.

Theory of transplanting machines. Just as precision planters meter individual seeds, transplanters plant individual seedlings. Thus, equation 6.4 is valid for transplanters if the word

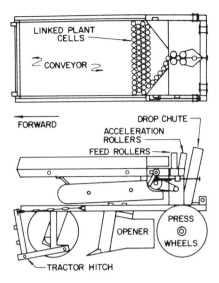

Figure 6.23–A roll-type feeding mechanism (Suggs et al., 1987).

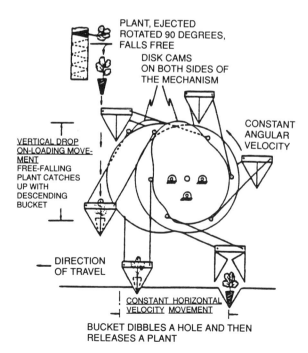

Figure 6.24–An experimental, dibble-type transplanter (Munilla and Shaw, 1987).

seedlings is substituted for seeds. A key limiting factor in the capacity of transplanters is the feed rate, i.e., the rate at which seedlings can be fed into the transplanter. The required feed rate is:

$$R_{st} = \frac{60 v \lambda_r}{x_s} \qquad (6.21)$$

where

R_{st} = required feed rate of seedlings (seedlings/min)
v = forward speed of transplanter (m/s)
x_s = seedling spacing along the row (m)
λ_r = number of rows planted simultaneously by transplanter

Kinematics theory must be used in designing the transplanters shown in figures 6.22, 6.23, and 6.24. In figure 6.22, the grippers must close and open at the proper times to grab a seedling cell, carry it to the furrow and release it in the furrow. The acceleration rolls in figure 6.23 must tear away a cell and convey it to the chute. The kinematics of these transplanters is beyond the scope of this book. For a complete kinematic analysis of the transplanter shown in figure 6.24, the reader is referred to the publication by Munilla and Shaw (1987).

Performance of transplanters. Seedlings suffer physiological damage when the roots are exposed to air as a part of the transplanting operation. Such seedling shock can be prevented by growing the seedlings in paper, peat, or other biodegradable containers which can be planted with the seedlings. For acceptable capacity, the feed rate of transplanters (eq. 6.21) should be at least 100 seedlings/min. Feeding capacities up to 140 seedlings/min have been observed. Maximum travel speeds have ranged from 0.9 to 1.8 m/s. For a feed rate of 100 seedlings/min, that speed range would accommodate seedling spacings from 0.93 to 1.85 m in a one-row machine or twice that spacing in a two-row machine. For a given feed rate, seedling spacing can be reduced only by reducing the travel speed. Thus, for reasonable seedling spacing, the feed rate clearly limits the maximum allowable travel speed of transplanting machines. A disadvantage of the dibbling transplanter of figure 6.24 is that the seedling spacing can be changed only if the shape of the cams is changed.

An important performance criterion for transplanters is that the seedlings must be oriented properly and in good contact with the soil. A successful planting has been defined as one in which the seedling is inclined less than 30° from the vertical (Munilla and Shaw, 1987). The transplanters in figures 6.23 and 6.24 allow the seedlings to be in free fall for a period of time. In the transplanter of figure 6.24, the seedling then impacts with the descending bucket and the impact must be minimized to prevent shattering of the root clump. Because the seedling was falling into a descending bucket, it was possible to achieve impacts corresponding to only a 50 mm free fall. When the seedling falls into a properly-shaped furrow, impacting can be useful in providing more intimate contact between the seedling root clump and the soil in the furrow. Soil firming wheels are usually used on these machines to improve the soil-to-root contact.

6.3 Evaluating Planter and Transplanter Performance

The rate of application is of interest in the evaluation of any planter and, in addition, the uniformity of seed or seedling placement is often important. ISO Standard 7256, Sowing Equipment – Test Methods, provides detailed guidelines for evaluating planter performance. The statistical formulas provided below are also given in ISO Standard 7256.

6.3.1 Broadcast Seeders

Broadcast seeders distribute seeds on the surface of the soil. Two aspects of performance require evaluation. The first is metering accuracy and the second is uniformity of distribution.

Seeders must be calibrated to allow the seeder operator to obtain desired seeding rates. Calibration charts can be prepared based on equations 6.1 and 6.2. A separate chart is required for each type of seed and travel speed combination. Specifying the type of seed and travel speed fixes the values for ρ_s and v in equation 6.1. Equations 6.6 through 6.17 can be used in estimating the swath width but, for best accuracy, the swath width should be measured experimentally. With ρ_s, w, and v held constant, the seeding rate then varies proportionally with Q (eq. 6.1) and Q varies proportionally with orifice area (eq. 6.2). The lever that controls the orifice area should be positioned near a numerical scale (fig. 6.7) to allow repeatable orifice settings. Then the numerical scale values can be included in the calibration charts. Although equation 6.2 can be used to predict the volume flow rate, it is more accurate to measure the flow rate experimentally by collecting a measured volume of seed discharged through the orifice and measuring the time required to collect that volume. The measurements should be repeated for several different orifice openings to obtain an experimentally-verified relationship between the orifice setting and the flow rate for each type of seed.

In assessing uniformity of seed distribution, variability can be assumed to exist across the width of the swath. ASAE Standard

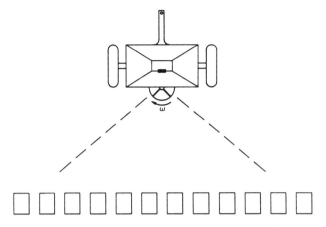

Figure 6.25–Evaluation of uniformity of broadcast seeding.

S341.2, for measuring swath uniformity when broadcasting granular materials, offers guidance in evaluating broadcast seeders. To assess seed distribution uniformity across the swath, a row of shallow trays is arrayed across the swath and the seeder discharges into the trays (fig. 6.25). If q_i is the quantity of seed caught in tray i and there are λ_t trays, then the following equations can be used to assess the uniformity of distribution:

$$\bar{q} = \frac{\sum_{i=0}^{i=\lambda_t} q_i}{\lambda_t} \qquad (6.22)$$

$$sd = \sqrt{\frac{\sum_{i=0}^{i=\lambda_t} (q_i - \bar{q})^2}{\lambda_t - 1}} \qquad (6.23)$$

$$CV = \frac{100\,sd}{\bar{q}} \qquad (6.24)$$

where
q_i = quantity of seed in tray i, either mass or volume
λ_t = number of trays
$\bar{q}$ = average amount in trays
sd   = standard deviation of amounts in trays
CV = coefficient of variation (percent)

The simplest method of testing pattern uniformity is to drive the seeder across the lateral row of trays while the seeder is operating. Since the spinning disk tends to deposit seeds in a circular pattern until the seeder begins moving forward, it is necessary to ensure that the full pattern has passed over the seed trays before measuring the quantities in the trays. A perfectly uniform distribution would have a CV equal to zero. With good design, broadcast seeders can achieve a CV in the range from 20 to 30%. Since broadcast seeders cannot produce a rectangular distribution pattern (fig. 6.17), it is reasonable to calculate the CV based on the uniformity created by multiple, properly-overlapped passes of the seeder.

6.3.2 Drills
Both the calibration and the distribution of drills require evaluation. The calibration procedure is similar to that for broadcast seeders, except that W is equal to the row spacing. Although equation 6.3 can be used to predict the volume flow rate, it is more accurate to measure the flow rate experimentally by collecting a measured volume of seed discharged through each metering unit and measuring the time required to collect that volume. The measurements should be repeated for several different cell volumes to establish a calibration chart. Uniformity can be checked in a stationary test in the laboratory by placing the drive wheels of the drill on a treadmill, placing a collection tray under each drop tube, and operating the drill for a fixed time period to accumulate seed in each tray. Then, if q_i is the quantity of seed in tray i, equations 6.22, 6.23 and 6.24 can be used to calculate the CV as an indication of uniformity. Uniformity can be assessed based on a single pass of the drill, since the patterns are not ordinarily overlapped. Seed metering can be assessed quantitatively, but other aspects of performance are assessed qualitatively. An example of qualitative assessment is the ability of the furrow openers to cut through surface residue in making a furrow.

6.3.3 Precision Planters
Precision planters are designed to meter one seed at a time and to place the seeds in a furrow at a desired spacing. It is common practice to check metering accuracy in the laboratory using stationary tests. The drive wheels of the planter are placed on a treadmill and turned at the speed which simulates the desired travel speed. An elongated seed collection device is pulled under the drop tube at the desired travel speed. The collection device must be able to capture the seeds as they exit from the drop tube; in the greased-board technique, sticky grease is placed on a board which is pulled

under the drop tube. The grease prevents seed bounce in capturing each seed as it exits the planter. Spacing of the seeds on the greased board can then be assessed, either manually or by an automatic counter. The numbers of skips or multiples can be determined by observation. A skip is created when a cell fails to deliver a seed to the drop tube. Multiples are created when more than one seed is delivered by a cell. Skips and multiples can be reported as a percentage of the total number of cells that passed the drop point during the run. After skips and multiples are removed from the data, the average spacing can be calculated using the remaining data and the average can be compared to the desired average seed spacing. Finally, using equations 6.22, 6.23, and 6.24, the CV of the seed spacings can be calculated. Perfect metering is achieved when there are no skips or multiples, the CV of the spacings is zero and the seed spacing is equal to the desired spacing.

Uniformity of planting depth and firming of soil around the seeds are important considerations for precision planters and are assessed during field tests. Futral and Verma (1973) suggest that, ideally, seeds should be placed in a narrow trench of uniform width which has a firm bottom. For many crops, the seed should be covered with approximately 12 mm of compacted soil and the remainder of the furrow should be filled with loose soil. The compacted soil aids moisture transfer to germinate the seed, while the loose soil inhibits moisture transfer and loss through the soil surface. Uniformity of depth can be measured by careful digging to expose planted seeds. Other observations, such as ability of the furrow openers to cut through surface residue and degree soil firming around the seed are usually reported qualitatively.

6.3.4 Transplanters

Automatic transplanters are still in their infancy and thus procedures for evaluating them are not well established. Since seedlings are planted in rows and uniform spacing is desirable, equations 6.22, 6.23, and 6.24 can also be used to quantify the ability of the transplanter to provide the desired spacing and the uniformity of spacing. In an analogy with precision planting of individual seeds, multiples are very unlikely to occur during transplanting. Skips could occur if the feeding mechanism ruins a seedling or fails to deliver it to the furrow. In successful transplanting, the seedlings should be planted with stems within a specified angle relative to a vertical line, e.g., within 15° of vertical. By measuring these angles for a number of plants, the average angle and standard deviation of the angle can be reported. Depth of planting may also be important; if the seedlings are uniform, depth of planting can be assessed by measuring the length of seedling protruding above the soil and subtracting from the total seedling length. The gentleness of the transplanter in handling the seedlings is also a consideration. Gentleness may be difficult to quantify except through study of survival rate of seedlings. In using survival rates for comparative evaluation of transplanters, it is important to ensure that all transplanters are evaluated under the same environmental conditions, since moisture, temperature and other factors can markedly influence survival rates of seedlings.

Problems

6.1   A centrifugal seeder is to be able to seed any of the top six crops in table 6.1 above at the maximum rate while traveling at a speed of 16 km/h with a swath width of 10 m, (a) what is the largest required flow rate of seeds through the metering orifice? (b) Calculate the required dimensions of the orifice if the orifice is square when open to the maximum. (c) The seeder must also provide the minimum flow rate required for any of the same six seeding jobs in the table. Calculate the minimum flow rate assuming no change in the travel speed or swath width. (d) Assuming the orifice size is reduced by partially covering the orifice, the reduced orifice will be rectangular. Calculate the dimensions of the rectangular orifice needed to provide the flow rate of part c.

6.2   Similar to problem 6.1, except now a drill is used to do the planting. The row spacing is 0.18 m and the travel speed is 7 km/h. The seeds are to be metered with a fluted wheel with 12 cells on the periphery (see fig. 6.8). (a) What is the maximum flow rate each fluted wheel must deliver to provide the maximum seeding rate as described in problem 6.1? (b) How fast must the fluted wheel turn to deliver this flow rate if the maximum volume of individual cells is 155 mm^3? (c) Assuming that the fluted wheel speed is the same for all seeding jobs, what fraction of the length of the fluted wheel must be covered to accommodate the minimum flow rate as described in problem 6.1?

6.3   Same as problem 6.2, except that wheat is to be drilled.

6.4   Same as problem 6.2, except that soybeans are to be drilled.

6.5   Soybeans are to be planted with a precision planter that meters 54 seeds per revolution of a metering disk; the row width is to be 75 cm and the planter speed is to be 7 km/h. A plant population of 480,000 plants per hectare is desired. Calculate (a) the required seeding rate assuming the lowest seed germination from table 6.1, (b) the required seed spacing along the row, and (c) the required rotational speed of the metering device. If the rolling radius of the planter wheels is 0.38 m, also calculate (d) the rotational speed of the wheels assuming 10% slip, and (e) the ratio of the metering disk speed to the planter wheel speed.

6.6   Same as problem 6.5, except that corn is to be planted for a plant population of 50,000 plants per hectare and the metering device meters 12 seeds per revolution.

6.7   Soybeans are to be planted using an air planter (fig. 6.12). Drums are available with 24, 36, 72, 96, 144, and 240 holes per row and rotate at 35 rev/min. If the planter travels at 2 m/s and the row spacing is 0.75 m, calculate (a) the seed spacing, and (b) the theoretical seeding rate in seeds/ha for each of the available drums. (c) From data in table 6.1 above, calculate the normal range of seeding rates (in seeds/ha). (d) Which of the drums should be used in this planting application, i.e., how many holes should be in the drum?

6.8   Same as problem 6.7, except that corn is to be planted.

6.9   A centrifugal spreader similar to fig. 6.15 is to be designed. The known specifications of the spinner are:

r_i = 0.05 m
f = 0.28
δ = 0.2 radians
α = 0.25 radians
ω = 50 rad/s
r_o = 0.15 m

(a) Calculate the angle of disk rotation during which the seeds will be in sliding contact with the disk (note that angle also specifies the gate location if the seed is to leave the disk at the point shown in fig. 6.15), (b) the velocity of the seeds relative to the blades at the outer edge of the disk, (c) the tangential velocity of the disk, (d) the horizontal component of velocity, v_{hr}, and (e) the upward component of velocity, V_{gv}, relative to the disk as the seed leaves the disk. (f) At what

TABLE 6.1. TYPICAL DATA IN THE TABLE BELOW ARE FOR ILLUSTRATING THE DESIGN OF
PLANTERS; SEED PROPERTIES MAY VARY FROM LISTED VALUES DEPENDING ON
VARIETIES, GROWING CONDITIONS, ETC.

Crop	Bulk Density (kg / L)	Seed Count (seeds / L)	Germ. Rate (%)	Seed Rate (kg / ha)	Mean* Diam. (mm)	Seed Density (kg / m³)	Term. Vel. (M / s)†
Alfalfa	0.77	339,000	72 - 94	8 - 13	1.53	1184 ‡	5.69
Sweet clover	0.77	441,000	73 - 94	7 - 11	1.41§	1184 ‡	5.39
Red clover	0.77	446,000	73 - 94	7 - 11	1.41§	1184 ‡	5.39
Brome grass	0.18	53,800	53 - 86	17 - 22	2.08	550 ‡	4.55
Orchard grass	0.18	259,000	53 - 81	9 - 11	1.59	440 ‡	3.37
Tall Fescue	0.31	154,000	68 - 92	13 - 17	1.82	430 ‡	4.64
Wheat	0.68	22,500	80 - 97	100	4.10	1120	9.81
Sorghum	0.64	21,200	67 - 77	3 - 6	3.88§	985 ‡	8.91
Soybeans	0.77	5,100	85 - 89	50 - 90	6.76	1176	13.11
Corn	0.72	2,370	85 - 95	10 - 15	7.29	1170	13.61

* Geometric mean = (length · width · depth)$^{0.333}$.
† Calculated terminal fall velocity in still air at 20° C and 100 kPa.
‡ Estimated values.
§ Calculated based on bulk density, seed count, and seed density.

forward speed, v_g, would the absolute velocity of the seed be perpendicular to the direction of travel of the seeder?

6.10 Same as problem 6.9, except that the coefficient of friction is 0.15.

6.11 Same as problem 6.9, except that the disk speed is 40 rad/s.

6.12 Same as problem 6.9, except that $\delta = 0$.

6.13 Same as problem 6.9, except that $\alpha = 0$.

6.14 Equation 6.11 can be used to calculate the terminal velocity of seeds, i.e., the value of fall velocity that gives zero vertical acceleration when the velocity is zero in the x- direction. Typically, the terminal velocity and Reynold's number for seeds are sufficiently large that equation 6.13 must be used to calculate drag coefficient and the solution for terminal velocity must be done iteratively. Using data from table 6.1, use equations 6.11 and 6.13 to verify that the listed terminal velocities are correct, i.e., that they give negligibly small vertical accelerations.

6.15   Calculation of a seed trajectory requires a value for drag
        coefficient. The drag coefficient can be calculated from
        Reynold's number using equation 6.12 or 6.13, but note that
        Reynold's number changes with seed velocity. The seed
        velocity begins losing velocity at point of release from the
        spreader, at which point it may be traveling 15 m/s or more,
        but never slows below its terminal velocity. Therefore, for
        each of the seeds listed in the above table, (a) calculate and
        plot Reynold's number vs. seed velocity for velocities ranging
        from 15 m/s down to terminal velocity. (b) For each seed, also
        calculate and plot the corresponding drag coefficient versus
        velocity. (c) Note that the drag coefficient will vary as the
        seed moves through its trajectory. For each seed, estimate
        the average height of the drag curve, i.e., the best value of
        drag coefficient to represent the entire trajectory of the seed.

6.16   Assuming that a centrifugal seeder releases alfalfa seeds at a
        height of 0.9 m and at an initial velocity of 9 m/s horizontally,
        calculate (a) the time of flight, and (b) the horizontal distance
        travelled. Use data from table 6.1 and a drag coefficient as
        discussed in problem 6.15. Note that sweet clover and red
        clover have properties similar to alfalfa and should have
        similar trajectories.

6.17   The situation is the same as in problem 6.16, except that you
        are to develop a computer program based on equations 6.10
        and 6.11 to simulate the flight of the seed. The program
        should be designed to accept input data that will allow it to
        simulate the trajectory of any of the seeds in the table.

6.18   Same as problem 6.16, except use bromegrass. Note that
        orchardgrass and tall fescue have somewhat similar
        properties to bromegrass.

6.19   Same as problem 6.16, except use sorghum.

6.20   Same as problem 6.16, except use soybeans.

6.21   After seeds are released by the metering unit in a precision
        planter (fig. 6.14), they fall through a drop tube whose
        vertical length is 0.6 m and which curves rearward to give
        the exiting seeds a rearward velocity relative to the planter.
        Assuming that the seeds being planted are corn, calculate
        (a) the time required for the seeds to fall through the drop

tube, (b) the vertical fall velocity at the exit of the tube, and (c) the required exit angle, θ_e, to give the seeds zero horizontal velocity relative to the ground if the planter speed is 2 m/s. (Use a drag coefficient as discussed in problem 6.15).

6.22   Same as problem 6.21, except soybeans are being planted.

6.23   Same as problem 6.21, except sorghum is being planted.

6.24   Seeds from an air planter (fig. 6.12) are transported through hoses to the furrow. If the 4 kPa pressure in the seed drum produces a seed velocity of 3.5 m/s at the exit of the hose and the planter is moving forward at 12 km/h, at what angle from the vertical, e, should the tube be directed rearward to produce zero horizontal velocity of the seed relative to the ground?

6.25   Same as problem 6.24, except planter speed is 8 km/h.

6.26   A one-row transplanter is to transplant strawberry plants at a spacing of 0.15 m within the row and with a 0.75 m row spacing. (a) If the feeding mechanism can deliver up to 100 seedlings/min, what is the maximum allowable travel speed of the transplanter? (b) What is the maximum allowable speed if the transplanter is a two-row machine? (c) Calculate the area (in m^2) covered per hour by the one- and two-row machines. (d) Is there any advantage in using a two-row machine in this case if only one feeder serves both rows?

6.27   A row of 10 square trays, each 15 cm by 15 cm in size, are arrayed across the 20 meter swath of a centrifugal seeder which is seeding alfalfa. After passage of the seeder, the following amounts of seed (in mg) are found in trays one through ten, respectively: 20.0, 32.8, 32.0, 30.5, 29.3, 29.1, 30.3, 31.5, 32.7, 23.5. Calculate (a) the mean, (b) the standard deviation, and (c) the coefficient of variation of the amounts of seed in the trays. (d) Also calculate the average seeding rate across the swath in kilograms per hectare.

6.28   Same as problem 6.27, except orchardgrass is being seeded and 18 cm by 18 cm trays are arranged across a 14 m swath. The amounts of seed in the trays are as given in problem 6.27.

7

Chemical Application

Introduction

The purpose of applying agricultural chemicals is to provide nutrients for plant growth and to control weeds, insects, and plant diseases.

Proper application of agricultural chemicals is crucial to successful modern agriculture. Agricultural chemicals, over the years, have become more sophisticated and expensive. The major classifications of agricultural chemicals are: fertilizers, pesticides and other growth regulatory chemicals. A pesticide is defined as a chemical that kills pests. Pests may be defined as weeds, fungi, insects, etc. Thus, a weed killing chemical is called a herbicide. A chemical that kills fungus is called a fungicide. These chemicals may be in either dry granular or liquid forms. The chemicals may be applied before planting during the seed bed preparation, during planting, and after germination during the active growth period.

In Chapter 7 we will discuss the chemical application methods and related equipment, functional components, and their operating principles, equipment calibration, testing, and other related topics.

7.1 Application of Dry Chemicals

Dry granular solids include primarily fertilizers, herbicides, and insecticides. A large percentage of dry granular solids are fertilizers. Granular pesticides are liquid chemicals impregnated on inert granular carriers such as clay, sand and corn cobs.

Application of dry granules has certain advantages. It eliminates the need to haul water and mixing required with liquid chemicals. Chemical drift is generally not as great a problem. The application equipment is less expensive and more trouble free since no mixing, pumping, and agitation is involved. While practicing conservation tillage, better control is possible with granules than sprays since granules filter through the foliage on to the soil. Granules are generally safer to use than liquid formulations.

Granular material is more expensive than the liquid chemicals. Granular material has poor metering characteristics and uniform distribution is a problem. The use of granules is limited to soil applications as they require moisture to become activated. Granular pesticides must be kept is a dry place and they are more bulky to store and transport.

Traditional granular pesticide rates have been 12 to 24 kg/ha (15 to 30 lb/ac) with 5 to 15% active ingredient. With the availability of 20-50% active ingredient there is a trend toward smaller rates of application. Some new formulations have 75 to 90% active ingredient with recommended application rate as low as 1.12 kg/ha (1 lb/ac) With the increase in the concentration of active ingredient there has been a shift toward smaller granular particles. Smaller particles tend to give better coverage by increasing the number of particles per unit area, however, they are more prone to drift.

7.1.1 Methods and Equipment
Granular fertilizer may be spread uniformly over the entire field, called the broadcast application, or it may be applied in narrow rows, called the banded application. The equipment for applying granular material includes drop type (gravity), rotary (centrifugal), and air (pneumatic) spreader.

Drop type equipment may be for either broadcast application or banded application. A truck mounted drop type spreader for broadcast application with a 15.24 m (50 ft) boom is shown in figure 7.1. Tractor drawn units have 2.4 to 3.7 m (8 to 12 ft) long hoppers with narrowly spaced openings in the bottom. The openings are

Figure 7.1–A drop type fertilizer distributor (Courtesy of Ag-Chem Equipment Co.).

generally 150 mm apart. A ground wheel-driven shaft located inside the hopper near the bottom carries agitators to help flow the material. A slide gate is used to control the openings and to shut-off flow during turn around. A drop-type applicator for banded application is shown in figure 7.2. This applicator utilizes several small hoppers as compared to one long one. The material is metered and dropped through a tube and is spread in a wide band by a diffuser. Some fertilizer distributors have furrow openers to place the material below the surface. This type of spreader is most commonly used as an attachment to planting equipment.

The rotary spreaders have one or two rotating disks with multiple vanes to impart energy to the granules and are suited for broadcast application. The material is metered on to the disks and is

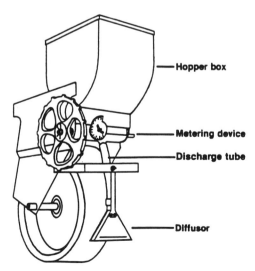

Figure 7.2–A drop type applicator for banded application (Reprinted from Bode and Pearson, 1985).

Figure 7.3–A truck mounted commercial rotary applicator (Courtesy of Ag. Chem Equipment Co.).

thrown wide due to the centrifugal force. The rotary spreaders are generally tractor mounted type but some of the larger commercial units are truck mounted with twin spinners as shown in figure 7.3. The trucks used for chemical application use high flotation tires.

Pneumatic applicators have a centrally located hopper from which granules are metered, delivered by air through tubes across the width of the machine, and spread by being impinged onto deflector plates. Pneumatic applicators allow central tank filling, easier installation on tillage implements, improved distribution, and easier transporting of trailer-mounted applicators. A pneumatic applicator is shown in figure 7.4. The pneumatic applicator can be used for either broadcast or band application.

Fertilizers may be broadcast by aircraft in areas that are either too large or too difficult (rough terrain, flooded rice fields) for ground rigs. Airplanes carry a maximum payload of 500 to 1100 kg (1100 to 2400 lb) at working speeds of 130 to 190 km/h (80 to 120 mph). The height of application usually varies from 9 to 15 m (30 to 50 ft). Ram-air spreaders located underneath the fuselage consist of an air scoop, a venturi or restricted-throat section where the material is introduced, and a diverging section with dividers to give the proper lateral velocity components to the material being carried by the air streams. The air stream is generated by the propeller blast. Many ram-air spreaders give a trapezoidal distribution pattern that allows for a fairly uniform application with proper overlap at swath widths of 12 to 14 m (40 to 45 ft). At application rates above 280 kg/ha (250 lb/ac) the particles are not accelerated properly and the distribution is not very uniform. The uniformity of application is also severely affected by cross winds. Another type of spreader used in aircraft application is rotating disk(s). The spinners used in aerial applications rotate at a much faster speed as compared to the ground

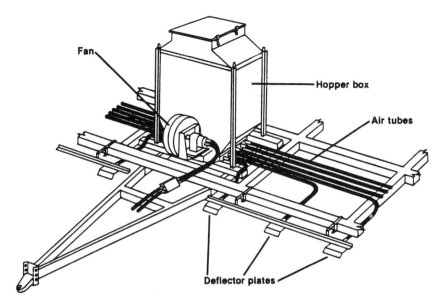

Figure 7.4–A pneumatic applicator (Reprinted from Bode and Pearson, 1985).

rigs in order to cover a much broader swath. Helicopters are used in areas where fixed wing aircraft are not suitable such as rugged, hilly terrain that is far away from a suitable landing site. The operating cost of helicopters is 2-3 times higher as compared to the fixed wing airplanes. The methods of application may be divided into the following:

Pre-plant application. Pre-plant application includes applying the material either on the soil surface or placing it below the surface using an appropriate tillage attachment. Material applied on the surface may be incorporated into the soil using an appropriate tillage tool (generally a field cultivator or a disk harrow) as part of normal seed bed preparation. Fertilizers may be placed deep into the soil with a chisel type cultivator. A fertilizer distributor may be used as an attachment to a plow which places it in the furrows below the surface at plowing depth.

During planting application. Fertilizer drills are commonly used to apply fertilizer during planting. Hoppers, tubes, and furrow openers are built in the drills to place the fertilizer below and to the side of the seed rows. Similarly, row crop planters have attachments to place fertilizers in a narrow band on either side of the seed row. The furrow openers for fertilizer are separate from the seed furrow openers and they can be adjusted independently in the vertical and horizontal directions.

Application in established crops. Chemicals may be applied either on the surface or below the surface in established crops. The

Figure 7.5–The functional diagram of a granular chemical applicator.

method of application depends upon the crop and the planting method. In solid planted crops, fertilizers may be surface applied using either a drop type or a rotary spreader. In row crops, granular chemicals may be banded between the rows or applied on either side of the rows as side dressing.

7.1.2 Functional Processes

A functional diagram of a granular chemical applicator is shown in figure 7.5. The main functions are *metering*, *distribution*, and *placement*. These functions are discussed below.

Metering. Many different types of metering devices have been developed to obtain a consistent and uniform metering action. These devices are generally driven by a ground wheel which stops metering when the implement is either stopped or lifted off the ground. Metering devices may be divided into *positive flow* and *gravity flow*.

The *star-wheel feed* (fig 7.6) is used on some grain drills and a few row-crop side-dressing attachments. Fertilizer, carried between the teeth of the feed wheel, falls into the delivery tube by gravity while material carried on top of the wheel is scraped off into the delivery opening. The discharge rate is controlled by raising or lowering a gate above the wheel.

Metering devices for some row-crop attachments have horizontal *rotating bottom plates* that fit up against the stationary bottom ring of the hopper base (fig. 7.7). The discharge rate is controlled by an adjustable gate over a side outlet. Sometimes there are two outlets permitting two bands from one hopper.

Auger-type metering devices are illustrated in figure 7.8 and 7.9. The type shown in figure 7.8 has a close-fitting auger tube and the

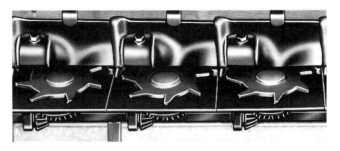

Figure 7.6–Star wheel metering mechanism of a grain drill (Reprinted from *Principles of Farm Machinery*, Kepner et al., 1978).

Figure 7.7–A rotating bottom metering device (Reprinted from *Principles of Farm Machinery*, Kepner et al., 1978).

auger has relatively large displacement per revolution. The loose-fitting or floating-auger arrangement shown in figure 7.9a is widely used on row crop attachments. The inside diameter of the tube is about 12.5 mm greater than the auger diameter. Each of the two

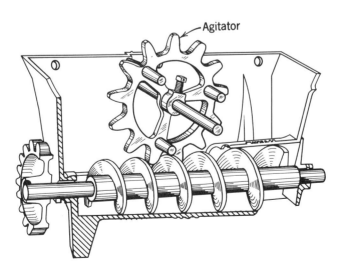

Figure 7.8–A metering device with close fitting auger (Reprinted from *Principles of Farm Machinery*, Kepner et al., 1978).

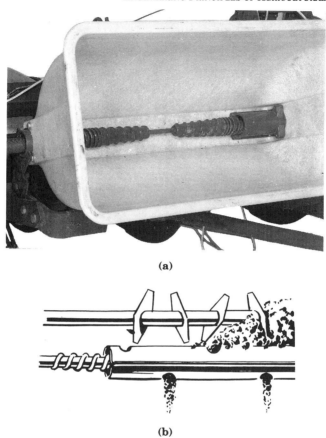

(a)

(b)

**Figure 7.9–Metering devices with loose-fitting auger
(a) for row crop attachments, (b) for row crop
attachment or drop-type broadcasters (Reprinted from
Principles of Farm Machinery, Kepner et al., 1978).**

auger sections move the material toward one end of the hopper,
where it is discharged from the end of the tube or dropped through
an outlet opening. One hopper serves two rows. Augers are easily
removable for cleaning.

Figure 7.9b shows a variation of the *loose-fitting auger* principle
in which the material enters the auger tube from the top instead of
from the end, is transported a short distance through the chute, and
is then discharged from a bottom outlet. The tube assembly forms the
bottom of the hopper and is removable. A series of openings along the
tube provide multiple outlets for row crop use or for drop type
broadcasters. With any of the auger-type metering devices, the
discharge rate is adjusted by changing the speed ratio between the
auger and the ground wheel.

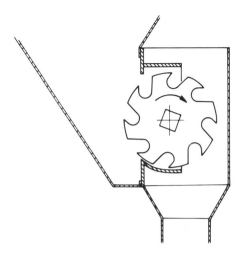

Figure 7.10–An edge-cell vertical rotor metering device (Reprinted from *Principles of Farm Machinery*, Kepner et al., 1978).

An *edge-cell*, positive-feed is shown in figure 7.10. Metering wheel assemblies are spaced as required along the hopper and are driven by a common shaft. Rotor width ranging from 6 mm to 32 mm are employed for different rate ranges. The discharge rate for a given rotor is controlled by changing the rotor speed.

Belt-type metering devices are sometimes employed where relatively large application rates are required, as on centrifugal broadcasters with large hoppers. Some units have a flat wire belt (usually stainless steel) that drags the material along the hopper bottom (fig. 7.11) and others employ rubberized-fabric belts. The discharge rate is controlled by an adjustable gate above the belt. The discharge can be split into two or more streams if desired.

The metering devices on most granular-pesticide applicators consists of a ground-driven *vaned* or *fluted rotor* above an adjustable discharge opening (fig. 7.12). Hopper for row crops sometimes have two or four openings whose outputs can be used separately or combined. Rotors fit closely in the hopper bottoms thus providing positive shut off when the rotor is not turning.

Ideally, discharge rate should be proportional to the rotor speed so that the application rate will not be affected by the forward speed. Tests have shown that this is not the case. Discharge rates are not proportional to the forward speed. This is due to incomplete filling of the inter-vane cavities which is affected by the material flow characteristics. Fluted metering devices like many other devices produce a cycle variation in the uniformity of the application rate.

Figure 7.11–A wire-belt metering device on a centrifugal broadcaster (Reprinted from *Principles of Farm Machinery*, Kepner et al., 1978).

Gravity type metering devices are common on drop-type broadcasters (fig. 7.13). The rate is controlled by adjusting the size of the openings. A rotating agitator breaks up lumps and moves the material across the opening to assist in feeding. Rotating broadcasters have hoppers of a size that can be tapered down to a small bottom area and usually employ stationary-opening metering devices. Gravity metering devices are sensitive to ground speed.

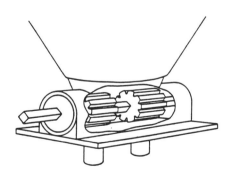

Figure 7.12–A positive feed fluted roll type metering device (Reprinted from Bode and Pearson, 1985).

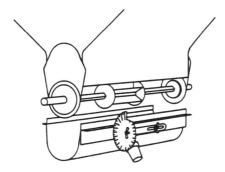

Figure 7.13–A gravity flow type metering device
(Reprinted from Bode and Pearson, 1985).

Spreading. Spreading devices may be divided into three categories: centrifugal, gravity, and ram-air.

Rotary spreaders. A rotary spreader usually consists of an either single or a double counter-rotating horizontal spinner. The direction of rotation is such that the adjacent sides in the counter-rotating spinners move the material rearward. The spinners have blades that may be radial, forward pitched or rear-ward pitched with respect to the radius. The blades may be either straight or curved. Forward pitched blades give greater carrying distances for free-flowing materials and rear-ward pitched blades unload sticky material (e.g., moist lime) more readily. These spinners are shown in figure 7.14. Rotary spreaders are used with broadcast types of chemical applicators. A stream of granular fertilizer is dropped on the spinner and is thrown out by the action of centrifugal force. For a double

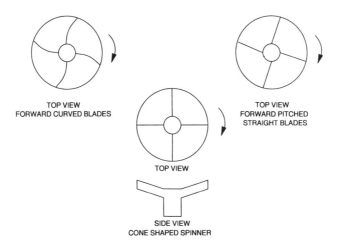

Figure 7.14–Different types of spinners for centrifugal distributors.

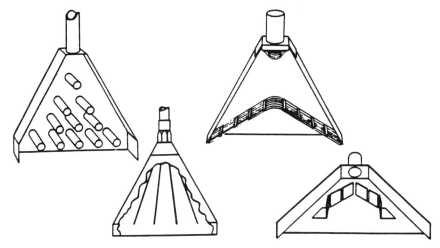

Figure 7.15–Various types of diffuser used in drop type applicators (Reprinted from Bode and Pearson, 1985).

spinner the stream is usually split in two by an inverted v-shaped splitter.

One of the most important performance criteria is the uniformity of coverage. The horizontal distance through which the particles are thrown is affected by the particle size, density, and shape in addition to the spinner speed and geometric configuration. The components of a dry blend tend to separate as the larger particles of the same density travel farther. Wind also affects the carrying distance, and hence, the distribution pattern.

Uniformity of application is influenced by the shape of the pattern from the spreader and by the amount of overlap. Most patterns from rotary spreaders can be approximated by one of the shapes shown in figure 6.17 (Chapter 6). Theoretically, pyramid, flat-top, and oval patterns give uniform distribution if they are symmetrical, straight-sided, and overlapped as shown. The pyramid pattern allows more leeway for driving error. Humped patterns are undesirable from the standpoint of the uniformity, but of the shapes shown would give reasonably uniform distribution, if the swath width were not over 40% of the overall pattern width, or if there were 60% overlap.

Gravity diffusors. Gravity diffusers are made of an inverted v-shaped housing made of either plastic or sheet metal plate at the bottom of the drop tube. The housing has distributing vanes or other patterns which take the stream of granular material and distribute it evenly into a wide band. Unlike rotary spreaders, the gravity type apply chemicals in more controlled manner and, therefore, they are more suitable as attachments to row-crop planters and cultivators.

They are also available in open field fertilizer drills for full coverage of the field. Figure 7.15 shows a gravity type diffuser.

Ram-air spreader. Ram-air spreaders are found in aircraft equipment. These are located in the propeller blast beneath the fuselage. A spreader of this type consists of an air scoop, a venturi or restricted-throat section where the material is introduced, and a diverging section with dividers to give the proper lateral velocity components to the material being carried by the air streams. Many different designs of the ram-air distributors have been developed. Most of those for spreading fertilizers or seeds are 910 to 1140 mm long, have a throat 610 to 760 mm wide and 150 to 200 mm high, and have a discharge area at least twice the throat area. The discharge angle for the outer sections is usually at least 45° from the line of travel.

Many of the ram-air spreaders give a trapezoidal pattern with a fairly flat top so that reasonably uniform distribution can be obtained with proper overlap at swath width of 12m to 14m. However, as the material flow rate increases, the air velocity through the spreader is decreased and there is less energy available to accelerate the particles. Consequently, distribution patterns are poor for discharge rates greater than 900 kg/min. Another limitation of the ram-air distributors is the high aerodynamic drag and power requirement (Yates and Akesson, 1973).

Placement. Placement devices may be divided into those that apply the chemical on the surface or below the surface. Surface application is often incorporated into soil by a tillage tool if it is done before planting. On growing crops a chemical is applied as top dressing and is not incorporated into soil, especially in solid-planted crops. Often fertilizer is placed below surface by a planter or a cultivator. Fertilizer is also placed deep in the soil using chisel plows or drilled into established pastures and other sods with special equipment.

Band placement during row crop planting is accomplished with applicators that are independent from the seed furrow opener. Double disk, single disk, and runner type openers, similar to seed furrow openers are often used.

Fertilizer grain drills often deliver the fertilizer through the seed tube, placing it in direct contact with the seeds in furrow. Separate disk openers are sometimes provided in front of the seed openers to not disturb the seed row.

7.2 Application of Liquid Chemicals

Liquid chemicals include fertilizers, pesticides and other growth regulating hormones. These may be water emulsions, solutions, or suspensions of wettable powders. Liquid pesticides may be either *contact* or *systemic* type. Contact pesticides kill weeds, insects, fungi, etc., by coming in contact. To be effective full coverage of the target, normally achieved by smaller droplets, is necessary. Systemic pesticides are taken in by the plant and they translocate within the plant. Full coverage of the plant is not required and larger droplets that are less prone to drift are acceptable.

7.2.1 Methods and Equipment

The methods of applying liquid chemicals may be divided into *pre-planting, during planting,* and *post-planting* application methods. Pre-plant applications generally are fertilizers and herbicides to control weeds. Pre-plant application may include sub-surface or surface application. Subsurface applications of fertilizer include aqua and anhydrous ammonia. The application is accomplished by means of specially designed knives or chisel injectors. During-planting applications generally include fertilizers and herbicides. Post-planting applications may include fertilizers and all types of pesticides. The application method may be further divided based on the area covered. This may be broadcast, banded, and directed spray. In a broadcast application the chemical is applied uniformly on the ground or on the crop. In banded application the chemical is applied in narrow bands or strips. Several nozzles are used in directed spray for row crop applications for a more complete coverage of the plants. Figure 7.16 shows the three methods of application.

Common liquid chemical application equipment may be divided into the following categories based on the system pressure:

Non-pressure liquid applicators. Non-pressure liquids can be applied directly to the soil surface, as on pasture and other solid-planted crops. Band application of non-pressure liquids are sometimes made during a row-crop planting operation or as later side dressing. Non-pressure liquid chemicals are available for many planters. Usually one tank is provided for each two rows. Liquid is discharged close to the furrow through small tubes.

Flow of liquid is due to gravity and the rate is controlled by fixed orifices. The attachments generally have a sediment bowl, a filter, one or two orifice disks with a range of orifice sizes, and a quick shut-off valve. Unless the tank elevation is large in relation to its depth, or bottom venting is employed, head changes will cause appreciable variations in flow rate. Bottom venting (inverted siphon)

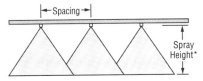

* Adjust spray height in the field to
overlap approximately 30% of each
edge of pattern.

Broadcast

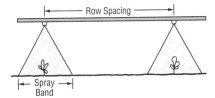

Banded

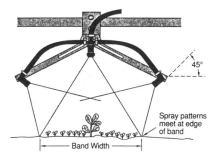

Directed

Figure 7.16–Methods of liquid chemical application (Courtesy of Spraying Systems Co. 1991).

is obtained by the tank sealed so air can enter only through an open tube that runs from the top of the tank to a point inside the tank near the bottom. The height of the bottom end in relation to the orifice then establishes the liquid head. This tube may be attached to a sealing-type filler cap. With a given orifice size and head, the application rate per hectare is inversely proportional to the forward speed.

A simple squeeze pump as shown in figure 7.17 has been developed for many non-pressure liquid applicators. Units are available with as many as 20 tubes, each serving one applicator outlet. The positive displacement ground-wheel-driven pump produces flow rate proportional to ground speed. The application rate

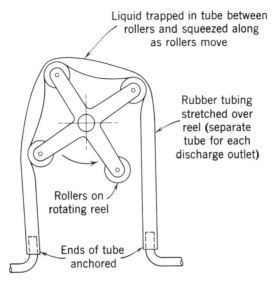

Figure 7.17–A squeeze pump (Reprinted from *Principles of Farm Machinery*, Kepner et al., 1978).

is adjusted by changing the speed ratio between the reel and the ground wheel.

Low-pressure sprayers. A tractor-mounted boom-type of field sprayer is shown in figure 7.18. These sprayers are used to apply pre- and post- emergent chemicals to control weeds, insects, and diseases. Boom-type sprayers are used on tractors, trucks, or trailers. Low pressure units usually operate in 150 to 350 kPa range and apply 50 to 200 L/ha. However, in some ultra low volume (ULV) applications, the rates may be as low as 10 L/ha to a few mL/ha. Tank on tractor mounted sprayers hold from 575 to 1000 L. For application in the standing row crop, high-clearance sprayers have been developed. They have a frame high enough to clear corn, cotton and other tall

Figure 7.18–A boom-type field sprayer (Reproduced by permission of Deere and Co. © 1991. All rights reserved).

crops. The spray boom may be raised or lowered depending upon the crop height. The sprayer may be mounted on a trailer or wheels and pulled through the field by a tractor. With tank capacity as high as 3750 L. The boom width may vary from 4 to 12 m. Skid mounted sprayers may be placed on a pick-up truck or a flat-bed truck. The tank size may be up to 10,000 L and the boom width may be up to 18 m. The trucks are fitted with flotation tires so they can operate in wet conditions. Aircraft-mounted sprayers have the advantage of rapid coverage and applying chemicals when conditions are otherwise unsuitable for ground rigs. Because of the limited weight carrying capacities, the aircraft mounted sprayers are most suited for low application rates of less than 50 L/ha. The aircraft speed varies between 50 to 125 km/h for helicopters and 175 to 250 km/h for airplanes as they fly about 1 to 8 m above the crop height.

High-pressure sprayers. High-pressure sprayers are similar to low pressure sprayers except they operate under much higher pressure up to 7000 kPa and generally do not have a boom with multiple nozzles. High pressure sprayers are used in orchards where it is necessary to spray to the top of the trees and to penetrate the thick tree canopy. High pressure sprayers are more expensive because the parts are made to withstand higher pressures.

Air-carrier sprayers. Air-carrier sprayers are sometimes called air-blast sprayers, or mist blowers. The liquid is atomized either by pressure nozzles or rotary atomizers in a high velocity airstream. The atomized liquid is then carried to the target by the air stream. The sprayers are capable of generating air flow rates in the range of 2.5 to 30 m^3/s with air speeds ranging from 125 to 240 km/h. Since air is used to carry the pesticide to the target, concentrated pesticides can be used resulting in a substantial savings in the

Figure 7.19–An air-blast sprayer (Courtesy of Durand-Wayland, Inc.).

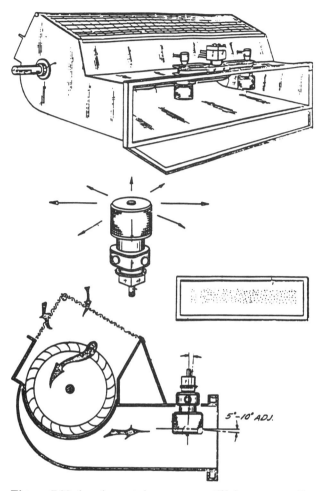

Figure 7.20–An air-curtain sprayer utilizing a cross-flow fan and a rotary controlled droplet atomizer (Van Ee and Ledebuhr, 1987).

amount of water needed and the time required for refilling. Figures 7.19 and 7.20 show two different types of air-carrier sprayers.

Sub-surface application. A liquid chemical applied below surface is generally fertilizer in the form of aqua or anhydrous ammonia. With anhydrous ammonia, aqua ammonia, and other low pressure liquids, it is essential that the material be released in narrow furrows at a depth of at least 10 to 15 cm and covered immediately to prevent escape of ammonia. Anhydrous ammonia contains 82% nitrogen. The boiling point is −28° F. A loose, friable soil with adequate moisture is important for good sealing and for absorption of ammonia on the soil particles. Under some conditions a press wheel or some other covering devices follow immediately

FLOW REGULATOR ASSEMBLY

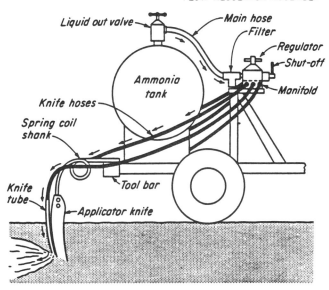

Figure 7.21–A schematic of a liquid ammonia applicator (Reproduced from Smith, 1964, by permission of McGraw-Hill Book Co.).

behind the applicators. Figure 7.21 shows a schematic of a trailing ammonia applicator. Note that there is no pump in the system. The vapor pressure of liquid ammonia is used to pump the liquid. A regulator valve is needed to control the flow as the vapor pressure varies with the amount and concentration of ammonia in the tank and temperature. For example, at 15.6° F the vapor pressure is 620 kPa (93 psi) but at 37.8° C the pressure rises to 1.3 MPa (197 psi). A typical narrow applicator blade is shown in figure 7.22. The liquid is discharged from holes in the sides of the delivery tubes near the lower end. The spacing of the knives depends on the crop being grown. When water is added to anhydrous ammonia to reduce the vapor pressure it is called aqua ammonia. It contains only 20 to 25% nitrogen and is termed low pressure liquid fertilizer. For subsurface application a pump is necessary. Ground driven, variable stroke pumps are also employed to meter ammonia. Aqua ammonia is applied about 5 cm below surface since it is not as volatile as anhydrous ammonia. Both mounted and pull-type implements are available for applying pressure liquids.

7.2.2 Functional Processes

Figure 7.23 shows a typical schematic arrangement for a hydraulic sprayer. A sprayer consists of a tank to hold the liquid chemical, an agitation system to keep the chemical well mixed and

Figure 7.22–An applicator blade for
anhydrous ammonia (Reprinted from
Principles of Farm Machinery, Kepner
et al., 1978).

uniform; a pump to create flow; a pressure regulator valve to control
rate of flow; a series of nozzles to atomize the liquid and
miscellaneous components such as boom, shut-off valves, fittings and
strainers. Main functional components are discussed below:

Pumping. *Positive displacement pumps.* Positive-displacement pumps found on sprayers include piston or plunger, rotary, and
diaphragm types. These types are self-priming, and they all require
automatic (spring-loaded) bypass valves to control the pressure and
to protect the equipment against mechanical damage if the flow is
shut off. Piston or plunger pumps are well-suited for high-pressure
applications such as high-pressure orchard sprayers and
multipurpose sprayers that are designed for both high- and low-
pressure spraying. They are more expensive than other types, occupy
more space, and are heavy, but they are durable and can be
constructed so they will handle abrasive materials without excessive
wear.

The volumetric efficiency of a plunger pump in good condition is
generally high (90% or more), and the discharge rate is essentially a
direct function of crank speed and volumetric displacement. Crank
speeds on the smaller sprayer pumps [38 L/min (10 gpm) and less]
are mostly 400 to 600 rev/min. High-pressure sprayer pumps
[4.1 to 5.5 MPa (600 to 800 psi)] are usually operated at 125 to

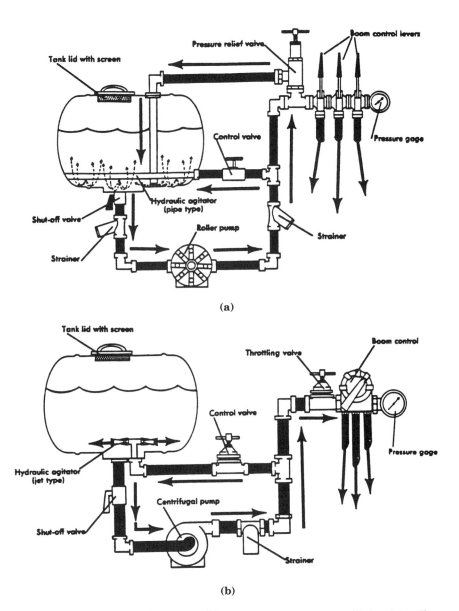

(a)

(b)

Figure 7.23–Schematic diagrams of low pressure sprayers utilizing (a) roller pump, (b) centrifugal pump (Reprinted from Bode and Butler, 1981).

300 rev/min have capacities of 75 to 225 L/min (20 to 60 gpm). Mechanical efficiencies may range from 50 to 90%, depending on the size and condition of the pump.

Rotary pumps are popular for low-pressure sprayers, the most common types being roller pumps (fig. 7.24). Roller pumps have a

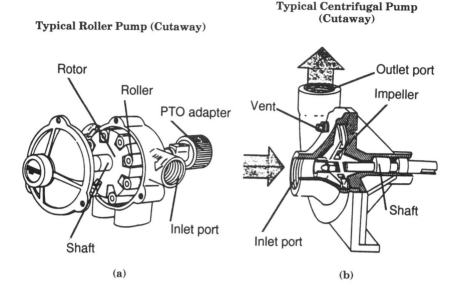

Figure 7.24–(a) A typical roller pump, (b) a typical centrifugal pump, (c) performance curves of roller and centrifugal pumps (Reprinted from Bode and Butler, 1981).

slotted rotor that rotates in an eccentric housing. Rollers in each slot seal the space between the rotor and the wall of the case. The rollers are held against the case by centrifugal force during pump operation. As the rollers go past the inlet the space expands creating low pressure and causing the liquid to be drawn in toward the housing. The liquid trapped between the rollers is moved towards the outlet as the rotor turns. Now the cavity between the rollers contracts expelling the liquid out through the outlet port. Pump output is determined by the length and diameter of the housing, its eccentricity, and the speed of rotation.

Teflon is a common material for the rollers, although rubber, steel, and carbon are also used. Rotary pumps of these type are compact and relatively inexpensive, and can be operated at speeds suitable for direct connection to the tractor pto. Although they are classed as positive-displacement pumps, leakage past the rollers causes a moderate decrease in flow as the pressure is increased. Normal output of roller pumps ranges from 19 to 114 L/min (5 to 30 gpm) and maximum pressures range from 1 to 3 MPa (150 to 300 psi). However, pressures above 690 kPa (100 psi) are not generally recommended for rotary pumps when pumping non-lubricating liquids. Roller pumps wear rather rapidly under abrasive conditions, but the rollers can be replaced economically.

Centrifugal pumps. Centrifugal pumps, as shown in figure 7.24b, depend upon centrifugal force for their pumping action. They are essentially high-speed (3000 to 4500 rev/min), high-volume (70 to 130 gpm) devices not suitable for high pressure applications. The pump output drops off rapidly when the outlet pressure is above 206 to 275 KPa (30 to 40 psi). The pressure or head developed by a given centrifugal pump at a particular speed is a function of the discharge rate, as indicated by the typical performance curves in figure 7.24c. Note that the peak efficiency, which occurs at a relatively high flow rate, is well above 70% for this particular unit, whereas efficiencies at small flows are low.

For a given pump and a given point on the efficiency curve, the discharge rate varies directly with the speed, the head varies as the square of the speed, and the power varies as the cube of the speed. If two or more stages are connected in series, the head and power at a given discharge rate are increased in proportion to the number of stages. Thus, multi-staging provides increased pressures without increasing the capacity range.

Centrifugal pumps are popular for certain types and sizes of sprayers because of their simplicity and their ability to handle abrasive materials satisfactorily. They are well suited to equipment such as air-blast sprayers and aircraft sprayers, for which high flow rates are needed and the required pressures are relatively low, and are used on many low pressure field sprayers. The high capacities are advantageous for hydraulic agitation and for tank-filling

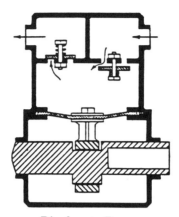

Diaphragm Pump

Figure 7.25–A positive displacement diaphragm pump (Reproduced by permission of Deere and Co. © 1991. All rights reserved).

arrangements. Speeds in these applications are generally in the range between 1000 and 4000 rev/min, depending upon the pressure required and the diameter of the impeller.

Since centrifugal pumps do not have positive displacement, they are not self-priming and do not require pressure relief valves for mechanical protection. Priming is usually accomplished by mounting the pump below the minimum liquid level of the tank or providing a built-in reservoir on the pump that always retains sufficient liquid for automatic priming.

Diaphragm pumps. Diaphragm pumps are becoming more widely used and are available with flow rates up to 19 to 23 L/min (5 to 6 gpm) and pressures up to 3.4 MPa (500 psi). Since the valves and the diaphragm are the only moving parts in contact with the spray material, these pumps can readily handle abrasive materials (fig. 7.25).

The power requirement of a pump is determined by its flow rate, the operating pressure, and its mechanical efficiency. The mechanical efficiency used for estimating the power requirements is between 50 to 60%. The pump input power can be calculated using the following formula:

$$P = \frac{Qp}{60,000\,\eta_m} \qquad (7.1)$$

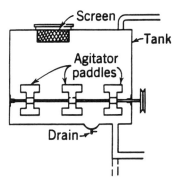

Figure 7.26–Mechanical agitation (Reprinted from *Principles of Farm Machinery*, Kepner et al., 1978).

where

P = power (kW)
Q = flow rate (L/min)
p = pressure (kPa)
η_m = mechanical efficiency (decimal)

Agitation. Many spray materials are suspensions of insoluble powders or are emulsions. Consequently, most sprayers are equipped with either mechanical or hydraulic agitating systems.

Mechanical agitation. Mechanical agitation is commonly obtained by means of either flat blades or propellers on a shaft running lengthwise in the tank near the bottom and rotating at a speed of 100 to 200 rev/min (fig. 7.26). The following relations apply to round-bottom tanks with flat, I-shaped paddles sweeping close to the bottom of the tank. They are based on results originally reported by French (1942) as cited in Kepner (1978).

$$s_m = 5.39 A^{0.422} R^{-0.531} F_e^{0.293} \qquad (7.2)$$

$$P_s = 3.26 \times 10^{-11} R^{0.582} s^{3.41} L \qquad (7.3)$$

where

s_m = minimum peripheral speed of paddles (m/min)
A = depth of liquid above agitator shaft center line (mm)
R = total combined width of all paddles divided by tank length
L = length of tank (mm)
P_s = shaft input power at any peripheral speed, s (kW)
F_e = factor indicating relative difficulty of agitating a given oil-water emulsion (hydraulically or mechanically)

TABLE 7.1. VALUES OF AGITATION FACTORS (F_E) FOR
OIL-IN-WATER EMULSIONS (KEPNER ET AL., 1978)

Oil (%)	Water (%)	Emulsifier (%)	Jet Position (fig. 7.29b)	Factor F_e
60	40	0	Emulsion	0.83
50	50	0	"	1.00
40	60	0	"	1.00
10	90	0	"	0.89
1-2	99-98	0	"	0.50
40	59.9	0.1	"	0.50
40	59.9	0.1	W.P.*	0.68

* Wettable powders.

Values of F_e for various oil-in-water emulsions are shown in table 7.1. These were established during tests with hydraulic agitation but are assumed to apply reasonably well for mechanical agitation. French's tests were conducted with an emulsion containing 1 to 2% oil. No data are available to indicate mechanical agitation requirements for suspensions of wettable powders.

Paddle tip speeds in excess of about 150 m/min (500 ft/min) may cause significant foaming of some mixtures. For mechanical agitation of emulsions in flat-bottom tanks with rounded corners, the minimum tip speed from equation 7.2 must be multiplied by the factor, 1.11. This increase in minimum speed causes the minimum power requirement to be approximately doubled (eq. 7.3).

Hydraulic agitation. A portion of the pump's output is discharged into the spray tank through a series of jet nozzles or orifices located in a pipe along the bottom of the tank to obtain hydraulic agitation. The energy and turbulence from the jets provide the mixing action. Figure 7.27a shows different hydraulic agitator nozzles. In tests with various sizes of cylindrical tanks, Yates and Akesson (1963) found that best results were obtained when the jet nozzles were mounted as shown in figure 7.27b. The location shown for wettable powders was satisfactory for an emulsion containing 40% oil and 60% water only when a suitable emulsifier was included in the formulation. Nozzle spacings from 75 to 710 mm (3 to 28 in.) were satisfactory for oil-water emulsions but not to exceed 305 mm (12 in.) for wettable powders.

The minimum total recirculation rates for hydraulic agitation in a cylindrical or round-bottom tank, based on complete mixing of a full tank of material in 60 s, were found to be as follows.

For oil-water emulsions:

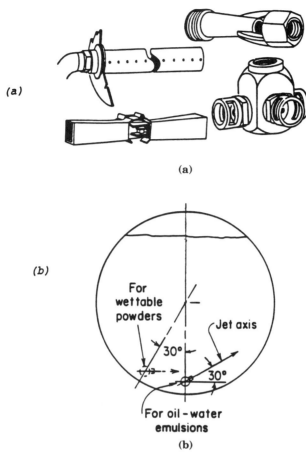

(a)

(b)

Figure 7.27–(a) Various types of nozzles for hydraulic agitation (Bode and Butler 1981), (b) locations of nozzles in the tank for agitation (Reprinted from *Principles of Farm Machinery*, Kepner et al., 1978).

$$Q_m = 3830 \, \frac{VF_e}{p^{0.56}} \qquad (7.4)$$

For wettable powders,

$$Q_m = 1380 \, \frac{VF_e}{p^{0.35}} \qquad (7.5)$$

where
Q_m = minimum total recirculation rate (L/min)
V = tank volume (m³)

p   = pressure at the agitation jet nozzle (kPa) (ordinarily this will be essentially the same as the spray nozzle-pressure)

The value of F_e was arbitrarily taken as 1.00 for a mixture of 120 g wettable sulfur per liter of water (1 lb/gal), since this is a difficult material to keep in suspension. Values of F_e for concentrations of 60, 12, and 6 g/L (0.5, 0.1, and 0.05 lb/gal) were found to be 0.87, 0.43, and 0.27, respectively. Table 7.1 indicates that adding an emulsifier to an oil-water mixture reduces the agitation requirements and also shows that F_e is greater when the jets are in the wettable powder optimum position (fig. 7.27b) instead of the emulsion position.

From basic hydraulic relations, the hydraulic useful power output required for any recirculation rate and pressure is:

$$P_h = \frac{Q_m \, p \times 10^{-3}}{60} \qquad (7.6)$$

where
     P_h = hydraulic power (kW)
     Q_m = total recirculation rate (L/min)

The principal advantage of hydraulic agitation is its simplicity as compared with the mechanism and drive required for mechanical agitation. With hydraulic agitation, however, the spray pump must have additional capacity and the power requirements will be considerably greater than for mechanical agitation, especially at high pressures. For high-pressure sprayers, mechanical agitation is definitely the more economical system.

Example 7.1

Determine the power requirements of a boom-type orchard sprayer if the spray gun pressure is 1.375 MPa, and the flow rate is 15 L/min. The hose has an inside diameter of 2.54 cm, and it is 50 m long. The volume of the tank is 375 L and contains wettable powder. It is also recommended that a 20% over capacity of flow should be designed to compensate for normal pump wear. The mechanical efficiency of the pump ranges from 50 to 60%. Assume the viscosity of the chemical is the same as that of water at 21° C or 0.98 MPa·s.

Solution. First we determine the pressure loss in the hose. Determine the flow regime by calculating the value of the Reynolds number as follows:

$$Re = \frac{4C\rho Q}{\pi \mu d}$$

$$= \frac{4(16.67)1000(15 \cdot 1.2)}{\pi(0.98)25.4} = 15,348$$

Note that $Q = 15 \cdot 1.2$ to account for 20% over capacity as desired in the problem statement. The flow is fully developed turbulent flow since the Reynolds number is above 4000. To calculate the pressure drop, we use the following equation (eq. 3.49):

$$\frac{\Delta p}{L} = \frac{0.0333\mu^{0.25}\rho^{0.75}Q^{1.75}}{d^{4.25}}$$

$$= \frac{0.0333(0.98)^{0.25}(1000)^{0.75}(15 \cdot 1.2)^{1.75}}{(25.4)^{4.25}}$$

$$= 0.992 \text{ kPa/m}$$

and $\Delta_p = 0.992 \cdot 50 = 49.59$ kPa. Thus, the total pressure required at the pump is:

$$p = 1375 + 49.59 \text{ kPa}$$
$$= 1424.59 \text{ kPa}$$

Now, determine the flow rate required for hydraulic agitation using the following equation for wettable powder:

$$Q_m = 1380 \frac{VF_e}{p^{0.35}}$$

$$Q_m = \frac{1380 \ (0.375) \ 0.68}{(1425)^{0.35}}$$

$$= 27.7 \text{ L/min}$$

Thus, the total flow that the pump must generate is:

$$Q = 15 \ (1.2) + 27.2 \text{ L/min}$$
$$= 45.2 \text{ L/min}$$

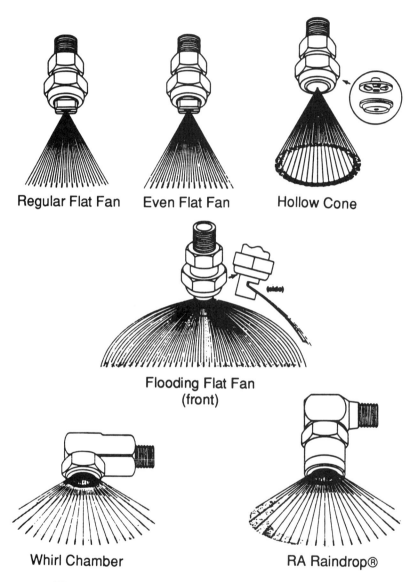

Regular Flat Fan   Even Flat Fan   Hollow Cone

Flooding Flat Fan
(front)

Whirl Chamber   RA Raindrop®

Figure 7.28–Various types of spray nozzles (Reprinted from Bode and Butler, 1981).

Pump output power is, from equation (7.14):

$$P = 1.667 \times 10^{-5} QP$$
$$= 1.667 \times 10^{-5} (45.2)\,(1424.59)\ kW$$
$$= 1.07\ kW$$

Figure 7.29–A typical nozzle assembly (Reproduced by permission of Deere and Co. © 1991. All rights reserved).

Considering the lowest efficiency of 50%, the input power is:

$$P_{input} = \frac{1.07}{0.5} = 2.14 \, kW \quad Ans.$$

Atomization. The main objective of atomization is to increase the surface area of the liquid by breaking it into many small droplets for effective coverage of plant and soil surfaces. During atomization, energy is imparted to the liquid to break it into small droplets by overcoming surface tension, viscosity and inertia. Based on the form of energy applied to produce atomization, the atomizers may be divided into either pressure, rotary, or pneumatic atomizers. Pressure atomizers are the most common type used in agriculture whereas use of the pneumatic kind is virtually non-existent.

Pressure atomizers. The pressure energy is used to break-up a liquid jet. Depending upon the pattern of spray, pressure atomizers, often referred to as nozzles, may be divided into the following categories (fig. 7.28). Figure 7.29 shows a typical nozzle assembly.

Regular flat-fan nozzle. Regular flat-fan nozzles are used for most solid application of herbicides and for certain pesticides when it is not necessary to penetrate foliage. These nozzles produce a tapered edge flat-fan spray that requires overlapping of pattern to obtain uniformity of coverage. The spray angle varies from 65° to 110° with 80° being the most common. Nozzle spacing is generally 50 cm on the boom. The boom height varies with spray angle and the amount of overlap desired. A minimum of 50% overlap is needed for a uniform coverage.

The operating pressure is generally 100 to 200 kPa (15 to 30 psi) when applying herbicides to produce medium to coarse droplets that are not susceptible to drift. Finer droplet are produced as the pressure is increased. Some herbicides are applied at pressure of 275 to 413 (40 to 60 psi) to generate finer droplets for maximum coverage. The LP or "low pressure" flat-fan nozzle is available that develops normal pattern at pressures of 69 to 172 kPa (10 to 25 psi). Operating at lower pressures results in larger drops and less drift.

Even flat-fan spray nozzle. As the name suggests the spray density is more even across the width of the spray as compared to the standard flat-fan spray which has a tapered spray distribution. Since overlapping would produce very uneven spray pattern, these nozzles are only for band application over the rows or in between them. Band width is determined by adjusting the boom height. The common spray angles are 80° and 95° and the operating pressures range from 100-200 kPa (15-30 psi).

Flooding flat-fan nozzles. Flooding flat-fan nozzles produce wider spray pattern than the flat-fan nozzles. They are most suited for broadcast application where uniform surface application is critical. Uniform spray application is obtained by 100% overlap of individual spray patterns. These nozzles produce large droplets and reduce drift, when operated at 55 to 170 kPa (8 to 25 psi) pressure. Pressure changes affect the uniformity of spray pattern more with flooding flat-fan nozzles than with regular flat-fan nozzles.

Hollow cone spray nozzles (disk and core type). As the name suggests the nozzle utilizes a two-piece, disk-core, hollow-cone spray tip. The core gives the fluid a swirling action before it is metered through the orifice disk, resulting in a circular, hollow-cone spray pattern. These nozzles are most suited for directed spray in row crop application when drift is not a concern as these nozzles are operated at 275 to 550 kPa (40 to 80 psi) pressures. Since the droplets are small, these nozzles are most suited for contact herbicides, insecticides, and fungicides where full coverage of plant foliage is essential.

Whirl-chamber hollow-cone nozzles. These nozzles have a whirl-chamber above a conical outlet that produces a hollow-cone pattern of

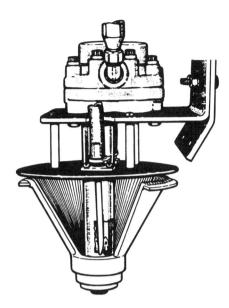

Figure 7.30–A controlled droplet atomizer (Courtesy of Farm Fans, Inc.).

cone angles up to 130°. These nozzles are best suited for broadcast surface application of herbicides. For best results the nozzle is tilted towards to the rear at a 45° angle. Since the droplets tend to be larger, these nozzles are most suited for systemic herbicides and where drift may be a problem. The operating pressure ranges from 35 to 138 kPa (5 to 20 psi).

Rotary atomizers. In rotary atomizers, the energy to produce droplets comes from a rotating device which could be a wheel, a disk or a cup. Figure 7.30 shows a rotary atomizer. Rotary atomizers are not as common in agricultural applications as the pressure nozzles. Rotary atomizers are also called controlled droplet atomizers (CDA) for their ability to produce more uniform droplets of the desired size.

Theory of pressure atomization. Atomization is a very complex process and depends highly upon the type of atomizer. To get a better understanding of the process we will discuss break-up of liquid jets, liquid sheets and liquid droplets.

Liquid jet break-up. As the liquid flow rate is increased through a horizontal nozzle, it goes through the following phases based on the Reynolds number (fig. 7.31).

Drop formation – At low flow rates drops form individually at the tip of the nozzle and grow in size until the weight overcomes the interfacial tension and the drop is released (fig. 7.32).

Varicose region – As the jet velocity is increased, symmetrical bulges and contractions appear and the jet lengthens. The drops become smaller and less uniform.

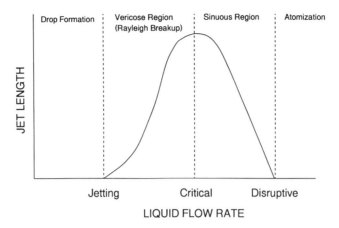

Figure 7.31–Phases of jet break-up (Keith and Hixon, 1955).

Sinuous region – Further increase in the velocity results in the transverse oscillations of the jet. The jet waves irregularly in an s-curve fashion. The jet becomes shorter and the drops become larger.

Atomization – Finally, the jet breaks down into small droplets, usually within a distance of 15 times jet diameter of the orifice. The break-up is highly chaotic. The ligaments shed at the crest as the jet oscillates which further break down into droplets. This condition corresponds to normal condition when a simple orifice is employed for atomization.

The following criterion is given for transition to this region:

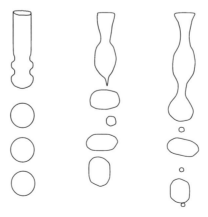

Figure 7.32–Idealized and actual jet break-up (Marshall, 1954).

$$\left(\frac{d_j v_j \rho_l}{\mu_l}\right) > 2.8 \times 10^2 \left[\frac{\mu_l}{\left(\sigma \rho_l d_j\right)^{1/2}}\right]^{-0.82} \tag{7.7}$$

where
  d_j = jet diameter (m)
  v_j = jet velocity (m/s)
  ρ_l = liquid density (kj/m^3)
  μ_l = liquid viscosity (Pa·s)
  σ = surface tension (N/m)

The jet velocity can be computed as follows once flow through the nozzle is known:

$$v_j = C_v \left(2\frac{\Delta p}{\rho_l}\right)^n \tag{7.8}$$

where
  C_v = velocity coefficient (–)
  Δp = total pressure drop (Pa)
  n = 0.5 for turbulent flow

The discharge coefficient represents the ratio of the actual liquid discharge rate to that theoretically possible. The volumetric flow rate is determined by:

$$Q = v_j C_A A \tag{7.9}$$

where
  C_A = area coefficient (–)
  A = nozzle orifice area (m^2)

C_A takes into account the vena-contracta effects. Combining equations 7.8 and 7.9 we obtain:

$$Q = C_v \left(2\frac{\Delta p}{\rho_l}\right)^{1/2} C_A A \tag{7.10}$$

Now, if we let discharge coefficient $C_D = C_v C_A$, the above equation becomes:

$$Q = C_D A (2gh)^{1/2} = C_D A \left(2 \frac{\Delta p}{\rho_1} \right)^{1/2} \qquad (7.11)$$

The average jet velocity may be computed from the above equation as follows:

$$v_j = \frac{Q}{C_D A} \qquad (7.12)$$

The discharge coefficient (C_D) varies depending upon the size of the orifice and the nozzle design. For a given nozzle, if we plot flow rate against the square root of the pressure drop, the slope of the line will be $C_D A \sqrt{2} / \sqrt{\rho_1}$ from which the discharge coefficient (C_D) may be computed.

Example 7.2

A spray nozzle manufacturer has provided the following pressure-flow rate data for a hollow cone nozzle spraying water.

Orifice Dia. (mm)	Nozzle Flow Rate (L/min) @ Pressure (kPa)									
	207	276	345	414	552	689	862	1034	1379	2068
2.39	1.17	1.63	1.82	2.00	2.31	2.57	2.95	3.14	3.71	4.54

For the above nozzle determine the flow required to produce atomization phase of a jet of water issuing from the nozzle.

Solution. Equation 7.7 is to be used to determine the jet velocity required to produce atomization. This equation can be rewritten as:

$$v_j > 280 \, \frac{\sigma^{0.42} \, \mu_1^{0.18}}{\rho_1^{0.59} \, d_j^{0.59}}$$

For water, σ = 0.0728 N/m
μ_1 = 1 mPa·s
ρ_1 = 1000 kg/m^3
d_j = 2.39 mm

Using the above values, $v_j > 16.06$ m/s

Equation 7.12 may be used to calculate the flow corresponding to the minimum jet velocity of 16.06 m/s as:

$$Q = C_D \, A \, v_j$$

However, the discharge coefficient (C_D) is to be determined from the data given by the manufacturer. If we plot the nozzle flow against the square root of the nozzle pressure as shown below, we find the slope as:

$$0.104 \, \frac{\text{L/min}}{\sqrt{\text{kPa}}} \quad \text{or} \quad 1.735{\times}10^{-6} \, \frac{\text{m}^3/\text{s}}{\sqrt{\text{kPa}}}$$

Plot of Spray Nozzle Performance

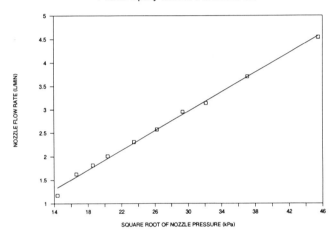

Using equation 7.11 we get:

$$\frac{C_D A \sqrt{2}}{\sqrt{\rho_1}} = 1.735{\times}10^{-6} \, \frac{\text{m}^3/\text{s}}{\sqrt{\text{kPa}}} = \frac{1.735{\times}10^{-6}}{\sqrt{1000}} \, \frac{\text{m}^3/\text{s}}{\sqrt{\text{Pa}}}$$

or

$$C_D = \frac{\sqrt{\rho_1}}{A \sqrt{2}} \times \frac{1.735{\times}10^{-6}}{\sqrt{1000}}$$

Substituting the values of ρ_1 and A, C_D is found to be 0.274. Note that this value of considerably less than 0.611 normally used for turbulent orifice flow. This is due to the inserts and screens used in a working nozzle.

Once C_D is known, the flow is calculated as:

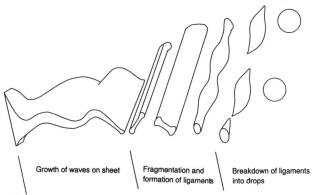

Growth of waves on sheet | Fragmentation and formation of ligaments | Breakdown of ligaments into drops

Figure 7.33–Break-up of a liquid sheet (After Dombrowski and Johns, 1963).

$$Q = 0.274 \left[\frac{\pi}{4} \left(2.39 \times 10^{-3}\right)^2 \right] 16.06 \ \text{m}^3/\text{s}$$

$$= 19.7 \times 10^{-6} \ \text{m}^3/\text{s}$$

$$= 1.18 \ \text{L/min}$$

It should be noted that this value corresponds to a pressure drop of 207 kPa. If the nozzle is operated at pressure less than 207 kPa, complete atomization will not occur. It should also be noted that this value corresponds to the minimum value of pressure given by the manufacturer. If lesser flow is desired, a smaller orifice should be used.

Liquid sheet break-up. When the liquid is pumped through a pressure nozzle, either a fanjet or a swirl nozzle, a sheet of liquid is formed. The liquid sheet breaks up into droplets of many sizes. The mechanism of sheet break up is complex and depends upon many factors. However, four main mechanism, have been observed (fig. 7.33):

Rim disintegration. The free edge of the sheet contract into a cylinder, which then breaks from the surface as large drops followed by their liquid fingers.

SPRAY NOZZLE   DROPLET BREAKDOWN   AIR RESISTANCE

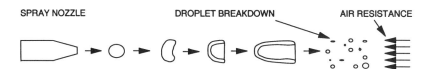

Figure 7.34–Break-up of a droplet.

TABLE 7.2. SPRAY DROPLET SIZE AND ITS EFFECT ON COVERAGE (BODE AND BUTLER, 1981)

Droplet Diameter (μ)	Type of Droplet	Area Relative to a 10μ Droplet	Volume Relative to a 10μ Droplet	No. of Droplets / cm² (10 L / ha application rate)	Coverage Relative to 1000μ Droplet
5	Dry fog	1/4	1/8	1 524 647	200
10		1	1	190 581	100
20	Wet fog	4	8	23 822	50
50		25	125	1525	20
100	Misty rain	100	1000	191	10
150		225	3375	56	6.7
200	Light rain	400	8000	24	5
500		2500	125 000	1.5	2
1000	Heavy rain	10 000	1 000 000	0.2	1

Sheet perforations. Perforations appear in the sheet which expand under the influence of surface tension until ligaments remain.

Unstable waves are formed in the sheet at a right angle to the direction of flow of liquid. The amplitude increases until the sheet breaks up.

Thick sheet break up. The crests of sheet are shed as ligaments.

Droplet break-up. Droplets further break down in an air stream if the aerodynamic forces exceed the surface tension force. This may occur in air carrier sprayers. A sequence of droplet breakup is shown in figure 7.34.

Droplet size and distribution. Spray droplets produced by an atomizer are classified by their diameters. The droplet diameter is measured in micrometers (μm) or microns (μ). One micron is one millionth of a meter or 1/25,400 of an inch. A person with normal eye sight can see 100μ without any magnification. When liquid is atomized, droplets of various sizes are formed. The performance and effectiveness of an atomizer depends upon the droplet size and its distribution. Table 7.2 shows some of the characteristics of various size droplets. The area covered and the volume of liquid in individual droplets is important in achieving effective and efficient application. Smaller droplets of the same volume provide more coverage. For example, a 200 μ droplet when broken into 64 droplets of 50 μ size will cover four times more area than one 200 μ droplet. The droplet distribution is important from the point of view of spray drift. As seen in table 7.5 the smaller the droplet size the longer it takes for it

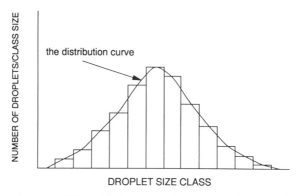

Figure 7.35–A histogram of droplet sizes and associated frequency.

to settle and the higher the probability of drift. It should be noted that droplets evaporate in flight. As they evaporate they become smaller thereby increasing the chances of drift.

Droplet size distribution can be represented by a plot of the number of particles of a given diameter, as in figure 7.35. The plot is called a histogram. A smooth curve through the center points of the maxima of each size class gives the distribution curve. This curve represented by a function, f(x), is commonly called a distribution function. If the distribution function is known explicitly, then only a few parameters (e.g., mean diameter and standard deviation) are needed to define a given distribution. Minimum and maximum size are additional parameters, often associated with a distribution. Sometimes, the surface area or the volume of a droplet is more relevant in certain applications rather than the diameter. If this is used as the ordinate then the curve in figure 7.35 would skew to the right because of the weighting effect of the surface area or volume associated with a droplet diameter.

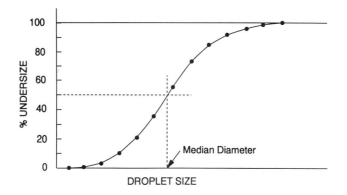

Figure 7.36–A cumulative frequency plot.

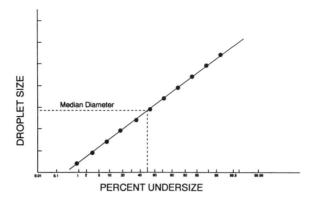

Figure 7.37–A cumulative frequency plot on a normal probability paper.

A more convenient method of representing particle size distribution is to plot the cumulative fraction of the total number smaller than a given size against that given size. This plot is called a cumulative frequency plot and is shown in figure 7.36. A more convenient way is to plot the data on a probability paper is shown in figure 7.37. The droplet diameter is plotted on the ordinate (y-axis) and the abscissa is the cumulative percentage of droplet number, length, surface area or volume. In pesticide application the cumulative number and cumulative volume are the most commonly used plot. The slope of the curve is an indication of the uniformity of the droplet size distribution.

Median droplet diameters. Median diameter divides the spray into two equal parts by number, length, surface area, or volume. Number and volume median diameters are determined from

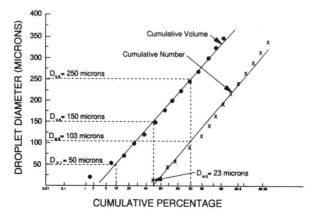

Figure 7.38–Cumulative number and volume curves for a typical spray nozzle after (Bode and Butler, 1981).

the cumulative probability plots such as shown in figures 7.38. A uniform method has been proposed to express the median diameters as D_{xf}. Whereas x can be V for volume, A for area, L for length, or N for number and f is the fraction on the cumulative distribution plot. Thus, $D_{v.5}$ = volume median diameter (VMD) indicates that 50% percent of liquid volume is in droplets smaller than this diameter and 50% in droplets larger than this diameter.

Mean droplet diameters. Mean droplet diameters are weighted averages. Their names depend on the method used to compute the average. The following equation can be used to calculate the mean diameters:

$$\overline{D}_{pq}^{\,p-q} = \left(\frac{\sum\limits_{i=1}^{n} N_i D_i^p}{\sum\limits_{i=1}^{n} N_i D_i^q} \right)^{1/(p-q)} \tag{7.13}$$

p,q = 1, 2, 3, or 4 and p > q
D_i = droplet diameter for the ith size class
N_i = number of droplets in the ith size class
i   = number of the size class
n   = total number of size classes

Various weighted averages may be computed based on the number of droplets in each class size. Commonly used means include: arithmetic mean $(\overline{D}_{10})$, surface mean $(\overline{D}_{20})$, volume mean $(\overline{D}_{30})$ and Sauter mean $(\overline{D}_{32})$. The arithmetic mean is computed by letting p = 1 and q = 0 in the above equation and it is the weighted average of all droplet diameters in the spray. Volume mean diameter (p = 3 and q = 0) is the diameter of the droplet whose volume times the number of droplets in the spray equals the total volume sprayed. Sauter mean diameter is calculated by equating p = 3 and q = 2 and it is an indicator of the volume to surface ratio of droplets in the spray. Similarly, the surface mean diameter, (p = 2 and q = 0), is the diameter of the droplet whose surface area times the number of droplets in the spray equals the total surface area of all droplets.

There is no general agreement as to which method of specifying droplet diameters is the best in agricultural chemical application. However, volume mean and Sauter mean diameters are most commonly used. Median diameters have a better physical significance in that they divide the droplet spectra equally based on the count, area, volume, etc.

Example 7.3

For the data given below, determine the mean and median droplet diameters.

Size Class Range (micron)	No. in Each Size Class
19-46	699
46-72	326
72-99	282
99-125	286
125-152	243
152-178	201
178-204	150
204-231	88
231-259	50
259-284	43
284-310	13
310-336	12
336-363	5
363-389	2
389-415	1

Solution. Mean droplet diameters are computed from the table below (Bode and Butler, 1981).

Size Class Range (micron)	Size Class Midpoint-D (micron)	No. in Each Size Class N	ND (μ)	ND^2 (μ^2)	ND^3 (μ^3)
19-46	32	699	22 368	715 776	22 904 832
46-72	59	326	19 234	1 134 806	66 953 554
72-99	85	282	23 970	2 037 450	173 183 250
99-125	112	286	32 032	3 587 584	401 809 408
125-152	138	243	33 534	4 627 692	638 621 496
152-178	165	201	33 165	5 472 225	902 917 125
178-204	191	150	28 650	5 472 225	1 045 180 650
204-231	217	88	19 096	4 143 832	899 211 544
231-259	245	50	12 250	3 001 250	735 306 250
259-284	272	43	11 696	3 181 312	865 316 864
284-310	297	13	3 861	1 146 717	340 574 949
310-336	323	12	3 876	1 251 948	404 379 204
336-363	349	5	1 745	609 005	212 542 745
363-389	376	2	752	282 752	106 314 752
389-415	402	1	402	161 604	64 964 808
		2401	246 631	36 826 178	6 880 181 431

$$\overline{D}_{10} = 102.7 \qquad \overline{D}_{20} = 123.8 \qquad \overline{D}_{30} = 142.0$$

$$\overline{D}_{21} = 149.3 \qquad \overline{D}_{31} = 167.0$$

$$\overline{D}_{32} = 186.8$$

To determine median diameters, complete the table as shown below and then plot the data on a probability paper as shown. Mean diameters are determined from the plot.

Size Class Midpoint (μ)	No. in Each Size Class	No. in Each Class (%)	Cum. % by No.	Vol. in Each Class (%)	Cum. % by Vol.
32	699	29.1	29.1	0.3	0.3
59	326	13.6	42.7	1.0	1.3
85	282	11.7	54.4	2.5	3.8
112	286	11.9	66.3	5.8	9.6
138	243	10.1	76.4	9.3	18.9
165	201	8.4	84.8	13.1	32.0
191	150	6.2	91.0	15.2	47.2
217	88	3.7	94.7	13.1	60.3
245	50	2.1	96.8	10.7	71.0
272	43	1.8	98.6	12.6	83.6
297	13	0.5	99.1	4.9	88.5
323	12	0.5	99.6	5.9	94.4
349	5	0.2	99.8	3.1	97.5
376	2	0.1	99.8	1.6	99.1
402	1	-	99.9	0.9	100
			100		

$$D_{N.1} = ----- \qquad D_{V.1} = 50\mu$$

$$D_{N.5} = 75\mu \qquad D_{V.5} = 195\mu$$

$$D_{N.9} = 188\mu \qquad D_{V.9} = 300\mu$$

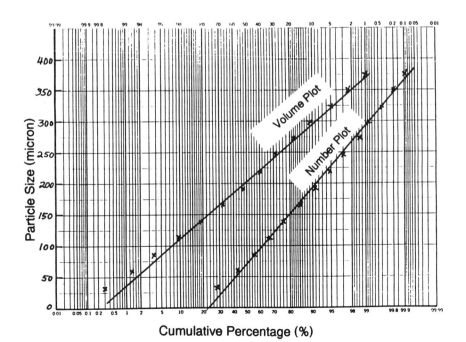

Cumulative Percentage (%)

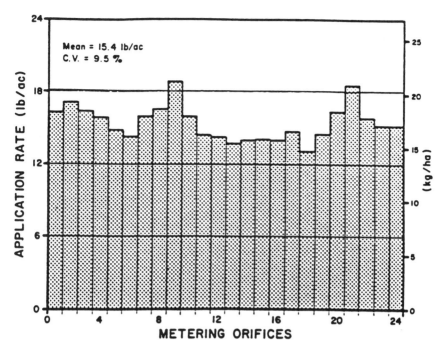

Figure 7.39–Typical variation in delivery rates from individual outlets with the original set of hopper bottoms while applying Avadex BW at 17.3 kg/ha (15.4 lb/ac) and 8 km/h (5 mph) (Courtesy of Prairie Agricultural Machinery Institute, Canada).

7.3 Performance Evaluation

7.3.1 Dry Chemical Application

The performance of a dry chemical application equipment is measured by the uniformity of coverage and calibration accuracy. The uniformity of coverage is based on the uniformity of metering and spreading or distribution. Field variables affect the uniformity and calibration accuracy. Bumpy and sloping fields result in undesirable performance. The material being applied also affects the performance. Free flowing materials produce more uniform application as opposed to the materials that tend to form clumps and do not meter well. A typical metering uniformity is shown in figure 7.39 (PAMI, 1985) for 24 outlets across the width of the applicator are shown. The mean delivery rate was 17.3 kg/ha at 8 km/h and the coefficient of variation (C.V.) was found to be 9.5%. The coefficient of C.V. is a measure of the scatter in a data set and it is computed by diving the standard deviation by the sample mean. The higher the C.V., the greater the scatter in the data. The uniformity of spreading is expressed in terms of application rate at a

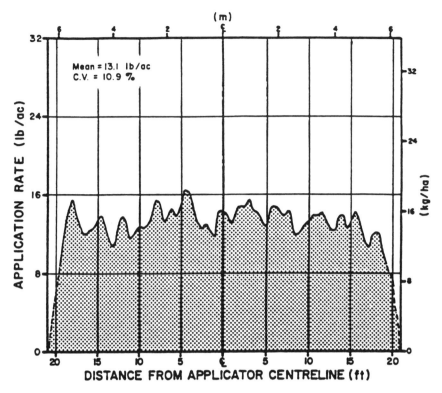

Figure 7.40–Typical distribution pattern using the original hopper bottoms when applying 14.7 kg/ha (13.1 lb/ac) of Avadex BW at 8 km/h (5 mph) using 610 mm (24 in.) deflector spacing and a 610 mm (24 in.) deflector discharge height (Courtesy of Prairie Agricultural Machinery Institute, Canada).

given location across the width of the applicator as shown in figure 7.40. The data as shown in the figure correspond to an application rate of 14.7 kg/ha at 8 km/h. The C.V. was found to be 10.9%. In addition to the lateral uniformity of application, longitudinal uniformity also affects the applicator performance. The longitudinal uniformity usually is in the form of cyclic variations that are caused by the design of the metering mechanisms. Figure 7.41 shows different lateral distribution patterns for centrifugal spreaders. The overall uniformity is based on the individual pattern and the amount of overlap for each swath.

The performance of rotary broadcast type fertilizer distributors is affected by the speed of the spinning disk and the size of fertilizer granules among other factors. Crowther (1958) conducted a study of these effects. A commercial fertilizer was used in the study with size distribution such that 92% of particles passes through sieve opening 3353μ, 36% at 2411μ and 4% at 1190μ. Figure 7.41 shows that as the speed of the disk increased the particles were thrown farther which

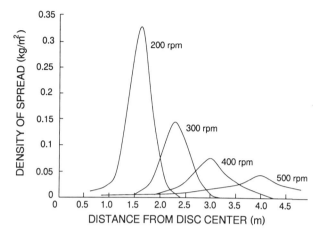

Figure 7.41–The effect of disk speed on the distance the particles are thrown by the distributor (Crowthers, 1958).

was expected. However, distribution of the spread density across the width of the distributor was also affected. Figure 7.42 shows the segregation of the particles at 400 rev/min. There is some segregation of particles according to their size, however, it is not likely to affect the overall distribution pattern.

7.3.2 Calibration

Gravity spreader. Calibration refers to the amount of chemical applied per unit area and is usually expressed as kilograms per hectare (kg/ha). The pesticide label indicates the recommended application rate. Sometimes the application rate is specified in terms of the amount of active ingredient to be applied per unit area since pesticides are available in different formulations. In this case the

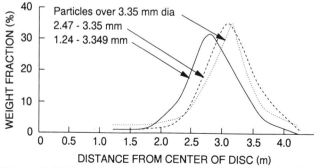

Figure 7.42–Segregation of particles due to their size by the spinning disk (Crowthers, 1958).

product application rate can be computed using the following formula:

$$AR = \frac{AR_{a.i.}}{FR_{a.i.}} \qquad (7.14)$$

Whereas AR is the product application rate in kg/ha, $AR_{a.i.}$ is the application rate of the active ingredient in the formulation, and $FR_{a.i.}$ is the fraction of the active ingredient in the formulation. The rate of application is independent of the ground speed of the applicator as the metering rate is proportional to the rate of travel. This is accomplished by driving the metering mechanism by the ground wheel. Different fertilizers and pesticides require different application rates. The manufactures of the applicators provide for the adjustment of the orifice to vary the application rate. The applicator should be properly calibrated to the desired rate of application.

An applicator may be calibrated in the laboratory although in-field calibration is recommended because the ground roughness affects the rate. To calibrate in the field, fill the hopper with material and adjust the gage to the recommended setting. Pull the applicator forward until a steady stream is flowing from the tubes. Mark a distance at least 200 m. Remove the tubes and attach bags to collect the material. After traveling the marked distance at the desired speed, collect and weigh the material. The following formulas may be used to determine the application rate.

$$A = \frac{d \cdot w}{10,000} \qquad (7.15)$$

$$A = \frac{m}{A} \qquad (7.16)$$

Whereas A is the treated area (ha), d is the distance travelled (m), w is the swath width (m), and m is the amount of material collected (kg). For laboratory calibration, the applicator is jacked up and the ground wheel is turned several times to simulate field travel. The granules are collected and weighed. The distance traveled in the above formula is determined by:

$$d = \pi D_w N \qquad (7.17)$$

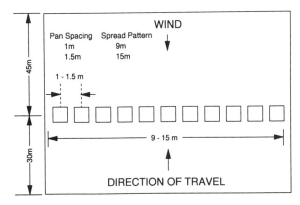

WIND

Pan Spacing   Spread Pattern
1m   9m
1.5m   15m

1 - 1.5 m

45m

30m

9 - 15 m

DIRECTION OF TRAVEL

Figure 7.43–Diagram showing the minimum requirements for a spread pattern test area.

where D_w is the ground wheel diameter (m) and N is the number of revolutions. If the application rate is not correct the applicator should be adjusted and the calibration should be performed again.

For banded application the rate of application in the band is the same as the recommended field application rate. Less total product is applied since treated area is less than the total area. The following formula is used to compute the treated area in band application:

$$A_b = \frac{d_b \cdot A}{d_r} \qquad (7.18)$$

Whereas A_b is the band treated area (ha), d_b is the band width (m), and d_r is the row spacing (m).

Rotary spreaders. The objective of calibrating a rotary spreader is to apply fertilizer at a desired application rate (kg/ha) and to obtain a uniform coverage. It is essential to establish the effective swath width and the spread pattern as they affect the amount of overlap. There are three acceptable spread patterns: flat top, pyramid, and oval, that result in a uniform coverage if proper overlap is maintained.

Most spreaders come with a calibration kit and a set of instructions to establish spread pattern and swath width. These instructions should be followed carefully. Generally, a test area is set up as shown in figure 7.43. Collection pans are placed according to the spacing as shown in table 7.3. Position the row of pans so that the spreader is running at least 100 ft before it reaches them and continues to spread at least 150 ft beyond. Select the desired application rate for the fertilizer to be applied and perform the test.

TABLE 7.3. PAN SPACING FOR COLLECTING SAMPLES TO
DETERMINE SPREAD PATTERN

Swath Width (m)	Pan Spacking (m) 9-Pans	Pan Spacing (m) 11-Pans
9.144	1.143	1.066 on each side of center pan 0.991 between all other pans
10.668	1.321	1.066
12.192	1.524	1.219
13.716	1.727	1.372
15.240	1.905	1.524

The application rate for each pan is then calculated based on the area of the pans and the weight of material collected in each pan. This data is then plotted in a manner similar to that shown in figure 7.44. The effective swath width is computed from this data by locating the point on either side of the center where the application rate is one half of that found in the center. The distance between these points is the effective swath width. The spread pattern can be visualized from the data given in figure 7.44. If this pattern is not acceptable necessary adjustments must be made according to the manufacturer's instructions. Finally, the application rate can be determined in field by keeping track of the amount of material applied and the area covered.

7.3.3 Liquid Chemical Application

The sprayer performance is determined by the uniformity of coverage and spray patterns, droplet size and its distribution, and target deposition and drift. The uniformity of coverage is affected by nozzle type, nozzle spacing, boom height, condition of nozzle, operating pressure, and field conditions.

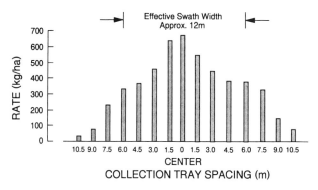

Figure 7.44–Diagram showing the experimentally obtained distribution pattern and the effective swath width.

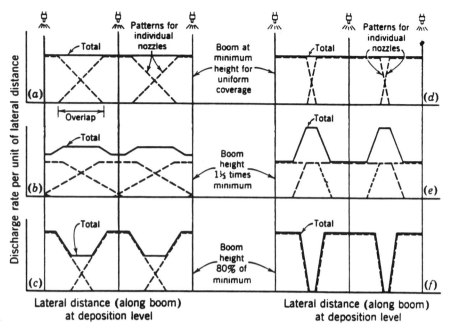

Figure 7.45–Effect of nozzle distribution pattern and boom height on uniformity of coverage. Broken-line curves indicate distribution patterns (at the deposition level) for individual nozzles; solid curve in each case shows the combined discharge pattern for all nozzles (i.e., the sum of the broken-line curves) (Reprinted from *Principles of Farm Machinery*, Kepner et al., 1978).

Uniformity of coverage. The uniformity of coverage is determined by (a) type of nozzle, (b) nozzle spacing, (c) boom height, and (d) the angle of spray nozzle. As shown in figure 7.45, most uniform coverage is produced with a flat fan nozzle with wide angle while the boom height is set at the minimum recommended height. Raising or lowering the boom results in over or under application. The figure also shows the effect of spray angle on the uniformity of spray pattern. For narrow spray angle nozzles, spray pattern is much more sensitive to the changes in boom height. It is generally recommended that for flat fan spray nozzles a 60% overlap should be obtained by adjusting the boom height. The overlap is defined as the width covered by two adjacent nozzles divided by the pattern width of a single nozzle expressed in percentage. The boom height can be calculated for a given amount of overlap and the nozzle spacing. However, manufacturers' recommended minimum boom height should be used because the actual spray width is somewhat less than the theoretical value as calculated by the spray angle and the boom height. The recommended amount of overlap for floodjet nozzles and some wide angle hollow cone nozzles is 100%.

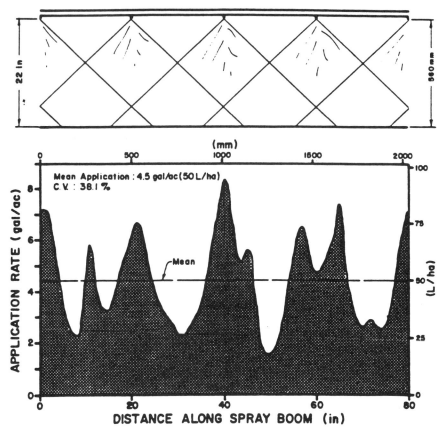

Figure 7.46–Typical distribution pattern along the boom using number 3 nozzles at 8.3 km/h (5.1 mph) at a 560 mm (22 in.) nozzle height (Courtesy of Prairie Agricultural Machinery Institute, Canada).

According to the tests conducted at the Prairie Agricultural Machinery Research Institute, Humboldt, Saskatchewan, Canada, the uniformity is affected by the nozzle pressure. Figure 7.46 shows poor distribution pattern along the boom at low nozzle pressure corresponding to a forward speed of 8.3 km/h. The distribution became more uniform when the pressure was increased to maintain the same application rate for a forward speed of 14.6 km/h as shown in figure 7.47. Worn and damaged nozzles result in an unacceptable spray distribution. Uneven ground causes boom height to vary thereby resulting in a non-uniform spray distribution.

Droplet Size. Droplet size, often expressed as $D_{v.5}$ (volume median diameter), is affected by nozzle type, spray angle, flow rate, and operating pressure. Generally, the hollow cone nozzles produce the finest droplets, flat spray being second while the full cone nozzles produce the coarsest spray. The droplets become finer as the width of

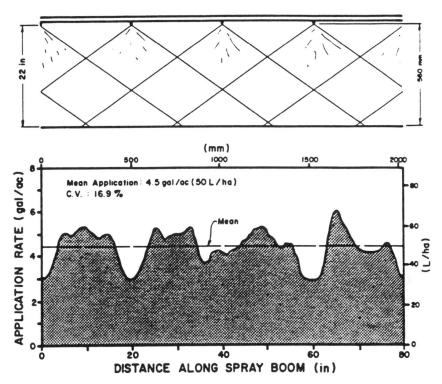

Courtesy of Figure 7.47–Typical distribution pattern along the boom using number 3 nozzles at 14.6 km/h (9.1 mph) at a 560 mm (22 in.) nozzle height (Courtesy of Prairie Agricultural Machinery Institute, Canada).

spray increases due to spreading of the liquid sheet to a greater angle which produces more fines at the edges. For a given type of nozzle the smallest capacity nozzle produces smaller droplets and vice versa. Table 7.4 shows the effects of spray angle and flow rate on droplet size (Spraying Systems Co., 1991). As the operating pressure increases the droplet size decreases. It is, therefore, important to realize that while increasing the application rate by increasing pressure, the droplet size would decrease and may result in higher drift. Liquid viscosity and density have very little effect on droplet size in the range commonly found in agricultural application. Increasing the surface tension increases the volume median diameter (VMD).

Often manufacturers of spray nozzles give droplet volume median diameter for a nozzle at a given pressure while spraying water. Droplet diameter may be estimated for a different pressure by the following equation:

TABLE 7.4. EFFECT OF SPRAY ANGLE AND FLOW RATE ON
DROPLET SIZE (SPRAYING SYSTEMS CO., 1991)

Spray Angle (°)	Nozzle Type (1.89 L min @ 275 kPa)	Volume Median Diameter (μ) (@ nozzle pressure of) (kPa)		
		103	275	550
40	4005 flat spray	900	810	780
65	6505 flat spray	600	550	530
80	8005 flat spray	530	470	450
110	11005 flat spray	410	380	360

Nozzle Type (275 kPa)	Volume Median Diameter (μ) (@ nozzle flow rate of) (L / min)		
	0.75	1.89	3
Std. TeeJet 80° Flat spray tip	390	470	560
XR TeeJet 80° Flat spray tip	360	460	560
TK-FloodJet Flat spray tip	370	450	540
FL-FullJet Full cone tip	—	680	770
TX ConeJet Hollow cone tip	220	360	—

$$\frac{D_{vm1}}{D_{vm2}} = \left(\frac{p_2}{p_1}\right)^{1/3} \tag{7.19}$$

where D_{vm1}, D_{vm2} = volume median diameters at pressures p_1 and p_2, respectively.

For similar nozzles and at constant pressure, the effect of different orifice size can be estimated from the manufacturers' data using the following equation:

$$\frac{D_{vm1}}{D_{vm2}} = \left(\frac{d_1}{d_2}\right)^{2/3} \tag{7.20}$$

where D_{vm1}, D_{vm2} = volume median diameters at orifice diameters d_1 and d_2, respectively.

Often surfactants are added to increase the surface tension to increase the droplet size and reduce drift. The effect of changing surface tension can be estimated from the following equation:

TABLE 7.5. SPRAY DROPLET SIZE AND ITS EFFECT ON DRIFT (BODE AND BUTLER, 1981)

Droplet Diameter	Steady State Fall Rate	Time to Fall 3.04 m in Still Air	Drift Distance in 3.04 m Fall with 4.82 km / h Wind	Lifetime of Droplet (sec)	Distance Fall in Lifetime (m)
(μ)	(m / s)	(sec)	(m)	Evaporating Water*	
5	0.00075	3960	4815	0.04	< 0.025
10	0.003	1020	1372	0.2	< 0.025
20	0.012	230	338	0.7	< 0.025
50	0.076	40	54.25	4	0.076
100	0.122	11	14.63	16	2.44
150	0.457	8.5	7.62	36	12.2
200	0.9274	5.4	4.57	65	38.4
500	1.158	1.6	2.13	400	> 380
1000	2.133	1.1	1.52	1,620	>> 380

* Air temperature: 30° C; relative humidity: 50%.

$$\frac{D_{v\,m,chemical}}{D_{v\,m,water}} = \left(\frac{\sigma_{chemical}}{73}\right)^{1/2} \tag{7.21}$$

where $\sigma_{chemical}$ = surface tension of the chemical [mN/m (dyne/cm)].

Drift and Coverage. Droplets that do not land on the intended target are considered drift. Spray drift poses significant hazard to the environment as most pesticides are highly toxic. Smaller droplets tend to drift more than the larger ones. Table 7.5 shows the time required for different size non-evaporating droplets to settle from a 10 ft height. It can be seen in the table that as the droplet size decreases settling time increases in a logarithmic manner. Droplets taking longer to settle are very prone to drift. Every nozzle produces different size droplets. If the distribution is very wide a lot of droplets would be undersize and be prone to drift. It is, therefore, desirable to produce a narrow distribution of droplet sizes near the desired size. Generally, a balance has to be struck between the large droplets and the small droplets. Large droplets give greater penetration of plant canopy while smaller droplets give greater coverage. Table 7.2 shows the effects of droplet size on coverage. As the droplets become smaller the coverage increases for the same application rate. For systemic herbicides larger droplets would be acceptable but for contact herbicides or fungicides full coverage made possible by smaller droplets is more desirable. Although smaller droplets give better coverage they evaporate at a faster rate adding to the drift. Table 7.5 shows evaporation rates for different size droplets.

Research is under way to improve sprayer efficiency and reduce drift. Electrostatic charging and air-curtain sprayers are but a few examples of the efforts in this direction. Droplets are electrostatically charged to improve their tendency to adhere to the plants thereby increasing efficiency of coverage and reducing drift. In air-curtain sprayers, the droplets are introduced in a fast moving air stream to increase penetration into the plant canopy.

7.3.4 Sprayer Calibration

Sprayer calibration refers to adjusting the chemical application rate in terms of L/ha. Application rate depends on the sprayer forward speed, effective sprayer width, and the nozzle flow rate. The following formula can be used to determine the required nozzle flow rating for broadcast application:

$$Q_n = \frac{AR \ S \ d_n}{600} \qquad (7.22)$$

where

Q_n = nozzle flow rate (L/min)
AR = application rate (L/ha)
S = sprayer speed (km/h)
d_n = nozzle spacing (m)

Once the desired nozzle flow rate is determined an appropriate nozzle may now be selected from the manufacturers' catalog. The next step is to adjust the system pressure to obtain the desired flow rate. The following formula may be used to determine the desired pressure (p):

$$p = \left(\frac{Q_n}{Q_r}\right)^2 p_r \qquad (7.23)$$

where

Q_r = rated nozzle flow rate (L/min)
p_r = rated nozzle pressure (kPa)

For banded application, use the spray band width or swath width for spacing in equation 7.22. For multiple nozzle directed spray, the value to be used for spacing is the row width divided by the number of nozzles per row. Keeping sprayer calibrated properly is very important to maximize chemical effectiveness and to minimize environmental hazard. Sprayer controllers are now available that monitor the tractor/sprayer speed and the flow rate, and continuously adjust flow to the desired application rate.

Example 7.4

Determine the nozzle flow rate for a hollow cone nozzle for an application rate of 200 L/ha. The sprayer speed is 10 km/h and the nozzle spacing is 50 cm. The available 0.787 mm orifice diameter nozzle is rated at 0.473 L/min at 275 kPa pressure. Determine what pressure would be required to produce the desired nozzle flow? If the nozzle produces a VMD of 200 μ at 1000 kPa, determine the droplet size at the desired flow rate. If a VMD of 350 μ is needed, determine the surface tension that should be achieved by adding adjuvants.

Solution. Determine nozzle flow rate as:

$$Q_n = \frac{200 \cdot 7.5 \cdot 0.5}{600} = 1.24 \text{ L/min}$$

Now determine the desired pressure for the given nozzle as:

$$P = \left(\frac{1.24}{0.473}\right)^2 275 = 1889 \text{ kPa}$$

VMD at the above pressure is calculated next:

$$d_{vml} = \left(\frac{1000}{1889}\right)^{1/3} 200 = 162\,\mu$$

Surface tension has to be increased to get the desired droplet size of 350μ. The necessary surface tension is calculated as:

$$\sigma_{chemical} = \left(\frac{350}{200}\right)^2 73 = 223.5 \text{ dynes/cm}$$

Manufacturers of adjuvants should be consulted to determine the appropriate compound and its proportion to achieve the desired surface tension.

Problems

7.1.   A side-dressing fertilizer unit is to place two bands per row on a crop with a 1-m row spacing. It is desired to apply a fertilizer having an apparent specific gravity of 0.85 at a rate of 560 kg/ha. If the distributor is calibrated by driving the machine forward a distance of 30 m, what mass of material should be collected from each delivery tube when the distributor is properly adjusted?

7.2.   A distributor for liquid fertilizer has gravity feed through fixed orifices. The tank is 460 mm deep and is top-vented. The bottom of the tank is 610 mm above the ground and the ends of the delivery tubes are 75 mm below ground level. The metering heads (including orifices) are just below the tank, but the delivery tubes are small enough so each one remains full of liquid between the orifice and the outlet end (thereby producing a negative head on the orifice). (a) Calculate the ratio between flow rates with the tank full and with a depth of only 25 mm remaining in the tank. (b) List three possible changes in the system that would reduce the variation in rates.

7.3.   A 0.95-m^3 round-bottom sprayer tank is 1.5 m long and has a depth of 0.9 m. Mechanical agitation is to be provided with four paddles 280 mm long (tip - diameter) and 200 mm wide mounted on a shaft 150 mm above the bottom of the tank. (a) Calculate the minimum rev/min for agitating a mixture of 10% oil and 90% water. (b) If the mechanical efficiency of the power transmission system is 90%, what input power would be needed for agitation.

7.4.   Under the conditions of Problem 3. (a) What recirculation rates would be required for hydraulic agitation at 400 kPa and 2.75 MPa? (b) If the pump efficiency is 50%, what pump input power would be needed for hydraulic agitation at each pressure. (c) Prepare a table to summarize and compare the results of problems 7.3 and 7.4. Note the decreased recirculation rate and increased power requirement when the hydraulic-agitation pressure is increased.

7.5.   A field sprayer having a horizontal boom with 20 nozzles spaced 46 cm apart is to to be designed for a maximum application rate of 750 L/ha at 520 kPa and 6.5 km/h. (a) Determine the required pump capacity in liters per minute, assuming 10% of the flow is bypassed under the above maximum conditions. (b) If mechanical agitation requires 375 input watts and the pump efficiency is 50%, what should be the engine rating if the engine is to be loaded to not more than 80% of its rated power? (c) What discharge rate per nozzle (L/min) is required under the above conditions? (d) If the nozzles have 70° spray angles and the pattern is such that 50% overlap is needed for uniform coverage (i.e., spray pattern 50% wider than nozzle spacing), at what height above the tops of the plants should the boom be operated?

7.6.   A field sprayer is equipped with nozzles having a rated delivery of 0.42 L/min of water at 275 kPa. The nozzle spacing on the boom is 51 cm. Each kilogram of active ingredient (2,4-D) is mixed with 80 L of water and the desired application rate is 0.95 kg of chemical per hectare. What is the correct forward speed for a nozzle pressure of 200 kPa?

7.7.   A hollow-cone spray nozzle deposits most droplets between two concentric circles. Assume the diameter of the inner circle is 70% of the diameter of the outer circle and that the distribution of droplets is uniform between the circles. Plot the theoretical distribution pattern that would be expected as the nozzle is moved forward past a transverse line. Graphical solution is acceptable.

7.8.   At a deposition level 410 mm below the tip of a particular fan-spray nozzle, the discharge rate-across a 20-cm width at the center of sprayed strip is essentially constant at 15 mL/min per centimeter of width and decreases uniformly to zero at a lateral distance of 36 cm from the nozzle centerline. (a) Plot the distribution curve to scale. (b) On the same graph, draw a curve for this nozzle at a deposition level 585 mm below the nozzle tip. (c) Calculate the nozzle spray angle. (d) If nozzles having this pattern are 50 cm apart on the boom, what tip height above the deposition level would give uniform coverage?

7.9.   An airblast sprayer is to be operated at 4 km/h and the desired application rate is 19 L per tree. The tree spacing is 9×9 m and each nozzle delivers 4.0 L/min at the operating pressure of 415 kPa. (a) If one-half row is sprayed from each side of the machine, how many nozzles will be needed?

(b) How many hectares can be covered with a 2-m^3 tank full of spray?

7.10. A manufacture of pressure nozzles specifies that a volume median diameter of 135 μm is obtained at 345 kPa using water. The same nozzle is to be used for a chemical whose surface tension is 50 dynes/cm. Determine the volume median diameter droplet size if the nozzle is to be operated at 525 kPa.

7.11. One hundred droplets from an atomizer were determined to have diameters in microns as shown below. Determine (a) arithmetic mean, surface, volume, and Sauter mean diameters, (b) Complete a probability distribution plot and determine number, surface, and volume median diameters.

70	250	490	160	150	370	370	330	210	500
340	210	150	340	290	110	580	760	350	290
260	270	1130	730	650	470	130	380	760	190
210	870	650	310	150	340	340	190	970	660
340	390	640	640	750	1140	450	280	160	270
250	620	150	200	520	190	440	700	280	360
140	470	470	180	1010	170	210	410	800	390
340	460	230	630	1070	570	460	550	310	170
150	150	490	100	780	370	330	520	350	250
470	540	330	150	170	370	270	370	160	190

Hay and Forage Harvesting

Introduction

Domesticated animals have been used as power sources and/or as food during the entire recorded history of agriculture. Through grazing, animals are able to make use of grasses, legumes, and other forage crops that people cannot consume directly. The climate permits year around grazing in some parts of the world. Because grazing is selective and management intensive, however, forages are generally machine harvested and stored for later feeding. The two most common methods of preserving forage crops are as direct cut or field wilting. Ensilage involves cutting the forage at 70 to 80% moisture, allowing it to field dry to 50 to 65% moisture, chopping it into short lengths to obtain adequate packing, and preserving it by fermentation in an airtight chamber. For hay harvest, the forage must be cut and allowed to dry to a moisture content of 15 to 23% before it can be stored. Hay has low bulk density and does not flow readily; silage has the same limitations, plus it will spoil if it is not fed soon after removal from storage. Thus, both hay

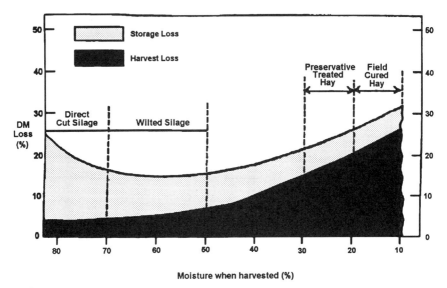

Figure 8.1–Effect of moisture on dry matter losses from forage during harvest and storage.

and silage are often fed close to the point of production. There are, however, commercial hay farms that produce high-quality hay, bale it and ship it considerable distances to customers.

Forages are unique because they are harvested at the peak of moisture content. Because of the large volume of water that must be removed and the limited crop value, it is generally not feasible to dry forages by artificial means. Losses and storage properties are highly dependent on crop moisture (fig. 8.1).

8.1 Methods and Equipment

Figure 8.2 illustrates two common methods for harvesting forage. For harvesting as silage, the standing or wilted crop is cut, field cured and then chopped into short lengths by a forage harvester (fig. 8.3). The same machine conveys the chopped forage into a wagon or truck for transport to the silo. There, the chopped forage is dumped directly

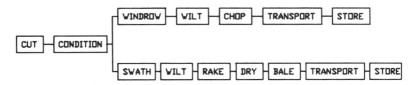

Figure 8.2–Block diagrams of two common forage harvesting methods.

Figure 8.3–A forage harvester (Courtesy of Deere and Co.).

into a bunker silo or, with a tower silo, a forage blower is used to convey the chopped forage into the silo (fig. 8.4). Most grass and legume forage is allowed to partially dry by wilting before chopping; silage stored too wet produces effluents and causes poor fermentation, while that too dry packs poorly and spoils. Therefore, once the crop has reached the proper moisture content (fig. 8.1), the forage harvester and its complementary equipment must provide for a rapid harvest. Direct-cut corn (maize) can be ensiled without drying, since the fermentation process prevents spoilage.

Forages are field dried in either a swath or a windrow. A swath approaches the width of the cut strip, generally leaving enough stubble uncovered to permit wheel traffic during subsequent operations. Swaths dry more rapidly due to greater area exposed to solar radiation, but they must be raked into a windrow for harvesting. A windrow is a narrow strip of forage that dries at a slower rate but does not require further manipulation before harvest. Forages to be made into dry hay are usually placed in a swath while those to be made into silage are placed directly into a windrow to control the drying rate.

Leaves dry faster than stems with legume and grass-type forages. The leaves, especially in legumes, are higher in nutritional value than the stems. Brittle, dry leaves may be lost during raking and harvesting. To reduce such losses, the forage will be conditioned

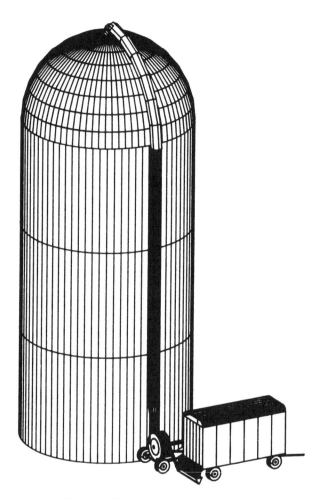

Figure 8.4–Conveying forage into a silo.

so that the stems dry at a rate approaching that of the leaves. Conditioning is a physical process of crushing, cracking or abrading the stems, or a chemical process which dissolves the waxy cutin layer of the stems. Either process improves the stem-drying rate by reducing the natural resistance to moisture removal from the stems.

Grass and legume forages are usually cut with a machine which combines the cutting and the conditioning process (fig. 8.5). The mower-conditioner can place the forage into either a wide swath or a narrow windrow. A windrower can be used to harvest either forages or small grains, but can only place the material into a narrow windrow.

After the forage dries to 23% moisture or less, it is usually compressed to some degree before being transported to storage.

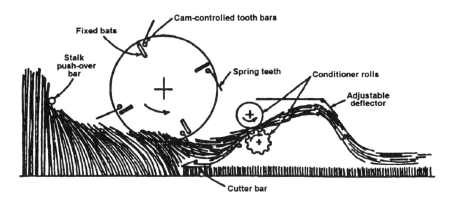

Figure 8.5–Schematic, cross-sectional view of a mower-conditioner. Side deflectors that can be used to form a windrow are not shown.

Baling the hay into rectangular bales of 25 to 40 kg mass (fig. 8.6) provides hay packages that are convenient to store and can be lifted by a single person or by machine. Because they do not resist water penetration very well, rectangular bales are usually transported and stored under a roof soon after baling. In another alternative, the hay is rolled into large round bales of 100 to 500 kg mass (fig. 8.7) which are more resistant to water penetration, especially if plastic wrapped, and are sometimes stored outdoors, although storage losses will be higher. The large round bales are too heavy to be handled by hand, so specialized powered equipment has been developed for handling and transporting such bales. Another approach is to package the hay into

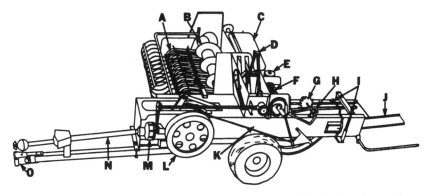

Figure 8.6–A baler that compresses hay into rectangular bales: A = pickup, B = feed auger, C = twine box, D = feed fork, E = hydraulic pump for density control, F = knotter, G = metering wheel, H = metering arm, I = density control rams, J = bale chute, K = bale chamber, L = flywheel, M = slip clutch, N = pto drive, O = hitch (Courtesy of Prairie Agricultural Machinery Institute, Canada).

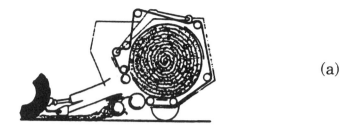

(a)

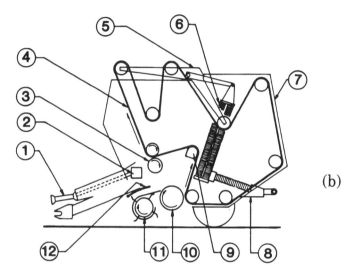

(b)

Figure 8.7–Baler for large round bales showing
(a) operation and (b) construction details: 1 = drive shaft,
2 = gear box, 3 = stripper roll, 4 = chamber belt,
5 = tensioning arms, 6 = tensioning springs, 7 = tailgate,
8 = bale ejector, 9 = core-forming cam idler, 10 = floor roll,
11 = pickup, 12 = windguard (Courtesy of Prairie
Agricultural Machinery Institute, Canada).

large rectangular bales which are similar in weight and density to
large round bales. The large rectangular bales will not shed water
and thus cannot be stored outdoors, but are better suited to shipping
by truck than large round bales.

In addition to those mentioned above, numerous other methods
have been developed for harvesting hay. These include pelleting,
stacking the hay into stacks in the field, compressing the hay into
large loaves, and other methods. Specialized equipment has been
developed to support each of these methods. Space does not permit
an engineering analysis of all of this diverse equipment, so such
analyses will be confined to mowing, conditioning, raking, forage
chopping, and baling.

8.2 Functional Processes

8.2.1 Cutting Mechanics and Plant Structure

Mowing and forage chopping involve the cutting of plant materials and cutting will be subjected to engineering analyses in this chapter. Those same analyses have wider application. For example, sickle bar mowers are used for cutting hay and forage, but similar sickle bars are included on the combines that harvest wheat, soybeans and other crops. Thus theory learned in this chapter will be useful in understanding Chapter 9 and perhaps in analyzing machines not covered in this textbook.

Cutting geometry. In a number of agricultural machines, a knife is used to sever plant material. Often severing is accomplished by shearing the material between a moving knife and a stationary countershear. In designing equipment to accomplish the severing, the objectives are to maintain the quality of the harvested product while minimizing the force and energy needed to accomplish the task. The characteristics of both the cutting device and the plant must be considered in pursuing these objectives.

Figure 8.8 illustrates the geometry associated with a mower in which a knife (sickle section) moves with reciprocating motion. The plant material is sheared as the sickle section reaches and passes over the countershear (ledger plate) on the right. At the instant illustrated in figure 8.8, the knife is just leaving the left end of its stroke and moving toward the ledger plate. Guards direct the plant material between the knife and ledger plate and also shield the blunt ends of the sickle sections while they reverse directions at the ends of their stroke.

Typically, in cutting theory, the x-axis of the coordinate system is in the direction of knife movement relative to the plant material. In figure 8.8, the knife has a velocity component, v_{km}, relative to the mower and a component, v_f, due to the forward speed of the mower. The vector sum of these two components gives the knife velocity, v_{kg}, relative to the ground. Since the plants to be cut are attached to the ground, v_{kg} is also the knife velocity relative to the uncut plants. Therefore, the x-axis is in the direction of v_{kg}, the y-axis is in the plane of the paper but perpendicular to x, and the z-axis is perpendicular to the plane of the paper and points upward. Note that the orientation of the coordinate system in figure 8.8 is for only one instant in time, since the magnitude of v_{km} varies during the cutting stroke and thus the coordinate system rotates about the z-axis as the direction of v_{kg} varies.

It is common knowledge that a sharp knife aids cutting. It is important, however, to distinguish between sharpness and fineness. A fine knife has a small bevel angle, ϕ_{bk}, while a blunt knife has a

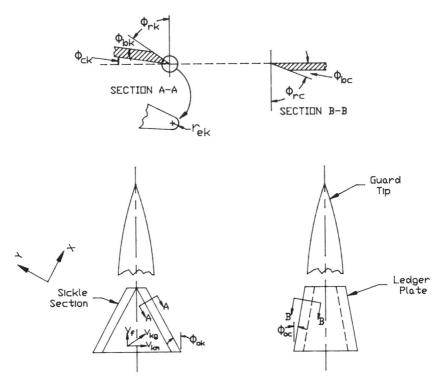

Figure 8.8–Illustration of geometry of a knife and countershear.

large bevel angle. Sharpness is defined by the edge radius, r_{ek}, of the knife, i.e., a sharp knife has a small radius while a dull knife has a larger radius. Initial penetration of the knife into the plant material is aided if the knife rake angle, ϕ_{rk}, is large. The knife clearance angle, ϕ_{ck}, is the angle formed between the bottom edge of the knife and the x-y plane. In general, the following relationship holds between the rake, bevel and clearance angles:

$$\phi_{rk} + \phi_{bk} + \phi_{ck} = 90° \qquad (8.1)$$

The chip angle on the knife, ϕ_{chk}, is defined as follows:

$$\phi_{chk} = \phi_{bk} + \phi_{ck} \qquad (8.2)$$

The oblique angle of the knife, ϕ_{ok}, is the angle between the y-axis and the cutting edge. The ϕ_{ok} illustrated in figure 8.8 is for the special case where $V_f=0$. A straight cut is one in which $\phi_{ok}=0$.

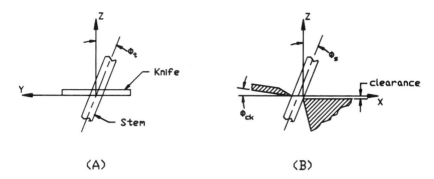

Figure 8.9–Illustrations of stem misalignment.

Conversely, an oblique cut is one in which ϕ_{ok} is not equal to zero. Oblique cutting reduces the peak cutting force because the plant material is sheared progressively rather than all at once as in a straight cut.

The bevel, rake, clearance, and oblique angles all have their counterparts on the countershear, as shown in figure 8.8. For each of these angles, the subscript k indicates that it relates to the knife, while a subscript c indicates the corresponding angle on the countershear. The clip angle, ϕ_{cl}, is the angle formed between the knife and countershear, i.e.:

$$\phi_{cl} = \phi_{ok} + \phi_{oc} \tag{8.3}$$

Frequently, plant stems are not parallel to the z-axis. Figure 8.9 illustrates the tilt angle, ϕ_t, and the slant angle, ϕ_s, which are used to define the orientation of such stems. The tilt angle is the angle between the stem axis and the z axis projected into the y-z plane, while the slant angle is the angle between the stem axis and the z axis projected into the x-z plane. Figure 8.9 also illustrates a positive clearance angle on the knife and the clearance that may be present between the knife and the countershear.

When ϕ_{ok} is not zero and the plant material is not yet in contact with the countershear, the possibility exists that the plant material may slide along the edge of the knife before or while being cut. The sliding is expected if the oblique angle is greater than the following maximum angle:

$$\phi_{okmax} = \arctan f_{ek} \tag{8.4}$$

where f_{ek} = knife edge friction coefficient. The edge friction coefficient is the lateral force (parallel to the knife edge) imposed by the plant on the knife edge divided by the normal force imposed by the plant. When the plant is in contact with both the knife and countershear, sliding is expected if the clip angle is greater than the following maximum:

$$\phi_{clmax} = \arctan \frac{f_{ek} + f_{ec}}{1 - f_{ek} \, f_{ec}} \qquad (8.5)$$

where

ϕ_{clmax} = maximum value of ϕ_{cl} that will prevent sliding
f_{ek} = friction coefficient for knife edge
f_{ec} = friction coefficient for countershear edge

Since the forward motion of the mower helps to push the plants toward the rear of the knife sections, sliding is most likely to occur when V_f is small. To increase friction and thus prevent sliding, serrations may be cut into the edge of the knife and/or countershear. For example, values of $f_{ek}=0.306$ for a smooth knife edge and $f_{ec}=0.364$ for a serrated ledger plate were observed during cutting of flax straw.

Plant structure. Cutting is a process which causes mechanical failure of plant stems and/or leaves and thus the structure and strength of plant materials are of interest. The engineering properties of plant parts are not as well understood as those of more common engineering materials such as steel, but some engineering studies of plant materials have been made. Living plants consist of solid materials which surround air and liquid-filled cavities. Fiber cells, with diameters of 10 to 50 μm and lengths exceeding 30 mm, provide the main strength of the plant material. Fiber cell walls include three basic layers, the middle lamella, the primary wall, and the secondary wall, with combined thicknesses on the order of 500 nm. The secondary wall lies inside the primary wall and provides the strength and flexibility of the structure. Cellulose chains, the main ingredient of the secondary wall, are bound together in parallel microfibrils of considerable length and with cross-sectional dimension of 2.5 to 20 nm (fig. 8.10). The microfibrils are oriented in spirals, and the angle of the spiral relative to the cell axis determines the elasticity of the cell wall. The cell wall density is approximately 1.45 g/mm^3, but makes up only a small proportion of the cross-section. Some cell walls have strength approaching that of steel, but the numerous cavities greatly reduce the average strength of the plant cross-section.

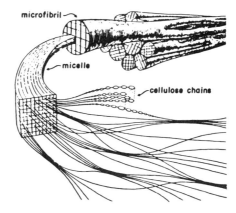

microfibril

micelle

cellulose chains

Figure 8.10–Arrangement and structure
of microfibrils (Reprinted from
Mechanics of Cutting Plant Materials,
Persson, 1987).

Plant stems and leaves consist of large numbers of similar cells. Structurally, the stems can be viewed as materials with fibers of high tensile strength oriented in a common direction and bound together by material of much lower strength. The softer cells make use of their turgor (liquid pressure) to connect and support the fibers. Grasses, including small grains and corn (maize), and legumes are the materials most commonly involved in agricultural cutting processes, so their structure and strength are of special interest. Many grass stems have hollow internode sections joined by solid nodes (fig. 8.11). The internode sections are much weaker than the nodes and thus determine the stem strength. The corn stalk has internode sections which are not hollow but have a more uniform cross-section. Figure 8.12 shows simplified models that were drawn to represent the actual cross-section of a hollow stem for analyzing stem strength in bending. The strength is determined by the amount of structural fibers and their locations in the plant, rather than by the outside dimensions.

Secondary cell walls in their natural position have ultimate tensile strengths ranging up to 1100 N/mm^2, a modulus of elasticity in the range from 10,000 to 100,000 N/mm^2, and ultimate strain of 0.5 to 5%. Those subject to compression in the growing plant have lower tensile strength but greater elasticity. Other cell walls have much lower strength; for example, tensile strength of the epidermis (skin) ranges from 2 to 14 N/mm^2. Ultimate tensile strength of the solids portion of timothy or alfalfa stems ranges from 90 to 470 N/mm^2; when the entire cross-section of the alfalfa stem is used, the ultimate strength is only 8 to 35 N/mm^2.

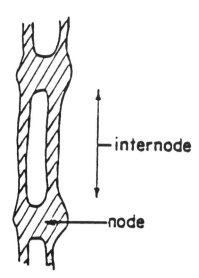

Figure 8.11–Longitudinal section through a stem, showing nodes and internodes (Reprinted from *Mechanics of Cutting Plant Materials*, Persson, 1987).

The bending strength of a plant stem may be important during cutting. For example, some devices cut a plant in the absence of a countershear; the plant stem below the cutting plane is loaded as a cantilever beam. In other situations, the stem may be loaded as a simply-supported beam. In either case, the direction of loading is radial (perpendicular to the longitudinal axis of the plant stem). The radial load that would cause failure in bending can be calculated using the following equation:

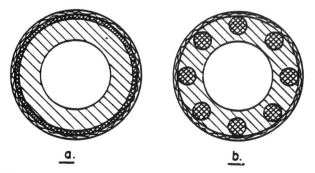

a.   b.

Figure 8.12–Mechanical equivalents stem cross-sections, showing the main structural components arranged as (a) a concentric cylinder, and (b) eight reinforcement rods. Drawn to approximate scale with regard to area and moments of inertia in bending (Reprinted from *Mechanics of Cutting Plant Materials*, Persson, 1987).

$$F_{bu} = \frac{I}{c} \frac{S_u}{L} \qquad (8.6)$$

where
  F_{bu} = ultimate load at bending failure (N)
  I   = moment of inertia of the cross-section (mm^4)
  c   = radius from neutral axis of stem to most distant load-
        carrying fiber (mm) or, alternately
  I/c = section modulus (mm^3)
  S_u = ultimate stress of plant fibers (N/mm^2)
  L   = distance from concentrated load to point of support (mm)

The deflection of the stem is given by equation 8.7, i.e.:

$$\delta_r = \frac{F_r L^3}{C_b E I} \qquad (8.7)$$

where
  δ_r = radial deflection (mm)
  F_r = radial concentrated load (N)
  E = modulus of elasticity of stem fibers (N/mm^2)
  C_b = constant (3 for cantilevered beams, 48 for simply-
        supported beams)

The moment of inertia of a homogeneous solid, circular section is:

$$I = \frac{\pi d^4}{64} \qquad (8.8)$$

where d = diameter of the section (mm). For a hollow, thin-walled
section, the moment of inertia is:

$$I = \frac{3 \pi d^3 t}{32} \qquad (8.9)$$

where t = wall thickness (mm). From comparing equations 8.8
and 8.9, we note that the moment of inertia of a natural stem should
be proportional to the section diameter raised to an exponent
between 3 and 4. Similarly, assuming that the neutral axis is
centered in the stem, the section modulus should be proportional to

before

after

Figure 8.13–Cross-section of a stem (a) before and
(b) after compression (Reprinted from *Mechanics of
Cutting Plant Materials*, Persson, 1987).

the diameter raised to an exponent between 2 and 3. The appropriate
section diameter is determined by the location of the cell-wall fibers
rather than the outside diameter (see fig. 8.12) and thus, if the
outside diameter is used, the bending strength will be somewhat over
estimated. If loading crushes a stem prior to cutting (see fig. 8.13),
the circular cross-section no longer exists; the moment of inertia and
section modulus must then be calculated for the new geometry of the
cross-section.

The size and bending strength of plant stems increases with
plant maturity (Persson, 1987). For example, the stem dry mass of
timothy increased from 0.6 to 1.4 mg/mm of length as the plant
matured; the corresponding stiffness (EI) increased from 1260 to
3900 N·mm^2. For red fescue (which has a much finer stem) at 67%
moisture content, the corresponding figures were stem dry mass
increasing from 0.017 to 0.083 mg/mm as the plant matured, while
the stem stiffness increased from 0.53 to 5.7 N·mm^2. The stiffness of
timothy stems was found to vary with diameter raised to an exponent
between 2.66 and 2.99. For cotton stalks ranging in diameter from
7 to 16 mm, the stiffness varied with diameter to the 3.0 power. The
modulus of elasticity of cotton stalks ranged from 600 to
3500 N/mm^2. Moisture content affects the strength of plants, since
the turgor pressure in the cells affects stem rigidity and strength.
Since plants must resist wind loading, strength also varies with
height on the plant, i.e., most plants are larger and stronger near the
ground than at the top. Near the base of rice straw at 62% moisture

content, for example, the stems were 3.5 to 4 times heavier per unit length than near the top. Calculation of plant strength and deflection is illustrated in example problem 8.1.

Example Problem 8.1

A living alfalfa stem of 2.5 mm diameter is loaded horizontally at a distance 30 mm above the soil surface, that is, it is loaded as a cantilever beam. Based on the entire stem cross-section, the modulus of elasticity is 1500 N/mm^2 and the ultimate tensile strength is 35 N/mm^2. (a) Calculate the horizontal force that would cause bending failure. (b) Calculate the horizontal deflection of the stem at point of failure.

Solution. (a) Before using equation 8.6 to calculate the ultimate load, it is necessary to calculate the section modulus, I/c, of the stem. The value of c is half the stem diameter, or 1.25 mm. From equation 8.8, the moment of inertia is:

$$\pi \cdot 2.5^4/64 = 1.92 \text{ mm}^4$$

The $I/c = 1.92/1.25 = 1.53$ mm^3. Then, from equation 8.6, the ultimate bending load is:

$$F_u = 1.53 \cdot 35/30 = 1.79 \text{ N}$$

(b) Now, equation 8.7 can be used to calculate the stem deflection:

$$\delta_r = 1.79 \cdot 30^3/(3 \cdot 1500 \cdot 1.92) = 5.6 \text{ mm}$$

For this example, the stem would deflect 5.6 mm before the stem fibers failed in bending.

Mechanics of cutting. Several different modes of tissue failure can occur during cutting, depending upon the knife characteristics. Initial penetration of the knife results in localized plastic deformation (flow) of the plant material. In moist stems and with high knife speeds, turgor pressure in the stems limits initial compression of the plant. With further knife movement, considerable stem buckling and compression occurs (see fig. 8.13); depending on knife sharpness and speed, the compression can advance well ahead of and to the sides of the knife edge. The precompression before failure results in a gradual buildup of force on the knife and the energy for precompression can consume 40 to 60% of the total cutting energy. As the fibers are deflected ahead of the knife edge, the shear strength of the material is mobilized to produce fiber tensile stresses. These stresses become sufficiently large to cause the fibers to fail in tension, whereupon loading is transferred to fibers further ahead of

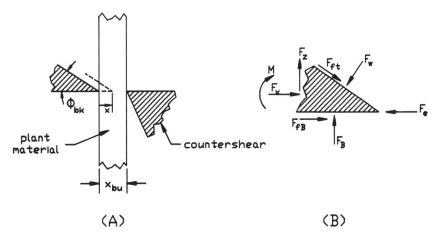

Figure 8.14–Illustration of knife forces during cutting.

the knife edge. For common crop materials, cutting occurs when the pressure exerted ahead of the knife edge exceeds 9 to 30 N/mm².

Figure 8.14a illustrates a knife and countershear cutting a bed of plant material. Forces on the knife are illustrated in figure 8.14b. The force, F_x, in the direction of knife motion is the sum of the knife edge force plus x-components of forces imposed on the top and bottom surfaces of the knife as it compresses and penetrates the plant material. By assuming that only the material directly ahead of the knife is compressed and by use of the bulk modulus for the plant material, the following equation for knife force was derived:

$$\frac{F_x}{w} = \frac{F_{ek}}{w} + \frac{B_f x^\lambda}{2 X_{bu}} \cdot (\tan\phi_{bk} + 2 \cdot f) \qquad (8.10)$$

where
- F_x = knife driving force in x direction (N)
- F_{ek} = force imposed by plant on the knife edge (N)
- w = width of knife (mm)
- x = knife displacement after initial contact (mm)
- λ = exponent
- B_f = bulk modulus of forage (N/mm²)
- X_{bu} = uncompressed depth of material between knife and countershear (mm)
- f = coefficient of friction of forage on knife
- ϕ_{bk} = bevel angle of knife edge

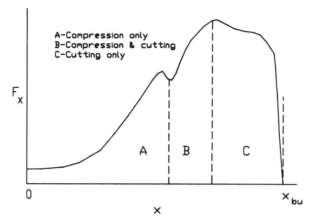

Figure 8.15–Knife force-displacement curve for a straight cut against a countersheet.

Theoretically, $\lambda=2$ in equation 8.10. However, a smaller exponent gives a better fit to some experimental cutting data. In an experiment in which a thin (8.9 mm) bed of timothy at 20% moisture was cut at a very low (0.42 mm/s) knife speed, equation 8.10 fits the data when $\lambda=1.46$ and $B_f=10$ N/mm^2. The knife edge force is calculated as the product of the projected frontal area of the knife edge times the pressure imposed on that edge by the forage. The approximate frontal area can be calculated from the following equation:

$$A_{ek} = r_{ek} \left(1 + \cos\left(\phi_{bk} + \phi_{ck}\right)\right) \qquad (8.11)$$

where
   A_{ek} = frontal area of knife edge per mm of width (mm^2)
   r_{ek} = radius of knife edge (mm)

Figure 8.15 shows the typical shape of the force-displacement curve when plant material is cut by a knife and countershear. In Section A, only compression occurs as the knife edge force is not yet high enough to cause cutting. After initial stem failure, some compression continues in Section B along with cutting. In section C, the material is fully compressed; cutting continues and then the force drops rapidly as the knife edge crosses the edge of the countershear. With suitable choice of parameters, the force in sections A and B could be calculated using equation 8.10. Section C does not involve compression so equation 8.10 does not fit that section. The diagram in figure 8.15 is for a straight cut, i.e., with $\phi_{cl}=0$. For an oblique cut, the peak cutting force would be reduced and the duration of cut would be extended compared to figure 8.15.

Figure 8.15 is useful in calculating the power requirement for cutting with a knife and countershear. The energy per cut is equal to the area under the cutting force curve; multiplying by the cutting frequency gives the power. The following equation can be used to compute the power requirement for cutting:

$$P_{cut} = \frac{C_F \, F_{xmax} \, X_{bu} \, f_{cut}}{60,000} \tag{8.12}$$

where
P_{cut} = power for cutting (kW)
F_{xmax} = maximum cutting force (kN)
X_{bu} = depth of material at initial contact with knife (mm)
        (see fig. 8.15)
f_{cut} = cutting frequency (cuts/min)
C_F = ratio of average to peak cutting force

C_F is always between 0 and 1 and, for a typical force-displacement curve as illustrated in figure 8.15, it is approximately equal to 0.64.

The cutting force, F_x, must be supported. If a countershear is present and clearance is small, the support force can be provided entirely by the countershear. When no countershear is present, the support force must be provided entirely by the plant itself through the bending strength of the stump below the cut and the inertia of the plant above the cut. The resulting cut is called, alternatively, an impact cut, an inertia cut or a free cut. As clearance with a countershear increases, the plant strength and inertia come increasingly into play; thus, impact cutting is similar to countershear cutting with very large clearance. Figure 8.16 illustrates the forces and moments on the plant during impact cutting. The soil and the plant root system provide a force, F_B and a moment, M_r, which tend to keep the stump upright. Acceleration of the stump is considered to be negligible. Force F_B represents the combined effects of the root system and stalk strength in providing bending resistance at the height of the cut. The center of gravity of the cut portion of the plant is at a height, z_{cg}, above the cut. The impact shown in figure 8.16 tends to accelerate the cut plant to the right and counterclockwise; consequently, an inertia force and inertia moment appear on the plant at the center of gravity. The following equation results from summing moments about the center of gravity of the cut plant:

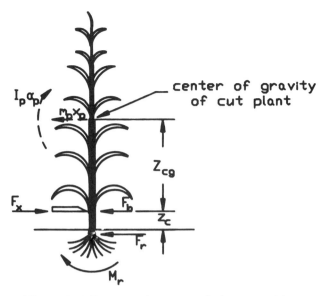

Figure 8.16–Forces and moments in impact cutting.

$$I_p \, \alpha_p = (F_x - F_b) \, z_{cg} \qquad\qquad (8.13)$$

where

α_p = angular acceleration of plant (rad/s^2)
F_x = cutting force (N)
F_b = bending resistance of stump (N)
z_{cg} = height of center of gravity of cut plant (m) (see fig. 8.16)
I_p = centroidal moment of inertia of plant (kg·m^2 = $m_p \cdot r_g^2$)
m_p = mass of cut portion of plant (kg)
r_g = radius of gyration of cut portion of plant (m)

An analysis of the kinematics (motions) of the plant gives the following equation for angular acceleration:

$$\alpha_p = \frac{a_c - a_{cg}}{z_{cg}} \qquad\qquad (8.14)$$

where

a_c = acceleration of plant at plane of cut (m/s^2)
a_{cg} = acceleration of plant center of gravity (m/s^2)

By assuming that the plant acquires knife velocity at the plane of cut, the following equation was derived:

$$a_c = \frac{1000 \, v_k^2}{d_s} \qquad (8.15)$$

where
    v_k = knife velocity (m/s)
    d_s = stalk diameter at plane of cut (mm)

Equations 8.13 through 8.15 can be combined to give the following equation for minimum knife velocity for impact cutting:

$$v_k = \sqrt{ d_s \, \frac{(F_x - F_b)}{1000 * m_p} \left(1 + \frac{z_{cg}^2}{r_g^2} \right) } \qquad (8.16)$$

When values for r_g and z_{cg} are not readily available, a simpler approximate equation can be obtained by assuming that $r_g = z_{cg}$. The simpler equation illustrates the key variables involved in impact cutting. If the stump bending resistance, F_b, is large enough to support the entire cutting force, F_x, the minimum required knife velocity is zero and cutting is equivalent to cutting with a countershear. Lowering the height of cut to increase F_b and reducing F_x by maintaining a sharp knife will both reduce the minimum required knife velocity. Tests of impact cutting of timothy, for example, have shown that cutting could be accomplished at knife velocities as low as 25 m/s but velocities of 45 m/s were required for reliable cutting of all stems. To assure reliable cutting over a wide range of knife sharpness and stem stiffness, minimum knife velocities of 50 to 75 m/s are generally recommended. Example Problem 8.2 illustrates the calculation of minimum knife velocity for impact cutting.

Example Problem 8.2
    Impact cutting is to be used to cut the alfalfa stem of example problem 8.1 at a height 30 mm above the ground. The mass of the plant above the cut is 0.01 kg. Assume that cutting occurs when the pressure ahead of the knife edge reaches 25 N/mm². The knife has a bevel angle of 20°, zero clearance angle, and an edge radius of 0.3 mm. Calculate (a) the force imposed by the knife edge to achieve cutting, (b) the minimum knife speed required for impact cutting.
    Solution. (a) The frontal area of the knife edge can be calculated using equation 8.11:

$$A_{ek} = 0.3 \cdot (1 + \cos(20 + 0)) = 0.582 \text{ mm}^2/\text{mm width}$$

The width of knife is not known but, since only a single stem is being cut, the width will be assumed equal to the stem diameter, 2.5 mm. Then, using the critical pressure of 25 N/mm^2, the force required to initiate cutting will be:

$$F_{ek} = 0.582 \cdot 2.5 \cdot 25 = 36.4 \text{ N}$$

(b) Equation 8.16 is available for calculating the minimum knife velocity for impact cutting. Values for r_g and z_{cg} are not available, but we will assume $r_g = z_{cg}$. No value for F_b is given but we will assume it is equal to the ultimate bending load calculated in Example Problem 8.1, that is, $F_b = 1.79$ N. Then the minimum velocity is:

$$v_k = [2 \cdot 2.5 \cdot (36.4 - 1.79)/(1000 \cdot 0.01)]^{0.5} = 4.2 \text{ m/s}$$

In this idealized cutting of a single stem, the minimum velocity was low. Typically, to allow for interaction of multiple stems during cutting, velocities of 50 to 75 m/s are recommended.

8.2.2 Cutting and Chopping

Cutting with a countershear. The construction of a typical cutterbar is illustrated in figure 8.17. Terminology for the cutting elements is shown on the detailed cross-sectional view in figure 8.17a. The knife sections and sometimes the ledger plates are replaceable. Knife section edges can be smooth or serrated and either type of sickle can be removed for sharpening. Ledger plate edges are usually serrated on the underside and are not resharpened. The knife clips maintain correct clearance between the knife sections and ledger plates. The wear plates support the rear edges of the knife sections and must be replaced when vertical clearance becomes excessive. In addition to guarding the blunt ends of the knife sections from the oncoming material at each end of the stroke, the guards also help to protect the sickle from being damaged by rocks. Typical guard spacing is 76.2 mm; the sickle stroke can be equal to or up to about 15 mm less than or greater than the guard spacing.

Most forages are harvested with a machine that combines the mowing and conditioning process, hence the name, mower-conditioner. The cutterbar and associated reel (fig. 8.5) are mounted on a separate framework which is connected to the machine by a spring-loaded four-bar linkage. Adjustable shoes are placed at each end of the separate assembly to adjust the cutting height, typically in the range from 25 to 100 mm. The flotation springs are adjustable to provide from 0.3 to 0.4 kN of vertical ground reaction on the shoes.

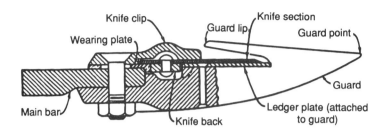

**Figure 8.17–A mower cutterbar with drive unit
(Reprinted from *Principles of Farm Machinery*, Kepner
et al., 1978).**

The cutterbar assembly should "float" easily over the ground without
bouncing.

The type of pickup reel that is used on a mower-conditioner is
also used on other machines, for example, forage harvesters and
combines. Figure 8.18 illustrates three different types of mechanisms
used in pickup reels. The mechanisms in figures 8.18a and 8.18c keep
all of the reel teeth parallel at all times but, because eccentric spider
control is simpler and less expensive, it has supplanted the planetary
gear control that was previously used. By adjusting the location of
the center of the bearing control plate (fig. 8.18a), the pitch of the
teeth can be adjusted. Although cam control (fig. 8.18b) is more
complex than eccentric spider control, the cam does permit changing
the pitch of the teeth on each tooth bar as the bar progresses through
its cycle. Thus, the teeth can be given a greater lifting action as they
pass near the cutterbar.

The cutterbar should have proper tilt, register, and alignment.
Tilt is adjusted by rotating the cutterbar about an axis parallel to the

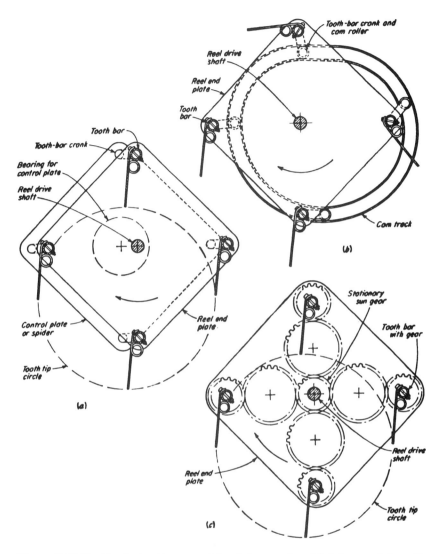

Figure 8.18–Feathering actions used in pickup reels with (a) eccentric spider control, (b) cam control, (c) planetary gear control (Reprinted from Richey et al., 1961).

sickle to raise or lower the guard tips. Proper register is achieved by moving the cutterbar in or out relative to the drive mechanism until the knife stroke is in symmetry with the guard spacing. The cutterbar is in proper alignment when it is perpendicular to the direction of travel while mowing. Alignment is generally not a problem when the cutterbar has horizontal support on both ends. On mowers which have the cutterbar extending outward from one side of the machine, however, the horizontal forces on the cutterbar create a

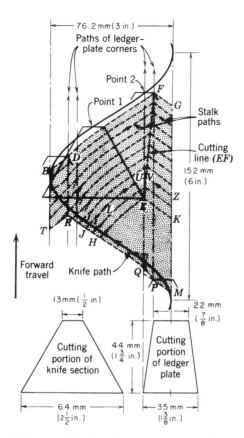

Figure 8.19–Cutting pattern of a conventional sickle bar mower (Reprinted from *Principles of Farm Machinery*, Kepner et al., 1978).

moment and the resulting deflection causes the outer end to lag behind the drive mechanism. To offset the lag, the outer end must lead the drive mechanism by about 20 mm/m of bar length when the mower is not operating. The driveline to the cutterbar should be protected to prevent damage if the sickle becomes jammed. A v-belt in the drive can provide overload protection but, if there is no belt in the drive, a slip clutch or jump clutch should be included in the driveline.

The cutting frequency is a key variable in the operation of a sickle bar mower. A higher cutting frequency aids cutting by increasing v_{km} (see fig. 8.8) and also allows higher travel speeds. Figure 8.19 shows typical dimensions of a sickle section and ledger plate, as well as a typical cutting pattern. Note that plants growing in the area bounded by points KMPQHE on the diagram must be deflected forward and cut ahead of point E. In figure 8.19, that area is equal to 25% of the total area cut per stroke; such bunching is undesirable because it leads to increased cutting forces and uneven stubble height. To avoid excessive bunching with a conventional mower, the forward travel of the mower should not exceed 150 mm per knife cycle; thus increasing the cutting frequency also increases the maximum allowable travel speed. Since the mowing capacity of the mower varies with the product of the cutterbar width and the forward speed, the maximum mowing capacity is proportional to the cutting frequency. Because the sickle must be reversed in direction at each end of its stroke, vibration imposes an upper limit on cutting frequency. The mower shown in figure 8.17b includes a counterweight which moves opposite in direction to the sickle to reduce the vibrations. Double sickle mowers are available; such mowers have no guards but have two reciprocating sickles moving in opposite directions. Double sickle mowers permit up to 220 mm of forward travel per cycle without excessive bunching and the opposite-moving sickles provide automatic balancing. A major limitation has been that the absence of guards has led to rock damage to the unprotected sickles. Also, some vibration of the cutterbar is desirable because it helps to keep the cut material flowing over the cutterbar.

Two well-known mechanisms are available for converting rotary motion into the reciprocating motion required to drive a sickle, i.e., a slider-crank or a spatial-crank mechanism. The spatial crank is more common because of its compact size and the ease with which it can be integrated into the drive train of a machine.

The spatial-crank oscillator is a mechanism from the Spherical Mechanism Group. Another well-known member of this group is the Cardan universal joint which was described in Chapter three. All of the joint axes in this group of mechanisms intersect at a common point. In the spatial-crank oscillator, the output shaft must be skewed with respect to the input shaft and the angle γ (fig. 8.20) must be smaller than the angle β. In the oscillator shown in figure 8.20, angle β is 90° or 1.57 radians. The following three equations govern the displacement, velocity and acceleration, respectively, of the oscillating shaft equation 8.19 assumes zero input acceleration:

$$\tan(\Gamma) = \tan(\gamma)\sin(\theta) \qquad (8.17a)$$

$$\dot{\Gamma} = \frac{\theta \tan(\gamma)\cos(\theta)}{1 + \tan^2(\gamma)\sin^2(\theta)} \qquad (8.18)$$

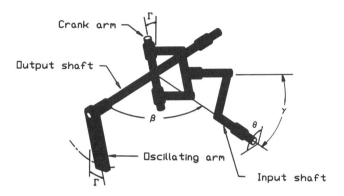

Figure 8.20–Isometric view of a spatial-crank oscillator.

$$\ddot{\Gamma} = \frac{-\dot{\theta}\tan(\gamma)\sin(\theta)\left[1 + \tan^2(\gamma)\left(1 + \cos^2(\theta)\right)\right]}{\left[1 + \tan^2(\gamma)\sin^2(\theta)\right]^2} \tag{8.19}$$

where
    Γ = displacement of the oscillating shaft (radians)
    θ = rotational displacement of input shaft (radians)
    γ = input shaft angle, radians (see fig. 8.20)

The dot notation used in equations 8.18 and 8.19 indicates time derivates of the variables indicated. If $\gamma < 0.33$ radians in equation 8.17, the tangent functions in the equation are approximately equal to the value of the argument in radians and thus the following simplified equation gives the displacement of the oscillating shaft with less than 0.2% error:

$$\Gamma = \gamma\sin(\theta) \tag{8.17b}$$

An oscillating arm is generally attached to the oscillating shaft to convert the shaft rotational oscillation to the required rectilinear motion required by the sickle. Note, however, that the tip of the oscillating arm travels on an arc rather than in a straight line. The problem is overcome by using a flexible bushing to connect the arm to the knife and by keeping the oscillation angle small and the arm length long within reasonable limits.

    Counterbalancing to reduce vibration caused by inertial forces is not generally required because the mass of the machine supporting the cutterbar is so large relative to the mass of the reciprocating knife. However, the vibrations generate stresses, increasing

maintenance problems and the possibility of early fatigue failure of
the moving parts. Essentially full dynamic balancing can be obtained
by attaching a countermass to the crank arm. For example, if a
countermass equal to the sickle mass were attached to the top of the
crank arm in figure 8.20 and if the sickle and countermass were
vertically equidistant from the output shaft, the horizontal oscillating
forces would cancel. There would be a residual oscillating couple due
to the vertical separation between the sickle and the countermass.

The approximate velocity of the knife relative to the mower
(v_{km}) can be calculated by assuming that the sickle moves with
sinusoidal motion. This assumption neglects some higher-order
harmonics that may be present depending upon the specific drive
used to power the sickle. Assuming sinusoidal motion, the relative
sickle speed is given by:

$$v_{km} = \frac{L_s\, \omega_c}{2000} \cos(\omega_c\, t) \qquad (8.20)$$

where
$\qquad v_{km}$ = velocity of knife relative to mower (m/s)
$\qquad L_s$ = stroke length of knife (mm)
$\qquad \omega_c$ = sickle frequency (rad/s)
$\qquad t$ = time measured from center of stroke (s)

Equation 8.20 is useful in estimating the speed of the knife through
the cutting zone. Also, as shown in example problem 8.3,
equation 8.20 is useful in determining the conditions under which
plant material may slide forward on the knife and escape cutting.

Example Problem 8.3.
The oblique angle of the sickle sections is 30° when $v_f = 0$, i.e.,
when the mower is not moving forward. If the stroke length is
76.2 mm and the cutting frequency is 105 rad/s, what is the
minimum v_f at which, during the entire knife stroke, the plant
material will move toward the rear of the knife sections rather than
moving toward the knife tips to possibly escape cutting?
Solution. Insight can be gained by calculating the conditions
under which the oblique angle is zero during cutting since, when the
oblique angle is zero, there is no tendency for the material to move
along the edge of the knife sections. The oblique angle is zero when
the knife movement relative to the ground is perpendicular to the
knife edge, i.e., when:

$$v_f/v_{km} = \tan 30°$$

or, by making use of equation 8.20, when:

$$v_f = (L_s \, \omega_c / 2\,000) \cos(\omega_c \, t) \tan(30°)$$

The most critical point is at midstroke (t=0) when the cosine term has its maximum value of 1.0. Then, substituting in the given values of L_s and ω_c, the minimum forward travel speed is:

$$v_f = 76.2 \cdot 105/2000) \cos(0) \tan(30°) = 2.31 \text{ m/s}$$

At $v_f = 2.31$ m/s, the material will have no y-component of velocity at midstroke but will tend to move toward the rear of the knife sections at all other parts of the stroke. At slower travel speeds, the material will tend to move toward the knife tips at midstroke. Of course, as equation 8.4 indicates, edge friction may be sufficient to keep the material from moving along the edge of the knife sections.

Equation 8.12 can be used to calculate the theoretical power requirement for mowing with a cutterbar mower. However, that equation does not include friction between the knife and cutterbar or other losses. By comparing pto power delivered to a mower while not cutting and while cutting moderately heavy mixed forage, Elfes(1954) found that cutting used only about 30% of the total pto power. Cutting frequency was 942 cycles/min and average total knife force was 1.2 kN/m of bar length. Harbage and Morr (1962) measured an average total knife force of 2.3 kN/m when mowing bluegrass at 1250 cycles/min. ASAE Data D497 suggests a pto power requirement of 1.2 kW/m of bar length for mowing alfalfa. To that must be added the tractive power required to overcome drag on the cutterbar and rolling resistance of the tractor and mower.

Impact cutting, horizontal axis. Impact cutting is used in flail mowers and rotary mowers. As shown in the schematic view of figure 8.21a, the flails in flail mowers rotate about a horizontal, transverse axis. Hinging of the flails provides flexibility for the flails to swing back and minimize damage in rocky fields. Some of the various types of knives used on flail mowers are shown in figure 8.21b. Staggering the flails in the successive rows provides complete coverage of the swath. Early flail mowers suffered excessive losses because short pieces of forage were lost in the stubble. Losses were reduced by designing the shroud to bend the plants forward to permit basal cutting and to provide clearance above the flail to reduce recutting. Bending the plants forward also permits lower knife velocities than calculated by equation 8.16 and the lower knife velocities also reduce recutting. Knife peripheral speeds of 43 m/s or less have been found to be satisfactory. The full-width gage roller

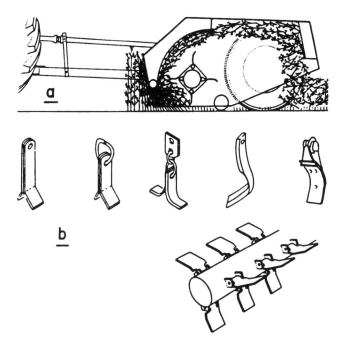

Figure 8.21–A flail mower, showing (a) side view and (b) flail detail (Reprinted from *Mechanics of Cutting Plant Materials*, Persson, 1987).

behind the flail (see fig. 8.21a) provides accurate control of cutting height and prevents scalping of high spots. The hitch of pull-type flail mowers is offset so that the tractor wheels run on cut forage rather than on the standing crop. The lacerating effect of the knives on the stems provides a conditioning effect that helps to increase the drying rate. In upright crops, the flail mower typically recovers 5 to 10% less of the crop than sickle bar mowers. Conversely, the flail mower can recover substantially more of a severely lodged crop.

The tips of the knives on the flail mower trace out cycloidal paths as the mower moves forward over the land. The x,z-coordinates of the path can be calculated using the following equations:

$$\frac{x}{r_f} = \frac{v_f\,t}{r_f} + \sin\theta_r \qquad\qquad (8.21)$$

$$\frac{z}{r_f} = 1 - \cos\theta_f \qquad\qquad (8.22)$$

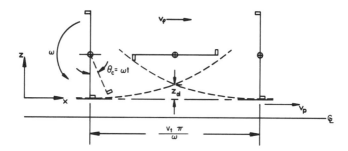

Figure 8.22–Flail mower cutting analysis.

where
    x = displacement of the tip in the x-direction (m)
    z = corresponding displacement of the tip in the z-direction (m)
    r_f = radius to tip of flail (m)
    v_f = forward velocity of mower (m/s)
    θ_r = angular displacement of rotor, rad (see fig. 8.22
    t = time (s)

Theoretically, the stubble height can become uneven if v_f becomes too large in relation to the knife peripheral speed, v_p. The distance, z_d, in figure 8.22 illustrates the uneven stubble height. The following equation can be used to calculate the approximate value of z_d:

$$\frac{z_d}{r_f} = 1 - \cos\frac{\pi}{\lambda_r(1 + C_v)} \qquad (8.23)$$

where
    z_d = stubble height difference (m)
    C_v = velocity ratio = v_p/v_f
    λ_r = number of rows of flails on the rotor

Equation 8.23 includes the assumption that the sine of the rotor angle is approximately equal to the value of the angle in radians. For realistic values of C_v, that assumption is valid. Note in figure 8.21b that alternate rows of flails are staggered to assure cutting over the entire swath width. Because of the staggered arrangement and the lateral gaps between the flails, $\lambda_r = 2$ for the rotor shown in figure 8.21a. Given that a typical v_p for flail mowers is about 43 m/s, C_v is 10 or greater for reasonable travel speeds. Equation 8.23 shows that the flail mower can produce good stubble uniformity under such conditions.

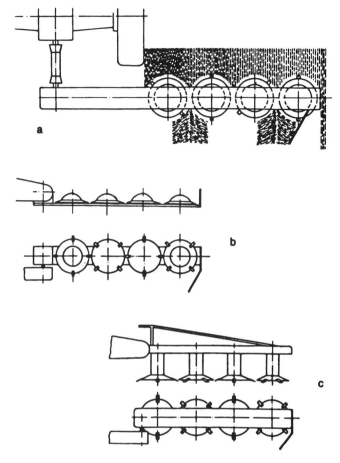

Figure 8.23–Rotary mowers, showing (a) cutting action,
(b) disk-type mower, (c) drum-type mower (Reprinted
form *Mechanics of Cutting Plant Materials*, Persson,
1987).

The power requirement of a flail mower is considerably higher
than for a sickle bar mower of the same width, because impact
cutting requires greater power than cutting with a countershear and
because of the air pumping done by the rotor. Therefore,
equation 8.12 is not valid for flail mowers because of the lack of a
countershear. ASAE Data D497 suggests the following equation for
calculating the power requirement of a flail mower mowing alfalfa:

$$P_{mow} = 8.2 + 2.13 \, \dot{m}_f \tag{8.24}$$

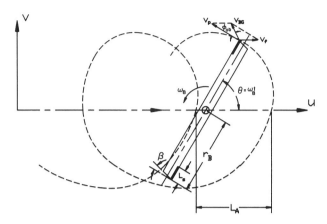

Figure 8.24–Analysis of cutting action of a rotary mower.

where
$$P_{mow} = \text{pto power required for flail mower (kW)}$$
$$\dot{m}_f = \text{feed rate (kg/s)}$$

Drawbar power needed to overcome rolling resistance of the mower must be added to obtain the full power requirement. The feed rate of any mower can be calculated from the following equation:

$$\dot{m}_f = \frac{Y \, w_s \, v_f}{10} \tag{8.25}$$

where
$$Y = \text{forage yield, wet basis (Mg/ha)}$$
$$w_s = \text{swath width cut by mower (m)}$$
$$v_f = \text{travel speed (m/s)}$$

Combining equations 8.24 and 8.25 shows that, as expected, the power requirement increases with the speed and cutting width of the flail mower. Since the mower must convey the material (see fig. 8.21) as well as cut it, the power requirement also increases with crop yield. The power requirement with zero yield is an indication of the power needed for air pumping and to overcome friction in the mower.

Impact cutting, vertical axis. Figure 8.23, a rotary mower for mowing forage, is an example of impact cutting using a vertical axis. Figure 8.23b shows the disk-type mower in which the drive mechanism is below the cutting blades. In the drum-type mower shown in figure 8.23c, the drive is above the cutting blades and

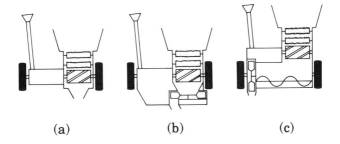

(a)   (b)   (c)

Figure 8.25–Forage harvesters with (a) cut and throw away delivery, (b) cut and blow delivery, (c) cut and blow with intermediate auger transport (Courtesy of Deere and Co.).

adjacent drums are counter-rotating so that the cut crop falls in distinct bands rather than being uniformly distributed across the cutting width. Mowers are also available in which all blades rotate in the same direction. Blades of adjacent disks or drums are designed to overlap to assure complete cutting. As each blade rotates about its center with velocity ω_b while the center moves forward with velocity v_f, the blade tip follows a cycloidal path over the ground (fig. 8.24). The velocity of a blade tip relative to the ground is the vector sum of the forward velocity and the peripheral velocity of a blade tip, i.e.:

$$v_{bg} = v_f + v_p \qquad (8.26)$$

where

$\quad v_{bg}$ = velocity of blade tip relative to ground (m/s)
$\quad v_f$ = forward velocity of mower (m/s)
$\quad v_p$ = peripheral velocity of blade tip (m/s = $r_b \cdot b$)
$\quad r_b$ = radius out to blade tip (m)
$\quad \omega_b$ = rotational speed of blade (rad/s)

Since the x-direction is defined as the direction of the blade relative to the material, it is in the direction of v_{bg} and constantly changes in direction as the blade rotates. In the nonrotating u,v coordinate system shown in figure 8.24, the mower moves in the u-direction. The u and v components of blade tip velocity are:

$$v_u = v_f - r_b \, \omega_b \, \sin\left(\omega_b \, t\right) \qquad (8.27)$$

$$v_v = r_b \, \omega_b \, \cos\left(\omega_b \, t\right) \qquad (8.28)$$

where

v_u = component of blade tip velocity in u-direction (m/s)
v_v = component of blade tip velocity in v-direction (m/s)
t = time (s) measured from point where θ = .
θ = angle between blade and direction of travel = $\omega_b \cdot t$
     (see fig. 8.24)

The oblique angle, ϕ_{ob}, can be calculated using the following equation:

$$\tan (\phi_{ob}) = \frac{1}{C_v \cdot \sec (\theta) - \tan (\theta)} \qquad (8.29)$$

where $C_v = V_p/V_f$. If $v_f = 0$, then $\phi_{ob} = 0$. Since v_f is always much smaller than v_p, the oblique angle is always close to zero in a rotary mower and sliding of plant material along the blade is not a problem.

The crescent shaped area between two successive passes of a blade (fig 8.24) defines the area cut by each pass of a blade. The advance per blade, L_a, is given by:

$$L_a = \frac{2 \pi v_f}{\lambda_b \omega_b} \qquad (8.30)$$

where

L_a = advance per blade passage (m)
λ_b = number of blades on each disk or drum

The width of the sharpened ends of the blades, L_s, must be greater than L_a. Because the blade velocity must be high for impact cutting (see eq. 8.16) and the blade peripheral velocity declines toward zero at the center, L_a must be limited to assure reliable cutting. The permissible L_a would be considerably less than is shown in figure 8.24, where L_a was enlarged for clarity. To avoid crop drag against the ends of the blades (which are not sharpened), the ends must be tapered at angle β (see fig. 8.24). The most critical point for crop drag is at $\theta = 0$, when the blade is aligned with the direction of travel. The minimum required angle β is:

$$\beta = \arctan \frac{v_f}{r_b \omega_b} \qquad (8.31)$$

The maximum width cut by each disk or drum is $2 \cdot r_b$ but, to assure complete cutting, some overlap is necessary and the disks or drums must be spaced less than the maximum cutting width. The drive provides timing such that knives on any disk (or drum) do not strike those on adjacent units. Example problem 8.4 illustrates design considerations for a vertical-axis mower.

Example Problem 8.4

In a rotary mower as shown in figure 8.23b, each disk carries four blades and rotates at 3000 rev/min. Each disk is to cut a 0.4 m swath. If the maximum travel speed is 15 km/h, calculate (a) the minimum required length of each knife. (b) Select an actual blade length, and (c) base diameter of each disk onto which the knives are to be attached. (d) Finally, calculate the minimum taper angle on the end of each blade.

Solution. (a) Equation 8.30 can be used to calculate the minimum length of each of the four blades on each disk. The travel speed is 15 km/h or 4.17 m/s; the disk rotation speed is 3000 rev/min or 314 rad/s. Then the minimum blade length is:

$$L_a = 2 \, \pi \, 4.17/(4 \cdot 314) = 0.021 \text{ m or } 21 \text{ mm}$$

(b) Such short blades would leave little room for accumulation of cut plants to be carried from the front to the side of the disk for discharge. Thus, we will select a longer blade length, 0.05 m or 50 mm. (c) The base disk diameter will then be:

disk diameter = $0.4 - 2 \cdot 0.05 = 0.3$ m or 300 mm

(d) Equation 8.31 can be used to calculate the minimum taper of the ends of the blades:

$$\beta = \arctan [4.17/(0.2 \cdot 314)] = 3.8°$$

Several design features are included on rotary mowers for safety purposes. The knives are hinged to the disk or drum so that they can swing back if they hit a rock or other obstruction; centrifugal force keeps the knives in cutting position during normal operation. Since the rotating cutters have appreciable inertia, an over-running clutch is usually provided in the drive to allow the mower to coast to a stop when power is interrupted. When rocks are encountered, the high-speed knives are capable of launching them as projectiles that could injure the operator or bystanders. Thus, for safety reasons, the entire cutterbar is covered by a canvas or flexible plastic shroud.

The power requirement of a rotary mower is much higher than that of a sickle bar mower of the same width, because the forage is not only cut but also accelerated by the knives during impact. Tests at the NIAE, National Institute of Agricultural Engineering, (Persson, 1987, p. 176) in England suggest the following equation for calculating power requirements of a rotary mower:

$$P_{mt} = (P_{Ls} + E_{sc} \, v_f) \, w_c \qquad\qquad (8.32)$$

where
P_{mt} = total pto power to mower (kW)
P_{Ls} = specific power losses due to air, stubble and gear-train friction (kW/m of width)
E_{sc} = specific cutting energy (kJ/m^2)
w_c = width of mower (m)

The NIAE data suggest that $1.5 < P_{Ls} < 4$ kW/m for disk and drum-type rotary mowers; disk mowers are at the lower end of the range, while drum mowers are at the upper end. Values of E_{sc} ranged from 1.5 kJ/m^2 for sharp blades to 2.1 kJ/m^2 for mowers with worn blades. A more recent survey of rotary mowers on the market indicated total pto power requirements ranging from 11 to 16 kW/m of cutting width while mowing at 15 km/h. Power to propel the mower and tractor must be added to obtain the total power requirement for mowing. Disks on typical mowers rotate at 3000 rev/min while cutting a 0.4 m swath per disk. Typical peripheral knife speeds are between 60 and 70 m/s. Mowers are available with from three to seven disks to provide a range of swath widths.

Chopping. Forage harvesters include means for gathering the crop into the machine, chopping it into short pieces and conveying the chopped forage into a wagon or truck. ASAE Standard S472 defines two basic types of forages harvesters, i.e., precision cut and nonprecision cut. A cylindrical cutterhead and stationary countershear are used for chopping in most precision-cut forage harvesters. Nonprecision-cut forage harvesters, to be discussed later, make use of a flail cutter for cutting and chopping the standing crop. Precision-cut forage harvesters can be further subdivided into cut-and-throw and cut-and-blow types. The cut-and-throw harvesters (fig. 8.25a) utilize energy imparted to the forage during cutting to transport the chopped material from the harvester. The cut-and-blow configuration (fig. 8.25b) uses an auxiliary blower for material transport. An auger conveyor is used between the chopper and blower on some forage harvesters (fig. 8.25c). The cut-and-blow

configurations allow the blower and wagon to be placed directly
behind the tractor, thus eliminating side draft. The cut-and-throw
configuration requires fewer components and can require less energy.

Three different types of headers are available for the precision-
cut harvesters, i.e., direct-cut, windrow pickup, or row-crop headers
(fig. 8.26). Direct-cut headers with widths up to 4.3 m include a
reciprocating sickle and reel similar to those on combine harvesters
(fig. 8.26a). Pick-up headers (fig. 8.26b) are for chopping haylage, i.e.,
forage that has been allowed to partially dry in the windrow. Row-
crop headers (fig. 8.26c) with up to six-row capacity are used when
maize or other row crops are to be chopped. Reciprocating sickles on
earlier row crop headers have given way to a pair of rotating cutting
disks for cutting each row. A pair of gathering chains, or a pair of
fluted rubber gathering belts backed by roller chains, grab the cut
stalks and pull them into the feed mechanism with the base of the
stalks leading (fig. 8.27).

Figure 8.28 shows two types of feeding mechanisms for
precision-cut forage harvesters. In either type, the upper feed rolls
are spring-loaded to pre-compress the forage before it reaches the
cylinder. The length of cut is controlled by the peripheral speed of the
feed rolls relative to the speed of the cutterhead. A smooth feed roll is
placed near the shear bar to maintain the grip on the forage as close
to the shear bar as possible. In determining peripheral speeds of
fluted feed rolls, the pitch (effective) diameter is slightly less than the
outside diameter.

The theoretical length of cut can be calculated using the
following equation:

$$L_c = \frac{60000 \; v_f}{\lambda_k \; n_c} \tag{8.33}$$

where
  L_c = theoretical length of cut (mm)
  v_f = feed velocity (m/s = peripheral speed of feed rolls)
  λ_k = number of knives on the cutterhead
  n_c = rotational speed of cutterhead (rev/min)

Some particles will be longer than the theoretical length when stems
are not oriented parallel to the direction of feed. Others will be
shorter than the theoretical length when the arrival of the ends of
stems does not coincide with the arrival of a cutterhead knife.
Theoretical lengths of cut range from 3 to 90 mm. The actual length
of cut is usually close to the theoretical length for row crops because
the stalks are oriented nearly perpendicular to the shear bar. For

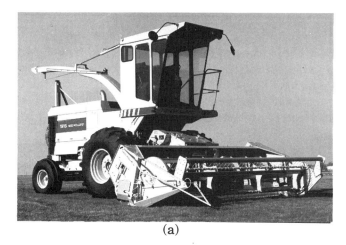

(a)

(b)

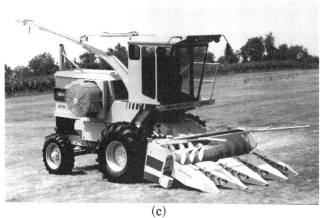

(c)

Figure 8.26–Gathering units for forage harvesters (Courtesy of New Holland, Inc.).

Figure 8.27–Rotary cut-off knives and gathering chains on a row unit of a forage harvester (Courtesy of Case-IH).

direct-cut forages, actual average lengths of cut are generally about 50% longer than the theoretical length. When windrowed crops are being chopped, the average actual length of cut is much longer than the theoretical length due to the random stem alignment. On a specific forage harvester, large increases in theoretical length of cut are made by removing knives from the cutterhead. For example, by going from 12 to 6 to 3 knives, the length of cut can be doubled twice. Another popular pattern is 8 to 4 to 2 knives. Smaller changes in length of cut are made by adjusting the feed velocity. The feed rolls will separate further to accommodate the reduced feed velocity until the maximum separation distance is reached; further reductions in feed velocity will then reduce the capacity of the harvester. The cutterhead speed is normally maintained at its maximum design value, typically 850 to 1000 rev/min, and thus is not adjusted.

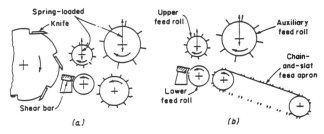

Figure 8.28–Two types of feed mechanisms for a forage harvester (Reprinted from *Principles of Farm Machinery*, Kepner et al., 1978).

Cutterhead diameters normally range from 520 to 770 mm and widths range from 450 to 620 mm.

The theoretical capacity of a precision-cut forage chopper can be calculated using the following equation:

$$\dot{m}_f = \frac{\rho_f \, A_t \, L_c \, \lambda_k \, n_c}{6 \times 10^8} \qquad (8.34)$$

where
$\dot{m}_f$ = theoretical capacity or feed rate (kg/s)
ρ_f = density of forage in the throat (kg/m^3)
A_t = throat area (cm^2)

Throat areas vary considerably among forage harvesters, but usually are within the range from 770 to 1350 cm^2. Based on research at the University of Wisconsin, typical forage densities between the feed rolls range from 56 kg/m^3 for hay at 26% moisture to 340 kg/m^3 for green corn (maize). If the forage yield changes during any given pass through a field, the corresponding change in capacity is accommodated through changes in the depth of forage between the feed rolls. Thus, the top feed rolls must be spring loaded to permit such changes in depth. The throat area is equal to the product of cylinder width times maximum forage depth between the upper and lower feed rolls. Maximum depths are typically in the range from 140 to 180 mm.

After the forage is chopped by the cutterhead, centrifugal force holds it against the housing as the cutterhead moves it toward the exit; the housing terminates at the bottom or rear of the cutterhead to allow the chopped material to escape. In a cut-and-throw machine, the cutterhead imparts sufficient energy to throw the chopped material to a trailing wagon or truck. Alternatively, in a cut-and-blow machine, a separate impeller-blower is used to convey the chopped material. Sometimes a recutter screen is installed at the exit of the cutterhead housing. Working against the recutter screen, the cutterhead further reduces the average length of cut of the exiting material (fig. 8.29). On machines with a recutter, an impeller-blower must be used to convey the chopped material. Electric motors or a hydraulic actuator controllable from the operator's seat permit swiveling the spout and/or tipping the end deflector to direct the forage to completely fill the truck or wagon (fig. 8.30). Figure 8.29 illustrates one method for providing access to the cutterhead and recutter screen. The impeller-blower is hinge-connected to the forage harvester. Swinging the impeller-blower away from the cutterhead

Figure 8.29–Recutter screen installed between cutterhead and impeller-blower (Courtesy of Gehl Equipment Co.).

permits access for installing or removing a recutter screen or for servicing the cutterhead.

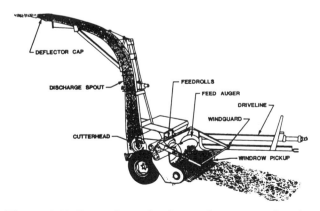

Figure 8.30–Rear view of a forage harvester showing adjustable discharge spout and deflector cap (Courtesy of Prairie Agricultural Machinery Institute, Canada).

The power demand of a precision-cut forage harvester is so large that harvesting capacity can be limited by available power. Power is consumed in gathering, conveying and compressing the material to be cut, in chopping the material and in conveying it to the truck or wagon. Parasitic power losses in a forage harvester include bearing friction, friction of the cut material on the cutterhead housing, and pumping of air at the cutterhead and blower. Numerous researchers have found that power use in cut-and-blow forage harvesters can be divided roughly as follows: 20% to gathering and feeding, 40% to the cutterhead, and 40% for blowing. Within the cutterhead, energy is required for compressing and shearing, for acceleration and air movement, and for overcoming friction at the housing. Within the blower, energy is required for acceleration, for air movement and for overcoming friction. Material parameters such as shear strength, moisture content and friction coefficient, and machine parameters such as sharpness of the knife and length of cut will all affect the distribution of power in the harvester. However, cutting usually requires the greatest energy at the cutterhead, while friction generates the greatest energy requirement at the blower. The power requirement for chopping can be calculated using the following equation:

$$P_c = \frac{1000 \, C_f \, F_{smax} \, \dot{m}_f}{\rho_f \, L_c} \qquad (8.35)$$

where
$\quad$ P_c $\quad$ = power required for chopping (kW)
$\quad$ $\dot{m}_f$ $\quad$ = feed rate (kg/s)
$\quad$ ρ_f $\quad$ = density of material in throat (kg/m^3)
$\quad$ L_c $\quad$ = theoretical length of cut (mm)
$\quad$ F_{smax} = maximum specific cutting force (N/mm of countershear length)
$\quad$ C_f $\quad$ = ratio of average to maximum specific cutting force

The knives on the cutterhead in forage harvesters are normally helix-shaped; the resulting oblique cutting extends the duration of each cut while reducing the peak cutting force. Compared to the force-displacement diagram for a straight cut (fig. 8.15), oblique cutting would lengthen and lower the diagram without changing the area under the curve. Thus, as with straight cutting, C_f is about equal to 0.64 for typical oblique cutting. Power for chopping varies with feed rate and length of cut; the specific cutting energy provides a better index for comparing forage harvesters of differing design. Specific cutting energy is defined as follows:

$$E_{sc} = \frac{1000 \, C_f \, F_{smax}}{\rho_f} \qquad (8.36)$$

where E_{sc} = specific cutting energy per unit mass on the countershear (J·m/kg)

By measuring power consumption while changing feed velocity and removing knives to change the theoretical length of cut and by assuming that such changes did not change other power requirements in the forage harvester, Richey (1958) estimated the specific energy requirements of two cylindrical cutterheads. For those tests, chopping alfalfa at 73% moisture and a 13-mm length of cut consumed 0.33 kW·h/Mg, giving a value of E_{sc} = 15.4 J·m/kg. Once a value of E_{sc} is known, the following equation can be used to calculate power:

$$P_c = \frac{E_{sc} \, \dot{m}_f}{L_c} \qquad (8.37)$$

Notice from equation 8.36 that E_{sc} is proportional to the maximum specific cutting force. Thus, maintaining sharp knives and shearbar/knife clearance is very important to reduce the power requirement for forage chopping. As the knife edge wears from a 0.1 mm (sharp) to a 0.3 mm radius (dull), the cutting energy approximately doubles. The cutting energy also doubles as the clearance increases from 0.1 to 0.4 mm. The combined effect of dulling the knife and increasing the clearance as indicated above is approximately a tripling of the cutting energy. Dull knives and excessive clearance cause the crop to be torn rather than sheared and also accelerates wear due to wedging between the knife and shearbar. A sharpening stone with automatic traversing along the cutterhead is included as a standard feature of many forage harvesters. The automatic sharpener permits the operator to interrupt harvesting and sharpen the knives without leaving the field. The clearance should also be easy to adjust. The adjustment must be done with the cutterhead running at normal speed to accommodate the centrifugal expansion of the cutterhead.

Metal detectors are another valuable option on forage harvesters. Metal can damage the chopper and/or kill livestock that consumes the metal in the forage. When a magnetic sensor detects metal in the throat, the feed rolls are automatically stopped to prevent the metal from reaching the cutterhead. The feed rolls must be reversed to expel the metal-bearing forage before harvesting can be resumed.

Power to overcome friction between the cut forage and the cutterhead or blower housing can be calculated by using the following equation:

$$P_f = \frac{\beta \, \mu \, \dot{m}_f \, v_{pc}^2}{1000} \qquad (8.38)$$

where

P_f = power absorbed by rubbing friction (kW)
β = average arc of housing rubbed by chopped material (radians)
μ = coefficient of friction between forage and steel housing
$\dot{m}_f$ = feed rate (kg/s)
v_{pc} = peripheral velocity of cutterhead (m/s)

Material leaving the cutterhead does not all strike the housing at the same place, so angle β is the average angle of contact. Manufacturers have realized that a short cutterhead housing is desirable to reduce friction power and thus have minimized arc β in most modern forage harvesters. ASAE Data D251 presents data on friction coefficients between chopped forages and metal surfaces. Friction coefficients for forage on steel range from 0.2 to 0.8 depending on type of forage, moisture content, peripheral velocity and other factors. Peripheral velocities of cutterheads typically range from 20 to 28 m/s and, for such velocities, both chopped corn and chopped alfalfa have a coefficient of approximately 0.49 on polished stainless steel.

Power required to accelerate the forage at the cutterhead or blower is derived by assuming that the forage leaves the blades at about the peripheral speed of the blades:

$$P_{accel} = \frac{\dot{m}_f \, v_{ip}^2}{2000} \qquad (8.39)$$

where

P_{accel} = power to accelerate the forage (kW)
v_p = peripheral velocity of the cutter or blower (m/s)

Both the cutterhead and the blower move air, although the latter at a greater rate. According to well-established fan laws, fan power varies with the cube of the peripheral speed. Making use of data by Blevins and Hansen (1956), the following equation was derived for the approximate air power:

$$P_{air} = \frac{v_p^3}{16,600} \qquad (8.40)$$

where P_{air} = power to move air (in kW).

The header power, including power for the feed rolls, varies with the feed rate and is not large except at very high feed rates. The following equation can be used to estimate the header power:

$$P_h = C_{h0} + C_{h1} \dot{m}_f \qquad (8.41)$$

where
$\quad P_h \qquad$ = power consumed by header (kW)
$\quad C_{h0}, C_{h1}$ = constants for any given header (kW and kW·s/kg)

C_{h0} is the amount of power required to overcome friction when the harvester is running empty. Cutting, conveying and compressing the forage between the feed rolls absorbs power in proportion to the feedrate.

By combining equations 8.36 and 8.38 through 8.41, an equation for the total power consumption, P_{fh}, of a forage harvester can be obtained. Note that air power is independent of feed rate, but power to all other components is proportional to feed rate. The form of the equation for P_{fh} is thus similar to the following equation from ASAE Data D497 for the total power consumption of a precision-cut forage harvester:

$$P_{fh} = 1.5 + 3.3 \, C_r \, C_c \, \dot{m}_f \qquad (8.42)$$

where
$\quad P_{fh}$ = total power consumed by forage harvester (kW)
$\quad C_r$ = recutter factor = 1.0 for no recutter or 2.0 with recutter screen
$\quad C_c$ = crop factor = 1.0 for green corn, 1.33 for green alfalfa or 2.0 for low-moisture forage or hay

Although equation 8.42 has the proper form, the constants in it represent only average conditions and the equation is not useful for exploring the effect of various design variables. The design of a precision forage harvester is illustrated in example problem 8.5.

Example Problem 8.5

A cut-and-throw forage harvester has a cylindrical cutter head with width of 500 mm and diameter of 600 mm carries eight knives and rotates at 950 rev/min. The average length of cut is to be 7 mm. The maximum height of the throat is 18 cm. When cutting corn, the compressed density of material in the throat is 320 kg/m^3, and the specific cutting energy is 15 J·m/kg. The coefficient of friction between the forage and the housing is 0.49, and the material is in contact with the housing through 2.5 radians of arc. Assume the power coefficients for the header are 0.6 kW and 0.3 kW·s/kg. Calculate (a) the required feed velocity into the cutterhead, (b) the maximum allowable feedrate into the harvester and (c) the total power requirement of the harvester.

Solution. (a) The required feed velocity can be calculated by solving equation 8.33 for v_f:

$$v_f = L_c \lambda_k n_c/60\ 000 = 7 \cdot 8 \cdot 950/60\ 000 = 0.887 \text{ m/s}$$

(b) Before using equation 8.34 to calculate the maximum allowable feedrate, the maximum throat area must be calculated. It is:

$$A_t = \text{cutterhead width} \cdot \text{throat height} = 50 \cdot 18 = 900 \text{ cm}^2$$

Then the maximum allowable feedrate is:

$$\dot{m}_f = 320 \cdot 900 \cdot 7 \cdot 8 \cdot 950/(6 \times 10^8) = 25.5 \text{ kg/s or 92 Mg/h}$$

(c) The various component power requirements must be calculated using equations 8.37 through 8.41 to get the total power requirement. The peripheral velocity of the cutterhead is needed to calculate the power used in friction, in accelerating the forage and in moving air. The radius of the cutterhead is 0.3 m and the rotation speed is 99.5 rad/s. Then the peripheral velocity is:

$$v_{pc} = v_{pi} = 0.3 \cdot 99.5 = 29.9 \text{ m/s}$$

Now the various power requirements can be calculated:

$$P_c = 15 \cdot 25.5/7 = 54.6 \text{ kW}$$

$$P_f = 2.5 \cdot 0.49 \cdot 25.5 \cdot 29.9^2/1000 = 27.9 \text{ kW}$$

Figure 8.31–A flail-type forage harvester (Courtesy of Ford New-Holland, Inc.).

$P_{accel} = 25.5 \cdot 29.9^2/2000 = 11.4$ kW

$P_{air} = 29.9^3/16600 = 1.6$ kW

$P_h = 0.6 + 0.3 \cdot 25.5 = 8.3$ kW

$P_{fh} = 54.6 + 27.9 + 11.4 + 1.6 + 8.3 = 103.8$ kW

In this example of a cut-and-throw harvester, the power delivered to the shaft of the cutterhead would be the sum of P_c, P_f, P_{accel}, and P_{air}. Thus, 95.5 kW, or 92% of the total power requirement would be delivered to the shaft of the cutterhead.

Forage harvesters with nonprecision cut represent a lower-cost alternative to precision-cut harvesters. Figure 8.31 shows a flail-type forage harvester, which has a nonprecision cut. Flails similar to those in a flail mower (fig. 8.21) cut the standing crop and deliver it into a cross auger. Rotor speeds are usually in the range from 1100 to 1600 rev/min, giving flail peripheral speeds in the range from 45 to 60 m/s. The auger conveys the cut forage to an impeller-blower to be conveyed to the trailing wagon. On some flail harvesters, a flywheel-type cutterhead is substituted for the impeller-blower. The cutterhead recuts the forage and conveys it to the wagon. Recutters generally have two, three, or six knives to provide varying lengths of cut. The average recut lengths are comparable to those from precision-cut forage harvesters except that the lengths are less uniform. Power requirements of a flail-type forage harvester with recutter are typically double or greater compared to those of a precision-cut forage harvester. Thus, the lower initial cost of the flail-type harvester is partially offset by higher operating costs. The flail-type harvesters are also less versatile because they cannot be used to harvest row crops.

8.2.3 Curing and Preservation of Forage

Losses of dry matter and quality can be very large during harvest of hay, especially for leafy hay such as alfalfa or other legumes. In alfalfa, for example, crude protein accounts for about 28% of the leaf dry matter but only 11% of the stem dry matter. Protein and nonstructural carbohydrates provide most of the nutritional value from the forage; NDF (nondetergent fiber) is less digestible and serves primarily as roughage (a coarse substance, usually high in cellulose, whose bulk stimulates peristalsis in the intestines). Dry matter and quality losses occur due to plant respiration, rain, and machine losses during harvesting. Typically, 3 to 5% of the plant dry matter, consisting primarily of nonstructural carbohydrate, is lost through respiration after cutting. Respiration losses thus increase the concentration of crude protein and NDF in the forage. Respiration ceases when the plants dry to 40% moisture. Rain causes leaf shatter and leaching losses. Leaf losses readjust the leaf to stem ratio, resulting in an overall loss in crude protein concentration and increased fiber concentration. Leaching losses from both leaves and stems consist of nonfiber; the leaching loss of crude protein is typically 20% greater than leaching loss of other dry matter. Machine losses include both leaves and stems but leaves are lost more readily; thus the reduction in the leaf-stem ratio caused by machines can reduce the overall protein concentration in the forage. Since fast drying of forage reduces respiration losses and also the opportunity for rain to fall on the cut forage, losses of both dry matter and quality are decreased by faster drying.

Leaves of legume crops dry much faster than the stems because the surface-volume ratio of leaves is much greater than that for stems. Also, a waxy cutin layer on the surface of stems acts as a natural moisture barrier and reduces their drying rate. Conditioning is a process in which the stems are crushed, cracked or abraded such that they dry at approximately the same rate as the leaves. Magnified cross-sections of conditioned and unconditioned stems is shown in figure 8.32. Conditioning of legumes is usually accomplished by running the forage between a set of rolls, either of the corrugated crimper type or the intermeshing crushing type. The corrugated crimper, which has deep flutes that feed aggressively, is less likely to plug but can cause excessive leaf loss. Conditioning occurs through splitting each stem as it is bent to pass through the rolls. Intermeshing crushing rolls are less aggressive and thus less

 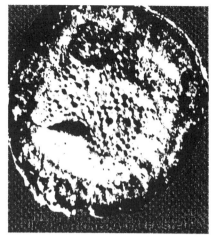

Figure 8.32–Magnified compression of conditioned and unconditioned alfalfa stems (Courtesy of Deere and Co.).

likely to cause leaf loss. Conditioning is accomplished by crushing the stems. The peripheral speed of conditioners should be three to four times the travel speed of the machine to maintain a thin layer of forage between the rolls, since thin layers are conditioned more effectively and uniformly than thick layers. Thin layers are also facilitated when the reel provides a uniform feed rate to the conditioner and by use of the widest possible rolls; however, stiffness limitations place a practical limit on roll width. Roll spacing must automatically vary to accommodate different crop yields. Springs are used to maintain pressure between the rolls and the spring force is adjustable to control the degree of conditioning. An adjustable minimum clearance is also provided between the rolls; minimum clearance is increased for crops with larger stems, since excessive roll pressure or insufficient clearance can cause excessive leaf loss. Rolls are usually constructed from steel, neoprene or tire carcasses. Shinners et al. (1990) found no difference in leaf loss or drying rate of alfalfa due to type of rolls.

Using conventional techniques for harvesting, hay curing in the field required from three to five days depending on weather conditions. Use of crop conditioners to crush the stems (fig. 8.5) accelerated the drying and reduced curing time to two to four days. Use of chemical agents to accelerate drying of crushed hay can reduce curing time by an additional day. Spraying an aqueous solution of potassium and/or sodium carbonate on the forage increases the permeability of the waxy cutin surface of the plants, thus allowing faster escape of moisture (Rotz et al., 1990). A recent technique, in which alfalfa is shredded and pressed into a mat, may allow alfalfa to cure in as little as four hours (Rotz et al., 1990).

A model of drying of swathed alfalfa was developed by Rotz and Chen (1985); drying dynamics may differ when the swath is raked. For the swathed alfalfa, Rotz and Chen found that two environmental factors predominate in driving the drying process; solar radiation provides the energy for moisture evaporation, while the vapor pressure deficit provides the moisture gradient to move the water vapor away from the plants. The two most important variables which limited the drying rate were swath density and soil moisture. Drying theory shows that, as material density approaches infinity, the drying rate approaches zero. Drying is also slowed when soil moisture keeps a wet surface at the bottom of the swath. The equilibrium moisture content is an important variable in drying theory. However, the model of Rotz and Chen best described actual drying when the equilibrium moisture content was assumed to be zero. Then the following equation gives the moisture content at any time during daylight drying:

$$M_f = M_{fo} \, e^{-C_{dr} \, t} \qquad (8.43)$$

where

M_f = moisture content (dry basis) at end of time t
M_{fo} = moisture content (dry basis) at t=0
t   = drying period (h)
C_{dr} = drying rate constant (1/h)

On the basis of 5000 experimental observations on the drying of alfalfa, the following two empirical equations were developed for the drying rate constant:

$$C_{dr} = \frac{S_{rad}(1 + 9.30 \, R_c) + 5.42 \, \Theta_{db}}{66.4 \, M_s + \rho_s (2.06 - 0.97 \, \lambda_d)(1.55 + 2.19 R_c) + 3037} \qquad (8.44)$$

or,

$$C_{dr} = \frac{S_{rad}(1 + 9.03 \, R_c) + 43.8 \, p_{vd}}{61.4 \, M_s + \rho_s (1.82 - 0.83 \, \lambda_d)(1.68 + 24.8 R_c) + 2767} \qquad (8.45)$$

where

S_{rad} = solar radiation (W/m^2)
R_c = application rate of chemical drying agent or conditioner (g of solution/g of dry matter)

M_s = soil moisture content (dry basis, %)
ρ_s = swath density (g/m^2)
λ_d = one on day of cutting, else 0
Θ_{db} = dry bulb temperature (°C)
p_{vd} = vapor pressure deficit (kPa)

The above equations apply only to daytime drying; rewetting by rain or dew will slow the drying process. Both models gave realistic prediction of alfalfa daytime drying rates in the East Lansing, Michigan, area and also in the semi-arid regions of California; the models have not yet been validated for other areas. Solar insolation rates typically range from 0 to 950 W/m^2. It is easier to measure dry bulb temperature than vapor pressure deficit and thus equation 8.44 may be best in areas of relatively high relative humidity. In very dry areas, equation 8.45 may give more realistic predictions of drying rate of alfalfa. The factor, λ_d, is in the model because drying is faster on the day of cutting when the moisture is still uniformly distributed through the swath. The top of the swath dries first and later moisture removal from the bottom of the swath occurs more slowly. Swath densities range from 150 to 1500 g/m^2, with 450 g/m^2 being a typical value. Note that the model makes no reference to the concentration of chemicals in the drying solution; tests have shown that the effectiveness was nearly independent of the concentration of the chemicals in the solution but was very dependent on the rate at which the solution was applied to the forage. Rates range from 0 to 0.25 grams of solution per gram of forage dry matter, with 0.075 g/g being a typical rate. Higher rates provide more complete coverage of the plant surfaces and thus promote drying. Example problem 8.6 illustrates the calculation of alfalfa drying.

Example Problem 8.6

On a day when the dry bulb temperature is 20° C, the solar radiation is 650 W/m^2, and the soil moisture is 18%, alfalfa is cut at 80% moisture in a humid area. The density of alfalfa in the swath is 450 g/m^2. Potassium carbonate drying agent is applied at the rate of 0.075 g/g. Calculate the moisture content of the hay at the end of the first hour and at the end of the second hour.

Solution. The hay was cut in a humid area and thus, from equation 8.44, the drying rate constant is:

$$C_{dr} = \frac{650\,(1 + 9.3 \cdot 0.075) + 5.42 \cdot 20}{66.4 \cdot 18 + 450\,(2.06 - 97 \cdot 1)\,(1.55 + 2.19 \cdot 0.075) + 3037} = 0.234$$

Then, from equation 8.43, the crop moisture at the end of the first hour is:

$$M_f = 89 \ e^{-0.234 \cdot 1} = 63.3\%$$

At the end of the second hour, the crop moisture is:

$$M_f = 63.3 \ e^{-0.234 \cdot 1} = 50.1\%$$

Thus, the forage lost 16.7 points of moisture in the first hour and 12.6 points in the second hour. Since the moisture loss during any hour is proportional to the beginning moisture, the hourly moisture loss continues to decline as the forage dries.

8.2.4 Windrowing

In some methods of forage harvesting, the forage is formed into windrows which can then be picked up directly by the harvester. This is common practice when harvesting forage for silage or where the climate is very dry. When dry hay is desired in humid climates, the forage is placed in a swath and then raked into a windrow. When cutting and windrowing are done in two separate operations, a side-delivery rake can be used to roll the swaths left by the mower into windrows. Rakes can also be used to invert previously-formed windrows to promote faster drying, especially after rain has wetted the windrows. Dry matter losses during raking typically range from 3 to 6% and more leaves than stems are usually lost. Thus, gentle handling is an important goal in rake design. The two most popular types of side delivery rakes are the oblique-reelhead rake and the finger-wheel rake.

A parallel bar (oblique-reelhead) rake is illustrated in figure 8.33. The two reelheads are parallel but at an acute angle with the tooth bars. Thus, when one of the reelheads is driven, either by pto power or by a ground wheel, every rake tooth follows a circular path in a plane parallel to the reelheads. All teeth automatically maintain parallel positions, usually vertical, but the pitch of the teeth can be changed by changing the tilt of the reelhead axes. Pitching the bottoms of the teeth forward gives a more vigorous raking action in heavy crops.

Figure 8.33 was used in deriving velocity relationships for a parallel-bar rake. Rake teeth contact the hay at angle α_1 from the lowest tooth position and release it at angle α_2 at the top of the windrow. Teeth are in contact with the hay during forward travel x_1 and out of contact during forward travel x_2. One expression for x_2 can be derived from figure 8.33a, i.e.:

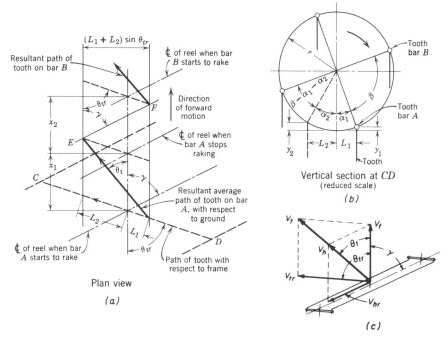

Plan view

(a)

Vertical section at *CD*
(reduced scale)

(b)

(c)

(d)

Figure 8.33–A side delivery rake with oblique reel-head (Courtesy of Ford-New Holland, Inc.).

$$x_2 = (L_1 + L_2) \left(\cos \theta_{tr} + \frac{\sin \theta_{tr}}{\tan \gamma} \right) \tag{8.46}$$

Another expression for x_2 can be derived from figure 8.33b, i.e.:

$$x_2 = r \frac{v_f}{v_p} \cdot (\beta - \alpha_1 - \alpha_2) \tag{8.47}$$

Then, since $L_1 = r \sin(\alpha_1)$ and $L_2 = r \sin(\alpha_2)$, equations 8.46 and 8.47 can be combined into the following equation:

$$\frac{\beta - \alpha_1 - \alpha_2}{\sin \alpha_1 + \sin \alpha_2} = \frac{v_p}{v_f} \left(\cos \theta_{tr} + \frac{\sin \theta_{tr}}{\tan \gamma} \right) \tag{8.48}$$

All terms in equation 8.47 are design variables except α_1 and α_2, which are unknowns depending upon operating conditions. From figure 8.33b:

$$\alpha_2 = \arccos \left(1 - \frac{y_2}{r} \right) \tag{8.49}$$

Distance y_2 can be determined as the height of the top of the windrow relative to the lowest position of the rake teeth. Then equation 8.49 can be solved for α_2 and equation 8.48 can be solved (iteratively) for α_1. Note that α_1 can be negative if the effective raking stroke begins beyond the lowest point of tooth travel. After α_1 and α_2 are known, the magnitude of vector v_{tr} can be calculated using the following equation:

$$\frac{v_{tr}}{v_p} = \frac{\sin \alpha_1 + \sin \alpha_2}{\alpha_1 + \alpha_2} \tag{8.50}$$

The direction of v_{tr} is parallel to the planes of the reelheads. After vector V_{tr} is determined, the direction and magnitude of v_t can be calculated. Angle θ_t can be calculated from:

$$\theta_t = \arctan \frac{v_{tr} \sin \theta_{tr}}{v_f + v_{tr} \cos \theta_{tr}} \tag{8.51}$$

and the magnitude, v_t can be calculated from:

$$V_t = \frac{V_{tr} \sin \theta_{tr}}{\sin \theta_t} \qquad (8.52)$$

The direction of v_h is coincident with v_t. The magnitude of v_h can be calculated using the following equation:

$$V_h = \frac{V_f}{\cos \theta_t + \sin \theta_t + \cot \gamma} \qquad (8.53)$$

The theoretical maximum distance travelled by the hay during raking is given by the following equation:

$$L_h = \frac{W_r}{\sin \theta_t} \qquad (8.54)$$

Definitions of symbols in equations 8.46 through 8.54 are as follows:

α_1 = angle before bottom at which raking begins (radians) (see fig. 8.33)

α_2 = angle at which raking ends (radians)

β = angle between tooth bars (radians)

γ = acute angle between raking front and direction of travel (radians)

θ_{tr} = angle between direction of travel and planes of reelheads (radians)

θ_t = angle between v_t and direction of travel (radians)

x_2 = horizontal distance travelled by teeth during nonraking (m)

y_2 = vertical distance from lowest position of rake teeth to top of windrow (m)

$L_1 + L_2$ = horizontal distance travelled by teeth during raking (m)

r = reel radius (m)

v_f = forward velocity of rake (m/s)

v_{tr} = reel component = average horizontal velocity of teeth during raking, relative to rake (m/s)

v_p = peripheral speed of reel (m/s)

v_t = resultant tooth velocity = vector sum of v_f and v_{tr} (m/s)

v_{hr} = average horizontal velocity of hay relative to rake (m/s)

v_h = average resultant hay velocity = vector sum of v_f and v_{hr} (m/s)

L_h = maximum theoretical distance travelled by hay during raking (m)

w_r = width of rake (m)

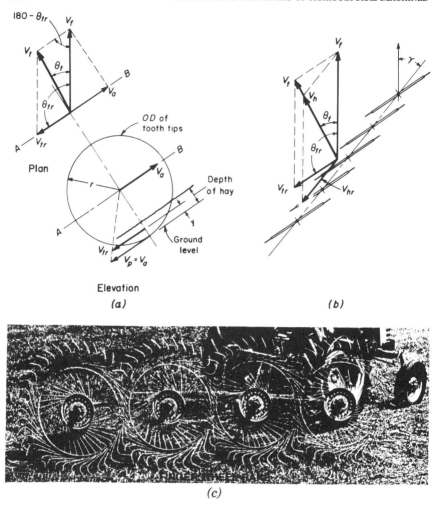

Figure 8.34–A finger-wheel side delivery rake (Courtesy of Deere and Co).

A finger-wheel side-delivery rake is illustrated in figure 8.34. The action of one raking wheel is illustrated in figure 8.34a, while velocity relationships for the complete rake are shown in figure 8.34b. Raking teeth are carried on wheels whose planes of orientation allow each wheel to be ground driven. Thus, no separate drive train is required. As was true for the oblique-reelhead rake, the vector v_{hr} is parallel to the raking front and v_{tr} is parallel to the planes of the raking wheels.

Since the tooth wheels are each ground driven, the magnitude of v_p can be calculated from the following equation (see fig. 8.34a):

$$\frac{v_p}{v_f} = \cos\left(\pi - \theta_{tr}\right) = \cos\theta_{tr} \qquad (8.55)$$

The reel component, v_{tr}, is proportionally less than v_p as shown in the following equation:

$$v_{tr} = \frac{r - y}{r} v_p \qquad (8.56)$$

where
$\quad$ y $\;=\;$ half of the windrow height (m) (see fig. 8.34a)
$\quad$ r $\;=\;$ radius from center of tooth wheels to tooth tips (m)

The angle, θ_t of the resultant tooth and hay path is given by the following equation:

$$\theta_t = \arctan\frac{v_{tr}\,\sin\theta_{tr}}{v_f} \qquad (8.57)$$

The magnitudes of v_t and v_h can be calculated using equations 8.52 and 8.53, respectively. The theoretical maximum length of hay travel for the finger wheel rake can be calculated using equation 8.54.

$\quad$ The gentleness with which the hay is handled during raking is influenced by rake design variables. Gentleness is promoted by maintaining low hay velocity, v_h, by keeping v_t as close as possible to v_h to reduce tooth impacting on the hay, and by keeping hay travel, L_h, as small as possible. The ratio of v_h/v_t is closer to unity for the finger-wheel rake, thus providing a smoother raking action than for the parallel-bar rake. However, the finger-wheel rake has a somewhat longer hay path (compare figs. 8.33c and 8.34a). For the parallel-bar rake, reducing the ratio v_p/v_f lengthens the hay path but reduces the frequency of tooth impacts on the hay and also reduces the ratio v_t/v_h. Reducing v_f also provides gentler handing of the hay but decreases the raking capacity. The theoretical effects of the various raking parameters were determined analytically, but there is little published information on the effect of raking parameters on losses. Example problem 8.7 illustrates calculations for a side delivery rake with oblique reel head.

Example Problem 8.7
$\quad$ A five-bar side delivery rake with an oblique reel head has a raking front angle, $\gamma = 65°$ (6.81 rad) and a raking width of 2.4 m. The reel radius is 0.3 m and the head angle is $\theta_{tr} = 72°$ (7.54 rad). The reel is ground driven with a speed ratio, $v_f/v_p = 0.8$. When the rake is

traveling at 8 km/h while raking a windrow of height 0.45 m, calculate the (a) direction and (b) magnitude of the resultant tooth path, (c) the average hay velocity, (d) the maximum theoretical distance travelled by the hay during raking, and (e) ratio, v_h/v_t, of the average hay velocity to the resultant tooth velocity.

Solution. (a) Angles α_1 and α_2 must be calculated to begin the analysis. Since the angles and their trigonometric functions will be used, radians will be used instead of degrees in all of the trigonometric calculations. The value of α_2 can be calculated using equation 8.49:

$$\alpha_2 = \arccos\,(1 - 0.45/0.3) = 2.09 \text{ rad}$$

then all variables in equation 8.48 are known except for α_1. Because the reel has five bars, $\beta = 2\pi/5 = 1.26$ rad. Then:

$$\frac{1.26 - \alpha_1 - 2.09}{\sin(\alpha_1) + \sin(2.09)} = \frac{1}{0.8}\left[\cos\,(7.54) + \frac{\sin\,(7.54}{\tan\,(6.81)}\right]$$

Solving the above equation by iteration gives α_1=5.45 rad. The forward speed of the rake is 8/3.6 = 2.22 m/s and the peripheral speed of the reel is v_p=2.22/0.8=2.78 m/s. Equation 8.50 can be used to calculate the reel component, v_{tr}:

$$v_{tr} = 2.78\,[\sin(5.45) + \sin(2.09)]/[5.45 + 2.09] = 1.53 \text{ m/s}$$

Next, the direction of the resultant tooth path can be calculated using equation 8.51:

$$\theta_t = \arctan[1.53\,\sin(7.54)/(2.22 + 1.53\,\cos(7.54))] = 2.97 \text{ rad or } 28.4°$$

(b) From equation 8.52, the magnitude of the resultant tooth velocity is:

$$v_t = 1.53\ \sin(7.54)/\sin(2.97) = 3.06 \text{ m/s}$$

(c) Next, from equation 8.53, the average hay velocity is:

$$v_h = 2.22/[\cos(2.97) + \sin(2.97) + \cot an(6.81)] = 1.22 \text{ m/s}$$

(d) The maximum length of the hay path, from equation 8.54, is:

$$L_h = 2.4/\sin(2.97) = 5.1 \text{ m}$$

(e) Finally, the ratio of hay velocity to tooth velocity is:

$$v_h/v_t = 1.22/3.06 = 0.40$$

The maximum hay path length is over twice the swath width and the average travel speed of the hay is only 40% of the tooth velocity. The teeth impact the hay repeatedly in moving it into the windrow and thus the leaves of legumes can be lost if the hay is very dry during raking.

Power requirements for side delivery raking are small and data are sparse. ASAE Data D497 suggests the following power requirement for a side delivery rake 2.44 m in width:

$$P_{rake} = -0.186 + 0.052\ v_f \qquad (8.58)$$

where
$\quad P_{rake}$ = power requirement for raking (kW)
$\quad v_f$ = raking speed (m/s)

Power requirements for mower-conditioners or windrowers are also sparse. Limited data suggests that the power requirement for a pto-powered windrower with sicklebar cutting, a reel and a roll-type conditioner is approximately 3.2 kW/m of width (Rotz and Sprott, 1984).

8.2.5 Baling

Hay can be harvested as loose hay in stacks or as chopped hay, but baling is the most popular method of hay harvest. The two types of balers in popular use are rectangular balers (fig. 8.6) and round balers (fig. 8.7). Although the discussion in this chapter relates to baling of hay, the same machines are used for baling straw and other fibrous materials.

Rectangular Balers. Virtually all rectangular balers have the baling chamber oriented in the direction of travel of the baler. A windrow pickup unit feeds the windrow into a cross conveyor which, in turn, feeds the hay into the baling chamber. There are three types of cross conveyors. In one type, an auger conveys the hay to a set of packer fingers which sweep the hay into the bale chamber. In a second type, linear moving packer fingers travel the full width of the pickup in conveying the hay into the bale chamber. In the third type, rotating finger wheels move the hay laterally to the packer fingers. The bale chamber is fed from below rather than from the side in one available baler. Material is fed from the pickup to the bale chamber by a crank-actuated feed fork. Feeding from the bottom allows the

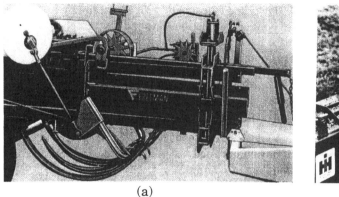

(a)   (b)

Figure 8.35–Control of bale density (a) hydraulically and (b) with manually-adjustable springs (Reprinted from *Principles of Farm Machinery*, Kepner et al., 1978).

baler to travel directly behind the tractor. In all feeder designs, the packer fingers must be timed to the movement of the reciprocating plunger so that the fingers are out of the bale chamber except when the plunger is in its forward ($\theta_c = 90°$ in fig. 8.38) position.

As the feeder delivers each charge of hay, a knife on the edge of the plunger and a countershear at the rear edge of the feed opening shear off the charge of hay as the plunger moves rearward. Continued movement of the plunger compresses the charge of hay and pushes previously accumulated compressed hay through the bale chamber. Controlled convergence of the bale chamber (fig. 8.35a) provides resistance to bale movement and thus controls bale density. Fixed wedges and spring-loaded dogs extend into the bale chamber and minimize re-expansion of the compressed hay during forward movement of the plunger. During compression, a star wheel at the top of the bale chamber (the leftmost star wheel in fig. 8.35a) is driven by the moving bale to trigger the tying mechanism when a bale of sufficient length has been formed. When the plunger reaches its rearmost position after the tying mechanism has been triggered, needles (visible at bottom of fig. 8.35a) move through slots in the plunger face to deliver twine or wire to the knotter. The knotter completes the knots and the needles retract as the plunger begins moving forward.

The density of hay in the bales is determined by the type of material being baled, its moisture content, and by the resistance provided by the convergence of the bale chamber. The convergence causes the hay to be compressed laterally as the bale moves through the chamber. Assuming the hay is an elastic material, the plunger force generated by convergence can be calculated using the following equation:

$$F_c = \frac{E_h \, y}{d_c} L_c \, w_c \, f_h \qquad (8.59)$$

where

F_c	=	compressive force supplied by plunger (N)
E_h	=	effective modulus of elasticity of the hay (kPa)
L_c	=	length of converging section (m)
y	=	total convergence in converging section (mm)
d_c	=	depth of bale chamber (m)
w_c	=	width of bale chamber (m)
f_h	=	coefficient of friction between hay and bale chamber

The quantity, $(E_h \, y/2 \, d_c)$ is the lateral pressure to compress the hay a distance y, and $(2 \, L_c \, w_c)$ is the total area on which the lateral pressure acts assuming only two sides converge. Multiplying by the coefficient of friction gives the contribution of convergence to the plunger force. There will be some friction against the nonconverging sides. If all four sides converge, convergence of each pair of sides is usually controlled independently. In either case, the friction against all sides should be included in calculating F_c. Equation 8.59 is difficult to use to compute actual forces because of difficulty in determining values for E_h. However, the equation does provide insights into the problems of density control. Both E_h and f_h increase with moisture content of the hay, thus increasing the plunger force and the bale density. The tension-control springs in figure 8.35b provide the lateral force for squeezing the bales in the convergence section. Hand cranks are provided to adjust the amount of spring tension and the tension must be adjusted to compensate for changes in moisture and crop. During operation, the springs extend when E_h increases and, although y declines, the lateral force increases. Zero-rate springs would be preferable and the equivalent effect is achieved by substituting a hydraulic cylinder to provide the convergence force (fig. 8.35a). The hydraulic pressure can be adjusted from the operator's station but remains at the set value, thus providing constant force. One large rectangular baler uses several load cells placed on the plunger face to monitor the compression force. The signals from the load cells are sent to a microprocessor. The microprocessor controls bale density by sending output signals to electrohydraulic valves which control oil pressure in hydraulic cylinders which regulate bale chamber convergence. The microprocessor system ensures uniform, constant bale density as crop conditions change.

Both twine-tie and wire-tie balers are available but the twine-tie balers are much more popular. ASAE Standards S229.6 and

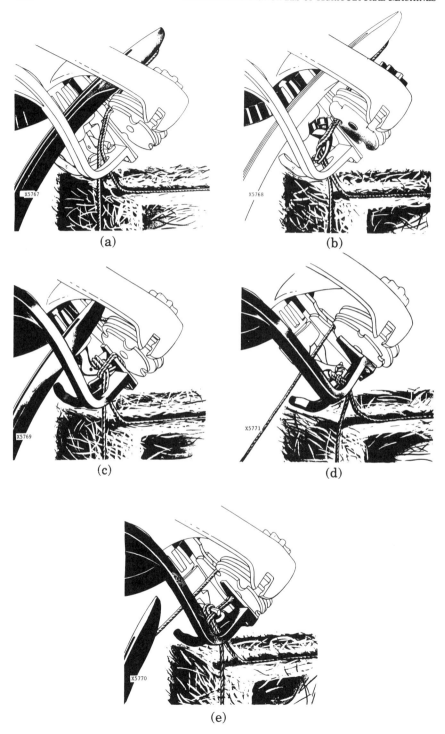

Figure 8.36–Operation of a twine knotter (Courtesy of Deere and Co.).

S315.2 provide specifications for baling wire and twine, respectively. Figure 8.36 shows a twine knotter tying a bale. In the most popular-sized baler, each bale is tied by two loops of twine and thus two knotters are included on the baler. When tying a bale, each knotter grips the cut end of its twine as the needles retract. As the next bale advances through the chamber pushing the twine strands on its leading edge, twine is pulled from two twine balls though the needle eyes. When the bale tying mechanism is triggered by the star wheel through a limited-motion pawl clutch, the needles rise through the plunger slots, carrying the twine strands to the respective knotters. Figure 8.36a shows the start of the tying cycle. The needle has brought the twine around the bale and placed it in the twine holder. The two outside disks of the holder have rotated through the angle between adjacent notches while the center disk remained stationary, thus pinching the twine between the spring-loaded disks to hold it when the needle withdraws. The knotter-bill assembly in figure 8.36b has begun rotating to form a loop in the string about the knotter bills. The loop is completed in figure 8.36c, the knotter bills have opened and, with continued rotation, the bills close over the strings held by the twine holder. As the bills grip the strings, the knife attached to the stripper arm cuts the twine between the knotter and the twine holder, thus releasing the formed bale. The bills have gripped the strings and the knife has completed the cutting in figure 8.36d and, in figure 8.36e, the wiper has completed the knot by moving forward to push the loop from the bills over the twine held by the twine holder. Note that, in figure 8.36d, the twine holder has already gripped the twine end for the next bale and continues to hold it while the current bale is being tied and the next bale is being formed. Wires are tied around bales in a manner similar to that described above, except that the wire ends are twisted, not knotted. Thus a wire-tie baler has a wire twister instead of a twine knotter. Because of the greater tensile strength of wires, wire-tied bales can have greater density than string-tied bales.

The baling rate (in kg/s) can be limited by the rate at which forage is fed into the baler, by the design of the baler or by available power. The following equation relates the first of these possible limits:

$$\dot{m}_f = \frac{d_c \, w_c \, \delta_s \, \rho_c \, n_c}{60} \tag{8.60}$$

where

$\dot{m}_f$ = baling rate or material feed rate (kg/s)
d_c = depth of bale chamber (m)
w_c = width of bale chamber (m)

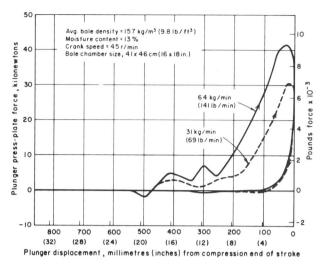

Figure 8.37–Plunger work diagrams for two feed rates in alfalfa (Burrough and Graham, 1954).

δ_s = thickness of each compressed hay slice (m)
ρ_c = compressed density of hay in bale (kg/m^3)
n_c = crank speed (rev/min)

By far the most popular chamber size is w_c = 0.46 m and d_c = 0.36 m. However, much larger balers with chambers 1.2 m by 1.2 m are on the market and several intermediate sizes are also available. Densities of hay in bales, including moisture at time of baling, range from 130 to 225 kg/m^3 with the lower end of that range being the most popular. Use of low crank speeds limits capacity and increases stress loads. Tests by Burroughs and Graham (1954) have shown that, for a given feed rate and bale density, peak plunger force fell 20% as crank speed increased from 40 to 50 rev/min but showed little decline with further increases in speed. Use of high speeds generates excessive inertia forces in the reciprocating plunger and causes greater losses of hay from the bale chamber. Practical crank speeds range from 45 rev/min for some large balers to 100 rev/min for smaller balers. Each time the baler plunger moves rearward, it shears off the incoming hay and compresses the hay charge into a flake or slice. The flake thickness varies with the rate at which hay can be fed into the bale chamber. Typically, flake thickness ranges from zero to about 20 cm. From equation 8.60, for a baler with chamber dimensions of 36 by 46 cm, crank speed of 50 rev/min, bale density of 225 kg/m^3 and flake thickness of 20 cm, the baling capacity would be 6.21 kg/s or 22.4 Mg/h. In NIAE (1965) tests of balers with the 36- by 46-cm bale chamber, rates as high as 22 Mg/h

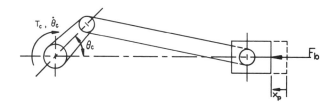

Figure 8.38–Diagram of a slider-crank mechanism in a baler.

were recorded for short time periods, but maximum rates fell to 16.3 Mg/h for continuous tests.

Instantaneous crank torque varies widely on a baler and a flywheel is used to maintain a relatively constant crank speed. Figure 8.37 shows two typical force-deflection curves for a baler plunger working with two different feed rates. The curves are similar except that compression starts earlier with the larger hay charge and the peak force is higher. The small peaks near 300 to 400 mm displacement are knife forces for shearing the hay charge; on most hay charges, these cutting peaks occur later and closer to the force peak. The force reaches a peak and begins declining when the hay compressed on earlier strokes begins moving in the chamber; the decline occurs because the sliding friction is less than the static friction in the chamber. Both force curves merge after the plunger starts forward. The force is greater than zero during the first 100 mm of return travel only because the compressed hay re-expands somewhat. During the re-expansion, a small amount of potential energy in the compressed hay is returned to the plunger in the form of kinetic energy. A force-displacement curve (fig. 8.37) can be converted to a torque versus angular displacement curve for the crank. For any given crank angle, θ_c, the plunger displacement (x_p) can be calculated using the following equation from slider-crank theory:

$$x_p = r_c \left(1 - \cos\theta_c\right) + L_{cr} - \sqrt{L_{cr}^2 - r_c^2 \sin^2\theta_c} \qquad (8.61)$$

where
    x_p = plunger displacement (m) (see fig. 8.38)
    r_c = crank radius (m)
    L_{cr} = length of connecting rod (m)
    θ_c = crank arm displacement (radians)

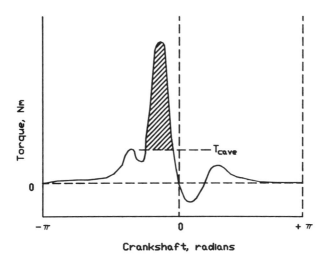

Figure 8.39–Instantaneous torque in the crank arm.

For the x_p corresponding to each θ_c, a force-displacement curve similar to the one in figure 8.37 can be used to find the corresponding plunger force. Then the instantaneous torque at that crank angle is given by the following equation:

$$T_c = \frac{-\dot{x}_p}{\dot{\theta}_c} F_p \qquad (8.62)$$

where
$\quad T_c \;=\;$ torque in crank arm (N·m)
$\quad F_p \;=\;$ force on plunger (N) and

$$\frac{\dot{x}_p}{\dot{\theta}_c} = r_c \sin\theta_c + \frac{r_c \sin\theta_c \cos\theta_c}{\sqrt{\dfrac{L_{cr}^2}{r_c^2} - \sin^2\theta_c}} \qquad (8.63)$$

where
$\quad \dot{x}_p \;=\;$ plunger speed (m/s)
$\quad \dot{\theta}_c \;=\;$ crank speed (rad/s)

Figure 8.39 is an illustration of instantaneous crank torque. The small peak on the left is the cutting peak. The data representing instantaneous torque as a function of crank angle can be integrated numerically to obtain the average torque. The average torque, T_{cave},

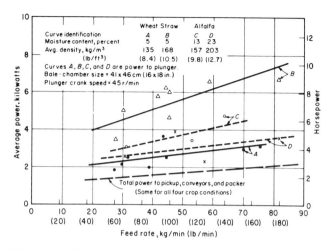

Figure 8.40–Relation of average power requirements to baling rate (Graham, 1953).

that must be supplied by the engine is shown by the dashed line across the peak. The cross-hatched area represents energy that must be supplied by a flywheel when the instantaneous torque exceeds the torque output supplied by the engine. The required flywheel size can be calculated using the following equation:

$$I_f = \frac{\Delta E_k}{R_s \, \dot\theta_{cave}^2} \tag{8.64}$$

where

I_f = mass moment of inertia of flywheel (kg·m²)

$\dot\theta_{cave}$ = average crankshaft speed (rad/s) = (max speed – min speed)/2

ΔE_k = kinetic energy required from flywheel (J) (see fig. 8.39)

R_s = speed regulation = (max speed - min speed)/average speed

The average power required to operate the plunger can be calculated from the product of the average torque and speed at the crankshaft. It can be shown that the average torque is proportional to the area within the plunger force-displacement diagram (fig. 8.37). Note that the average torque and thus the average power requirement increase with the feed rate. The power required by the pick-up, conveyors, and packer also increase with feed rate (see fig. 8.40). The equation for the total power requirement of a baler thus has the following form:

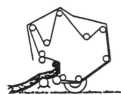  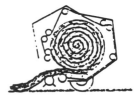

Figure 8.41–A round baler with variable geometry (Courtesy of Prairie Agricultural Machinery Institute, Canada).

$$P_{baler} = C_0 + C_1 \dot{m}_f \qquad (8.65)$$

where
P_{baler} = total power requirement of baler (kW)
$\dot{m}_f$ = feed rate (kg/s)
C_0, C_1 = constants that vary with baler design, type and moisture content of material being baled. Units are kW for C_0 and kW·s/kg for C_1

Values for constants C_0 and C_1 can be determined from field tests of balers. From figure 8.40, for example, values for (C_0, C_1) are (1.75, 1.17), (2.84, 3.37), (1.88, 2.23), and (1.97, 1.23) for curves A, B, C, and D, respectively. Calculation of baler capacity and power are illustrated in example problem 8.8.

Example Problem 8.8
    A rectangular baler with chamber cross-section of 0.36 m by 0.46 m is operated at a crank speed of 70 rev/min. The feed rate is such that the thickness of each compressed slice is 0.2 m and slice density is 180 kg/m^3. Power constants are C_0 = 1.88 kW and C_1 = 2.23 kW·s/kg. Calculate (a) the baler capacity, and (b) the power requirement.
    Solution. (a) From equation 8.60, the capacity is:

$$\dot{m}_f = 0.36 \cdot 0.46 \cdot 0.2 \cdot 180 \cdot 70/60 = 6.95 \text{ kg/s or 25 Mg/h}$$

(b) The baler conforms to varying feed rates by changing the slice thickness. For example, if the feed rate is increased by increasing the travel speed along the windrow, the slice thickness increases accordingly. The power requirement for the entire baler is:

$$P_{baler} = 1.88 + 2.23 \cdot 6.95 = 17.4 \text{ kW}$$

Most of the power is used in driving the plunger.

Figure 8.42–A round baler with fixed geometry (Courtesy of Prairie Agricultural Machinery Institute, Canada).

Round balers. Machines to make large round bales (fig. 8.7) entered the marketplace in 1971. ASAE Standard X498 provides terminology relating to round balers. Early machines employed a variety of techniques for forming bales, including use of variable-geometry chambers (fig. 8.41), fixed-geometry chambers, (fig. 8.42) and chambers without a floor (not shown) in which the forming bale is rolled on the ground. A pickup similar to those on rectangular balers but smaller in diameter is used to convey the windrow into the baler. When the windrow is narrower than the bale chamber, a certain amount of weaving is required by the operator to deliver hay to the full width of the chamber.

The variable-geometry chamber of figure 8.41 is the most widely used design; it creates a bale of nearly uniform density whereas the other types create bales with a low-density core. In the design of figure 8.41, a group of parallel, flat belts form the chamber. Typically, the belts are each 100 to 150 mm wide and have 50 to 100 mm wide spaces between them. The rollers on spring-loaded idler arms retract and allow the chamber to enlarge as the bale grows to full size. Power must be supplied to the chamber belts so that the moving periphery of the chamber will rotate the incoming hay and cause it to form into a tight roll. Peripheral speeds of the belts and floor conveyor typically range from 1.3 to 2.8 m/s. The chamber forms a bale with a low-density core. As additional layers are added, the density increases and is controlled by the belt tension. When the bale reaches the desired diameter, the operator stops forward motion and engages the twine-wrapping mechanism as the bale continues to rotate. A manual or powered traversing guide spaces the twine wraps at 150 to 200 mm intervals across the face of the bale. The twine is not tied; the twine end is inserted into the chamber, wraps on the bale as it rotates, is cut and left with a free end when the bale is completed. On some balers, dual-tying mechanisms allow both ends of the bale to be tied simultaneously for faster tying. As an alternative to tying with twine, the baler may be equipped with facilities for wrapping the bales in a full-width plastic netting. Only 1.5 to 2 turns of the bale are needed to wrap with netting, compared to 10 to 20 turns to wrap with twine. The netting

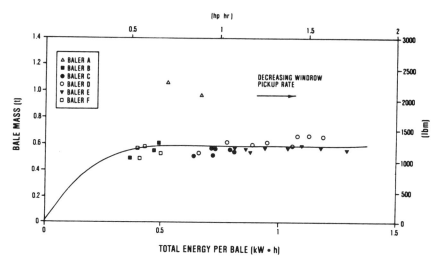

Figure 8.43–Cumulative bale mass versus energy required to form a bale (Freeland and Bledsoe, 1988).

gives the exterior of the bale a more closed structure, thus reducing leaf loss and improving weatherability compared to twine-wrapped bales. Although the netting is more expensive than twine, the improved productivity from faster wrapping, coupled with the reduced losses and improved weatherability generally offset the higher cost of the netting. After tying, the operator backs the baler approximately 6 m and raises the tailgate to eject the completed bale onto the ground. The baler is moved ahead 6 m before lowering the tail gate to allow the gate to clear the discharged bale and then baling resumes. Typical bale dimensions are 1.22 to 1.52 m in width and 1.22 to 1.83 m in diameter. Average densities range from 100 to 240 kg/m^3, giving bale masses ranging from 320 to 1050 kg per bale. Bale density varies with belt or chain tension and with belt-to-ground speed ratio. Increasing the belt speed relative to the ground speed causes thinner layers to enter the chamber and thus produces more dense bales. Good judgement must be used when ejecting bales on sloping land; ejecting bales while traveling up or down slope can allow the bales to roll downhill with great destructive potential.

Maximum instantaneous harvesting capacity of a large round baler is a product of the size of the windrow (in kg/m) and the allowable forward speed of the baler. Forward speed is typically limited by the pickup, i.e., pickup losses become excessive at very high speeds. Average travel speeds are generally in the range from 5 to 12 km/h, but average speeds up to 19 km/h have been observed. Average capacity is reduced by the time lost in tying and discharging a bale. Depending upon the windrow size, formation of a bale can take from 2 to 15 or more minutes. The tying and unloading cycle

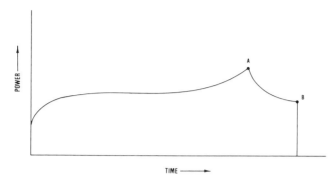

Figure 8.44–Characteristic power curve of a variable-geometry baler (Freeland and Bledsoe, 1988).

typically requires about 1 min with twine wrapping. Observed average baling rates, including the unloading cycle, have ranged from about 1 to 12 Mg/h. Since power requirements stay relatively high throughout the bale-forming process, the energy use per bale increases with the time required to form a bale (fig. 8.43). Thus, to save energy, it is advantageous to form the bales as quickly as possible.

Power requirements for operating a large round baler include pto power to form and discharge the bales, and drawbar power to propel the baler. The pto requirements follow the characteristic curve of figure 8.44, in which point A is the end of the bale-forming cycle and point B is the end of the tying cycle. The pto power requirements when the baler is running empty are typically 2 to 4 kW, but increase as the bale forms as shown in figure 8.44. With a full bale in the chamber, pto power requirements range from 12 kW to 55 kW depending on bale density and baler design. Drawbar power requirements depend heavily on field conditions as well as bale size. On firm, level fields, drawbar requirements typically range from 2.5 to 10.5 kW but the requirements can increase by 50 kW in soft, hilly fields.

8.3 Performance Evaluation

Techniques for evaluating performance can be specific to a particular machine and a wide variety of machines are used in hay and forage harvesting. For any machine, however, three types of evaluation are generally included. These are measurement of capacity, power requirements and quality of the finished product. The Prairie Agricultural Machinery Institute (PAMI) of Humboldt, Saskatchewan, Canada, conducts independent tests of various farm machines under sponsorship of several Canadian provinces. The

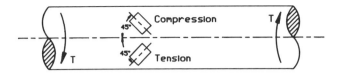

Figure 8.45–Use of strain gages to measure shaft torque.

PAMI reports are an excellent source of performance data on hay and forage harvesting equipment that is tested by PAMI.

Capacity measurements can be on the basis of area covered per unit time (in ha/h) or of material processed per unit time (in Mg/h). The amount of area that can be covered in unit time is called field capacity and is a product of the processing width and speed of the machine. Since width and speed are easily measured, field capacity measurements are not complex. For machines such as mowers, rakes, mower-conditioners, or windrowers, where the forage receives a minimum of processing, the materials handling capacity is not important and only the field capacity is measured. Conversely, the materials handling capacity is very important for forage harvesters or balers. Materials handling capacity is the maximum feed rate that can be accommodated on a sustained basis. Forage harvester feed rate is the product of mass processed per unit travel distance (for example, in kg/m) times the forward speed of the harvester. The mass per unit distance can be measured before the material enters the harvester or as it leaves. As indicated by equation 8.25, the former method involves measuring the crop yield and effective width processed by the harvester. In the latter method, the chopped material can be caught in a container for a given travel distance and then weighed. Baler feed rate can be determined by measuring the average time required to produce a bale and weighing to determine the mass in an average bale.

Power requirements of a machine include rotary power transmitted through the pto shaft and drawbar power to propel the machine. Rotary power is the product of shaft speed and shaft torque. Accurate measurement of shaft speed can be accomplished by positioning a magnetic pickup to detect passage of teeth on a gear attached to the shaft in question. Digital data loggers are available for recording the tooth passage frequency, from which the shaft speed can be determined. Measurement of torque generally involves measurement of the deflection in a given length of shaft; since shafts are designed to work within their elastic range, the deflection is proportional to the shaft torque. From strength of materials theory, shaft torque causes both tensile and compressive strains to appear on the shaft surface (see fig. 8.45). Electric resistance or semiconductor strain gages can be attached to measure these strains and thus to measure the shaft torque. By proper positioning of the speed and torque transducers, the power demand of the various components of the machine can be measured during operation. When measuring power, it is important to simultaneously measure the other variables which affect the power requirement. Since feed rate affects the power requirement of forage harvesters and balers, the feed rate should always be measured and reported with power measurements. The moisture content of the forage should also be reported. Finally, values for all relevant machine parameters should be reported. In the case of a forage harvester, for example, the condition of the cutter knives has a large influence on the power requirement of the cutterhead. Drawbar power required to propel hay and forage machinery is usually much less than pto power and is not always reported. If drawbar power is to be reported, it can be determined by measuring travel speed and drawbar pull. Radar units are available as optional or standard equipment on many tractors and can be used to determine travel speed. As in the case of torque measurement, strain gages can be used to make a drawbar force transducer and such transducers are commercially available.

Relevant measures of quality vary with the type of machine. As examples, uniformity of stubble height may be measured for sickle bar mowers, while length of cut is important for forage harvesters. ASAE Standard S424, an ASAE standard that has been adopted by ISO as a technical report, provides methods for determining and expressing particle sizes of chopped forage. The ISO Standard DP8909-1 deals with procedures for testing forage harvesters.

Forage loss is an important parameter for all of the machines. Koegel et al. (1985) used rolled plastic to evaluate losses. Plastic sheets 3.7 m in width by 30 m in length were folded along the length to a width of 2.2 m and rolled onto spindles. A spindle was attached to a mower-conditioner and, as the plastic was unrolled during operation, the swath was deposited on the plastic. Hedge shears were used to cut and a pitchfork was used to carefully remove sections of the swath. Material remaining after the swath was removed was gathered and weighed to determine mower-conditioner loss. Next, the part of the plastic sheet that was folded underneath was pulled out and the plastic was staked at its full 3.7 m width to provide space for raking on plastic. Again, hedge shears were used to cut and a pitchfork was used to remove sections of the windrow. Material remaining after windrow removal was gathered and weighed to determine mowing plus conditioning plus raking losses. Finally, a baler was used to bale the windrows from the plastic. Additional material deposited on the plastic were attributed to baler losses. The technique did not permit separation of pickup and chamber losses from the baler. Minor damage sustained by the plastic during raking and baling was repaired with tape. The above method used by Koegel et al. (1985) may over estimate losses. An alternative to using the plastic is to hand pick losses from the ground in small (0.25 to 0.5 m^2) sampling frames that are placed in representative areas of the field.

Length of cut is often measured when evaluating forage harvesters. Since one kilogram of chopped forage may contain over 500,000 pieces, a mechanical means of length analysis is essential (O'Dogherty, 1982). Sieving is the most common method used for length analysis, i.e., the chopped forage is passed through a series of sieves with increasingly smaller openings. A given sieve contains those lengths that passed through the sieve above but would not pass the given sieve, and the mass of that fraction is determined by weighing. The sieves must be able to size pieces which are long in relation to their cross-sectional dimensions, i.e., length to diameter ratios range up to 50:1. Sieves are oscillated to promote movement of the material; by keeping the screens horizontal and using a horizontal oscillation, the possibility of endwise movement of forage through the sieves is minimized.

Problems

8.1   A certain knife has a rake angle of 85° and a clearance angle of 2°. Calculate (a) the bevel angle and (b) the chip angle of the knife.

8.2   A rotary mower is cutting grass which leans 30° from the vertical in the direction the mower is traveling (the U-direction in fig. 8.24). Calculate the (a) tilt and (b) slant angles when $\theta = 0$, i.e., when the blade is aligned with the direction of travel. Next, calculate the (c) tilt and (d) slant angles when the blade is perpendicular to the direction of travel. Assume the forward speed of the mower is negligibly small compared to the peripheral speed of the blade.

8.3   In figure 8.8, the oblique angle of the sickle section is 30° when the forward velocity of the mower is zero, so that v_{kg} coincides with v_{km}. When the forward speed is 2.2 m/s, at what knife velocity, v_{km}, is the oblique angle zero?

8.4   In figure 8.8, the oblique angle of the sickle section is 30° when the forward speed of the mower is zero, so that v_{kg} coincides with v_{km}. (a) If the knife edge is smooth with an edge coefficient of friction of 0.306, will the plant material slide along the edge when the knife moves toward the countershear? (b) What is the minimum coefficient of edge friction that will prevent sliding?

8.5   Assume in figure 8.8 that the leading corner of the sickle section has reached the ledger plate and the forward velocity of the mower is essentially zero. The oblique angle of the sickle section is 30°, while the oblique angle of the ledger plate is 8.4°. (a) If both the sickle section and the ledger plate have smooth edges with a coefficient of friction of 0.306, is the clip angle small enough to prevent the plant material from sliding forward along the edges? (b) Repeat part (a), except that the ledger plate is now serrated and has an edge coefficient of friction of 0.364. (c) Repeat part a, except that both the section and ledger plate have serrated edges with coefficients of friction of 0.364. (d) Suppose that forward speed of the mower has reduced the oblique angles of both the knife and the countershear by 10° and both edges have the same coefficient of friction. What is the minimum coefficient of friction that would prevent sliding?

8.6   Assume an alfalfa plant with a stem diameter of 3 mm and ultimate tensile strength of 35 N/mm^2 is being cut at a height of 60 mm above the ground, i.e., the plant roots fix the stem to the ground and the knife loads the stem as a cantilever beam. (a) How large must the knife force be to load the plant fibers to their ultimate stress? (b) If the modulus of elasticity of the stem is 1,800 N/mm^2, how far would the stem deflect when the plant fibers reached their ultimate stress?

8.7   Same as problem 8.6, except use a cotton plant with a stem diameter of 12 mm, ultimate fiber stress of 70 N/mm^2 and modulus of elasticity of 2000 N/mm^2.

8.8   Use equations 8.10 and 8.11 to generate a curve of knife force versus knife displacement during the cutting of forage. The knife width is 10 mm, the bevel angle is 20°, the clearance angle is zero, the radius of the knife edge is 0.15 mm and initial penetration occurs when the knife edge pressure on the forage reaches 20 N/mm^2. The uncompressed depth of the forage is 9 mm, the bulk modulus is 10 N/mm^2 and the coefficient of friction between forage and knife is 0.3. Assume $\lambda = 2$ in equation 8.10. Plot for knife displacements from zero to 9 mm.

8.9   Same as problem 8.8, except that the radius of the knife edge is 1.5 mm and the coefficient of friction is 0.4.

8.10   A forage harvester has eight knives on the cutterhead, which rotates at 900 rev/min. The depth of forage at initial contact of the knife is 150 mm. If the maximum cutting force is 8 kN, use equation 8.12 to estimate the power required for cutting.

8.11   Same as problem 8.10, except that the cutterhead has only four knives.

8.12   Use equation 8.16 to study the effect of stem diameter on the theoretical minimum velocity required for impact cutting. Assume that $r_g = z_{cg}$ to simplify the equation. Use equation 8.6 to calculate the bending resistance of the solid (not hollow) stem, assuming that the roots fix the stem as a cantilever beam which is struck by the knife at a distance 100 mm above the soil and the ultimate bending strength of the stem is 50 N/mm². Use equations 8.10 and 8.11 to estimate the knife force. Let the knife width, the uncompressed depth of material and the total knife displacement all be equal to the stem diameter; assume $\lambda = 2$, $B_f = 10$ N/mm², $f = 0.25$ and $\phi_{bk} = 20°$. Also, assume that the edge radius of the knife is 0.1 mm (a sharp knife) and the pressure ahead of the knife edge is 30 N/mm² to initiate cutting. Finally, note that the mass, m_p will vary with stem diameter, i.e., more massive plants must have larger stems to support gravitational and wind loads on the plant. Assume that $m_p = 5 \cdot 10^{-6} \cdot d^4$, where d is the stem diameter in millimeters and m_p is the plant mass in kilograms. Plot the required v_k versus stem diameter for diameters from 1 to 25 mm.

8.13   Same as problem 8.12, except use a duller knife ($r_{ek} = 1$ mm).

8.14   Same as problem 8.12, except the cut is made 2 mm above the ground.

8.15   Assuming that $\gamma = 0.3$ radians for the spatial-crank oscillator, and the input crank speed is 105 rad/s, calculate and plot values of oscillator angular displacement (Γ), velocity, and acceleration versus θ for values of θ ranging from 0 to 2π, i.e., for one full cycle.

8.16   Same as problem 8.15, except that $\gamma = 0.5$ radians.

8.17   (a) Differentiate equation 8.17b to derive an expression for the velocity of the oscillating arm. (b) Plot velocity versus input angle for one full cycle for both your derived equation and for equation 8.18 using = 0.33 radians.

8.18   (a) Derive the following equation for the knife velocity, v_{km}, assuming that knife is driven by a spatial-crank oscillator whose oscillating arm has radius r_{oa}:

$$v_{km} = (r_{oa} \cdot \omega \cdot \tan(\gamma) \cdot \cos(\theta))/(1 + \tan^2(\gamma) \cdot \sin^2(\theta))^{1.5}$$

(b) Compare the above equation to equation 8.20 in the text, which is an approximate equation for knife velocity. Note that, from the comparison:

$$r_{oa} \cdot \tan(\gamma) = \left(\frac{L_{s'}}{2000}\right) \text{approximately}$$

(c) Further compare the two equations by plotting knife velocity versus crank angle for one full revolution of the crank. Use $\gamma = 0.3$ radians in the plots and let $L_s = 75$ mm. (d) How closely do the curves from the two equations match?

8.19   Same as problem 8.18, except $\gamma = 0.5$ radians.

8.20   Assume that the movement of the knife in figure 8.19 is governed by equation 8.20. The stroke length is 76.2 mm and the sickle frequency is constant at 105 rad/s (1000 rev/min). (Note that time, t, in equation 8.20 is measured from when the knife is in midstroke). Cutting is improved by maintaining a high knife speed through the cutting zone, i.e., from when the leading edge of the knife reaches the ledger plate until the trailing edge reaches the ledger plate. (a) Obtain an equation for knife displacement by integrating equation 8.20. Use the displacement equation to find the times when (b) the leading edge of the knife reaches the ledger plate (beginning of cutting), and (c) when the trailing edge of the knife reaches the ledger plate (end of cutting). Then, calculate the knife speed relative to the ledger plate at (d) start and (e) end of cutting. (f) Finally calculate the percent of the stroke during which cutting occurs.

8.21   Same as problem 8.20, except that the stroke length is 87 mm
        (i.e., the knife travels beyond the center of the ledger plate at
        each end of the stroke) and the sickle frequency is 84 rad/s.

8.22   Calculate the maximum inertia force on the sickle for the
        situation of problem 8.20 if the sickle mass is 5 kg. (Hint:
        differentiate equation 8.20 to obtain an equation for knife
        acceleration).

8.23   Calculate the maximum inertia force on the sickle for the
        situation of problem 8.21 if the sickle mass is 5 kg. (Hint:
        differentiate equation 8.20 to obtain an equation for knife
        acceleration).

8.24   (a) Use Elfes (1954) data that average total knife force was
        1.2 kN/m of bar length when cutting frequency was
        942 cycles/min in estimating the power required for cutting.
        Assume the standard cutting geometry as shown in figure
        8.19 and let X_{bu} be equal to the effective length of stroke, i.e,
        the distance travelled by the knife from when the leading
        until the trailing edge of the knife reaches the ledger plate.
        (b) Using Elfes' finding that cutting used only 30% of the
        total pto power, estimate the total required pto power per
        meter of bar length. (c) Compare the answer of part b with
        ASAE Data 497, which suggests a pto power requirement of
        1.2 kW/m for mowing alfalfa. (d) what are some of the factors
        that could account for differences between answers of parts b
        and c?

8.25   Repeat problem 8.24, except use Harbarge and Morr (1962)
        data that the total average knife force was 2.3 kN/m of bar
        length when the cutting frequency was 1250 cycles/min.

8.26   (a) A flail mower has a total of four rows of flails but, because
        of offsetting the flails as in figure 8.21b, there are effectively
        only two rows from the standpoint of stubble uniformity.
        Calculate and plot the ratio of stubble height difference over
        rotor radius (z_d/r_f) versus velocity ratio (v_f/v_p) for velocity
        ratios ranging from zero to 0.1. (b) On the same graph, plot a
        similar curve except for a six-row rotor with offset flails. If
        the radius of the rotor is 250 mm, what is the maximum z_d
        for the (c) four-row rotor and (d) six-row rotor? (d) Is a six-row
        rotor needed to achieve adequate stubble uniformity?

8.27   A flail mower with a rotor width of 2 m is used to mow alfalfa which has a yield of 3.2 Mg/ha. Plot the power requirement for the flail mower versus travel speed for travel speeds ranging from zero to 15 km/h.

8.28   Same as problem 8.27, except that the rotor width is 3 m.

8.29   The path of a rotary mower blade is as shown in figure 8.24. If the forward velocity, v_f, is 4% of the blade peripheral velocity, determine the maximum oblique angle and the blade angle, θ, at which it occurs. (Hint: you may find the answer either by differentiating equation 8.29 with respect to θ or by plotting oblique angle versus θ.

8.30   A rotary mower has a single blade with both ends sharpened as shown in figure 8.24. The radius of the blade is 300 mm and the blade rotates at 1900 rev/min. (a) What is the minimum width of the sharpened portion of each end of the blade, L_s, if the forward speed of the mower can be up to 4% of the peripheral speed of the blade? (b) Calculate the minimum taper of the end of the blade to prevent crop drag against the end of the blade.

8.31   Same as problem 8.30, except the blade radius is 250 mm and the blade rotates at 2200 rev/min.

8.32   (a) Estimate the power requirement of a disk-type rotary mower which has six disks, each cutting a 0.4 m width. The blades are sharp and the travel speed is 15 km/h. (b) Now estimate the power requirements for the same mower after the blades become worn.

8.33   Same as problem 8.31, except the mower is a drum-type mower.

8.34   A forage harvester has a cylindrical cutterhead 600 mm in width and 700 mm in diameter. It has eight knives and rotates at 900 rev/min. It is to harvest corn at a feed rate of 65 Mg/h while producing an average length of cut of 5 mm. The specific cutting energy can be held to 14 J·m/kg when the knives are sharp. The forage is in contact with the housing for 2.36 radians of arc and the coefficient of friction between the corn and the steel housing is 0.49. Calculate (a) the required peripheral speed of the feed rolls, (b) the maximum height of the throat area if the density between the rolls is 300 kg/m^3, and the power requirements for (c) chopping, (d) friction, (e) impelling (assume the impeller peripheral velocity equals that of the chopper), (f) moving air, (g) the header power assuming C_{ho} = 0.6 kW and C_{R1} = 0.3 kWs/kg, and (h) the total power requirement. (i) For comparison, calculate the total power requirements using equation 8.42. (j) What length of cut would cause the answers for parts g and h to agree?

8.35   Same as problem 8.34, except only four knives are used. Also calculate the new length of cut when only four knives are used.

8.36   Same as problem 8.34, except that dull knives have allowed the specific cutting energy to rise to 28 J·m/kg.

8.37   Same as problem 8.34, except alfalfa is being harvested at a rate of 50 Mg/h, the length of cut is to be 10 mm, the density in the throat is 55 kg/m^3 and the specific cutting energy is 16 J·m/kg.

8.38   Alfalfa is cut at 80% moisture on a day when the dry bulb temperature is 30° C, the solar radiation is 700 W/m^2, and the soil moisture is 17%. The density of alfalfa in the swath is 450 g/m^2. (a) Assuming the hay is cut in a humid area, so that equation 6.41 applies, plot the moisture content of the hay versus time for 8 h of drying on the day the hay is cut. Assume no drying agent is used. (b) Add a second curve to the graph, but with 0.08 g/g of drying agent used.

8.39   Same as problem 8.38, except that the temperature is only 20° C and the solar radiation is only 350 W/m^2, i.e., it is a poorer drying day.

8.40   Same as problem 8.38, except use equation 8.45 with a vapor pressure deficit of 2.5 kPa.

8.41   Same as problem 8.38, except the swath density is reduced 20%.

8.42   A side-delivery rake with five bars in its oblique reel head has the following parameters:

raking width=02.59 m
reel radius   =00.30 m

$$\theta_{tr} \qquad = 072°$$
$$\gamma \qquad = 065°$$

The reel is ground driven such that v_f / v_p = 0.82. Assuming y_2 = 0.2 m, calculate and plot (a) v_h/v_f and (b) L_h/w_r for travel speeds ranging from 3 to 11 km/h.

8.43   Same as problem 8.42, except that the rake is pto driven with v_p = 2.0 m/s.

8.44   Same as problem 8.42, except the rake is a finger-wheel rake with the following parameters:

raking width=03.20 m
reel radius =00.74 m
θ_{tr} =0130°

8.45   Estimate a value for E_h by using equation 8.59, data from figure 8.37 and assumed data as follows:

d_c = 0.46 m, from figure 8.37
w_c= 0.41 m, from figure 8.37
F_c= 42 kN, from figure 8.37
L_c= 0.70 m, assumed
y = 75 mm, assumed
f_h = 0.25, assumed

The assumed values were chosen to be realistic values for the baler used to develop figure 8.37. To provide a basis for evaluating your value for E_h, Persson (1987) presented a value of 35 MPa as a limiting value beyond which straw at 20% moisture content would not compress. When the moisture content of the straw was 70%, the limiting value was 5 MPa. Since the hay compressed in the baler of figure 8.37, the value of E_h must have been less than a similar limiting value.

8.46   (a) Generalize figure 8.37 by plotting plunger compressive pressure on the y-axis versus percent of plunger stroke on the x-axis. The compressive pressure is the plunger force divided by the cross-sectional area of the plunger (bale chamber cross-section dimensions are given on fig. 8.37). Percent of stroke is the actual plunger displacement divided by the maximum displacement (547 mm in fig. 8.37). (b) Be sure to include a curve for each of the two feed rates in figure 8.37.

Generalize by using data from figure 8.37 and equation 6.60 to calculate the slice thickness, δ_s, associated with each feed rate.

8.47 (a) Calculate and plot a torque-displacement curve similar to figure 8.39 for a baler baling alfalfa hay at 13% moisture content to an average bale density of 157 kg/m^3. The chamber is 0.36 m wide by 0.46 m high, the crank radius is 0.38 m, the connecting rod length is 1.12 m and the crank speed is 79 rev/min. Note that equation 8.61 can be used to calculate the plunger displacement, for each crank angle through the full cycle. For each plunger displacement, use the plot made in problem 8.46 (with the maximum slice thickness) to determine the pressure on the plunger face and then calculate the plunger force. Then equations 8.62 and 8.63 can be used to calculate torque at each crank angle. (b) Integrate the torque-displacement curve of part a to find the average torque through the cycle. (c) Calculate the required flywheel inertia to provide 10% speed regulation, i.e., $R_s = 0.2$. (d) Calculate the power required to operate the plunger.

8.48   Same as problem 8.47, except use the minimum slice thickness from problem 8.45 b.

8.49   A large round baler is making alfalfa bales with a width of 1.5 m, diameter of 1.75 m, and average density of 200 kg/m^3. The speed of the baler while making bales is 8 km/h and the windrows contain 0.9 kg of hay per meter of length. The peripheral speed of the chamber belts is 2.75 m/s. The pto power is 3 kW when the baler is running empty, and 30 kW when a bale reaches full size. Calculate (a) the time required to form a full bale, (b) the mass of a full bale, (c) the rotational speed of the bale in the chamber when full size, (d) the torque, and (e) peripheral force that must be supplied by the belts to turn the full bale, (f) the number of rotations of the bale required to wrap twine at 150 mm spacing across the full width of the bale, and (g) the time required to wrap the twine. (h) Calculate the time savings per bale if each bale is wrapped with 1.5 turns of net wrap instead of twine.

8.50   Same as problem 8.49, except that the peripheral speed of the chamber belts is 1.5 m/s.

9

Grain Harvesting

Introduction

The purpose of grain harvesting is to recover grains from the field and separate them from the rest of the crop material in a timely manner with minimum grain loss while maintaining highest grain quality. The methods and equipment used for harvesting depend upon the type of grain crop, planting method, and the climatic conditions. The major grain crops are barley, edible beans, soybeans, corn, oats, rice, sorghum, and wheat. Many other grain crops, such as oil-seed crops, are harvested using the methods and equipment described in this chapter.

9.1 Methods and Equipment

One of the oldest methods of harvesting grains is to cut the grain stocks by means of a hand sickle, transport the cut crop to a central location, thresh the crop to detach the grains, and separate the grains from the rest of the crop material. All of these operations required human and/or animal

Figure 9.1–A modern grain combine (Courtesy of Ford/New-Holland).

power. With the development of technology these operations are now performed by machines. However, in many parts of the world harvesting is still performed by human and/or animal power.

The entire harvesting operation may be divided into cutting, threshing, separation, and cleaning functions. Depending upon the method employed for harvesting, these functions are performed by different machines or they may be combined in a single machine. The methods commonly used in modern mechanized farming are discussed in the following sections.

9.1.1 Direct Harvesting

In the direct harvesting method, all functions, from cutting to cleaning, are performed by one machine called the combine (fig. 9.1). All major crops mentioned above can be harvested directly. The combines may be either a conventional type or a rotary type depending upon the threshing and separating mechanism employed. A combine may be self-propelled or pulled by a tractor and powered by the pto drive as shown in figure 9.2.

Figure 9.3 illustrates a schematic diagram of a conventional combine showing the functional components. During combine operation the uncut standing crop is pushed by the *reel* against the *cutterbar* and onto the *platform*. The cut crop is conveyed towards the center of the platform from either side by the *platform auger* and conveyed to the threshing cylinder by the *feeder conveyer*. The crop is

Figure 9.2–A typical pull-type combine drawn by a
tractor (Reproduced by permission of Deere and Co.
© 1991).

threshed by the *threshing cylinder*. The threshing cylinder rotates at
a very high speed (about 30 m/s peripheral speed). A large fraction of
threshed grain passes through the *concave* and *grate* (normally about
80%) along with chaff and broken pieces of straw. The rest of the crop
is forced through the concave-cylinder gap where the *beater* causes it
to slow down. The crop which is primarily straw and some chaff and
grain, is delivered to a separator. In a conventional combine the

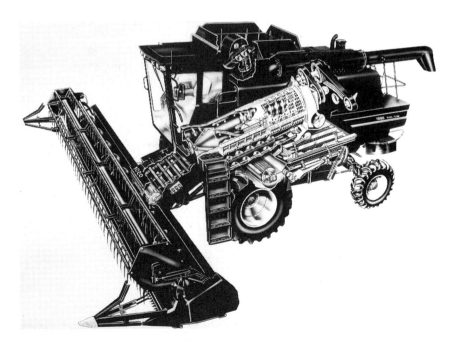

Figure 9.3–Internal construction of a modern self-propelled grain combine
(Courtesy of Case-IH Co.).

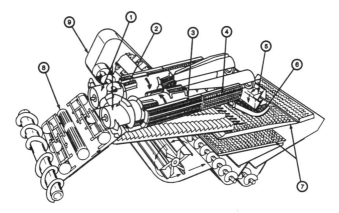

Figure 9.4–A rotary combine utilizing twin rotors: 1 Rotor; 2-Rasp bars; 3-Threshing concave; 4-Separating concave; 5-Discharge beater; 6-Beater grate; 7-Cleaning shoe; 8-Feeder housings; 9-Tailings auger (Courtesy of Prairie Agricultural Machinery Institute, Canada).

separator is made of oscillating channel sections called the straw walkers. Since early 1970's separator design has changed to a rotary design. These designs are discussed later in the chapter. The separated material falls into the channels and moves towards the front of the combine and is delivered on top of an oscillating *grain pan* where it is combined with the grain/chaff mixture separated at the cylinder/concave. This mixture of chaff and grain moves rearward due to the oscillating action of the pan and falls on the oscillating cleaning shoe. The cleaning shoe generally consists of two sieves and a fan to blow air upwards through the bottom of the sieves towards the rear of the combine. The top sieve is designed so that the openings may be adjusted and it is referred to as the *chaffer*. The air blows the chaff and the straw pieces off towards the rear of the combine while the clean grain falls through the sieves to the bottom of the cleaning shoe. The *clean-grain auger* carries the grain to the *grain tank*. Unthreshed grain heads that are too heavy to be blown off with chaff and too large to escape through sieve openings are called *tailings* and they are collected by the *tailings auger* and carried to the threshing cylinder for rethreshing. Different manufacturers have different designs for the functional components as illustrated in figure 9.3.

Figure 9.4 shows a schematic diagram of a rotary or axial flow combine utilizing twin rotors. Figure 9.5 shows an axial flow single rotor combine. In these combines, threshing and separation are performed by a rotor or a pair of rotors. The name rotary is used because the separation is accomplished by means of the rotating action of the rotor in place of the oscillating action of the straw walker. The name axial flow is used because the axis of the rotor is

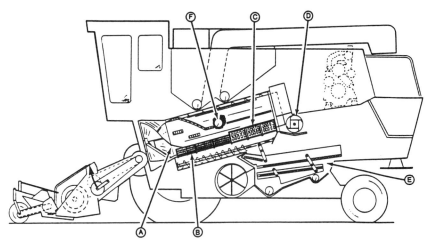

Figure 9.5–An axial flow rotary combine utilizing a single rotor: A-Rotor; B-Threshing concave; C-Separating concave; D-back beater; E-Cleaning shoe; F-Tailings return (Courtesy of Prairie Agricultural Machinery Institute, Canada).

parallel to the line of travel as compared to the transversely located threshing cylinder in a conventional combine. In one rotary combine design, the rotor is mounted transversely as shown in figure 9.6. In some combine designs multiple conventional threshing cylinders are used as shown in figure 9.7. Each cylinder rotates faster successively to thresh out increasingly hard to thresh grains. Figure 9.8 shows yet

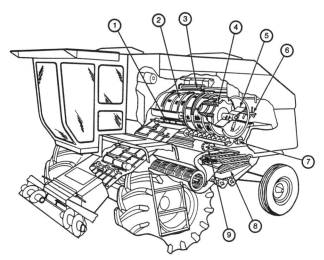

Figure 9.6–A rotary combine utilizing a single transversely mounted rotor : 1-Threshing concave; 2-Cage; 3-Cage sweeps; 4-Rotor; 5-Discharge paddles; 6-Straw choppers; 7-Distribution auger; 8-Cleaning shoe; 9-Accelerator rolls (Courtesy of Prairie Agricultural Machinery Institute, Canada).

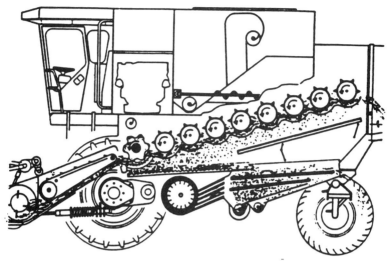

Figure 9.7–A combine design utilizing a conventional threshing cylinder and multiple separation cylinders (Courtesy of Prairie Agricultural Machinery Institute, Canada).

another arrangement. A transversely mounted conventional threshing cylinder is used in conjunction with a rotary tine separator. This design is especially suited for crops with tough straw such as rice.

Figure 9.8–A combine configuration utilizing a transversely mounted conventional threshing cylinder and a rotary tine separator (Courtesy of Deere and Co.).

Figure 9.9–A windrow pickup attachment and its operating principle (Reproduced by permission of Deere and Co. © 1991).

9.1.2 Cutting and Windrowing

Some crops that do not lend themselves to direct harvesting are better harvested by cutting and windrowing before threshing, separating, and cleaning. When the crop does not ripen evenly or, in some northern climates, does not mature fully, cutting and windrowing allows for the crop to cure in field before threshing. Some crops, such as edible beans, are cut below ground and windrowed to avoid cutting bean pods.

Equipment for cutting and windrowing is discussed in Chapter 8. Generally, cutting is accomplished by sickle bar and windrowing is done by draper type platform. The crop material in a swath width is placed in a narrow windrow for the purpose of drying. The reel and cutterbar header is replaced by a pickup attachment in the combine as shown in figure 9.9. The windrow is gently picked up by the pickup header and taken into the combine where the subsequent harvesting operations are completed. If the crop was planted in rows, several rows are combined to form a windrow.

9.2 Functional Processes

A modern grain combine performs many functional processes. These are gathering and cutting or picking (in case of windrows), threshing, separation, and cleaning. Figure 9.10 shows a process diagram of a combine.

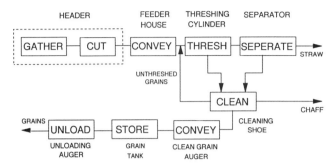

Figure 9.10–Process diagram of a combine.

9.2.1 Gathering, Cutting, Pickup, and Feeding

Grain header. Mechanisms to gather and cut the crop are located in the cutting platform (also called the header) as shown in figure 9.11. Bat or slat type and pickup type reels are commonly used for gathering most small grain crops. The pickup reel is used for lodged crops. The fingers whose orientation is controlled by either cam guides or parallel bar mechanism, reach into the lodged crops and help to pick up the crop for cutting.

Proper operation of the reel is critical to minimize header losses. Header losses are defined as shatter and cutterbar losses. During

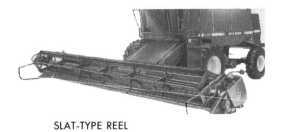

SLAT-TYPE REEL

PICKUP REEL

Figure 9.11–Slat (or bat) and pickup type reels (Reproduced by permission of Deere and Co. © 1991).

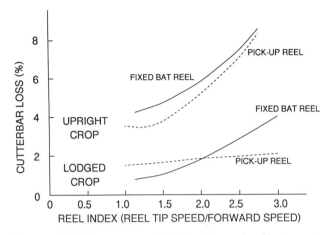

Figure 9.12–Losses associated with reel adjustments (Wilkinson and Braumbeck, 1977).

windrowing these losses include windrower losses as well as combine gathering losses in the pickup and conveying operations.

Factors affecting header losses are:
1. Cutting height
2. Reel position with respect to the cutterbar
3. Reel speed with respect to the forward speed

For optimum combine operation the crop should be cut just below the grain heads. If the crop height is uneven or if the crop is lodged in some places it may not be cut which will contribute to losses. Optimum reel position is affected by the crop height, amount of straw cut, and the condition of the straw. Normally, the reel should be set so the slats, when in their lowest position, will strike the straw 15 to 25 cm above and slightly ahead of the cutterbar. For lodged crops the reel should be set farther back. Proper reel speed is important to minimizing shattering and gathering losses. A reel turning too fast will result in excessive shatter loss whereas too slow a speed will result in the cut grain heads to fall off the platform. It is recommended that the peripheral speed of the reel should be about 25 to 50% faster than the forward speed of the combine. The reel index is defined as follows:

$$\text{Reel Index} = \frac{v_r}{v_c} \qquad (9.1)$$

where
v_r = tangential speed of the reel tip
v_c = forward speed of combine

Figure 9.13–A corn header (Reproduced by permission of Deere and Co. © 1991).

For proper operation the reel index should be between 1.25 to 1.5. The reel is powered by either a V-belt drive or a hydraulic motor. Many manufacturers provide control of the reel speed from the operator's station for proper operation. The position of the reel axis with respect to the cutterbar is adjustable and must be adjusted properly for satisfactory gathering operation. For example, in heavily lodged crops the reel is set well ahead of the cutterbar to improve lifting. Figure 9.12 shows the effect of reel position and reel index on cutter-bar losses for slat and pickup type reels.

For most small grain crops the cutting is accomplished by a cutterbar consisting of oscillating knife sections that shear the crop stems. The cutterbar operation was discussed in detail in Chapter 8. To minimize cutter-bar losses for crops with grains close to ground a flexible cutterbar has been designed. The flexible cutterbar follows the ground profile across the width of cut that results in a uniform cutting height and minimum losses.

Corn header. Gathering and cutting of seed corn is accomplished by a corn header, as shown in figure 9.13. A corn header can harvest three to twelve rows at a time. The row spacing is designed to match the planter row spacing. During the operation the gatherer points are positioned in between the corn rows. The corn head on a combine primarily performs *gathering*, and *snapping*, and *trash removal*. The gathering units are fitted with gathering chains equipped with finger links that assist in moving stalks into and through the snapping zone and prevent loose ears from sliding forward to be lost. The chain speed is approximately equal to the forward speed of travel when stalks are upright.

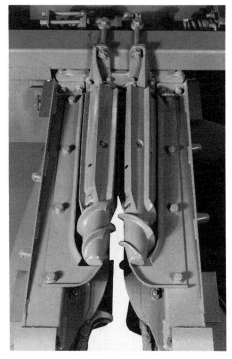

Figure 9.14–Corn-head fluted snapping rolls and its operating principles (Reprinted from (top) Wilkinson and Braumbeck, 1977; (bottom) Kepner et al., 1978).

Breaking of corn ears from its stalk is called snapping. Snapping is performed by fluted snapping rolls that grab the corn stalks and pull them between the snapping bars. The spacing between the snapping bars is such that the corn ears can not go through. As corn ears reach the snapping bars they are snapped off and carried in to the machine by the gathering chains as shown in figure 9.14. The entire corn stalk is pulled through causing all ears to

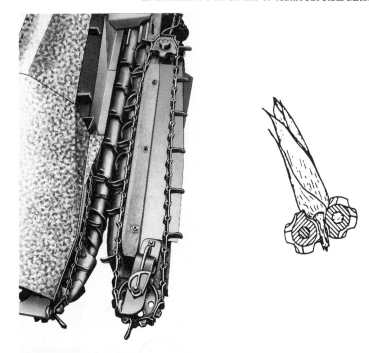

Figure 9.15–Spiral ribs and lugs type snapping rolls of a corn head and its operating principles (Reprinted from (left) Kepner et al., 1978; (right) Wilkinson and Braumbeck, 1977).

snap off. Another design of snapping rolls is referred to as spiral-ribbed or spiral-lugged rolls (fig. 9.15). As the name suggests, these rolls have spiral ribs on them and they are closer together. The ears snap off as they reach the rolls and the spiral is such that the stalks move rearward. The roll lengths generally ranges from 1 to 1.25 m and their diameters are 7.5 to 10 cm. Peripheral speeds are usually 180 m/min. Proper speed is important for adequate operation. Faster speeds would result in shelling of cobs at the point of attachment to the stalk while slower speeds may result in stalk slippage and trash buildup on the rolls. It is important to operate snapping rolls at speed proportional to the forward speed of the combine. If the snapping rolls operate too slow, the combine would run them down before they are pulled through. Too high a velocity would cause them to bounce off the snapping bars and fall to the ground. Roll spacing is also important to satisfactory roll operation. It is generally kept between 6 to 13 mm. Larger spacing may cause stalk slippage and narrower spacing stalk breakage.

Straight fluted rolls are more aggressive than spiral-ribbed rolls. Stripper plates located above the rolls prevent ears from contacting the rolls. Diameters are usually 9 to 12.5 cm and roll

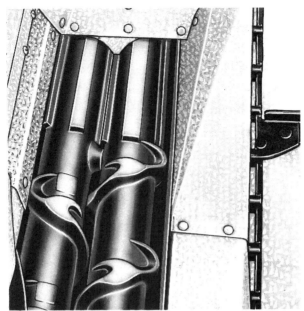

Figure 9.16–Fluted trash rolls on the upper ends of
snapping rolls (Reprinted from Kepner et al., 1978).

lengths of the fluted part are generally 40 to 60 cm. Because of their
positive action, fluted rolls permit faster capacities and higher
ground speeds.

Special trash rolls are often provided on corn pickers to remove
trash and broken stalks not expelled by spiral-ribbed snapping rolls.
Fluted sections may be incorporated on the upper end of the
snapping rolls as shown in figure 9.16.

9.2.2 Threshing

Mechanisms. Threshing is accomplished by a combination of
impact and rubbing action in both conventional and rotary combines.
A rotating cylinder and a concave grate are utilized to accomplish
threshing. As the cylinder rotates crop is forced through the gap
between the concave and the cylinder and is subjected to impact and
rubbing action that causes grains to be detached. In a conventional
combine the crop flow is transverse to the axis of rotation whereas in
a rotary combine the crop flow is parallel to the axis of rotor. There
are primarily three types of threshing cylinders in conventional
combines:

Rasp-bar cylinder and concave. The rasp-bar cylinder consists of
a number of steel bars that are mounted on several star shaped hubs
to form a cylinder. The hubs are mounted on a common shaft which
is supported by bearings and driven by means of V-belts. The bars

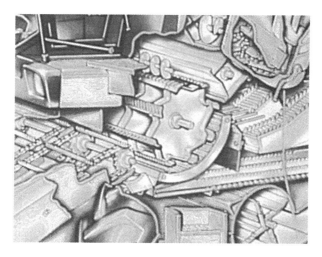

Figure 9.17–Rasp-bar thresher (Reproduced by permission of Deere and Co. © 1991).

are corrugated on the out side. The concave is made of parallel bars that are held together by parallel curved bars as shown in figure 9.17. As the cylinder rotates the crop is forced through the gap between the concave and the rasp bars and is subjected to a combination of impact and rubbing action to accomplish threshing. The rasp bar cylinder is most commonly used because most crops can be threshed by the action produced by this design.

Angle-bar cylinder and concave. The angle bar cylinder is made of helical rubber coated angle irons in place of rasp bars (fig. 9.18). The concave is also rubber coated. The threshing action is primarily that of flailing that results in a gentler threshing action. The angle-bar design is commonly used for crops such as clover and alfalfa.

Spike-tooth cylinder and concave. The spike-tooth cylinder has spikes on the bars in place of the rasps. The concave also has matching spikes as shown in figure 9.19. The threshing action in this design is that of tearing and shredding. The spike-tooth cylinder is used for tough rice straw to improve material handling and often for edible beans. There is less damage to the grain, however, it has an undesirable effect of breaking up the straw that must be removed from the grain.

The threshing cylinders vary from 38-56 cm in diameter and rotate between 150 to 1500 rev/min. The cylinder speed is determined by the crop type and condition. Wet, hard-to-thresh conditions require higher speeds. Grain damage increases as the cylinder speed is increased. Another factor affecting the quality of threshing is the cylinder-concave gap. If the gap is too large, the crop is not threshed completely. Too narrow a gap results in excessive

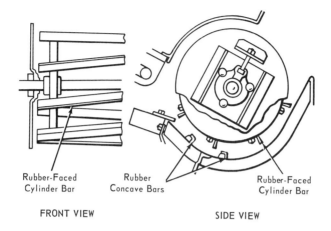

Rubber-Faced
Cylinder Bar

Rubber
Concave Bars

Rubber-Faced
Cylinder Bar

FRONT VIEW

SIDE VIEW

Figure 9.18–An angled-bar threshing cylinder and concave (Reproduced by permission of Deere and Co. © 1991).

power and grain damage. The threshing cylinder length is proportional to the width of the combine header.

Threshing cylinders in axial flow combines are part of the separator. The front part of the rotor has helical rasp bars mounted at equal distance. The twin rotor model has two helical bars mounted 180° apart (fig. 9.4). A single rotor design has three helical bars with staggered straight section between them (fig. 9.3). The rotor diameter for the twin rotor is 43.2 cm whereas for the single rotor design the diameter ranges from 61 to 76.2 cm. The crop take a helical path while being threshed in a rotary combine. The rotor speed is less and the concave gap is higher that results in more thorough threshing with less damage under most harvesting conditions.

Multiple threshing cylinders arranged in series have been utilized to thresh edible beans and peanuts. Each successive cylinder rotates at a higher speed.

Figure 9.19–A spike-tooth threshing cylinder and concave (Reproduced by permission of Deere and Co. © 1991).

Performance. The performance of threshing mechanisms is measured by:

1. Threshing efficiency
2. Separation efficiency
3. Grain damage
4. Amount of straw breakup

Threshing efficiency is defined as the percentage of the grains threshed as calculated on the basis of the total grains entering the threshing mechanism. *Separation efficiency* of the threshing cylinder is defined as the percent of grains separated at the concave (in case of the conventional design) or at the threshing part of the rotary combine, as compared to the total grains in the crop entering the threshing mechanism. It is important to have a high degree of separation during threshing to minimize losses during separation and cleaning. The separation efficiency varies from 60 to 90%. *Grain damage* refers to the mechanical damage to grain during the process of threshing. It includes broken kernels, kernels with skin damage, and kernels with internal damage. High mechanical damage results in poor germination, poor storability of the grains, and poor processing characteristics. There are many methods of measuring grain damage. These include visual inspection of a sample of grain, sieving through a standard sieve, and the germination test. Excessive straw break-up during threshing would result in an increased load on the cleaning shoe which would cause cleaning losses to go up. Also, power requirements of the threshing cylinder go up with increased straw break-up.

The threshing performance parameters are affected by the following factors:

1. Design factors
   a. Cylinder diameter
   b. Concave length
   c. Number of rasp bars
2. Operating parameters
   a. Cylinder speed
   b. Cylinder/concave gap
   c. Material feed rate
3. Crop condition
   a. Crop moisture content
   b. Crop maturity
   c. Crop type

Threshing efficiency. Threshing efficiency increases asymptotically with concave length up to a certain point. Increasing concave length beyond this point does not increase threshing efficiency and might even decrease it under certain conditions. However, experiments show that under easy threshing conditions there is little advantage of increasing the concave length beyond 33 cm (Arnold, 1964). Increasing the diameter of the conventional threshing cylinder increases threshing losses at a rate of about 0.9% for each 7.5 cm increase in the diameter. Number of rasp bars and their spacing do not seem to have any affect on the threshing efficiency. Cylinder speed is one of the most important variables affecting threshing losses. For hard to thresh crops and/or conditions, threshing losses can be significantly reduced by increasing the cylinder speed. In one set of experiments increasing the speed from 23 to 33 m/s reduced losses from 8 to 4%. Cylinder/concave gap affects threshing losses adversely. An increase of 1/8 in. increased the unthreshed loss from 0.6 to 2.0%. Concave clearance ratio, is defined as the ratio of the gap at the front to that at the rear of the cylinder. This is done to facilitate crop feeding into the cylinder. The effect of this variable on the threshing efficiency is not consistent.

The threshing losses increase with material feed rate and MOG-to-grain ratio. The feed rate is generally expressed in terms of tons/h of material-other-than-grain (MOG). The other ways of expressing material feed rate are grain feed rate and total feed rate. Moisture content also affects threshing efficiency. Generally, the crop becomes hard to thresh at higher moisture content and as a result the threshing losses become higher. Also, if the crop is not fully mature and if there is a lot of green material in the crop, threshing becomes difficult and losses increase.

Separation efficiency. The efficiency of grain separation at the threshing cylinder is defined as the ratio of the grain separated through the concave grate to the total grain in the crop entering the threshing cylinder expressed in percent. A major portion of total grain separation is done at the threshing cylinder. A high cylinder separation efficiency generally translates into higher separation and cleaning efficiencies of the combine. Cylinder separation efficiency can be as high as 90%. Increasing the concave length increases the separation efficiency but at a diminishing rate. Grain separation increases with cylinder speed. Number of rasp bars have little effect while increasing the cylinder diameter tends to reduce the separation. Increasing the cylinder/concave clearance tends to reduce separation. Increasing the feed rate has a negative effect on the separation efficiency.

Grain damage. Cylinder speed has the most profound effect on grain damage during threshing. Increasing cylinder speed increases damage exponentially. Increasing concave length tends to increase grain damage slightly. Increasing cylinder diameter and cylinder concave gap reduces grain damage. Increasing feed rate provides more cushioning that may reduce grain damage. Grain moisture affects grain damage. Increasing grain moisture increases grain

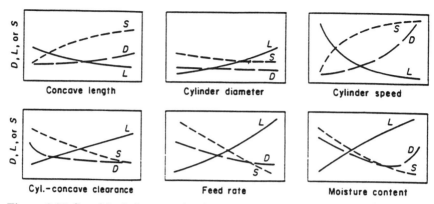

Figure 9.20–Graphical characterization of some of the performance relations for a rasp-bar cylinder with an open-grate concave. L = cylinder loss; D = grain damage; and S = percent of grain separated through concave grate (F. Wieneke, 1964).

damage, however, at very low moisture content the kernels tend to crack and increase grain damage. For shelling corn the optimum moisture content was reported by Byg (1968) to be around 20%.

Figure 9.20 shows the effect of the various factors on threshing performance of a combine. Typical cylinder threshing speeds and concave clearances are given in table 9.1. The effect of cylinder type, cylinder speed, and clearance on visible damage to barley having moisture content between 12 to 15% is given in figure 9.21.

9.2.3 Separation

Mechanisms. Grain separation in combines refers to the separation of grains from straw. A large percentage (70 to 90%) of grains are separated during the threshing process. Two types of grain separators are commonly used in combines to separate the grains

TABLE 9.1. TYPICAL CYLINDER PERIPHERAL SPEEDS AND
CLEARANCES FOR VARIOUS CROP (KEPNER ET AL., 1978)

Crop	Peripheral Speed (Rasp-bar or Spike-tooth) (m / s)	Mean Clearance (Rasp-bar Cylinders) (mm)
Alfalfa	23-30	3-10
Barley	23-28	6-13
Edible Beans	8-15	8-19
Beans for seed	5-8	8-19
Clovers	25-33	1.4-6
Corn	13-22	22-29
Flax	20-30	3-13
Grain Sorghum	20-25	6-13
Oats	25-30	1.5-6
Peas	10-15	5-13
Rice	25-30	5-10
Rye	25-30	5-13
Soybeans	15-20	10-19
Wheat	25-30	5-13

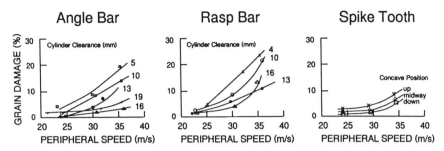

Figure 9.21–Effect of cylinder speed and clearance on visible damage to barley having a moisture content of 12 to 15% (Redrawn from Wilkinson and Braumbeck, 1977).

remaining in the straw after threshing. The conventional combines use straw walkers and the rotary combines use rotary separators.

Straw walkers. The straw walkers consist of several long channel sections mounted on a crankshaft. As the shaft turns the channel sections follow an elliptical or circular path that causes the straw to bounce on top of the channels and move toward the rear of the combine due to the design of the saw tooth shape of the top of the channel sections. The oscillating action causes the grains and some chaff to be sifted down and be separated from the straw. There are three to eight sections in a combine depending upon its size. The sections are about 20 to 30 cm wide and the crank throw is about 5 cm that rotates at approximately 200 rev/min. Figure 9.22 is a side view of a conventional separator showing the straw movement. The crank shaft used to create oscillatory action of the channel sections is shown in the end view in figure 9.23.

Rotary separators. The main force causing the grain to move through a mat of straw is the centrifugal force caused by rotation of the straw-mat by the rotor as compared to the gravity force in the straw walkers. The rotor generates a centrifugal force field which is several times that of the gravity. The rotor rotates inside of

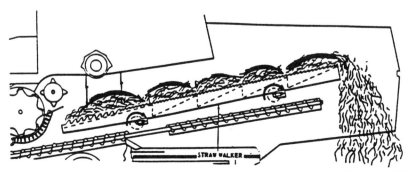

Figure 9.22–Straw walker action (Reproduced by permission of Deere and Co. © 1991).

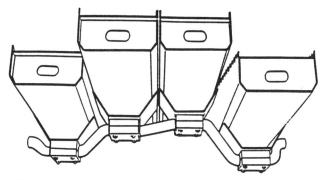

Figure 9.23–Straw walkers and the driving crankshaft
(Reproduced by permission of Deere and Co. © 1991).

stationary cylindrical screen. The paddles mounted on the rotor
surface cause the crop to take a helical path in the annular space
defined by the rotor and the screen. In rotary separators the crop
motion is forced rather than induced (as in the case of straw
walkers). This results in higher capacity per unit grate area but
requires higher power. Since the separation is not gravity dependent,
the ground surface irregularity has no effect on the separation
process. Figure 9.24 shows a rotary separator that utilizes two rotors.

Figure 9.24–The cylinder and tine rotary separator
(Courtesy of Deere and Co.).

The diameter of the front feed section of the rotor is 464 mm and the separator section is 502 mm providing a total separation area of 1.2 m². The rotors turn at 700 rev/min.

Theory. The grain separation theory presented here is based on the research conducted by Gregory and Fedler (1987). They compared grain movement through a mat of straw with the process of diffusion to develop a separation model. The model, based on Fick's Law, is given as follows:

$$Q_g = - D \, \frac{A}{L_d} \left(C_2 - C_1 \right) \tag{9.2}$$

where
Q_g = volumetric grain flow rate (m³/min)
A = cross-sectional area (m²)
D = coefficient of diffusion (m²)/min)
C_2 = concentration of grain in straw walkers (-)
C_1 = concentration of grain outside of straw walkers (-)
L_d = length through which diffusion is occurring (m)

For the straw walker, the grain flow rate is defined as the change in grain volume with time. The grain concentration under the straw walker is zero. The above equation becomes:

$$\frac{dV_g}{dt} = - D \, \frac{A}{L_d} \left(C_2 - C_1 \right) \tag{9.3}$$

where
V_g = volume of grain on straw walker (m³)
t = time (s)

The concentration of grain, C_2, on the straw walker is defined as the volume of grain divided by the total volume of material. Since the grain is contained in the volume of MOG, the total volume is equal to the volume of MOG. The area is defined in terms of the width and length of the straw walker. Equation (9.3) is expressed as:

$$\frac{dV_g}{dt} = - D \, \frac{WL}{L_d} \left(\frac{V_g}{V_{MOG}} \right) \tag{9.4}$$

where
   W   = width of separator area (m)
   L   = length of separator area (m)
   V_{MOG} = volume of material-other-than-grain on the straw
            walker (m^3)

The equation after rearranging and integrating becomes:

$$\ln\left(\frac{V_{gf}}{V_{gi}}\right) = -D\ \frac{WL}{L_d V_{MOG}}\ t \qquad (9.5)$$

Taking the exponential of both sides of the above equation gives,

$$\frac{V_{gf}}{V_{gi}} = e^{-[DWL/(L_d V_{MOG})]\ t} \qquad (9.6)$$

The grain volume can be replaced by grain mass divided by
grain density. The above equation is rewritten in terms of grain
masses as follows:

$$\frac{G_f}{G_i} = e^{-[DWL/(L_d V_{MOG})]\ t} \qquad (9.7)$$

where
   G_f = final grain mass (kg)
   G_i = initial grain mass (kg)

Replacing V_{MOG}/t by the MOG feed rate divided by MOG density:

$$\frac{G_f}{G_i} = e^{-[DW\rho_{MOG}/(L_d \dot{m})]\ L} \qquad (9.8)$$

where
   ρ_{MOG} = bulk density of MOG (kg/m^3)
   $\dot{m}$ = MOG flow rate (kg/min)

If all the variables, except for L, in the exponent on the right
hand side of the above equation were held constant (= K_L) the
resulting equation will be a decaying function of straw walker length

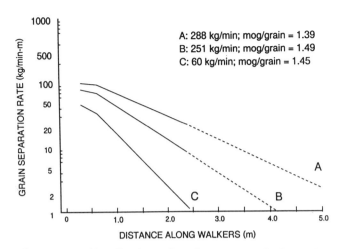

Figure 9.25–Distribution of grain separated along the walkers at three different feed rates. The number at each foot interval indicates the percentage of total separated at that foot of length (Redrawn from Reed et al., 1974).

as shown below. The values of K_L were found to be dependent on the MOG feed rate.

Reed et al. (1974) and Wang (1987) studied grain straw separation in conventional and rotary combines. They found that grain separation is an exponential function of the separator length as shown in figure 9.25 and 9.26. Reed suggested the following relationship for grain loss in a conventional combine:

$$GL = e^{-bL} \tag{9.9}$$

where

    GL = grain loss
    b   = constant
    L   = walker length

Comparing equation (9.8) with (9.9) we find that the two equations are identical and that K_L has the same meaning as b. Therefore, K_L may be determined using the data reported by Reed. The separator efficiency is determined by subtracting the grain loss from 1 and expressing the number in percentage. The walker length corresponding to 50% efficiency is determined as follows:

$$0.5 = e^{-bL_{1/2}}$$

or

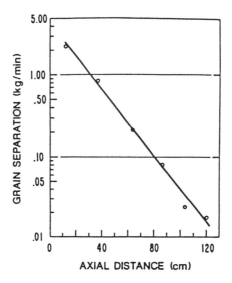

Figure 9.26–Typical separation distribution along and beneath the central region of the threshing and separation concave of a rotary combine in wheat (Wang et al., 1987).

$$\ln\left(0.5\right) = -bL_{1/2}$$

or

$$b = \frac{0.693}{L_{1/2}} \qquad (9.10)$$

The value of b can be determined from the data given in figure 9.25. It depends on the MOG feed rate and MOG/grain ratio. The following relationship was developed to estimate the value of b:

$$b = 648.4\dot{m}^{-1.296}\left(\frac{MOG}{Grain}\right)^{-0.662} \qquad (9.11)$$

where
$\dot{m}$ = MOG feed rate (kg/min)
MOG/Grain = MOG to grain ratio in the crop

Example 9.1

A combine, fitted with a 2.44 m long straw walker, is harvesting wheat at a MOG feedrate of 9 t/h. The MOG/grain ratio is 0.8. Determine the expected grain loss from the separator. Assume that 75% of the grain was separated at the cylinder concave.

Solution. The grain loss is determined from equation (9.9). Estimate the value of b from equation (9.11) as follows:

$$b = 648.4 \, (150)^{-1.296} \, (0.8)^{-0.662}$$
$$= 1.137 \text{ m}^{-1}$$

Substituting in equation (9.9) we get:
$$\text{grain loss} = e^{-1.137 \, (2.44)}$$
$$= 0.0624$$

or

$$\cong 6\%$$

Since only 25% of the total grain reaches the separator and 6% of which is lost, the grain loss on the total grain basis would be 0.25·0.06 = 0.015 or 1.5%. This is a reasonable amount for separation loss.

Performance. The performance of the separator is measured in two ways. *Walker efficiency*, measured in percent grain loss, and *walker capacity*, measured in tons/h of MOG feed rate corresponding to a given grain loss (usually 1 or 2%). The *walker efficiency* is calculated by dividing the amount of grains separated by the amount of grains entering the separator and expressed as percentage. The amount of grain still in the straw as it leaves the combine is considered the separator loss. This method is preferred for comparing the separation performance of different combines.

The separation performance parameters for the conventional combines are affected by the following factors:
1. Design factors
   a. Walker length
   b. Crank throw and speed
2. Operating Parameters
   a. Material feed rate
   b. Walker slope
3. Crop Conditions
   a. Grain to MOG ratio
   b. Physical and mechanical properties of the crop

Effect of design factors. The effect of separator length on the performance has been presented earlier. The size and speed of straw walker crank are designed to obtain an optimum combination of the straw agitation and crop throughput rate. Increasing the crank throw would increase the agitation but at a higher power requirements. Increasing the speed would increase the throughput rate but may not allow all grains to sift out before the straw escapes through the rear of the combine.

Effect of operating parameters. Increasing the MOG feed rate of the crop increases grain loss exponentially. A reasonable balance between the capacity and grain loss has to be maintained. Fig. 9.27 shows the effect of uphill and downhill ground slope on the separator performance. Downhill slope results in better performance. Hill and Frehlich (1985) reported that as the MOG/grain ratio increases, separator losses increase somewhat exponentially in wheat and barley as shown in figure 9.28. In wheat, reducing the MOG/grain ratio from maximum (1.2) to medium (0.85) reduced the average straw walker losses from 0.73 to 0.48%. Reducing the

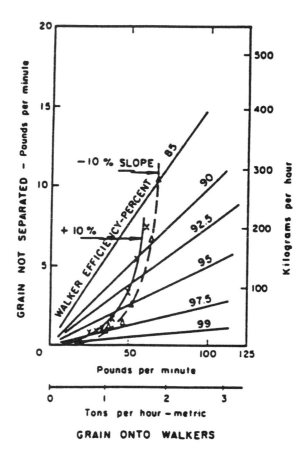

Figure 9.27–The effect of 10% slope on walker efficiency (Reed et al., 1974).

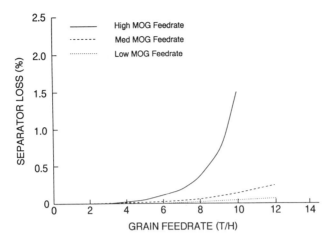

Figure 9.28–Typical effect of MOG/G ratio on straw walker loss for wheat crop (Redrawn from Hill and Frehlich, 1985).

MOG/grain ratio from 1.2 to 0.64 reduced losses to less than 0.3%. This suggests that an accurate header height control to cut the stalks just below the grain heads would improve separator performance.

Effect of crop properties. Srivastava (1990) reported that grain bulk density and angle of repose, and straw bulk density are related to separator performance while harvesting wheat and barley. Increasing grain density increases separator capacity while increasing the grain angle of repose has the opposite effect. Higher straw density reduces separator capacity.

9.2.4 Cleaning

Cleaning refers to the final separation of grain from other crop material which consists of mainly chaff and broken straw pieces. The grain separated at the threshing cylinder and the separation unit is combined on an oscillating conveyor or a set of augers that feed the mixture of grain and chaff to the cleaner, often referred to as the *cleaning shoe*.

Mechanisms. A common cleaning shoe arrangement is shown in figure 9.29. The separation is accomplished due to the aerodynamic and mechanical actions. The cleaning shoe design consists of two (or three) oscillating adjustable opening sieves and a paddle type fan to blow air through the sieve openings. The crop is dropped on the top sieve (*chaffer sieve*) near the front of the shoe. The chaff gets blown off by the air and the grain falls through the opening on to the lower sieve (*cleaning sieve*). The process is repeated once more as the clean grain passes through to the clean grain auger and conveyed to the grain tank. The separation occurs due to difference in

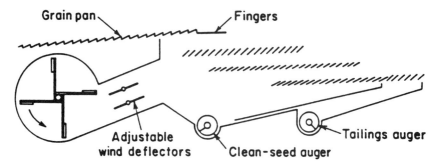

the terminal velocities of grain and chaff material. For example, the terminal velocity of wheat, oat, and barley grain range from 5 to 10 m/s whereas the terminal velocity for short pieces of straw from 2 to 6 m/s and from 1.5 to 2.5 m/s for chaff.

The two sieves oscillate in the same direction or opposite to each other for better balance. The rate of oscillation varies from 250 to 325 cycles per minute. The sieve area depends on the width of the threshing cylinder. Generally, the chaffer sieve area varies from 114 to 147 cm²/cm of the cylinder width for models having two sieves. Figure 9.30 shows the adjustable opening sieve design. The lips rotate to open or close the openings. The bottom sieve has smaller openings. For small grain the bottom sieve is replaced by round hole sieve. The unthreshed grain, commonly referred to as the tailings, too small to go through the sieves and too heavy to be blown off by the fan, travel on top of the chaffer towards the rear of the combine due to the oscillations. The tailings are collected by an auger and conveyed to the threshing cylinder for rethreshing.

Rotary combines utilize the same cleaning shoe design as the conventional machines. There are augers placed longitudinally under the rotor to carry the grain-chaff mixture to an oscillating grain pan

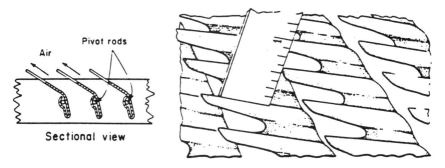

Figure 9.30–An adjustable chaffer sieve (Reprinted from Kepner et al., 1978).

which feeds the mixture to the cleaning shoe. Some rotary designs create air flow through the rotor to remove chaff. This may be considered a form of pre-cleaning.

Theory. To understand the theory that applies to the cleaning shoe it would be worthwhile to examine what happens to the crop material during the process of cleaning. The mixture of grain, chaff and small pieces of straw falls from the oscillating grain pan or an auger bed on to the front part of the chaffer sieve. As the mixture falls, a blast of air is directed at about 45° angletowards the rear of the combine. The air velocity is such that it carries most of the chaff with it while the grain and some chaff fall on the chaffer sieve. The remaining mixture of crop material is subjected to air movement as well as mechanical oscillations. The mat of the crop material moves towards the rear of the combine on the chaffer sieve due to the oscillations. The air moving through the mat causes the mat to lose chaff as it is carried by the air stream while the grain sifts down through the mat of chaff and small pieces of straw due to gravity and pass through the openings in the chaffer. The grain and a small fraction of chaff fall on the cleaning sieve where the process is repeated. Thus, the theoretical principles applicable to the cleaning process are:

1. Aerodynamic separation based on the terminal velocities
2. Movement of the crop material on the chaffer
3. Movement of the grain through the mat
4. Escape of the grain through the openings in the chaffer

Aerodynamic separation is based on the pneumatic conveying of chaff and straw which in turn depends upon the terminal velocities and the drag coefficients of the different components in the crop mixture. The crop movement on the chaffer is based on the theory of oscillating conveyors. Grain motion through the chaff and straw mat is due to the gravity and the resistive force caused by the straw mat. The escape of grain through the sieve opening is based on the theory of sieving which is based on the theory of probability.

The *aerodynamic model*, based on the research reported by Rumble and Lee (1970) on aerodynamic separation, is presented here. This model applies to the separation process that occurs as the crop falls from the grain pan and is subjected to an air blast and as it moves over the upper screen. The following assumptions apply:

1. The drag coefficient is independent of the air velocity
2. The particles are accelerated as free bodies and not as a mat
3. The velocity of air through the upper screen is constant
4. Air flow above the upper screen is streamlined parallel to the orientation of the chaffer lips

Summing forces acting on the particles in the vertical direction we get:

$$ma = F_g - F_d \qquad (9.12)$$

where
- m = particle mass (kg)
- a = particle acceleration (m/s^2)
- F_g = force of gravity acting on the particle (N)
- F_d = aerodynamic drag acting on the particle (N)

The aerodynamic drag force is expressed as:

$$F_d = C_d v_y^2 \qquad (9.13)$$

C_d = drag coefficient
v_y = relative velocity between the particles and air in the vertical direction (m/s)

At terminal velocity the drag force equals the weight of the particles, or:

$$F_d = mg = C_d v_t^2 \qquad (9.14)$$

where
v_t = terminal velocity of the particle

From the previous two equations the drag force can be computed as follows:

$$F_d = mg \left(\frac{v_y}{v_t}\right)^2 \qquad (9.15)$$

Substituting equation (9.15) in (9.12) the following equation is obtained:

$$\frac{d^2 y}{dt^2} = g - g \left(\frac{v_y}{v_t}\right)^2 \qquad (9.16)$$

Acceleration in the horizontal direction is given by:

$$\frac{d^2 x}{dt^2} = g \left(\frac{v_x}{v_t}\right)^2 \qquad (9.17)$$

where v_x = velocity of the particles relative to the air in the
      horizontal direction
Note that v_x and v_y are $dx/dt - v_{ax}$ and $dy/dt - v_{ay}$, respectively.
Whereas v_{ax} and v_{ay} are the horizontal and the vertical components
of the air velocity.

The above two equations are non-linear and require numerical
solution. The equations were solved using an analog computer by
Rumble and Lee (1970). The solution was obtained in two parts. First
part was related to the free fall of the particles from the grain pan
and the second part consisted of the particle motion on the chaffer.
The vertical motion would come to a stop when the particles reached
the chaffer sieve. After the particles fall 17.78 cm (7 in.), the second
condition applies. It was considered, based on the experimental
studies, that excessive loss would occur if the grain travelled 7.62 cm
(3 in.) towards the rear of the combine without landing on the
chaffer. Using this as the criterion, they developed the results as
shown in figure 9.31. The horizontal axis is the initial downward
velocity of the grain. If the initial downward velocity is too low grain
would travel farther toward the rear and will end up in grain loss.
Very high values would result in excessive chaff landing on the
screen which will also result in the grain loss. An optimum zone is
shown in the figure.

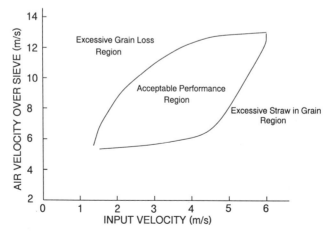

**Figure 9.31–Computer simulated results of a cleaning
shoe showing the combination of grain and air velocity
for acceptable performance (Redrawn from Rumble and
Lee, 1970).**

Performance. The performance of a cleaning shoe is expressed in the following terms:

1. Grain loss or cleaning efficiency
2. Cleaner capacity
3. Grain dockage

Grain loss is calculated by determining the percentage of lost grain on the basis of the total grain entering the cleaning shoe. The *cleaning efficiency* is the percentage of grain recovered by the shoe. The *cleaner capacity* is determined by first plotting a curve of grain loss against the material other than grain (cleaner MOG) feed rate passing through the cleaning shoe. A curve is fitted to the data, usually an exponential function, and the capacity of the cleaning shoe is determined corresponding to a given grain loss level. Grain dockage is the amount of chaff that is separated with grain. Grain dockage is determined by taking a sample of grain from the grain tank of the combine and cleaning the sample to determine the percentage of chaff in the sample.

The cleaning shoe performance is affected by the following factors:

1. Design factors
   Sieve size
   Oscillation amplitude and frequency
2. Operating parameters
   Material feed rate
   Cleaning shoe slope
   Air flow rate
   Chaffer openings
3. Crop conditions
   Grain to MOG ratio
   Crop properties

Design factors. Longer sieves would allow longer dwell time for more complete separation of grain. However, physical considerations limit the size of the cleaning shoe. Studies have indicated that the initial sieve length does not contribute much to the cleaning action. The cascade arrangement as shown in the figure permits a more complete cleaning while keeping the length of the sieves short. The frequency and the amplitude determine the level of acceleration imparted on the crop. This determines the level of agitation necessary to provide least resistance to grain separation. The material flow rate is also determined by these parameters. German and Lee (1969) reported on the effects of the frequency of oscillation on the shoe performance. The range of frequencies used were 260 to 460 cpm. Increasing the frequency of oscillation at 90 kg/min input rate reduced the grain loss significantly. However, they did not recommend increasing the frequency because of the increased mechanical vibrations.

Operating conditions. German and Lee (1969) also studied the effect of air volume on the cleaning performance. The air volume has to be matched with the feed rate. They developed a relationship between the air volume and the debris found in the grain sample as follows:

$$Z = 2 - 50 \cdot 10^{-6}V + 0.4 \cdot 10^{-9}V^2 \qquad (9.18)$$

where
    Z = amount of debris (kg/min)
    V = air flow rate (m³/min)

Bottinger and Kutzbach (1987) reported on the effect of the fan speed and feed rate. Their results are shown in figure 9.32. As shown in the figure, the grain loss increases somewhat exponentially with the fan speed and feed rate. Nyborg et al. (1969) found that the cleaning losses increase with MOG feed rate and with grain/straw ratio. The results are shown in figure 9.33. As shown in the figure the effect of feed rate becomes more significant at high grain/straw ratio and vice versa. Increasing the lip angle from 30 to 36° reduced grain loss according to a study reported by Lee and Winfield (1969). The lip

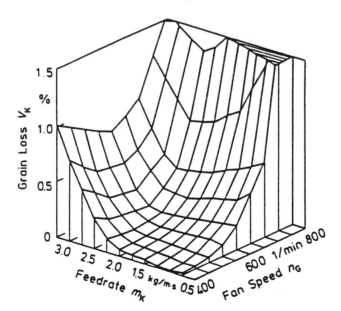

Figure 9.32–Performance characteristics of a cleaning shoe (Bottinger and Kutzbach, 1987).

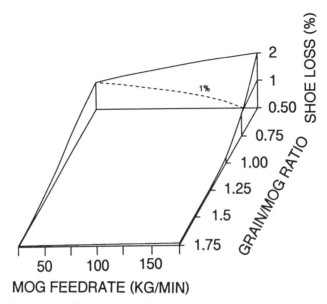

Figure 9.33–Shoe-loss surface for a standard combine in wheat (Nyborg et al., 1969).

angle effect is highly dependent on other factors such as the material feed rate.

Crop properties. Srivastava et al. (1990) studied the effect of chaff and grain properties of wheat and barley on the capacity of the cleaning shoe. He found that the grain angle of repose had a negative effect on the cleaner capacity. Increasing the chaff friction also decreases the capacity. Increasing grain density increases the cleaner capacity. Increasing chaff mean length tends to reduce the cleaner capacity. Both grain and chaff moisture tended to decrease the cleaner capacity.

9.2.5 Power Requirements

Rotz et al. (1991) reported a simplified method for estimating rotary power requirements for agricultural machines by the following equation:

$$P_r = a + c \cdot F \tag{9.19}$$

where
    P_r =   rotary power required (kW)
    F =   material throughput rate (t/h)
    a, c =   machine specific parameters

Use a = 20 kW and c = 3.6 kWh/t for small grain self-propelled combines. The material flow rate is based on MOG flow rate. To estimate power for grain corn use a = 35 kw and c = 1.6 kWh/t. The throughput rate for corn is based on grain flow rate. For pto driven combines the value of 'a' should be reduced by 10 kW. A variation of as much as 50% can be expected in the value of b depending on the crop and the harvesting conditions.

If F is set equal to zero, equation 9.19 can be used to estimate no-load or propulsion power. The cylinder generally accounts for a large portion of the total power. Power requirements for the separation and cleaning units are small and relatively independent of material flow rate. Short-time peak power requirements for the cylinder may be two to three times as great as the average requirement.

9.3 Combine Testing

The objectives of combine testing are to determine the performance characteristics of its functional components, power requirements, and durability. Only functional testing is discussed in this book. The objective of functional testing is to determine grain losses and capacity. Grain losses are expressed as percentages of total grain entering the combine. The capacity of a functional component is expressed as the MOG feed rate (t/h) through that component at a certain grain loss level. Combine testing is performed in the field as well as in the laboratory. Laboratory testing has the advantage of uniform crop and better control on test conditions. However, the crop has to be stored and that may cause changes in its properties which affect the performance characteristics of the component being tested. The test engineer has to be aware of this.

Combine losses are divided into the following categories:

Header losses. These losses include lodging, shatter and cutterbar loss. Lodged crop not cut by the cutterbar is considered lodging loss. Shatter loss is the grain that falls to the ground as the grain head is shattered due to the impact by the reel. Cutterbar loss is the cut grain heads that fail to land on the platform. The header losses may be expressed as kg/ha or as percentage of the crop yield. To determine the header losses, the combine is driven in the field and when the steady state operation is achieved, the combined is stopped. The combine is backed up a distance less than or equal to the longitudinal distance between the cutterbar and the discharge chute at the rear of the combine. A sample area is marked off in front of the combine and the losses collected from that area. Uncut grain heads still on the crop are considered lodging losses. Loose grain is

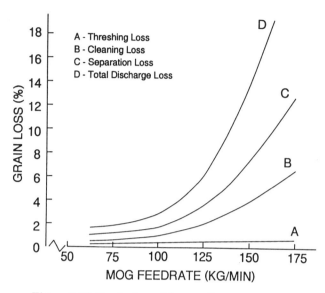

Figure 9.34–Typical combine performance curves.

considered shatter losses and the cut grain heads are considered cutterbar losses.

Threshing losses. Threshing or cylinder losses are those unthreshed grain heads that escape the combine at the rear with straw and are expressed as the percentage of total grain entering the combine.

Separation losses. Separation losses also called walker losses in conventional combines are lost grain with straw expressed as the percentage of total grain entering the combine.

Cleaning losses. Cleaning losses also called shoe losses are the grain lost with chaff expressed as the percentage of the total grain entering the combine.

Threshing, separation, and cleaning losses are also called the discharge losses. These losses are affected by the material-other-than-grain (MOG) flow rate through the machine. The plot of these losses at different MOG feed rate is referred to as the machine performance curve. The capacity of a functional component is the MOG feed rate at a certain loss level. This loss level is 1 or 2% for the separator capacity and 1/2 or 1% for the cleaner capacity.

To determine the discharge losses in field material, discharged from the separator and the cleaner is collected separately. A simple method of collecting the sample is to hang a canvas bag at the appropriate discharge chute at the rear of the combine. The combine is run in the field and when the steady state operation is reached the bag is opened to collect the material. At the same time grain coming out of the clean grain auger is also collected at the grain tank. When the bag is full it is closed and the sampling time is recorded. The material is weighed and the MOG flow rate is established. The grains are separated from the collected MOG and their percentage is computed. The procedure is repeated several times at different combine forward speed and a curve is plotted as in figure 9.34. To determine threshing losses the MOG collected from the separator is re-threshed in a stationary thresher after determining separator losses. Re-threshed grains are then separated to find cylinder losses. The separator and cleaner losses are often plotted against their own MOG feed rate rather than the total machine MOG feed rate. In this case it is necessary identify it as the separator MOG (primarily straw) and the cleaner MOG (primarily chaff). Various manufacturers have developed automated methods to develop loss curves that save time and increase accuracy.

Problems

9.1   The following data were collected in a field test while harvesting barley with a 4 m self-propelled combine: length of test = 12 m; time 21.3 s; total material over walkers = 9.4 kg; free seed over walkers = 76 g; unthreshed seed over walkers = 60 g; total material over shoe = 4.4 kg; free seed over shoe = 289 g; unthreshed seed over shoe = 81 g; total seed collected at grain tank = 17.6 kg. The average gathering loss was 10.2 g/m². Calculate: (a) Cylinder, walker, shoe, and total processing losses as percentage of total grain feed rate. (b) Gross yield, gathering loss, and processing losses in kg/ha. (c) Gathering loss as percentage of gross yield. (d) Walker, shoe, and total MOG feed rate in t/h.

9.2   For the case as described in example 9.1, what would be the separator length if the separation loss was to be under 1%? Is it practical? What other means do you have at your disposal to reduce the losses if the same separator length was used?

9.3   List possible causes and cure for each of the following combining losses: (a) Excessive header loss. (b) Excessive amount of unthreshed seed. (c) Broken kernels of grain. (d) Excessive seed loss over the separator. (e) Excessive amount of chaff in the grain tank. (f) Excessive cleaner seed loss.

9.4   Suppose you are the test engineer in charge of comparative functional performance testing of a new combine against a reference combine. Develop a detailed testing program that you would follow.

10

Fruit, Nut, and Vegetable Harvesting

Introduction

To appreciate the engineering complexities of fruit, nut, and vegetable field harvesting systems, one needs only to walk the isles of a modern supermarket. In the fresh produce section, fruits, nuts and vegetables are either recently harvested or have been maintained in a fresh condition by special extended shelf-life storage means. The canned goods section contains fruits and vegetables processed to assure shelf-lives of a year or more. The glass packed isles display a large array of products. Frozen fruits and vegetables are available in many fresh-frozen and preprocessed forms. Interestingly, some commodities can be found in more than one section. This fact is not unusual from the consumers' point of view, but, depending upon which section of the store the commodity is marketed, often requires an entirely different harvesting system. For example, peaches will have probably been harvested by hand in the fresh produce section but may have been mechanically harvested for fresh frozen sliced peaches, canned peach halves, or peach jam products.

In this chapter the underlying principles of mechanical harvesting of fruits, vegetables and nuts will be explained by examining a sampling of recent U.S. patents in the field of mechanical harvesting. While only selected patent figures will be used, the student will be introduced to the unique format of these drawings. The complete specifications of the patents are not presented here. All patents cited in this chapter are listed in the Patent Reference section in Appendix A, page 575. Students wishing to study these patents further, can find microfilm copies of all patents in Patent Depository Libraries located throughout the country that are selected for this purpose by the U.S. Patent and Trademark Office (PTO), Washington, DC. For a nominal fee, single paper copies of specific patents can be obtained by writing to the PTO. Thus, the secondary educational objective of Chapter 10 is to introduce the student to the patent literature and to the unique value of this literature in providing a functional understanding of harvesting machines.

10.1.1 Natural Constraints

Not only has the consumer demanded a wide selection of produce in different forms, but, nature has further complicated harvesting by imposing size and stage-of-maturity variables. Some varieties of grapes, for example, will continue to flower throughout the growing season so that late in the growing season, at the time of harvest, the vines will have flower buds still opening, green fruit in various stages of development, and large grapes at several stages of ripeness. Sweet potatoes will also continue to grow and increase the root size until the tops are destroyed by mowing or a heavy Fall frost. Harvesting systems must be able, in some cases, to accommodate a considerable variation in product size and maturity.

It is important to realize that the choice of one-time harvesting or multiple harvests is often a basic natural commodity constraint. In some cases, such as the tomato, genetic modifications to achieve uniform maturation have been introduced to facilitate field mechanized harvesting (Hightower, 1972). Plant materials are selected for their ability to synchronize the maturation process, thus, producing a higher percentage of ripe product for one-time harvest. Also, traits that enhance mechanical harvestability, such as firmness and bruise resistance, are selected by plant breeders.

Often food production results from crops produced only once per year on the natural yearly cycle of nature. Some food crops can be produced in repeated cycles in a given year. U.S. food production, by virtue of climatic differences, and World food production, by virtue of climatic and seasonal differences, tend to produce food more or less continuously throughout the year. However, in any given location, every commodity commercially produced results in an intense harvest activity of limited duration. Timing of harvest to ensure peak product quality may further intensify the harvest activity. This intense harvesting period requires high capacity harvesting systems that are very reliable.

10.1.2 Economic Constraints

Harvesting of fruits, nuts, and vegetables can be viewed as a value-added operation. In other words, a grower must look at the market opportunities for the crop at harvest to attempt to ensure maximum economic return to the enterprise. Sometimes this evaluation results in a choice between fresh or processed markets. The complex interrelationships between the harvesting system used and the resulting fresh product shelf-life often dictates that hand harvest methods be used for products destined for the fresh market. Hand harvesting is an important component of the food production system and will be employed in production enterprises as long as consumers are willing to support the resulting value-added pricing.

It is important to realize that the mechanized harvesting of any fruit, nut or vegetable commodities results only after that commodity has been produced (and harvested by hand) in sufficiently large quantities. Once the importance (and volume) of a commodity increases, there is often economic justification to replace hand harvesting with mechanical means, assuming product quality and market potential remain unchanged. Philosophically, this releases the hand labor to move to some other minor commodity and the cycle is repeated. It is most important to understand that many successful mechanical harvesting systems in use today were originally developed to "mimic" the hand harvesting system.

10.2 The Functional Processes

Before developing a detailed understanding of the important functional harvesting processes, it is important to consider their interrelationships. While removal, control, selection, and transportation are the required functional operations for a harvester, the order in which these functions are achieved is determined by the harvest requirements of the specific commodity. For example, hand harvesting almost always begins with selection. The hand is guided to the visually selected object after which control is achieved. Removal (detachment) is then accomplished by a cutting, pulling, twisting, or rolling motion to remove the object from the host plant.

After removal, the hand harvested object is carefully (hopefully) placed into a suitably selected transportation receptacle. In mechanical harvesting systems, as another example, detachment is seldom as selective as desirable, thus the selection function is achieved after detachment in the form of a sorting operation, either as part of the field harvesting operation or at some later processing, sorting, cleaning, grading, or packaging operation.

Given the four functional processes listed above, it is clear that there are numerous, viz 24, i.e. 4! ways in which to order the functions to effect the field harvesting operation. While certain of these combinations may appear to be impractical, the fact that the combinations exist offer an experienced engineer with the opportunity to explore "non-obvious" design alternatives. This checklist of design alternatives can be an important tool in understanding and classifying existing harvesting machines.

10.2.1 Removal

As defined earlier, removal is the actual separation of the harvested portion from the host plant. Application of energy is necessary to effect this result. The method in which this energy is applied is an important consideration, depending upon the commodity in question. Severing the attachment requires that the ultimate fatigue, tensile, or shear strength limits must be exceeded. Application of removal energy can affect one or more of these properties simultaneously. The necessary removal energy can be delivered by direct force application to the harvested portion or indirectly delivered as an inertial force response to the attachment as a result of a difference in relative acceleration. Hand and robotic harvesting effect control of the harvested portion and then exert the necessary force to cause detachment. In contrast, inertial removal methods cause detachment by accelerating the attachment support away from the harvest object. In some cases, cutting may be the preferred method of removal. The direct application of the necessary cutting forces is the most energy efficient method of removal (Persson, 1987). Cutting is usually employed only after achieving control. In most cases this control is explicit in that machine elements are in contact with plant materials such that the location of the attachment point or region is known. In some cases control is implicit since non-uniformity from plant to plant is negligible and the location of attachment can be assumed with a high degree of certainty.

Inertial application of energy usually results from accelerating plant materials with machine elements in a pattern and frequency that has been selected for the specific commodity. If the point of application of the inertial energy is the trunk or branch of a tree, then care must be exercised to minimize the possibilities of damage to the underlying plant tissues. When the machine elements interact directly with the commodity to be harvested, there is always the possibility of product damage.

Inertial shakers are commonly constructed as a slider-crank mechanism, two counter rotating masses with a common center of rotation, or a compound counter-rotating two-mass pendulum. It is possible to construct shakers with three synchronously rotating masses to effect a wide variety of shaking patterns. The kinematic analysis of the rotating mass shaker will be an example problem.

10.2.2 Control

Catching surfaces are often required to gain or maintain product control during harvesting operations. While padding is desirable to reduce the possibilities of product damage, careful selection of these padding materials is necessary. Good padding materials absorb the impact energy of the product, are easy to keep clean, and durable. Specialized catching surfaces and systems are used in the harvest of many bush, trellis, and tree crops.

If the product can be engaged by machine elements before separation, then subsequent operations are often simplified. In grape harvesting, for example, the row of plants enter the harvester where the engagement, separation and control of the product occur more or less simultaneously and in the same area. By directing the separation energy in the grape harvester, the harvested product flow can be controlled into the conveyors that will move the product to the transportation function.

Harvesting functions often interact with each other. For example if inertial separation is used by interacting with the plant material, then, the separated fruit usually has an associated kinetic energy. Now, the harvested product is unattached and moving, thus making it difficult to reestablish its control. Had inertial separation not been used, better opportunities for gaining and maintaining product control might have been achieved.

10.2.3 Selection

Selection is the process, in general, in which only the ripe, correctly sized, or desirable product is obtained from the entire product population on the plant, while the remainder is rejected. In principle this seems trivial. However, developing machines that are capable of implementing complex selection algorithms is neither simple in practice nor economically attractive. Often, a simple air blast selection means will provide a high degree of functionality while minimizing implementation complexities. This is not surprising when large aerodynamic property difference are observed between harvested product and leaves, for example. Effective design of these air separation sub-systems can be achieved with an understanding of terminal velocities usually in a turbulent air flow field.

Size or uniformity of size is often associated with product quality. Seldom are harvesting systems equipped to achieve size grading in the field. This would unnecessarily complicate the harvesting operations with the resulting need for transportation of multiple sizes.

Product maturity is an important parameter that requires special attention, especially in multiple pass harvest systems. Ideally, during any one harvest, all mature product (and only mature product) is harvested. This is important because unharvested mature product will likely be harvested on a subsequent harvest as over-mature. Harvest of immature product usually and unnecessarily reduces the available crop on subsequent harvests. Once harvested, both over-mature and immature product must be separated from the marketable product, and are liabilities to be avoided. Once-over harvest systems also need to consider these factors since the exact timing of the harvest is subject to horticultural and weather factors.

10.2.4 Transportation

Bulk handling systems are preferred where product considerations permit. In many cases, truckload lots for commodities such as tomatoes, field-packed lettuce, green beans, onions, sweet potatoes, wine and juice grapes, juice apples, and potatoes are handled from the field through the wholesale or process marketing systems.

Standard pallet sized containers (ASAE Standard: ASAE S337.1) can be handled with forklift equipment and are desirable when on-farm operations are limited to pallet sized lots. In small operations, the common means of transporting products in low volume has been the smaller sized, hand lug that holds about 15 to 25 kg of product. Lugs are often constructed from wood or plastic and have provided an important mode of transportation for many years. Many harvesting systems provide for direct filling of the hand lug on the harvester.

10.3 Methods and Equipment

Given the diversity of fruit, nut, and vegetable crops grown for human consumption, it should not be surprising that classifying harvesting systems into a small number of categories is difficult. In general, the harvest methods will be categorized by the physical

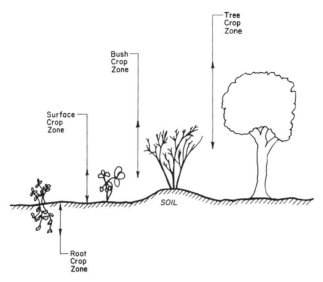

Figure 10.1–Illustration of the generalized production zones of interest.

location in which the harvestable portion of the crop is located. Figure 10.1 illustrates the production zones of interest. Certainly the location of the soil surface is more or less precisely known, but the transition between the surface crop zone and the bush and trellis zone is not always so clear. For example, tomatoes are grown as a surface crop and also as a trellis crop supported on wooden stakes. Blueberries grow on the surface (low-bush varieties), as a bush (high-bush varieties), and as small trees (mature rabbiteye varieties).

Even though some commodities belong to more than one harvesting zone classification, it is important to realize that harvesting functionality generally conforms to the harvesting zone. Surface crops are usually harvested in a once-over operation. This is certainly true for most processing tomatoes and low-bush blueberries. Bush blueberries and trellis tomatoes for fresh market are usually harvested by hand several times throughout the season. Peanuts, although not botanically a root crop, are harvested with methods common to root crops. Thus, an overview of harvesting methods and equipment will be considered by class within the four general harvesting zones. Figure 10.1 shows the generally overlapping vertical root, surface, bush, and tree harvest zones.

Finally, it is beyond the scope of this text to present a complete and comprehensive engineering functional analysis of each and every harvesting system employed in the field for agricultural food production. Furthermore, the variation in the degree of mechanization in specific commodities is based upon economic factors

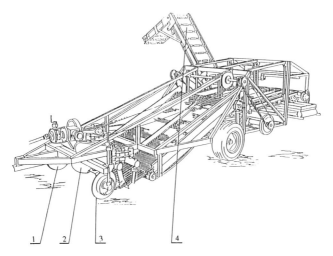

Figure 10.2–Root crop harvester (U.S. Patent #4,560,008).

and the relative degree of difficulty in engineering machines to achieve the harvesting operations. Several selected theoretical treatments of harvesting principles will, however, be presented later in this chapter.

Recent U.S. Patent literature will be used to illustrate example harvesting systems and survey important harvesting components for each harvest zone. The principles utilized by these systems will be explained and functionally analyzed from an engineering perspective. O'Brien, Cargill, and Fridley (1983), ASAE Publication 5-84 (1984), Cargill and Rossmiller (1969), and Ag Eng 88 (1988) are three excellent references on the status of world wide mechanization in fruit, vegetable, and nut harvesting mechanization.

10.3.1 Root Crops

Major root crops grown in the U.S. are carrots, beets for sugar, onions, peanuts, potatoes, and sweet potatoes. Minor root crops grown in the U.S. are radishes, rutabagas and turnips. Each of these crops are grown in rows with the average in-row spacing and between-row spacing being crop specific.

Bulk root crop harvesting. Potato harvesting is commercially achieved by bulk harvesting. Typically these machines will unearth relatively large volumes of soil that contain the roots to be harvested. The machine like that shown in figure 10.2 is designed to separate these large volumes of soil from the potatoes. In principle this machine moves through a defined volume of soil and engages the product by virtue of the product position within the volume of soil being processed. The actual process volume in this two-row machine is defined by the horizontal shear plates (**2**) and the vertical shearing

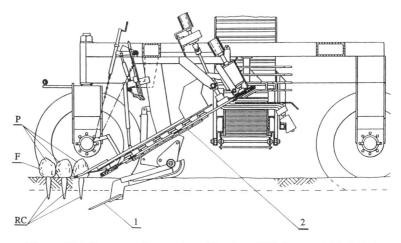

Figure 10.3–Row crop harvester, side view (U.S. Patent #4,416,334).

coulters (**1** and **3**). As the harvester moves forward, a defined mass of soil containing the potatoes to be harvested as well as the surrounding soil and above ground plant portions enter the machine. It is possible that the above ground plant material has been removed or harvested prior to the digging operation similar to the method of green peanut harvesting illustrated later in this chapter.

Once in the machine, the primary function is to sort the potatoes from the soil, soil clods and stones as gently and completely as possible. Machine elements are designed to remove the soil quickly with as little damage as possible and elevate (**4**) the clean potatoes into a storage and transport container (not shown) that is towed beside the machine.

Controlled root crop harvesting. Often root crops are harvested by initially engaging the above ground portion of the crop prior to actually digging or engaging the root portion that is to be harvested. In figure 10.3 the plants (**P**) with above ground portions (**F**) and root portions (**RC**) are engaged before the soil lifter (**1**) uproots the crop. The concept is to gain control of the root crop by the tops and transfer that control to the elevator means (**2**) prior to actual digging. If the soil conditions are favorable at harvest, then the digger will fracture the soil such that the root crop is extracted free, or nearly so, of soil. In this machine the next function is to separate the unwanted tops from the desired root portion by the general means (**4**) shown in figure 10.4.

In figure 10.4 we see two important functions being implemented. Top removal is desired at the lowest point on the plant with respect to the top of the harvested root. The interior surfaces (**2**) of the elevating belts (**1**) grasp and continue to elevate the crop until the top portion of the root crop engages the counter-rotating

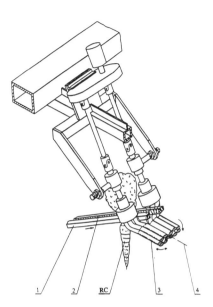

**Figure 10.4–Row crop harvester,
side view (U.S. Patent #4,185,696).**

toppers (**3**). This counter-rotation of the topper elements further
ensures that the top of the plant is pulled up to the desired topping
height. By adjusting the lateral clearance of the counter-rotating
elements, top removal is achieved at a very uniform position with
little top remaining on the root. This is the common method used for
carrot harvesting.

Peanut harvesting. Peanuts are harvested commercially in a
two-stage harvesting operation. At an optimum time the crop is dug
from the ground and the complete plant with attached peanuts is
inverted and left to air-dry on the soil surface. This operation is
accomplished by a peanut digger/inverter as shown in figure 10.5.
The initial functions performed by the peanut digger/inverter are the
same as the bulk potato harvester. A volume of soil, containing the
peanuts with the attached above ground portions, is engaged by a
series of disk coulters that are strategically positioned. In figure 10.5,
the initial four coulters on each row serve to loosen and break the soil
away from the peanuts. The final pair of opposing coulters (**1**) is
designed to provide an elevation and inversion of the peanut plant
while depositing the plant mass on windrowing and soil separating
finger-like elements at the rear end of the machine. In this machine,
the pto is used to vibrationally excite the separating elements to
increase their separation effectiveness and assist in moving the plant
material toward the central windrow position. When the peanut
moisture has been sufficiently lowered, a peanut combine, similar in

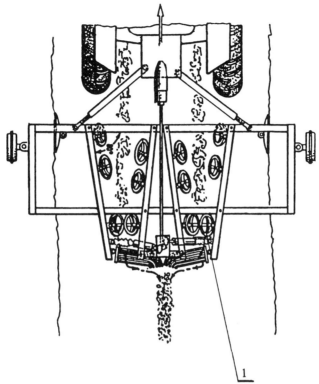

Figure 10.5–Peanut digger/inverter, top view (U.S. Patent #4,934,461).

function to a windrow grain combine, is used to move through the field and thresh (separate) the peanuts from the plant stem material. The functional elements of this combine are further illustrated in the green peanut harvester shown in figure 10.6.

In some cases it may be desirable to harvest the green peanut tops for animal forage. A forage harvester is used to chop the tops and blow the chopped material into a trailing wagon. Without the tops, the peanuts must be dug immediately, since they will deteriorate rapidly if left in the ground. In this case, the green peanut combine must also possess the functionality of a root crop harvester in addition to the threshing and separation functions of a grain combine as shown in figure 10.6. This detailed view shows how the dug plants with attached peanuts are introduced at the arrow (**2**) into the concave separation cylinder assembly that rotates about an axis. The tooth/tine arrangement of this threshing device is designed to remove the green peanut containing pods from the plant peg material while minimizing damage to the pods. The entire mass of threshed material is moved across a stationary screen grid (**7**) by the positive action of tines (**1**). Further separation is achieved with

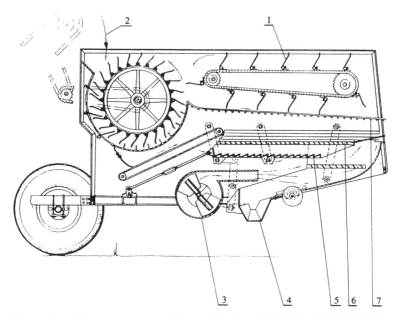

Figure 10.6–Green peanut combine, side view (U.S. Patent #4,166,505).

shakers (**5** and **6**), similar to straw walkers in grain combines, and a fan (**3**). Finally the cleaned pods are collected in conveyor means (**4**) where they are elevated to the storage and transport element of the machine.

10.3.2 Surface Crops

Major surface crops grown in the U.S. are beans (bush and dried), blueberries (low-bush), cabbage, celery, cranberries, cucumbers, lettuce, peas, strawberries, sweet corn, and tomatoes. Minor surface crops grown in the U.S. include artichokes, asparagus, broccoli, cauliflower, eggplant, peppers, spinach, squash, and melons (several types).

Cabbage harvesting. As seen earlier, root crop harvesting attempts to selectively remove the desirable root portion of the crop from the tops. In the case of cabbage harvesting, the reverse is true. The functional elements of the harvester are quite similar. Again the once-over harvest is initiated by the engagement of feed roller means (**1** and **2**) in figure 10.7. These rollers have helical spiral elements on their surface to provide a component of controlled motion in the horizontal direction parallel to the forward travel of the machine. This requires a synchronization between this forward motion component and the travel of the machine. This machine would normally be powered with a tractor that has a ground-synchronized

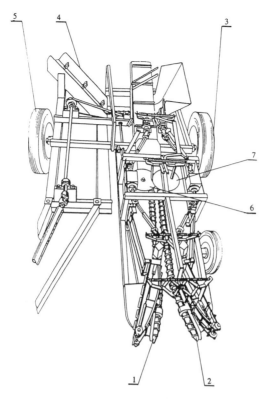

Figure 10.7–Cabbage harvester (U.S. Patent #3,858,660).

pto shaft or the feed roller elements could be driven by a ground wheel such as (**3** or **5**).

The elevation of the rollers increases as the cabbage plant moves toward the rear of the machine. Two actions occur. The resistance of the plant to being pulled up by the roots causes the cabbage head and lower leaves to seat down against the rollers until the resulting seating force is sufficient to begin to remove the plant root system from the soil. Complete up-rooting of the plant is undesirable since the restraining force of the roots is essential to maintaining proper head position. The counter rotation of the engagement rollers with the stem contact surface moving downward also keeps the heads properly seated as they approach the disk cutters (**6** and **7**). The severed heads are transferred to the elevator (**4**) for transport to the storage and transportation means.

Tomato harvesting. Tomato harvesting by machines is a well established practice in the industry for tomatoes that are destined to be processed into canned or frozen products. In general these harvesters will move over the crop only one time. The entire plant is

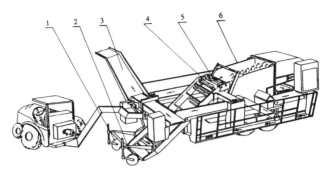

Figure 10.8–Tomato harvester (U.S. Patent #4,584,826).

harvested so uniform maturation is very important. The harvest begins in figure 10.8 with coulters (**1**) and a subsurface root cutter (**2**). Elevating means raise the harvested plants with the attached tomatoes while removing all remaining soil. At the top of the machine the pairs of counter-rotating rollers (**4** and **5**) pull the vines downward and rearward toward the walker-shaker assembly (**6**). The separated tomatoes are collected in a series of conveyors and deposited by conveyor (**3**) into the field bins.

On some field tomato harvesters the sorting is fully automated with electronic systems that color sort the tomatoes for stage of maturity. Immature tomatoes are left in the field.

Mechanically harvesting tomatoes for the fresh market is functionally identical to harvesting for the processed market, except, mechanical damage must be reduced. Designing machines that minimize bruising and scraping during the harvesting operations is much more difficult. On these harvesters all tomato contact surfaces must be covered with soft and resilient materials to protect the tomatoes from damage.

Strawberry harvesting. Mechanical harvesting of strawberries has received considerable attention over the years. Modification of cultural practices appears to be an important factor in moving towards mechanized systems. Figure 10.9 shows an integrated approach to strawberry production that begins with proper field site location. Postharvest practices are also important in preparing the plants for the next year's crop. Clearly the machine designed must rely on certain of these cultural practices to assure that the crop at the time of harvest will have the required properties. For example, the location of the strawberries will be greatly affected by site selection, weed control, variety selection, plant density, fertilization, irrigation and moisture control. This machine must have a uniform, solid mass of plant and strawberry material to harvest at one time.

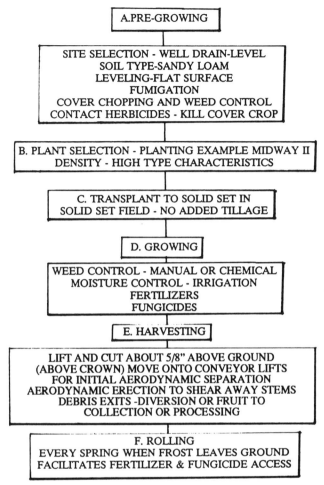

Figure 10.9–Strawberry harvesting, cultural practices (U.S. Patent #4,519,191).

The powered reel and cutter means at the right end of the machine in figure 10.10 cuts the plant material just above the surface of the ground (**4**). The entire mass of plant stems, leaves and strawberries is elevated into the initial air separation means which are more clearly shown in figure 10.11. The single leaves and lightest material are blown out the discharge chamber (**1**). The berries and attached material are heavier and fall to the conveyor means (**5**). This conveyor moves the plant material over two upwardly directed air blasts from fans (**6**) as shown in figure 10.12. The upward air velocity is carefully selected to aerodynamically orient the berries and stems for the cutter assemblies (**2 and 3**) to clip the stem and leaf material from the berries.

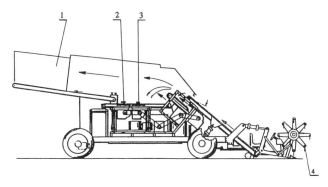

Figure 10.10–Strawberry harvester, side view (U.S. Patent #4,519,191).

The successful operation of a once-over harvester is a function of many factors. Clearly the ability of the machine to engage and cut all the material as close as possible to the soil surface is crucial. This fact is shown in a relative way in figure 10.13 where the relative distances are realistic and illustrate the need to sever each and every plant at the soil surface. The cutter knives (1) are often within 1 to 1.5 cm of the soil surface.

Another strawberry harvesting machine attempts to assist the lifting of the plant material into the cutters with opposed and intersecting air streams as shown in figures 10.14 and 10.15. Again, the important aerodynamic properties of lift and drag influence the operational success of this harvesting principle.

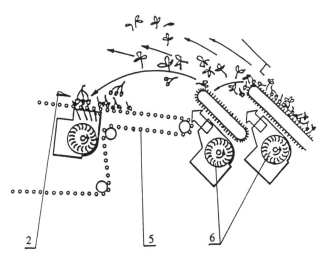

Figure 10.11–Strawberry harvester, air cleaning (U.S. Patent #4,519,191).

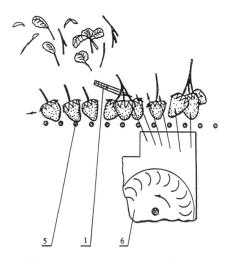

Figure 10.12–Strawberry harvester,
stem removal (U.S. Patent #4,519,191).

10.3.3 Bush and Trellis Crops

Major bush and trellis crops grown in the U.S. are blueberries (high-bush), boysenberries, grapes, pineapples, and table grapes. Minor bush and trellis crops grown in the U.S. are blackberries, black raspberries, coffee, currants, dewberries, kiwifruit, logan berries, marrion berries, okra, red raspberries, and young berries.

Grape harvesting. Worldwide a large percentage of grapes harvested for processing purposes are harvested by machines. A number of types of trellises are used for different varieties and in different growing areas. Functionally, grape harvesting is a machine operation in which the fruit is shaken from the vines and caught as they fall. Conveyors transport the collected fruit from the catching surfaces to the air blast cleaners and then into the field transport and storage bins. This basic functional harvesting approach has been used for many years. The design engineer is always interested in

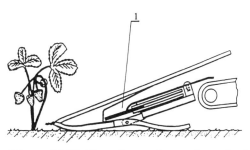

Figure 10.13–Strawberry harvester, plant
cutting (U.S. Patent #4,519,191).

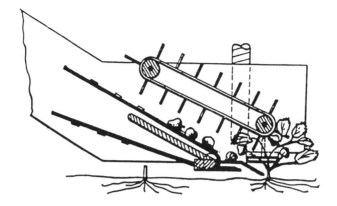

Figure 10.14–Strawberry harvester, air pickup, side view (U.S. Patent #3,964,245).

improving the performance or efficiency of these basic functional components which is the subject of the remainder of this section.

The overall harvesting effectiveness of shake-catch method is adversely affected by the trailing grape vines that originate from the cordon wires and generally overlay the grape bearing positions of the vines. One approach to reduce this effect is shown in figures 10.16 and 10.17 in which the inclined rods (**1**) at the front of the harvester are positioned to lift the trailing vines up and out of the way of the subsequent beaters (**2**). This improves the effectiveness of the beaters. Furthermore, if the trailing vines are not lifted, then they have a tendency to form a shielding curtain that encourage the detached grapes to fall in a vertically downward direction. Ground losses are normally highest around the vine trunks and trellis support posts, as we will review in the next section.

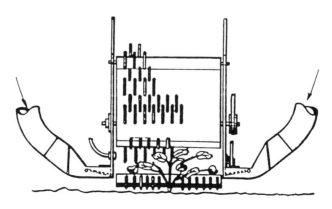

Figure 10.15–Strawberry harvester, air pickup, front view (U.S. Patent #3,964,245).

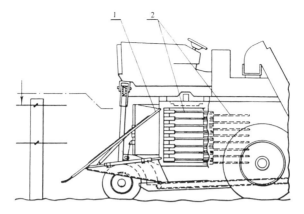

Figure 10.16–Grape harvester with cane lifter, side view (U.S. Patent #4,251,983).

Fruit Catchers. Forming a catching surface below the shakers is normally accomplished with a series of overlapping plates as shown in figure 10.18. As the harvester moves forward, the spring-loaded plates, while maintaining contact with the stationary vine trunk or post, rotate open and closed to form a catching surface. Clearly the area (**1**) is not covered so falling fruit will be lost to the ground. It is possible to improve this functional arrangement by modifying the shape, or number of plates used as shown in figure 10.19. Here we see that the relative geometry of figure 10.18 has been substantially improved by a reduction of the uncovered area (**1**) in the improved design.

Shakers. The interaction of machine elements with plant materials has many important results. Shakers or beaters that are used to remove grapes are subject to cyclic stresses that cause fatigue

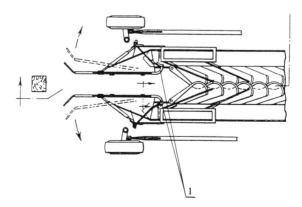

Figure 10.17–Grape harvester with cane lifter, top view (U.S. Patent #4,251,983).

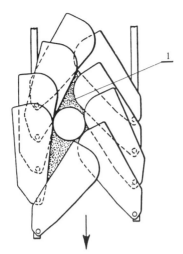

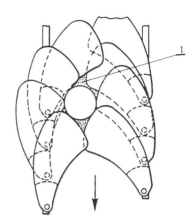

Figure 10.18–Fruit collector construction, prior art (U.S. Patent #4,464,888).

Figure 10.19–Fruit collector construction, improvement (U.S. Patent #4,464,888).

failures of the beater rods and drive components if not properly designed. It is important to realize that the plants are also subjected to mechanical and physiological stresses that result from the actions of the shakers or beaters. Tissue damage from impacts can reduce future crop productivity.

Shaking systems have been devised that are internally force balanced to reduce machine element fatigue as shown in figure 10.20 (see also fig. 10.21). In this embodiment, the shaker mechanism is located vertically above the single wire vertical cordon while the shaking action is imparted to the trellis/vine system by bars (**4** and **5**). Catching surfaces and conveyors (**3**) are strategically located below to receive the falling fruit. The entire arm assembly (**2**) with positioning means (**6**) is supported as a four-bar linkage by the two vertical links (**1**).

The isometric view (fig. 10.21) shows clearly the front and rear four-bar linkage assemblies. The horizontal component of force balance shaking is achieved by synchronously rotating two masses (**8** and **8'**) in one direction while simultaneously and synchronously rotating two additional masses (**7** and **7'**) in the opposite sense. Thus, primary vertical force balance is achieved.

The concept of force balancing can be achieved by many mechanisms as illustrated in a second example as shown in figure 10.22. Functionally this shaker interacts with the vines in an identical manner to the previous example shaker. However, the four bar linkage with non-parallel links (**1** and **2**) introduces a virtual

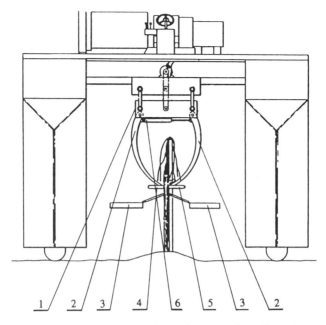

Figure 10.20–Horizontal force balanced shaker, front
view (U.S. Patent #4,793,128).

rotation point for the shaker action. This has the effect of amplifying
the displacement of the vine contact bars (**3** and **4**).

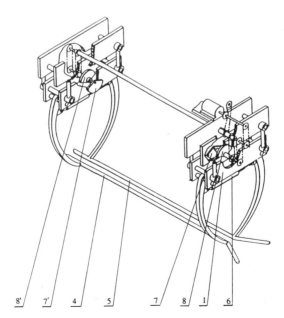

Figure 10.21–Horizontal force balanced shaker,
detailed front view (U.S. Patent #4,793,128).

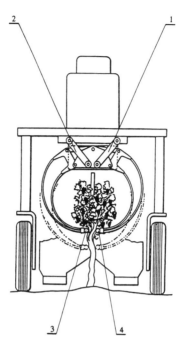

Figure 10.22–Oscillatory shaker, general front view (U.S. Patent #4,621,488).

In this second example, the method of generating the force balanced shaking component can be seen more easily by examining figures 10.23 and 10.24 as orthographic top and left side views, respectively. Two masses (**2** and **3**) rotate on a common shaft in the counter-clockwise sense while at the other end, two masses (**4** and **5**) rotate on a common shaft in the opposite sense. The direction of travel is from the left of these figures to the right and the resulting

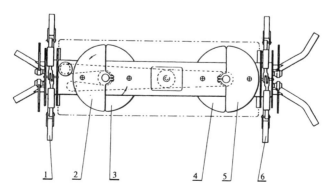

Figure 10.23–Oscillatory shaker, detailed top view (U.S. Patent #4,621,488).

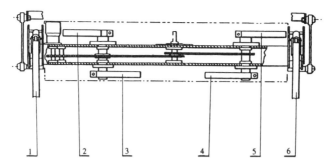

Figure 10.24–Oscillatory shaker, detailed side view (U.S. Patent #4,621,488).

unbalanced rocking force is imparted to the plant materials via the arm assemblies (**1** and **6**).

Shakers or beaters are often comprised of a rod-like structure that is fixed and activated from one end like those shown in figures 10.16 and 10.17 as pivotally mounted rods (**1**) that oscillate through a relatively small arc and strike the plant material. This type mechanism will generate whip-like internal vibrations that may produce substantially higher impact velocities as indicated by harmonic design.

One side of a grape harvester shaker design that restrains the displacement of both ends of the impact rod is shown in figure 10.25 and overcomes this high whip-like impact velocity . The lead ends of the shaker rods are fixed in common to a member (**2**) that is pivotally mounted on an axis (**3**) which is, in turn, excited by a bell crank (**1**) four-bar linkage. The trailing ends of the beater rods (**4**) are restrained in displacement but not in moment. The eccentric drive (**5**) sets the beater rods into a standing wave oscillation pattern. This design reduces impact damage potential while increasing the forward travel speed of the harvester.

Three orthographic views of a bramble harvesting shaker are shown in figures 10.26, 10.27, and 10.28. Eccentrics on synchronously rotating shafts (**2**) cause the diagonal braces to oscillate the vertical support arms at point (**3**) as well as the spiked bush impact drum assemblies (**1**) in force balance. The fruit harvesting spikes in the 4 o'clock-8 o'clock positions in figure 10.27 are moving with relatively uniform horizontal displacement, a significant functional advantage of this mechanism. Each spike drum is free to rotate through the plant material as the harvester moves forward. A rotational ratchet system restricts any reverse rotational component thus ensuring that a positive displacement of impacted material will occur in one direction.

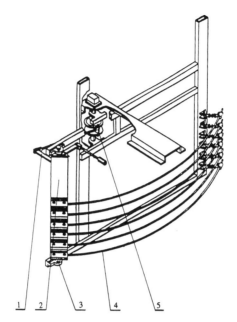

**Figure 10.25–Oscillatory shaker, top view
(U.S. Patent #4,769,979).**

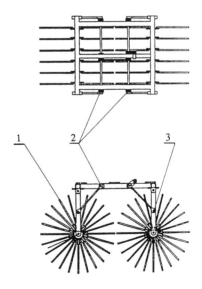

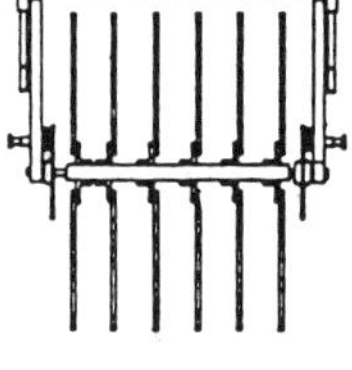

**Figure 10.26 (left)
–Shaking Mechani-
sm, front view (U.S.
Patent #4,860,529).**

**Figure 10.27 (bottom, right)–Shaking Mechanism,
side view (U.S. Patent #4,860,529).**

**Figure 10.28 (top)–Shaking Mechanism, top view
(U.S. Patent #4,860,529).**

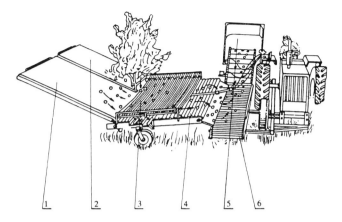

Figure 10.29–Tree fruit harvester, extended (U.S. Patent #3,896,612).

10.3.4 Tree Crops

Major tree crops grown in the U.S. are apples, apricots, avocados, cherries, citrus of several types, peaches, pears, pecans, and plums. Minor tree crops grown in the U.S. are almonds, dates, figs, filbert nuts, macadamia nuts, olives, prunes, and walnuts of several types.

Tree harvesters. The mechanical harvest of edible tree crops has been of interest to engineers for a number of years. Many factors influence the degree of success of these attempts to harvest by machine. The structure, size, and shape of the tree is important. Apple trees are quite different from date palm trees. The relative durability of the harvested crop is no less important. Peaches are much more subject to bruising damage that are pecans. Finally the relative value of the individual harvested unit is indicative of the harvest revenue that is available to mechanize the harvest. The value of a single red tart cherry for processing is small compared with the value of a freshmarket orange. In the last analysis the revenue that can be applied towards mechanization of any commodity is a complex issue. The important feature is that the general trends outlined above can provide initial insight and guidelines into the realistic expectations of providing mechanized harvesting systems.

Certain tree crops lend themselves to whole tree harvest by mechanical means. Figure 10.29 illustrates a harvester for trees that provides for a catching surface (**1** and **2**) that can be positioned within the row by a tractor and deployed across the row to form a complete catching surface beneath the tree canopy. The inclined surfaces, after deployment, collect the harvested fruit by gravity means while the decelerator strips (**3**) protect the fruit from directly impacting the collector means (**4**) that transfers the fruit to the transport conveyor (**6**) and then into the bulk storage and transport bin (**5**). The mechanisms used for shaking the tree to cause fruit release will be addressed in the following sections.

Tree shakers. In general, harvesting tree fruits by shaking the tree requires the transfer of relatively large amounts of energy into the tree structure. Application of this energy is achieved with trunk or limb shakers that attach to the pertinent tree member. The nature of the connection between the tree and the vibrator has evolved over many years. The application of shear stress to the bark must be avoided since "slipping" the bark can cause sufficient damage to kill the tree outright or may be accumulative over the years if the tree survives in a weakened state. The importance of proper design and operation of the shaker assembly is essential if trees are to be harvested successfully.

Eccentric rotating masses are used almost exclusively in tree shaker designs. Since these are inertial shaker designs, it should be clear that the resulting amplitude of shake is related to the relative mass of the rotating inertial shaker mass and the mass of the shaken tree or branch. The frequency of shake is also important but is usually much easier to monitor and control.

There is also a practical operational matter to be considered with tree shakers. If the eccentric displacement is fixed, then it is necessary for the shaking frequency to be zero while the shaker is attached or clamped to the tree. Additional time is required since the shaker must then be brought up to the desired operational shaking frequency. During this acceleration process, undesirable and potentially damaging low frequency structural harmonics may be excited within the tree. It is therefore important to have shakers that can be operated at one frequency with variable amplitudes of force.

Figure 10.30 has a rotating mass (**1**) that, in the position shown in the figure, has its center of gyration coincident with the axis of rotation of shaft (**2**). The eccentricity is controlled by a hydraulic cylinder (**3**). Synchronous combinations of this shaker can be used to force balance in a manner similar to the grape shaking systems examined earlier in the chapter.

In harvesting nuts and citrus for processing, it is common to shake the crop onto the ground for subsequent collection by a machine in a second field operation. Thus, tree shakers are used alone as shown in figure 10.31. Of more interest, this shaker can produce different patterns of shaking displacement, subject to the understanding that the resulting displacement of all inertial shakers is a function of the mass and resonant structural vibrational characteristics of the tree being shaken. Figure 10.32 illustrates

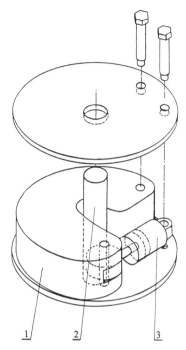

Figure 10.30–Variable eccentricity mass shaker (U.S. Patent #4,776,156).

three co-axial mounted eccentric masses that can be rotated in either direction and at independently selected speeds.

Pick-up systems. The functional requirements of ground collection systems like the one shown in figure 10.33 include product engagement and control elements. Once the product is elevated into the harvester, air is used to remove the lighter trash from the

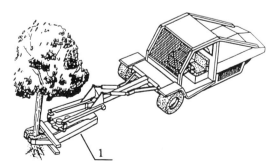

Figure 10.31–Multi-pattern mass shaker (U.S. Patent #4,409,782).

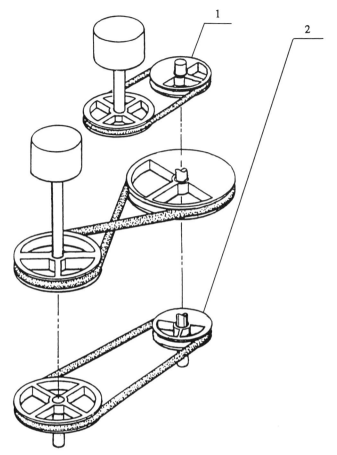

**Figure 10.32–Multi-pattern mass shaker,
isometric (U.S. Patent #4,409,782).**

product. Careful attention to the mechanics of aerodynamic cleaning
can be observed in figure 10.34. A combination of high air velocity in

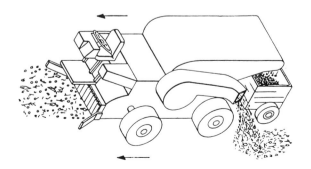

**Figure 10.33–Nut gathering machine (U.S. Patent
#4,364,222).**

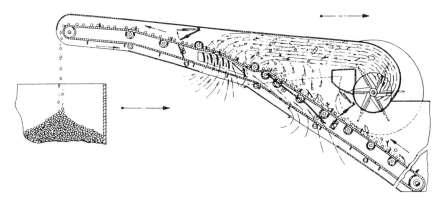

Figure 10.34–Nut gathering machine, side view (U.S. Patent #4,364,222).

the principle flow path as well as an alternating gradient in the conveyor assures that all light material is removed. Products that are inadvertently entrained into the air stream as well, have an opportunity to fall back out before entering the fan. This system has no means for separating stones or heavier material from the product.

Automatic tree harvesters. The advances in computer technology and vision systems have led to the development of field systems that are functionally capable of unattended operation in well established orchards harvesting single fruits at a time and carefully placing the harvested fruit into the storage bin. Functionally these systems are operationally similar to manual labor. Television cameras view the tree with harvestable fruit and computers process the images to determine which fruit to pick. As shown in figure 10.35, the computers then control the robotic arm with a vacuum gripper (**2**) that rotates to detach the fruit (**1**). The machine is self-propelled between the tree rows. The machine senses the

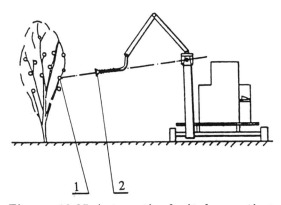

Figure 10.35–Automatic fruit harvesting machine (U.S. Patent #4,975,016).

position of the tree and stops to pick the fruit. At the end of the rows, the machine is computer-controlled to loop-back into the next middle and continue fruit picking operations. The only human interaction would be a forklift operator who removes filled bins of fruit and replaces them with empty bins.

10.4 Theoretical Considerations

Several principles have been successfully utilized in solving mechanization problems in fruit, vegetable, and nut harvesting. Appropriate engineering analyses are often used to explore the feasibility of a possible design solution or understand why an existing machine element or process functions. In each section that follows, important problem conditions are stated along with the necessary assumptions for the theoretical analyses and definitions of all engineering variables.

10.4.1 Aerodynamic Concepts

Often it is possible to effect an operational result based upon one physical parameter by implementing another. This concept is useful and effective as long as there exists a high correlation between the operational property and the desired result. For example, the size of an object is often used to effect a separation of product by mass. Similarly, color of product is used to indicate ripeness or maturity. The choice of physical property to utilize in the machine function is dependent upon several factors. First is the relative ease of implementation. It is much easier to subject products to the sizing by falling through a dimensionally controlled opening, than to effect a mass balance measurement of each item. Secondly, the two properties must be in fact significantly related. In some cases this relationship is functional as in the case of physical size and weight where the product density is known to be constant or nearly constant. Thus, it is a common and accepted design practice to utilize a strongly related property to effect a unit operation based upon another property.

Aerodynamic properties of strawberries. Cleaning the leaves, severed stems, straw and other light weight trash from harvested strawberries depends upon being able to introduce the unsorted materials into an air flow field that has an average flow velocity component lower than the relative terminal velocity of the berries, but, higher than the relative terminal velocity of the lighter materials.

Terminal velocity in air (V_t) is defined as the maximum free-falling velocity that is achieved by a body subject to gravitational

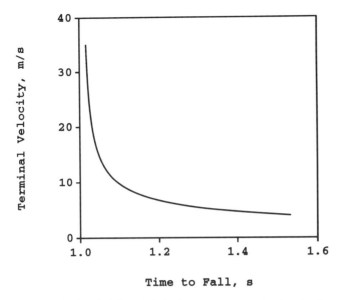

Figure 10.36–Relationship between the terminal velocity of an object and the time to fall for a given drop height (Bilanski et al., 1962).

acceleration. Relative terminal velocity in air (V_r) is defined as the velocity of air in a uniform flow field that, when directed vertically upward, will suspend or "float" a body that is subject to gravitational acceleration. Thus, the free falling terminal velocity of a strawberry will be different from the average upwardly directed air velocity necessary to suspend a berry in mid air within that flow field. The preferred units for both terminal and relative terminal velocities are meters per second.

In practice, terminal velocity can be measured by determining the time of free fall from a given height as determined by equation 10.1 (Bilanski et al., 1962):

$$S = \frac{V_t^2}{g} \ln\left[\cosh\left(\frac{gt}{V_t}\right)\right]$$ (10.1)

where
  S = free fall distance (m)
  V_t = terminal velocity in still air (m/s)
  g = gravitational acceleration, 9.807 m/s^2
  t = time to free fall a distance S (s)

TABLE 10.1. REGRESSION ANALYSIS COEFFICIENTS FOR
RELATIVE TERMINAL VELOCITY (V_r) AS A FUNCTION OF
STRAWBERRY MASS (m) FOR VARIOUS MATURITIES

$V_r = a + b \cdot (m)^{1/2}$			
Maturity	Mass (g)	a	b
Green	1-11	9.52	2.51
White	2-12	10.18	2.52
White-Pink	2-16	10.43	2.39
Pink	2-16	11.18	2.16
Red	3-19	11.98	1.92
Overall	1-19	10.08	2.53

Equation 10.1, for a free fall height of 5 m, is shown graphically in figure 10.36. If the terminal velocity exceeds about 15 m/s, then the drop height must be increased above practical limits. Alternatively, the relative terminal velocity must be considered by establishing an air flow field with an average velocity that suspends the body. Often this process is complicated by the fact that the suspended body rotates or otherwise becomes unstable, thus making experimental observation of relative terminal velocities difficult.

The factors affecting the relative terminal velocity are the berry mass and the drag coefficient. The drag coefficient is a function of berry shape, size, and surface characteristics, as well as the Reynolds number of the fluid flow field. DeBaerdemaeker and Segerlind (1974) combined the technique of free falling time measurement within a flow field that had an average upward velocity somewhat less than the terminal velocity of the body to be measured. Thus, they were able to experimentally determine the relative terminal velocities of strawberries as a function of mass as given by:

$$V_r = a + b\,(m)^{1/2} \tag{10.2}$$

where
V_r = relative terminal velocity (m/s)
a,b = coefficients from table 10.1
m = mass of individual berry (g)

Table 10.1 gives the values of the coefficients a and b that were derived from experimental data and these computational results are shown in figure 10.37. Clearly seen in this figure, the stage of ripeness has much less effect on relative terminal velocity than does the berry mass. With the exception of the green berries, little effect can be seen due to stage of ripeness.

Aerodynamic properties of blueberries. Lowbush blueberries are harvested by stripping the plants using either hand-held rakes (combs) or by a mechanized system of rakes. Both

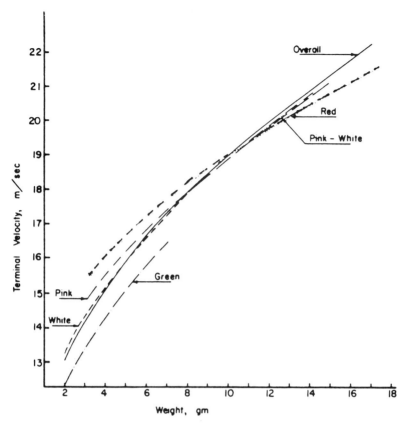

Figure 10.37–Terminal velocity of strawberries by mass for five color groups (DeBaerdemaeker and Segerlind, 1974).

methods require removal of trash and leaves which is most often achieved with the use of a vertical, upwardly directed air stream. If the mean velocity of the air stream is somewhat less than the relative terminal velocity of the berries, then the lighter trash with a lower relative terminal velocity will be removed. Since blueberries are nearly spherical, the drag coefficient can be expected to be nearly constant at 0.44 for fully developed turbulent flow ($N_{Re} > 10^3$). Soule (1970) reported mean drag coefficients (C_d) between 0.483-0.525, depending upon berry shape. Berry suspension occurs is the air stream when the drag force (F_d) is equal to the force due to gravity reduced by buoyant effects (F_g) as given by:

$$F_d = C_d \, A_b \, \rho \left(V_r\right)^2 / 2 \qquad (10.3)$$

and

$$F_g = g \, m_b \left(\rho_b - \rho \right) / \rho_b \qquad (10.4)$$

Combining equations 10.3 and 10.4, the general equation for the terminal relative velocity becomes:

$$V_r^2 = 2 \, g \, m_b \left(\rho_b - \rho \right) / \left[\left(\rho \, \rho_b \right) A_b \, C_d \right] \qquad (10.5)$$

where
   A_b = berry cross-sectional area perpendicular to the air flow direction (m2)
   C_d = coefficient of drag (dimensionless)
   ρ = density of air (kg/m3)
   ρ_b = density of berry (kg/m3)
   m_b = Mass of berry (kg)

Example Problem 10.1
   It is necessary to design a leaf removal station for a red tart cherry harvester using an upwardly directed vertical air stream. What is the maximum average air velocity needed to accomplish this function? Would you expect this cleaner to remove the very small cherries if they were also present and why?
   Solution. It is necessary to assume that all fruit and leaves are single and that if stems are present, their effects can be neglected. Furthermore we assume that red cherries are similar enough in shape and surface characteristics that equation 10.5 can be used after the student determines appropriate numeric values for the variables in the equation. The effect of small fruit can be determined by looking at the relative change in relative terminal velocity when the fruit size is, for example, reduced by 50%. Cross-sectional area is a function of radius squared, thus if the radius is reduced to 1/2 its previous value, the area reduces by $(1/2)^2$, or 1/4. Similarly, the mass is proportional to the volume which is a function of the radius cubed, thus volume (and mass) are reduced by $(1/2)^3$ or 1/8. We see from equation 10.5 that V_r^2 is proportional to M_b/A_b, or $1/8 \div 1/4 = 1/2$. Therefore, we conclude that reducing the cherry size to 1/2 the original radius reduces V_r^2 to 1/2 its original value, hence V_r is reduced to $1/(2)^{0.5}$ or 1/1.414 or 0.707 times the original value. If the air velocity is set at 85% of the relative terminal velocity of the large cherries, then the small (50% size) cherries will be removed with the leaves.

10.4.2 Fundamentals of Bush and Treeshakers
   Inertial vibrators have proven to be a simple and reliable means of imposing forced vibrational motion upon bush and tree structures.

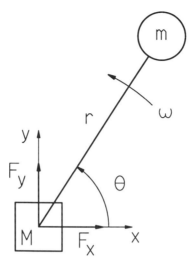

Figure 10.38–A single rotating mass inertial shaker.

The purpose of transmitting the vibrational energy to the plant structure is to cause detachment of the harvestable material. In addition to the mechanics of the vibrator itself, there are additional questions of damage to the harvested product, damage to the remaining plant structure itself and the actual mechanics of detachment. We shall treat each of these factors in subsequent sections.

A single moving mass shaker. A simple shaker with one moving mass (m) is shown in figure 10.38. We assume that the axis of rotation (0, 0) is fixed in space and that the inertial shaker mass (m), rotates with constant angular velocity (ω) in a counter clockwise direction. The angle of rotation is equal to the product of time (t) and ω. At any time (t) the center of mass (m) is located at point (x, y):

where
$$x = r \cos(\omega t)$$
and
$$y = r \sin(\omega t) \tag{10.6}$$

where x, y, r are displacements (m).

The centrifugal force (F) created by the circular motion of m about 0,0 can be resisted by the two component forces:

$$F_x = m\, d^2x/dt^2 = -m\, \omega^2 r \cos(\omega t)$$

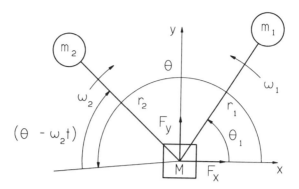

Figure 10.39–A double rotating mass inertial shaker.

and

$$F_y = m\, d^2y/dt^2 = -\, m\, \omega^2 r \sin(\omega t) \qquad (10.7)$$

Power is the vector cross product of force times velocity. In this case, since the center of rotation has been assumed to be fixed, the power needed to operate the system is clearly zero. This model of a rotating mass is useful for predicting shaking forces, subject to the assumed limits. Another limitation of this model is that control of the direction of shaking force or the shaking pattern is not possible since the centrifugal force is constant in magnitude and its direction rotates uniformly.

Before proceeding, it is important to differentiate between the number of masses in a vibrational system and the number of degrees of freedom in that system. For each degree of freedom in the system, it is necessary to have one linearly independent equation in order to be able to solve the resulting system of equations. Each mass in the system is capable of producing six possible orthogonally independent motions, three mutually perpendicular linear displacements and three rotational displacements about axes that are at 90° to each other. Another way to consider the number of degrees of freedom of a system is to determine the number of independent engineering dependent variables needed to completely describe the system under consideration.

A double moving mass shaker. Control of both the direction and pattern of shaking can be achieved by the addition of a second rotating mass as shown in figure 10.39. We also assume that the mass of the base, M, is very large such that the resulting "small" movements of M do not invalidate the inertial force summation calculations of F_x and F_y. Using the results of the single mass shaker, we have for figure 10.39:

$$\Sigma F_x = M\, d^2x/dt^2$$
$$= -\, m_1 \omega_1^2\, r_1 \cos(\omega_1 t) - m_2 \omega_2^2\, r_2 \cos(\Theta - \omega_2 t)$$

and

$$\Sigma F_y = M\, d^2y/dt^2$$
$$= -\, m_1 \omega_1^2\, r_1 \sin(\omega_1 t) - m_2 \omega_2^2\, r_2 \sin(\theta - \omega_2 t) \qquad (10.8)$$

In the special symmetric case where $\omega_1 = \omega_2 = \omega$, $m_1 = m_2 = m$, $r_1 = r_2 = r$, and $\Theta = \pi$, we have:

$$\Sigma F_x = 0$$

and

$$\Sigma F_y = -\, 2m\, \omega^2\, r \sin(\omega t) \qquad (10.9)$$

Under these assumptions, the shaker is force balanced in the x-direction with a pure sinusoidal excitation force in the y-direction.

If the y-direction force equation 10.9 is divided by the mass (m) and twice integrated with indefinite limits of integration, then the y-direction displacement equation is given as:

$$y = (2\, m\, r/M) \sin(\omega t) \qquad (10.10)$$

The general equations 10.8 can also undergo double indefinite integration to yield the general displacement equations for the center of mass (M) which is also assumed to be the center of rotation of masses m_1 and m_2. These general equations of displacement are:

$$x(t) = (m_1/M)\, r_1 \cos(\omega_1 t) + (m_2/M)\, r_2 \cos(\Theta - \omega_2 t)$$

and

$$y(t) = (m_1/M)\, r_1 \sin(\omega_1 t) + (m_2/M)\, r_2 \sin(\Theta - \omega_2 t) \qquad (10.11)$$

Example Problem 10.2

In the two rotating mass shaker analysis, the resulting motion was assumed to be "small". What conditions are necessary for the maximum displacement to be no more than 10% of the radius of the rotating masses in the case of the force-balanced shaker?

Solution. The amplitude of the resulting motion can be obtained from equation 10.10 in the y-direction. Thus:

$$2\, m\, r/M < 0.10\, r$$

or

$$m < 0.05\, M \qquad (10.12)$$

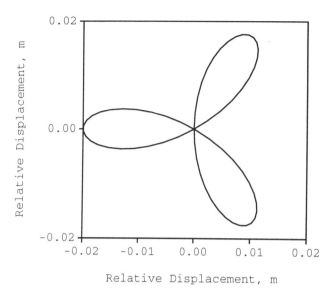

Figure 10.40–Displacement of the center of a double rotating mass inertial shaker.

Therefore, if the rotating mass (m) is less than 5% of the shaken mass (M) the resulting maximum displacement of shaking will be less than 10% of the rotating mass radius (r).

Example Problem 10.3

Using equations 10.11, subject to conditions of equation 10.12, determine the values for m_1, m_2, ω_1, ω_2, r_1, r_2 and M that result in a three lobe shaking displacement pattern shown in figure 10.40.

Solution. Equations 10.11 must be solved (by computer) for several incremental values of t between t=0 and t=$2\pi/\omega_1$ or t=$2\pi/\omega_2$, which ever is the greater value of time. In this example TK Solver™ was used and the rule and variable sheets are shown in Table 10.2.

A three moving mass shaker. Figure 10.32 shows a three moving mass shaker. All three masses rotate about a common axis. To this point, we have assumed the two-moving mass shaker as being force balanced in every direction except one. This is true, if the centers of gravity of the two masses rotate in a common plane perpendicular to the axis of rotation. In practice it is not so simple to achieve this result. A practical solution is to "split" one mass into two, placing one half above and the other half below the third mass in the middle as shown in figure 10.32. If equal masses (**1**) and (**2**) are synchronized to be in phase with each other at the same rotational direction and frequency, it should be obvious from

TABLE 10.2. TK SOLVER OUTPUT SHEETS FOR FIGURE 10.40

RULE SHEET For Academic Use Only

A1 = m1 • r1 / M
B1 = m2 • r2 / M
x = A1 • cos(w1 • t)+B1 • cos(theta-w2 • t)
y = A1 • sin(w1 • t)+B1 • sin(theta-w2 • t)

VARIABLE SHEET For Academic Use Only

St	Input	Name	Output	Units	Comment
		A1	0.01	(m)	Figure 10.40
	10	m1		(kg)	
	0.2	r1		(m)	
		B1	0.01	(m)	
	10	m2		(kg)	
	0.2	r		(m)	
	200	M		(kg)	
L		x	0	(m)	
	10	w1		(rad / s)	
L	0	t		(s)	
	3.1415927	theta		(rad)	
	20	w2		(rad / s)	
L		y	1.225E–18	(m)	

symmetry that the resulting shaker is force balanced in the plane perpendicular to the axis of rotation, but, also moment balanced such that there are no unbalanced moments "rocking" this plane. Furthermore this shaker is clearly capable of producing the two-dimensional shaking patterns in the tree shown in figure 10.31 if the entire mass of the shaker head (**1**) combined with the tree has an effective center of mass at the centerline of rotation of the three moving masses.

Shaker power. Consider the force balanced shaker shown in figure 10.41 where the forcing function F_y is given by equation 10.9. The resulting differential equation of motion in the y-direction is:

$$M\,d^2y/dt^2 + C\,dy/dt + K\,y = 2\,m\,r\,\omega^2\sin(\omega t) \qquad (10.13)$$

where

C = damping coefficient (N s/m)
K = stiffness (N/m)

The transient (complementary) solution to equation 10.13 is of little interest since it generally disappears relatively quickly. The steady state (particular) solution is of the form:

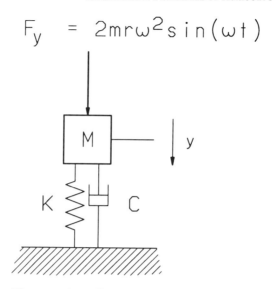

$$F_y = 2mr\omega^2 \sin(\omega t)$$

Figure 10.41–Forced vibrational two degree of freedom model excited with a force-balanced double rotating mass inertial shaker.

$$y(t) = \frac{2\,m\,r\,\omega^2}{\left[\left(K - M\,\omega^2\right)^2 + \left(C\,\omega\right)^2\right]^{0.5}}\sin\left(\omega t - \alpha\right)$$

where

$$\alpha = \tan^{-1}\left(\frac{C\,\omega}{K - M\,\omega^2}\right) \qquad (10.14)$$

If we define the natural frequency, $\omega_n{}^2 = K/M$, and, the damping ratio, $\xi = C/(2\cdot M\cdot\omega_n)$, then,

$$y(t) = \frac{2\,m\,r\,\omega^2/K}{\left\{\left[1 - \left(\omega/\omega_n\right)^2\right]^2 + 2\left(\xi\,\omega/\omega_n\right)^2\right\}^{0.5}}\sin\left(\omega t - \alpha\right) \qquad (10.15)$$

where

$$\alpha = \tan^{-1}\left(\frac{2\,\xi\,\omega/\omega_n}{1-\left(\omega/\omega_n\right)^2}\right) \qquad (10.16)$$

If the excitation frequency is much higher than the natural frequency, i.e., $\omega \gg \omega_n$, then, equation 8.15 reduces to:

$$y(t) = \left(\frac{2\,m\,r}{M}\right)\sin\left(\omega t - \alpha\right) \qquad (10.17)$$

This result should be compared with equation 10.10. The difference is that the damping effect has introduced a phase lag in the displacement with respect to the forcing function. The velocity is given by:

$$dy/dt = \frac{2\,m\,r\,\omega}{M}\cos\left(\omega t - \alpha\right) \qquad (10.18)$$

Finally, the instantaneous power can be written as the product of the force times the velocity as:

$$P_{inst} = \left[2\,m\,r\,\omega^2\sin\left(\omega t\right)\right]\left[\frac{2\,m\,r}{M}\cos\left(\omega t - \alpha\right)\right] \qquad (10.19)$$

The average power can be obtained by integrating equation 10.19 over the time required for one cycle of the slower rotating mass (T_f) as:

$$P_{avg} = 1/T_f \int_0^{T_f} P_{inst}\,dt$$

with, the limits of integration being 0 to T_f. Thus, the average power is given by:

$$P_{avg} = \left[2\,m^2\,r^2\,\omega^3/M\right]\cdot\sin(\alpha) \qquad (10.20)$$

Adrian and Fridley (1965) investigated the shaker power requirements under actual field conditions.

LaGrange's equation. Complex, forced vibrational problems with damping are often treated from the point of view of energy. Simply stated, LaGrange's equation is an energy balance applied to the entire vibratory system. Multi-degree of freedom systems are conveniently treated, but, the resulting systems of differential equations often requires a computer to solve. Closed-form (analytic) solutions to real, non-linear systems of equations that represent practical problems are virtually impossible to obtain. LaGrange's equation in generalized orthogonal coordinates (q_i) has the general form of:

$$\frac{d}{dt}\frac{\partial\left(K.E.\right)}{\partial q_i} - \frac{\partial\left(K.E.\right)}{\partial q_i} + \frac{\partial\left(P.E.\right)}{\partial q_i} + \frac{\partial\left(D.E.\right)}{\partial q_i} = Q_i \qquad (10.21)$$

where

K.E. = kinetic energy of the system = $1/2\ M\left(\frac{dx}{dt}\right)^2$

P.E. = potential energy of the system = $1/2\ K\ x^2$

D.E. = dissipation energy of the system = $1/2\ C\left(\frac{dx}{dt}\right)^2$

Q_i = generalized external force acting on the system

Example Problem 10.4
Apply the LaGrange equation to the forced vibrational of a single degree of freedom damped mass shown in figure 10.41. The parameters M, C, and K are defined in equation 10.13. Neglect gravity.
Solution. The kinetic energy of the system is given by:

$$K.E. = 1/2\ M\left(\frac{dy}{dt}\right)^2 \qquad (10.22)$$

The potential energy of the system is given by:

$$P.E. = 1/2\ K y^2 \qquad (10.23)$$

The dissipative energy of the system is given by:

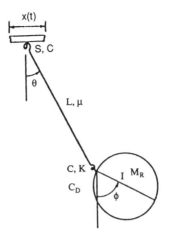

Figure 10.42–Two-degree of freedom fruit attachment vibrational model (from Tsatsarelis, 1987).

$$D.E. = 1/2 \; C \left(\frac{dy}{dt}\right)^2 \qquad (10.24)$$

The forcing function in the single degree of freedom direction of motion (y) is given by:

$$Q = F_o \sin(\omega t) \qquad (10.25)$$

After calculating the appropriate partial derivatives and substitution, equation 10.21 becomes:

$$\frac{d}{dt}\left[M\left(\frac{dy}{dt}\right)\right] - 0 + K\,y + C\left(\frac{dy}{dt}\right) = F_o \sin\left(\omega\, t\right) \qquad (10.26)$$

and finally reduces to:

$$M\left(\frac{d^2 y}{dt^2}\right) + C\left(\frac{dy}{dt}\right) + K\,y = F_o \sin\left(\omega\, t\right) \qquad (10.27)$$

10.4.3 Vibrational Detachment During Harvest

The LaGrange equation has been used to successfully analyze vibratory harvesting of olives (Tsatsarelis, 1987) and air-suspended

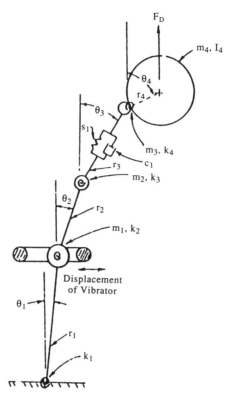

Figure 10.43–A five-degree of freedom vibrational model of an air-suspended depended, fruit-stem system (from Ruff, et al., 1980).

strawberries (Ruff et al., 1980). A two-degree of freedom model for olives is shown in figure 10.42 and a five-degree of freedom model is shown in figure 10.43. Both of these studies looked at the resulting vibrational mode shapes that resulted from forced vibrations and confirmed with experimental observation that the tilting mode of vibration shown in figure 10.44 is very important to fruit removal by causing detachment at the stem-fruit connection.

Three modes of vibration are important in understanding the mechanism of fruit detachment. The tilting mode is the most important and has been experimentally observed to be present at the time of detachment. This mode causes high tensile stresses to develop in the stem-calyx junction of the stem and the fruit. Under normal maturation processes this junction becomes weaker as the natural abscission layer develops. Furthermore, there is evidence that biological materials fatigue under repeated cycles of stress, each cycle of which is not individually capable of causing failure, but,

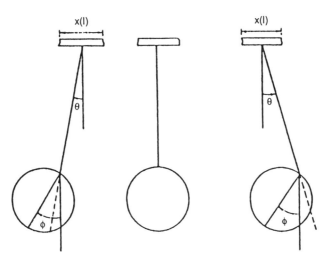

Figure 10.44–Vibrational modes defined; pendular, left; rest, middle; and tilting, right (Tsatsarelis, 1987).

accumulatively will produce failure of the stem or stem-calyx junction.

The second important vibrational mode is the axial tension mode. This mode is the result of the application of forces directed along the axis of the stem itself. In the forced vibrational excitement of the plant structure, it is relatively easy to imagine how the vibrating fruit-stem could achieve a relative position such that the next cycle of vibration, by the assumed geometry, would result in a sudden imposition of a relatively high axial stem force. This situation can be recognized by the common expression of "crack the whip" which results in an amplification of tensile forces by sudden redirection of momentum forces.

The pendular mode is the third mode and is important to excite if the fruit is to be detached with the stem intact. It is much more difficult to excite this mode if the stems are relatively long than the tilting mode. In fact all three modes are present to varying degrees and as such combine to produce detachment.

10.4.4 Impact Models and Mechanical Damage

Mechanical damage during harvesting operations can affect both the plant and the harvested product. In the case of a multiple pick crop, unharvested product can also be damaged. The focus of this section will be on models that attempt to characterize damage to the harvested product. There are four principal components of failure in fruits and vegetables that contribute to reduced product value. These four components are compressive stress, shear stress, creep stress and fatigue stress. Stress analysis in three dimensions in

complex shapes with non-isotropic bodies is very difficult. The
presence of a protective (usually tough) skin over a product is only
one example of non-isotropic condition. Most loading conditions that
are observed under practical conditions are a combination of the
above four component loadings. For engineering purposes, useful
information in equation form can be derived from empirical (physical)
observations. Care should be exercised in applying empirical results
to non-identical products or conditions.

Impact force response of a sphere on a flat plate. If a
stationary flat plate is impacted with a spherically shaped object
dropped under gravity, the resulting total force exerted on the plate
is a function of the mass, impacting and rebounding velocities of the
sphere. This results from the application of Newton's Second Law as
given by:

$$I = \int_0^{t_c} f(t)\,dt = m\left(v_2 - v_1\right) \tag{10.28}$$

where
   I = impulse (N · s)
   $f(t)$ = contact force as a function of time (N)
   t = time during contact (s)
   t_c = total contact time (s)
   m = mass of sphere (kg)
   v_1 = velocity of center of mass (m/s) before contact, i.e., $t=0$
   v_2 = velocity of center of mass (m/s) after contact, i.e., $t=t_c$

The coefficient of restitution (r) is defined as:

$$r = -v_2/v_1 \tag{10.29}$$

where velocities v_1 and v_2 are defined as above and the minus sign
reflects the fact that the direction of rebound is opposite the impact
direction.

If one assumes r is greater than zero and considers two
successive bounces, then on the first impact:

$$I_1 = m(v_2 - v_1)$$

and the second impact, neglecting air frictional losses:

$$I_2 = m(v_3 - v_2)$$

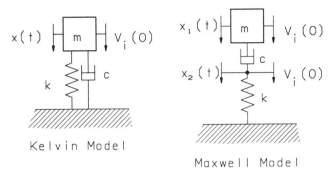

Figure 10.45–Kelvin model and Maxwell model of a
viscoelastic impact with a stationary surface.

If one assumes that the coefficient of restitution is constant for
both impacts, then, it can be shown that:

$$r = I_2/I_1 \qquad (10.30)$$

Hence, by measuring the impulse of two successive impacts, the
coefficient of restitution can be determined experimentally.

It is also possible to determine the fruit mass from the impact
response by:

$$I_1 = m(v_2 - v_1) = m\,v_1(v_2/v_1 - 1) \text{ or}$$

$$m = -I_1/[v_1(1 - r)] \qquad (10.31)$$

The pre-impact velocity (v_1) can be estimated by knowing the
free fall height under constant gravitational acceleration. Thus, it is
possible to experimentally determine the coefficient of restitution and
the mass of a sphere dropped from a known height onto a rigid flat
surface provided two consecutive impulses are measured and
analyzed.

Until this point, the actual shape of f(t) has not been considered
and, in fact, has no effect on the above equations. The shape of the
impact force curve [f(t)] is a function of the fruit firmness and
damping as shown in the next section.

Impact models with firmness and damping effects. For
ordinary engineering purposes, it is often assumed that the impact
force and contact deformations within a convex fruit or vegetable
product and a rigid flat surface can be modeled with one or two
degrees of freedom. Two models are shown in figure 10.45. The
Kelvin model is a single degree of freedom with lumped parameter
mass, spring and damping characteristics. Maxwell model contains
the same lumped physical elements as Kelvin model, but, is based

upon a different physical arrangement. Lumped parameter models are defined by parameter constants that represent invariant conditions. For example, in these models all mass is assumed to be "lumped" together and moves without internal deformations, hence the motion of the center of mass is assumed to be the motion of all mass.

Each model provides useful insight and engineering information. But, each model is also subject to certain restrictions and limitations. In addition to the lumped parameter assumption, the development of initial conditions, while physically justifiable, sometimes result in mathematical consequences that are not physically realizable. As each model is developed, further examples of differences between the physical and mathematical representations will be identified. The single degree of freedom Kelvin model will be considered first.

Before considering the equations of motion for the two models in figure 10.45, an understanding of initial conditions will be developed. The models are considered at rest, without the effects of gravity, at times prior to "impact". This condition is assumed to exist for all time, $t < 0$. At $t = 0^+$, the mass is considered to have an instantaneously achieved velocity of V_i in the direction noted in figure 10.45. At this time, contact with the stationary surface exists and the initial displacements of all displacement variables is taken to be zero. Neither model is subjected to an external forcing function.

Since contact continues to exist only if the contact force is positive, then the model equations of motion are only valid during the initial contact period. Once the contact force goes to zero, the initial impact event is considered to be complete and the velocity of the mass, if any, is considered to be the impact rebound velocity. The choice of units for the equations of motion can be made consistent with the equations themselves. Any consistent set of units may be used.

The Kelvin model, being a single degree of freedom system, is described by the following equation of motion:

$$m \frac{d^2 x}{dt^2} + c \frac{dx}{dt} + kx = 0 \qquad (10.32)$$

While the general solution for this equation is of the form:

$$x = x_c + x_p \qquad (10.33)$$

Only the complementary solution (x_c) is of interest since the particular solution (x_p) is in this case, zero. The characteristic equation (or auxiliary equation) is:

$$m\lambda^2 + c\lambda + k = 0 \qquad (10.34)$$

If $\omega^2_n = k/m$ and $\zeta = c/2m \cdot \omega_n$, where ζ is called the damping factor, then,

$$\lambda_1 = \omega_n \left(-\zeta + \sqrt{\zeta^2 - 1} \right) \qquad (10.35)$$

and

$$\lambda_2 = \omega_n \left(-\zeta - \sqrt{\zeta^2 - 1} \right) \qquad (10.36)$$

The roots of the characteristic equation (λ_1 and λ_2) will be real and distinct, real and equal, or complex conjugates for ζ being greater than one, equal to one or less than one, respectively.

If ζ is greater than one the system is overdamped and oscillatory motion is not possible as given by the overdamped complementary solution.

$$x_c = Ae^{-\lambda_1 t} + Be^{-\lambda_2 t} \qquad (10.37)$$

where A and B are constants determined from the initial conditions.

Critical damping is a very special mathematical condition, seldom seen in the physical world, where $\zeta = 1$, and clearly $\lambda_1 = \lambda_2 = -\omega_n$. In this special case, the complementary solution is given by:

$$x_c = (C + Dt)e^{-\omega_n t} \qquad (10.38)$$

again where C and D are constants determined from the initial conditions.

The underdamped condition, $\zeta < 1$, is often encountered in fresh, mature fruits and vegetables, and results in the complementary solution:

$$x_c = (A\cos\omega_d t + B\sin\omega_d t)e^{-\zeta\omega_n t} \qquad (10.39)$$

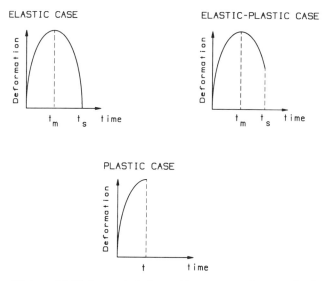

Figure 10.46–Impact deformation curves for products with elastic, plastic, or elastic-plastic properties.

where the damped natural frequency $[\omega^2_d=(1-\zeta^2)\omega^2_n]$ is given by definition. If the initial displacement is taken as zero and the initial velocity is V_i, then $A=0$ and $B=V_i/\omega_d$.

Maxwell's Model is more complex because it has two degrees of freedom. By example problem, these equations will be derived using the LaGrange equations. The complementary solution can then be obtained, by using a symbolic math package such as MAPLE™ resulting in rather than complex algebraic analytical solution. A TUTSIM™ computer solution to the differential equations could also be used.

Both the Kelvin and Maxwell models are useful in demonstrating the impact phenomena. Depending upon the relative mass, firmness, and internal energy absorption of the impacting body, elastic, plastic or elastic-plastic impact response can be demonstrated as illustrated in figure 10.46. The coefficient of restitution (r=1 for elastic, r=0 for plastic, and 0<r<1 for plastic-elastic, characterizes the impact behavior.

Example Problem 10.5

Use LaGrange's equation to find the equations of motion for Maxwell's Model shown in figure 10.45. Neglect gravity.

Solution. The needed expressions and terms of the LaGrange's equations are written as follows:

$$P.E. = \frac{kx_2^2}{2} \tag{10.40}$$

$$K.E. = \frac{m}{2}\left(\frac{dx_1}{dt}\right)^2 \tag{10.41}$$

$$D.E. = \frac{c}{2}\left[\left(\frac{dx_2}{dt}\right)^2 - \left(\frac{dx_1}{dt}\right)^2\right] \tag{10.42}$$

$$Q = 0$$

since there is no generalized forcing function.

After calculating the appropriate partial derivatives and substitution, equation 10.21 becomes:

$$m\ddot{x}_1 - c(\dot{x}_2 - \dot{x}_1) = 0 \tag{10.43}$$

and

$$kx_2 + c(\dot{x}_2 - \dot{x}_1) = 0 \tag{10.44}$$

subject to $x_1(0) = x_2(0) = 0$, and:

$$\frac{dx_1(0)}{dt} = \frac{dx_2(0)}{dt} = v$$

The solution to equations 10.43 and 10.44 are:

$$x_1(t) = -\frac{-vm}{c} - 2\frac{cvm^{1/2} e^{-kt/2c} \sinh(\beta)}{k^{1/2}\left(-4c^2 + mk\right)^{1/2}}$$

$$+ \frac{vm^{3/2} k^{1/2} e^{-kt/2c} \sinh(\beta)}{c\left(-4c^2 + mk\right)^{1/2}} + \frac{vm\, e^{-kt/2c} \cosh(\beta)}{c}$$

TABLE 10.3. IMPACT PARAMETERS AND RESULTS FOR THE
SOLUTION OF THE KELVIN AND MAXWELL EQUATIONS
OF MOTION FOR BLUEBERRY MODELS

m (g)	c (N·s / m)	k (N / m)	F_{peak} (N)	t_s (ms)	r	Figure	d_p (mm)
1.54	0.75	797	0.713	3.60	0.414	8.47	0.40
1.54	12.0	1000	1.27	3.85	0.414	8.48	0.28

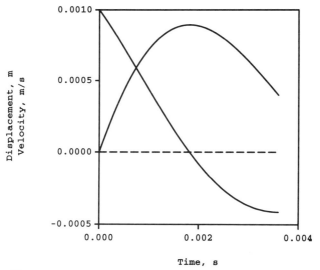

Figure 10.47–Solution to Kelvin model of a blueberry, see table 10.3 for model parameter values and results.

$$x_2(t) = -2\,\frac{cvm^{1/2}\,e^{-kt/2c}\,\sinh(\beta)}{k^{1/2}\left(-4\,c^2 + m\,k\right)^{1/2}}$$

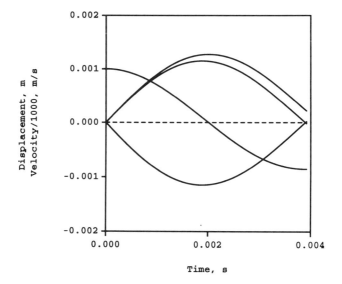

Figure 10.48–Solution to Maxwell model of a blueberry, see table 10.3 for model parameter values and results.

$$\beta = 1/2 \frac{k^{1/2} \left(- 4 c^{2} + m k\right)^{1/2} t}{m^{1/2} c}$$

Impact models results and applications. A Kelvin model (Bower and Rohrbach, 1976) and a double Kelvin model in series (Glass and Rohrbach, 1980) have been used to model blueberry fruit impacts. For blueberries, the mass ranges from less than 1 g to nearly 3 g, the damping constant between 0.1 and 0.8 N·S/m and the spring constant can take values between 500 and 8000 N/m. Actual model parameters were selected to match individual berry coefficient of restitution or contact force and velocity mechanical impedance criterion. Model berry mass is often found to be slightly less than the actual berry mass.

Table 10.3 summarizes the impact parameters used in computer solutions of blueberry impact results for the Kelvin model shown in figure 10.47 and the Maxwell model shown in figure 10.48. In both cases the coefficient of restitution is 0.414 with the model mass being 1.54 g. The damping constant and the spring constant values were empirically adjusted in the Maxwell model to obtain equal coefficients of restitution for the two different models.

Once the deformations within the spring model elements have been calculated, $x_1(t)$ for the Kelvin model and $x_2(t)$ for the Maxwell model, the impact force f(t) is easily calculated as the product of the deformation and the spring stiffness (k). However, the Kelvin model predicts a non-zero impact force at the time of rebound or separation, which is not particularly useful, but, results from the model's "attempt" to restore the initial free length of the unstressed spring element. If one attempts to "correct" for the non-zero contact force prediction at the time of rebound by subtracting the force component associated with the viscous damping element, then the initial contact force becomes a step at $t=0^{+}$ with a magnitude of $c \cdot (dx_1/dt)$. The Kelvin model does predict a permanent fruit deformation after separation in the case where separation does indeed occur.

The Maxwell model comes closer to predicting an impact force that exists during rebound which is consistent with physical observation as well as a permanent fruit deformation (d_p) with a magnitude of $x_2(t_r)$, where t_s is the time at separation. The comparative results of the two impact models in Table 10.3, show some differences between the predicted contact time, peak impact force, and permanent fruit deformations (d_p) after impact for identical coefficients of restitution. It is important to remember that engineering models are very useful to the extent that they help the engineer understand the physical situation represented and the engineering parameters of interest, but, not all physical aspects of the real situation are accurately modeled.

In practice, most values for K are obtained from empirical force-deformation tests (Instron Universal Tester™) or drop test data, and are only valid for the size and conditions of that test. The development of tri-axial contact stress during a fruit impact is beyond the scope of this text. Additional theoretical aspects of food rheology and physical properties are presented in Mohsenin (1970). Goldsmith (1960) is an excellent reference for additional discussion of impact events.

Coefficient of restitution in peaches has been reported to be successfully measured and used to identify individual fruit firmness (Meredith, Leffler and Lyon, 1988). The coefficient of restitution was determined from data collected from two consecutive bounces on an instrumented load cell. Neither variety, fruit size nor drop height affected the determination of the coefficient of restitution within the range of the investigated variables.

An impact probe for determining apple and pear firmness was developed and tested (Delwiche et al., 1991). A small air cylinder moves an impact surface towards the side of a "stationary" fruit. Impact force is sensed by an accelerometer attached to the impact surface. A strong correlation between peak impact deceleration and fruit firmness was obtained by testing.

10.5 Performance Factors

The fundamental concepts useful in reducing or eliminating damage to harvested products involves a number of complex issues. Basically, bruising results from the undesirable absorption of energy in the product tissue. Product that free-falls onto a receiving surface results in the application of a deceleration or impact force. This force, when distributed over the impact area or region, will damage the product if the critical values of shear or compressive stress are exceeded for the product being harvested. Often harvesting elements that are designed to transmit vibrational energy to the plant material cause bruising. Fruit impacting other fruit during free fall or at the collection surfaces are also a common source of damage.

10.5.1 Damage

Product bruising, cutting, scuffing, and direct damage to the remaining plant are all undesirable effects of field harvesting operations. Direct product damage reduces the value of the product in the market and the general desirability to the consumer. Plant damage, for multiple harvest enterprises, is also undesirable since subsequent harvests are reduced.

UNITED STATES STANDARDS FOR GRADES OF APPLES

	U. S. EXTRA FANCY	U. S. FANCY	U. S. NO. 1	U. S. UTILITY
Maturity	Mature but not overripe	Mature but not overripe	Mature but not overripe	Mature but not overripe
Scab	Free from	Not over ¼ inch dia.	Same as Fcy.	Not over ¾ inch dia.
Russeting	1. Net-like (not over 10% of surface) 2. Smooth solid (not over 5% of surface) 3. Slightly rough (not over ½ inch) 4. Rough (not over ¼ inch)	Not over 15% of surface Not over 5% of surface Same as Ex. Fcy. Same as Ex. Fcy.	Not over 25% Not over 10% Same as Ex. Fcy. Same as Ex. Fcy.	Any amount allowed Not over ½ of surface Not to detract from appearance More than smooth solid
Sunburn & Sprayburn	Must blend with color	Skin not cracked and must blend with color	Same as Fcy.	Not seriously detracting from appearance
Limb Rub	Not over ¼ inch	Not over ½ inch	Same as Fcy.	Not more than one-tenth of surface
Hail Marks	1. When skin not broken 2. When surface not discolored 3. When not over 1/16 inch deep 4. One spot not over ⅛ inch in diameter or aggregate not over ½ inch.	Unbroken skin, not over ½ inch in aggregate Not over ⅛ inch deep Well healed, not over ¼ inch in diameter	Same as Fcy.	Unbroken, not more than 1/10 of surface in aggregate Well healed broken skin not more than ½ inch in dia.
Stem & Calyx Cracks	When well healed or not over ¼ inch aggregate length	Same as Ex. Fcy.	Same as Ex. Fcy.	When well healed or not over ½ inch in length
Cedar Rust	Not over 3/16 inch in diameter	Not over ¼ inch in the aggregate	Same as Fcy.	Not more than 3/4 inch
Sooty Blotch or Fly Speck	Dark and heavy, not over ¼ inch Thin, not over 5% surface	Dark and heavy, not over ½ inch Not over 10% surface	Same as Fcy. Same as Fcy.	Not more than 1/3 of surface
Stings	Not over ⅛ inch in diameter	Not over 3/16 inch in diameter	Same as Fcy.	Not more than ¼ inch in diameter
Worm Holes	None	None	None	None
Decay	None	None	None	None
Percent of Color Required By Variety And Grade				
Red Delicious	66	40	25	None
Delicious	50	25	15	None
Red Rome	66	40	25	None
Rome	50	33	15	None
Red Stayman	66	40	25	None
Stayman	50	33	15	None
Winesap	66	40	25	None
Golden Delicious	75% characteristic color	Same as Ex. Fcy.	characteristic ground color	None

COMBINATION GRADES PERMITTED
    Comb. U.S. Extra Fancy and U.S. Fancy
    Comb. U.S. Fancy and U.S. No. 1
    Comb. U.S. No. 1 and U.S. Utility
    Note: At least 50% shall meet the higher grade to qualify as combination grade.
OTHER GRADES: U.S. No. 1 Early: Same as U.S. No. 1 except 2 inch min., no color requirements, need not be mature.
                U.S. No. 1 Hail: Must meet all requirements of U.S. No. 1 except unlimited well healed hail marks allowed provided apples are fairly well formed.

Prepared and distributed by Horticultural Crop Section, Division of Marketing, North Carolina Department of Agriculture, Raleigh, North Carolina 27611, telephone 919-733-7136. James A. Graham, Commissioner of Agriculture.

April, 1983

Figure 10.49–Summary table of United States standards for grades of apples.

Damage is often accumulative and proportional to the total energy absorbed by the fruit tissue. In blueberries, for example, sixteen 2-cm drops onto a rigid flat surface causes the same relative damage as eight 4-cm drops or four 8-cm drops. Clearly, the first and most important principle in minimizing bruising is to minimize the amount of kinetic energy that the fruit has at any time during machine operations.

The United States Department of Agriculture oversees the development of quality standards for most of the more popular commodities grown or marked in the U.S. as fresh or processed. In some cases these standards have evolved into an extensive collection of quality factors that are used to establish the marketing grade for a specific shipment of product. As an example, figure 10.49 is a summary table of the USDA Apple grade standards. In the case of apples, combined grade classifications are permitted.

10.5.2 Efficiency

Field harvest efficiencies for multiple harvest operations are only meaningful when compared with some existing or accepted standard. There is no single definition for field harvest efficiency. Usually it is defined as economic recovery of product as a percentage of total available harvest. Often this total available harvest is taken as the "hand harvest". However, most "hand harvest" methods have a measurable component of loss as either ground loss or unharvested product.

Ground loss is an important component of machine harvesting systems. Ground loss is defined as a percentage of either the total harvest or the net harvest. This is not to be confused with preharvest ground loss that may result from preharvest weather conditions or ground losses due to other harvest delays.

10.5.3 Reliability

Since fruit, vegetables, and nuts are usually high value commodities, harvesting systems should be designed for high mean times between failure (MBTF). Since the harvest period is often concentrated in a short time, harvesting systems must be serviced and have all preventative maintenance completed before the annual harvest season. In the design of these systems, standard parts should be used whenever possible to ensure local availability of repair parts in the event of a breakdown.

Since a food product for human consumption is being harvested, care should be exercised by the designer to avoid the possibilities of product contamination with hydraulic oil or other machine fluids. Special consideration should be given to minimize the sites on the machine that can accumulate unwanted residue. The machine itself will need to be cleaned periodically to eliminate the buildup of biological microbes that could adversely affect harvested product quality.

Safety of the people that are working with the harvesting system needs special attention. Often machine elements that perform useful harvesting functions must be accessible to the commodity for proper operation and cannot be guarded by position from human access. All such hazards must be shielded to the maximum extent possible and all individuals warned to the greatest extent possible of the potential hazard. Standard operating procedures should require that power be disengaged for all maintenance and repair activities. All applicable engineering safety design standards must be applied to fruit, vegetable and nut harvesting equipment.

Problems

10.1   For your state, determine the relative importance (rank among other states) of fruit, nut, and vegetable production. Which of these commodities is most important to your state's agricultural income?

10.2   For each of the possible 24 logical combinations of functional harvest operations, list at least one commodity example for as many combinations as possible. For example, hand harvesting of apples is the functional equivalent of selection, control, removal, and transportation.

10.3   Design a two-mass (coaxial and counter rotating at equal angular speeds) inertial shaker that will develop a linear +/− 4 cm stroke at 250 H_z operating on the shaker frame and plant material equivalent mass of 100 kg.

10.4   Modify (non equal angular speeds) the linear shaker designed in problem 10.8.3, above, to produce a six-directional shaking pattern, i.e., each successive stroke precesses 60° from the preceding stroke. Is it necessary to adjust the masses of the counter rotating masses?

10.5   Visit a large fruit, vegetable, or nut grower near your location. Interview the grower with the following list of questions after you add three of your own questions to this interview list: What new harvesting equipment or features do you need? What existing machine harvesting functions

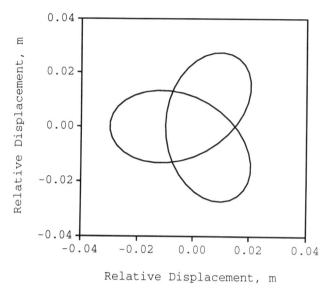

Figure 10.50–Displacement of the center of a double rotating mass inertial shaker, for problem 10.12.

need improvement? What are the safety concerns of the grower relative to harvesting equipment?

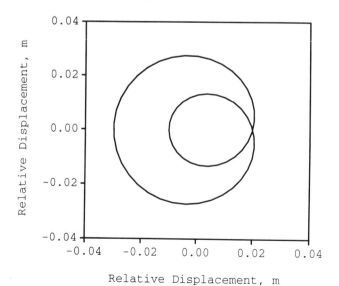

Figure 10.51–Displacement of the center of a double rotating mass inertial shaker, for problem 10.13.

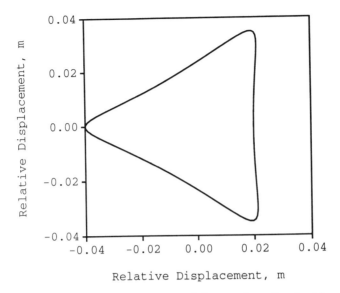

Figure 10.52–Displacement of the center of a double rotating mass inertial shaker, for problem 10.14.

10.6   What is the effect of the relative direction of rotation of the two masses in the inertial shaker shown in figure 10.39? And, the effect of the initial angular displacement?

10.7   Program equations 10.11 on a computer in a manner to allow for evaluation of various combinations of values for mass, frequencies, rotational radii, etc. Determine empirically the relationship between the relative angular frequencies and the number of "lobes" in the displacement pattern. What is the importance of the relative magnitudes of the rotating masses in establishing the "lobe shape?"

10.8   It is assumed that the relative amplitude of displacement in the base mass (M) in figure 10.39 should be only 1% of the minimum radius of rotation of either excitation mass. What is the maximum relative rotating mass that can be used compared with the base mass (M)? Does this result depend upon the resulting displacement pattern? And why?

10.9   The terminal velocity of a harvested product is believed to be in the range of 30 m/s. If you want to confirm this estimation by actual measurement of the free fall time, what drop height should be used?

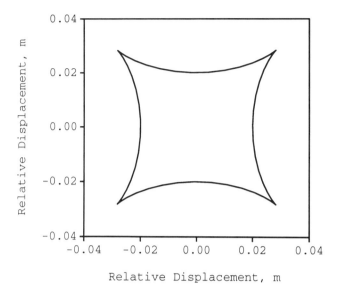

Figure 10.53–Displacement of the center of a double rotating mass inertial shaker, for problem 10.15.

10.10   Integrate equation 10.19 to obtain the average shaker power given by equation 10.20. Show all steps.

10.11   What air velocity would you propose to be used to separate green strawberries from ripe (red) strawberries in an

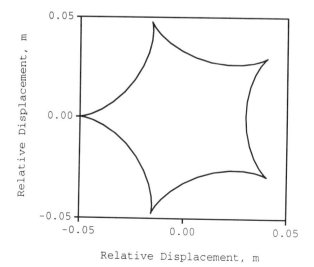

Figure 10.54–Displacement of the center of a double rotating mass inertial shaker, for problem 10.16.

upwardly directed air blast separator? Fully justify your answer.

10.12 Table 10.2 lists the model parameters for the inertial shaker displacements shown in figure 10.40. With a computer model of equations 10.11, determine one model parameter change that will result in the relative displacements shown in figure 10.50.

10.13 With a computer model of equations 10.11, determine one model parameter change from problem 10.8.12 that will result in the relative displacements shown in figure 10.51.

10.14 With a computer model of equations 10.11, experiment and determine the model parameter changes needed that will result in the relative displacements shown in figure 10.52.

10.15 With a computer model of equations 10.11, experiment and determine the model parameter changes needed that will result in the relative displacements shown in figure 10.53.

10.16 With a computer model of equations 10.11, experiment and determine the model parameter changes needed that will result in the relative displacements shown in figure 10.54.

10.17 With a computer model of the equations for Maxwell's impact model, experiment and determine how the model parameters are related to the coefficient of restitution. Is there a simple relationship between the model parameters m, c, and k and the resulting coefficient of restitution (r)? What is it?

10.18 For a fruit, vegetable or nut crop grown in your location, obtain a copy of the USDA Grade Standards. Develop a concise tabular summary of the standard similar to the USDA Apple Grades in figure 10.49.

10.19 For the Kelvin blueberry impact model shown in figure 10.47, find the exact time of rebound, i.e., the time when the model predicts the maximum rebound velocity. **Hint:** Calculate the appropriate derivatives of the displacement and investigate the maximums of the velocity expression.

10.20   Use a computer to solve the Maxwell blueberry model and calculate the contact force during impact. Evaluate the coefficient of restitution using equation 10.30. Compare this result with the coefficient of restitution from equation 10.29, and explain any differences.

10.21   Based upon interest, select one of the patents from the "Patents Cited" list in Appendix A and obtain a complete copy. Study the patent carefully and report to the class the exact nature of the patent coverage. (You may wish to find another interesting patent, within the scope of your course, to study and report.)

11

Conveying of Agricultural Materials

Introduction

There are several methods used to convey agricultural materials. The selection of conveying method depends upon the nature of application and on the type of material being conveyed. The agricultural material may be liquid, granular, powder, fibrous or any combination of these. This chapter does not cover conveying of liquid material.

Generally, conveying is accomplished by a combination of mechanical, inertial, pneumatic and gravity forces. Conveyors utilizing primarily mechanical forces are screw, and chain conveyors. Oscillatory conveyors rely on the inertial and the friction forces. Pneumatic conveyors employ the aerodynamic drag to accomplish conveying. Conveying by throwing combines both the inertial and aerodynamic forces. Silo loaders utilize these principles.

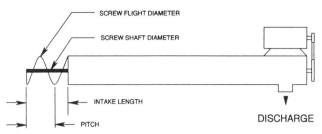

Figure 11.1–A schematic diagram of a screw conveyor.

11.1 Screw Conveyors

Augers are used to convey materials that are free flowing such as grain to difficult fibrous materials and powders. For example, in a grain combine, augers are used to move cut crop on the platform to the feeder housing, clean grain at the bottom of the cleaning shoe to the grain tank, and to unload the grain tank on to a wagon or a truck. Augers are used at the grain elevators and farmstead to load grain storage bins and on the feedlot for feed distribution.

11.1.1 Methods and Equipment

The screw conveyor consists of a shaft which carries helicoid flightings on its outer surface. These flighting are enclosed either in a trough for horizontal augers or in a tube for elevating augers. The tube or the trough is held stationary while the rotation of the flightings causes the material to move longitudinally. Figure 11.1 shows the essential components of a screw conveyor. At the inlet side, the auger flightings extend beyond the tube. Generally, a hopper is provided to hold the material while it is conveyed into the tube. Augers can be permanently installed in a machine, or at a site, or they can be portable. The augers are driven either at the intake side or the discharge side. There are some center drive augers but they are not common in agricultural applications.

The auger length is defined as the length of the tube assembly including any intake but not including the intake hopper and/or the head drive. The intake length is the visible flighting at the intake of the auger. The outside diameter of the tube is referred to as the auger size. A standard pitch auger is the one whose pitch is approximately equal to outside diameter of the helicoidal flighting. Generally, the pitch is not less than 0.9 and not more than 1.5 times the outside diameter. Standard pitch augers are used for horizontal and up to 20° inclination angles. For inclination angles greater than 20°, half standard pitch screws are used. Double and triple flight, variable pitch, and stepped-diameter screws are available for moving difficult materials and controlling feed rates.

11.1.2 Theory

The *theoretical volumetric capacity* of an auger is expressed as:

$$Q_t = \frac{\pi}{4}\left(d_{sf}^2 - d_{ss}^2\right)l_p n \qquad (11.1)$$

where
Q_t = theoretical volumetric capacity (m³/s)
d_{sf} = screw flighting diameter (m)
d_{ss} = screw shaft diameter (m)
l_p = pitch length (m)
n = screw rotational speed (rev/s)

In reality the actual capacity of an auger is considerably less than the theoretical capacity. This results in loss of volumetric efficiency. The *volumetric efficiency* is defined as:

$$\eta_v = \frac{Q_a}{Q_t} \qquad (11.2)$$

where
η_v = volumetric efficiency
Q_a = actual volumetric capacity (m³/s)

Generally, the throughput rate in terms of mass (or weight) per unit of time, for example, t/h or kg/min, is specified. The volumetric capacity is obtained by dividing the throughput rate by the bulk density of the material.

The power requirement of an auger is expressed by the specific power. The specific power is defined as follows:

$$P' = \frac{P/L}{Q_a \rho_b} \qquad (11.3)$$

where
P' = specific power (W·s/kg·m)
P = total power (W)
L = auger length (m)
ρ_b = material bulk density (kg/m³)

Thus, the specific power is the power required to convey a unit mass throughput rate per unit auger length.

**TABLE 11.1. A LIST OF VARIABLES AFFECTING
SCREW CONVEYOR PERFORMANCE**

Symbol	Variable Definition	Dimensions	Units
Q_a	Actual volumetric capacity	L^3/T	(m^3/s)
P	Power requirements	ML^2/T^3	(W)
d_t	Tube inside diameter	L	(m)
d_{sf}	Outside screw diameter	L	(m)
d_{ss}	Screw shaft diameter	L	(m)
L	Screw length	L	(m)
l_p	Screw pitch length	L	(m)
l_i	Exposed screw intake length	L	(m)
n	Angular speed	$1/T$	(rev/s)
θ	Angle of conveyor inclination	—	(degrees)
ρ_b	Material bulk density	M/L^3	(kg/m^3)
μ_1	Material-metal friction	—	—
μ_2	Material-material friction	—	—
g	Acceleration due to gravity	L/T^2	(m/s^2)

The process of conveying by a screw conveyor is a complex process. It is difficult to develop analytical models to predict volumetric capacity and power requirements without making overly simplified assumptions. Purely empirical models, on the other hand, are not general enough in nature and can not be used to predict auger performance in a variety of applications. Rehkugler and Boyd (1962) proposed the application of dimensional analysis as a tool to develop a comprehensive prediction model for screw conveyor performance. Table 11.1 shows a list of variables that are pertinent to the problem. These variables can be combined into ratios or dimensionless groups called the π-terms using Buckingham's π-theorem. The following equation includes the dimensionless terms:

$$\pi_1 = f\left(\frac{d_t}{d_p}, \frac{d_{sf}}{l_p}, \frac{d_{ss}}{l_p}, \frac{l_i}{l_p}, n\sqrt{\frac{l_p}{g}}, f(\theta), \mu_1, \mu_2\right) \qquad (11.4)$$

where

$$\pi_1 = \frac{Q_a}{\frac{\pi}{4}(d_{sf}^2 - d_{ss}^2)l_p n} \quad \text{or} \quad \frac{P/L}{Q_a \rho_b g} \qquad (11.5)$$

The first term in the right hand side of equation 11.5 is the ratio of the actual volumetric throughput rate to the theoretical volume swept by the screw per unit of time. This has been regarded as the volumetric efficiency of the screw conveyor. The second term in the right hand side of the above equation is the power required per unit length per unit mass flow rate of the material being conveyed. It has been defined as the specific power or the power efficiency of the conveyor. The conveyor length does not affect the volumetric efficiency.

The dimensionless terms of equation 11.4 are used to develop prediction equations using experimental data. Published data on the performance of auger conveyors conveying wheat, oats, and shelled corn were used to develop the performance equations. These equations may be used to estimate conveyor performance for similar materials.

$$\frac{Q_a}{\frac{\pi}{4}\left(d_{sf}^2 - d_{ss}^2\right)l_p n} = 432 \times 10^{-6} \left(2\pi n \sqrt{\frac{l_p}{g}}\right)^{-0.44} \left(\frac{l_i}{l_p}\right)^{0.31}$$

$$\times \left[f_1\left(\theta\right)\right]^{1.35}\left(\mu_1\right)^{-4.59}\left(\mu_2\right)^{-3.72} \tag{11.6}$$

$$\frac{P/L}{Q_a \rho_b g} = 3.54 \left(2\pi n \sqrt{\frac{l_p}{g}}\right)^{0.14} \left(\frac{d_{sf}}{l_p}\right)^{-10.12} \left(\frac{l_i}{l_p}\right)^{0.11} \left[f_2\left(\theta\right)\right]\left(\mu_2\right)^{2.05} \tag{11.7}$$

where
$f_1(\theta)$ $= 1 + \cos^2\theta$ (11.8)
$f_2(\theta)$ $= 6.94 \left(1.3 - \cos^2\theta\right)$
θ = conveyor angle as measured from the horizontal
         (degrees)
$0.414 > \mu_1 > 0.374$
$0.554 > \mu_2 > 0.466$

11.1.3 Performance

The performance of a screw conveyor, as characterized by its capacity, volumetric efficiency and power requirements, is affected by the conveyor geometry and size, the properties of the material being conveyed, and the conveyor operating parameters such as the screw speed and the angle of inclination. The effect of these factors is discussed below:

Capacity. Screw length has no effect on the capacity. The effect of speed and inclination is given in figure 11.2. As shown in the figure, there is a limiting value of speed beyond which the capacity does not increase. In fact it may even decrease beyond a certain speed. It is also seen from this figure that the capacity decreases as the angle of inclination increases. The limiting value of speed is

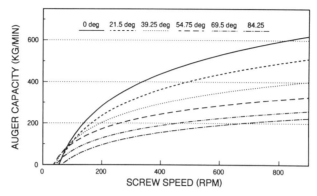

Figure 11.2–Effect of screw speed and angle of auger inclination on conveying capacity (Redrawn from Regan and Henderson, 1959).

independent of the angle of inclination. It has been suggested that there may be two factors responsible for this behavior; (a) The maximum possible rate of grain flow through an orifice; and (b) the centrifugal force due to the rotation of the grain mass. Initially, the capacity increases directly with speed up to 250 rev/min. After this point the centrifugal force restricts the flow of grain at the intake and causes the slope to decrease. If the speed is increased sufficiently the centrifugal force may become so restrictive as to cause a decline in the capacity.

Figure 11.3 shows the effect of screw angle of inclination on the capacity. The reduction in the capacity approximately follows the cosine function with two exceptions: (a) the capacity at higher speed is well below the cosine function; and (b) the capacity at 90° angle is about 30% of the horizontal capacity. This may be due to the

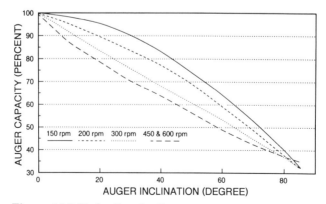

Figure 11.3–Reduction in the auger conveying capacity as affected by the angle of inclination at different speeds (Redrawn from Regan and Henderson, 1959).

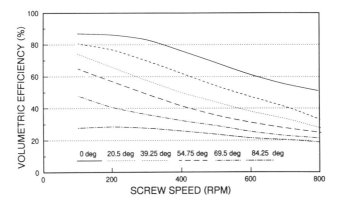

Figure 11.4–Effect of screw speed on volumetric capacity at various angles of inclination (Redrawn from Regan and Henderson, 1959).

restriction to grain flow into the intake of the conveyor at higher speeds and the fact that grain flows from a vertical orifice at one-third the rate from a comparable horizontal orifice.

Volumetric efficiency. Screw length has no effect on the capacity and volumetric efficiency. The effect of screw speed and inclination on volumetric efficiency is given in figure 11.4. Generally, volumetric efficiency decreases as the screw speed and the angle of inclination increase. Brusewitz and Persson (1969) reported that the screw clearance affects the volumetric efficiency. As shown in figure 11.5, the diametral clearances up to 5 to 7% have little affect on the volumetric efficiency but a drop in efficiency of 0.7% per 1% increase in clearance can be expected. No interaction of the conveyor inclination and screw clearance is evident.

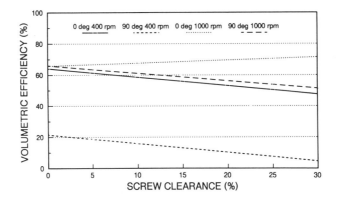

Figure 11.5–Effect of the clearance between screw flightings and the tube inside diameter on the volumetric conveying efficiency (Redrawn from Brusewitz and Persson, 1969).

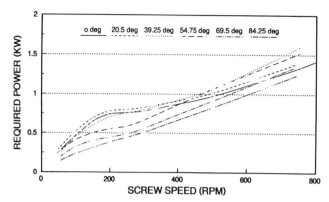

Figure 11.6–Auger conveyor power requirements at different screw speeds and angles of inclination (Redrawn from Regan and Henderson, 1959).

Power requirements. The effect of screw diameter on specific power as defined earlier is dependent on the speed. At low speeds there is a decrease in the specific power with increase in the screw diameter. The trend reverses with higher speeds. Screw length has no effect on specific power. There is a slight effect of the pitch on the specific power. An increase in pitch tends to reduce the specific power. For horizontal augers, an increase in the diametral clearance causes a slight decline in the specific power. However, for vertical augers, this results in a general increase in the power. An increase in screw speed results in an increase in the required power as shown in figure 11.6. The hump in the power curve below 300 rev/min is due to the high torque value at lower speeds. Increasing the angle of inclination causes the power to increase initially but a decrease follows beyond a certain angle. This is due to the decline in the volumetric efficiency. Moisture content which is associated with increase in friction causes the specific power to increase significantly.

Presently, concise data are not available for individual design problems. The selection is based on data provided by the manufacturers. Most data provided by the manufacturers are for low speed horizontal augers. However, the equations given above may be used for estimating auger capacity and power requirements for a given application.

Example 11.1

Determine the efficiency, volumetric capacity and power requirement of a horizontal standard pitch screw auger conveying wheat. The screw diameter is 15.24 cm (6 in.) and the shaft diameter is 2.54 cm (1 in.). The screw speed is 600 rev/min. The grain-metal friction may be taken as 0.414 while a value of 0.466 may be used for internal friction coefficient. The intake length of the screw is two times the pitch.

Solution.

Given:

$$d_{sf} = 0.1524 \text{ m (6 in.)}$$
$$d_{ss} = 0.0254 \text{ m (1 in.)}$$
$$l_p = 0.1524 \text{ m (6 in.)}$$
$$l_i = 0.3048 \text{ m (12 in.)}$$
$$\rho_b = 769 \text{ kg/m}^3 \text{ (table 11.2)}$$
$$\mu_1 = 0.414$$
$$\mu_2 = 0.466$$
$$n = 10 \text{ rev/s (600 rev/min)}$$
$$\theta = 0$$

Use equation 11.6 to determine the efficiency. The dimensionless groups are calculated as follows.

$$2\pi n \sqrt{\frac{l_p}{g}} = 2\pi(10)\sqrt{\frac{0.1524}{9.81}} = 7.83$$

$$\frac{d_{sf}}{l_p} = \frac{0.1524}{0.1524} = 1$$

$$f_1(\theta) = 2$$

$$\frac{l_i}{l_p} = \frac{0.3048}{0.1524} = 2$$

Substituting in equation 11.6 we get:

$$\frac{Q_a}{\frac{\pi}{4}\left(d_{sf}^2 - d_{ss}^2\right) l_p n} = 432 \times 10^{-6} (7.83)^{-0.44} (2)^{0.31} (2)^{1.35}$$

$$\times (0.414)^{-4.59} (0.466)^{-3.72}$$

$$= \left(432 \times 10^{-6}\right) (0.4) (1.24) (2.55) (57.3) (17.12)$$

$$= 0.53$$

$$\eta_v = 0.53 \quad \text{or} \quad 53\%$$

Volumetric capacity can be found as:

$$Q_a = 0.53 \times \frac{\pi}{4} \times \left[(0.1524)^2 - (0.0254)^2\right] \times 0.1524 \times 10$$

$$Q_a = 0.014 \text{ m}^3/\text{s} \quad (\text{or } 40.5 \text{ t / h})$$

Use equation 11.7 to determine the power requirement.

$$\frac{P/L}{Q_a \, \rho_b \, g} = 3.54 \, (7.83)^{0.14}(1)^{-10.12}(2)^{0.11}(3.23)^{1.0}$$

$$(0.466)^{2.05}$$

$$= 3.54 \times 1.334 \times 1 \times 1.079 \times 3.23 \times 0.209$$

$$= 3.345$$

P/L $\quad = 3.345 \times 0.014 \times 769 \times 9.81$

P/L $\quad = 368.4 \text{ Watt/m}$

11.2 Pneumatic Conveyors

Pneumatic conveyors move grain by imparting the kinetic energy of moving air to grain in conduits. Pneumatic conveyors are flexible in that they may be used to convey material to areas that are hard to reach by other mechanical conveyors. However, pneumatic conveyors require relatively higher specific power as compared to the screw conveyors.

11.2.1 Methods and Equipment

The pneumatic conveying systems can be divided into three types. These are negative pressure, positive pressure, and combination negative/positive pressure systems. However, negative pressure systems are not common in agricultural applications.

TABLE 11.2. GRAIN PROPERTIES RELATED TO PNEUMATIC CONVEYING (ASAE DATA D241.2)

Material	Bulk Density (kg / m³)	Particle Density (kg / m³)	Equivalent Particle Diameter (mm)
Wheat	769	1300	4.08
Oats	410	1050	4.19
Barley	615	1330	4.05
Soybeans	769	1180	6.74
Corn	718	1390	7.26

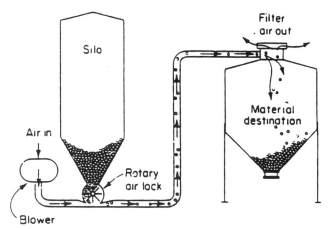

Figure 11.7–A positive pressure pneumatic conveying system (Reproduced from *Chemical Engineers' Handbook* by permission of McGraw-Hill Book Co.).

Positive pressure systems. Material is introduced into the high pressure stream of air by means of an air lock as shown in figure 11.7. The material may be transported from a single point to many destination points. There is no need for a cyclone separator and a dust collector. High capacities may be obtained from a relatively smaller unit due to the higher operating pressures. The system is limited to 10 psig pressure.

Combination negative/positive systems. Some systems employ a combination of both vacuum and positive pressure. Vacuum is used to draw the material into the system and then the positive pressure is used to convey the material to its destination. The air mover for this system is larger than either of the above systems. A combination system is shown in figure 11.8. The total range of

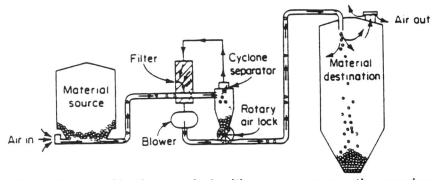

Figure 11.8–A combination negative/positive pressure pneumatic conveying system (Reproduced from *Chemical Engineers' Handbook* by permission of McGraw-Hill Book Co.).

pressure for the combination system is 33 cm (13 in.) Hg to 68.9 kPa (10 psig).

The necessary components used to complete a pneumatic conveying system may be classified into air moving system, feeding system, discharge system, and piping and fittings.

Air moving system. The selection of the air mover depends upon the pressure and air flow requirement of the system. The air movers may be divided into low volume high pressure or high volume low pressure systems. Figure 11.9 shows a rotary positive displacement blower and centrifugal blower. As shown in the figure, a pair of lobed rotors fitted inside a housing create the positive pumping action. These blowers are suitable for pressures up to 68.9 kPa (10 psig). A pressure relief valve and an air filter are essential for a positive displacement blower. A centrifugal blower can generate a large volume of air but at relatively low pressures — usually less than 34.5 kPa (5 psig). However, the blowers may be connected in series to generate higher pressures. Centrifugal blowers are more tolerant of dirt which is an advantage when used in a negative pressure system.

Feeding system. The design of a feeding system depends upon the type of the conveying system used. For a pipeline under vacuum the material may be metered in through a rotary air-lock, a controlled feed hopper, or a self-regulating pickup nozzle. For a pipeline under positive pressure the material must be metered in through a rotary air-lock to keep back pressure to a minimum. A vent is provided in the feed hopper to relieve back pressure. Figure 11.10 shows a rotary air-lock feeder. The speed of rotation is controlled to regulate the material flow rate.

Discharge system. For a pipeline under vacuum, the conveyed material must be separated from the conveying air. A

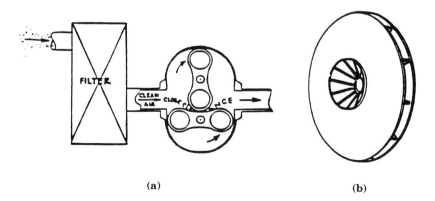

(a)   (b)

Figure 11.9–(a) A rotary positive displacement blower, (b) a centrifugal blower (Reprinted from Hellevang, 1985).

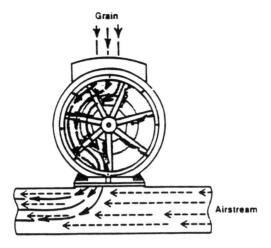

Figure 11.10–A rotary air lock (Reprinted from Hellevang, 1985).

cyclone type separator is used to slow the grain in order for it to settle in the bottom and be separated from the air. A screen or a filter is needed to remove the dirt from the air before it enters the blower. For pipelines under pressure, the material may be discharged directly into the bins or silos. The discharge is tangential to create a cyclone effect. Often, in high velocity low positive pressure systems, a cyclone separator is used to slow the material down to minimize damage to grain. A cyclone separator is shown in figure 11.11.

Pipelines and fittings. Pipeline diameter, wall thickness, and the pipe material are to be determined while selecting a pipeline. The pipe material should be wear resistant. Most piping has smooth bores and couplings that butt the pipes to minimize grain damage. Long

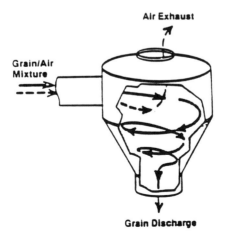

**Figure 11.11–A cyclone separator
(Reprinted from Hellevang, 1985).**

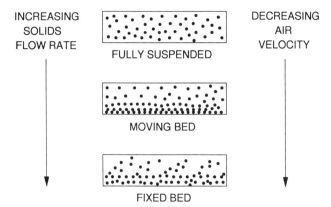

INCREASING SOLIDS FLOW RATE

DECREASING AIR VELOCITY

FULLY SUSPENDED

MOVING BED

FIXED BED

Figure 11.12–Different phases of solids flow in pneumatic conveying.

factory bends are preferred to minimize grain damage and pipe wear. It is recommended that the turning radius be six to eight times the tube diameter for bends of 45° or greater.

11.2.2 Theory

As solid particles are introduced to a flowing stream of air in a duct they are subjected to the aerodynamic drag. If the air velocity is sufficiently high the particles accelerate and the drag reduces because the relative velocity between the particles and the air also reduces. When the particles are being conveyed, the drag overcomes the forces of gravity, particle to particle interaction, and particle to conduit wall friction. As the number of particles in the air stream are increased as a result of higher conveying rate, the resistance to air flow increases. If the conveying rate of solids continues to increase, there comes a point when the particles no longer behave as discrete particles. They may form clusters and eventually a plug if the flow rate of solids continues to increase. The phase when the solids are in a uniform suspension is called the *dilute phase*. The *dense phase* occurs when the particles begin to form clusters. Conveying of agricultural material is done in the dilute phase also called the lean phase. Figure 11.12 shows the distribution of particles as the solids flow rate increases.

Figure 11.13 shows a plot of pressure drop per unit length versus superficial air flow velocity at different material flow rates. In the initial part of the curve the pressure drops as the velocity increases. Then after a certain velocity the pressure drop increases. The point of inflection of the curve essentially separates the dense phase from the dilute phase. The point that separates the two flow regimes is based on the mass flow rate of solids relative to that of the air. Generally, a solid/air mass flow ratio less than 15 would result in

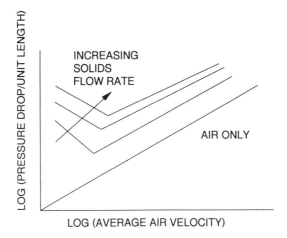

Figure 11.13–A pneumatic conveying state diagram.

the dilute phase. The minimum point on a curve represents the minimum velocity required to produce the dilute phase for that mass flow rate.

During transport, the solid particles are in a suspension and may be treated as an aggregate of solids with void space. The void ratio (e) is defined as:

$$e = \frac{V - V_s}{V} = 1 - \frac{V_s}{V} \tag{11.9}$$

where
V_s = volume occupied by solids (m^3)
V = total volume (m^3)

The total volume occupied by solids is the sum of each solid particle and may be expressed as follows:

$$V_s = nV_p = \frac{\dot{m}}{\rho_p c}\, dL \tag{11.10}$$

where
n   = number of solids in the control volume
V_p = volume of each solid particle (m^3)
$\dot{m}$ = mass flow rate of solids (kg/s)
ρ_p = density of solid particles (kg/m^3)
c   = velocity of solid particles (m/s)
dL = elemental length of the conveyor tube (m)

Density of solid particles may be determined from the data presented in table 11.2. Substituting equation 11.10 in equation 11.9 we get:

$$e = 1 - \frac{\rho^*}{\rho_p} \qquad (11.11)$$

where

ρ^* = apparent bulk density of solids during transport (kg/m^3)
  = $(\phi_m v \rho)/c$
v = velocity of air (m/s)
ρ = density of air (kg/m^3)
ϕ_m = mass flow ratio = $\dot{M}/(\rho Q)$
Q = volumetric flow rate of air (m^3/s)
c = solids velocity (m/s)

Marcus et al. (1990) have reported the following equation for estimating the solids velocity (c):

$$\frac{c}{v} = 1 - 0.68 d^{0.92} \rho_p^{0.5} \rho^{-0.2} D^{0.54} \qquad (11.12)$$

where d = particle mean diameter (m)

The design of a pneumatic conveying system involves determining the conveying air velocity, volume of conveying air, total pressure drop, and power requirement for the blower. The air velocity depends upon the size, shape, and the density of the particles to be conveyed. The volume of air depends on the desired mass flow rate. Figure 11.14 shows the desired air velocity and volumetric flow rate that would produce dilute phase transport conditions. The pressure drop in the conveying system is a sum of many terms as given by the following equation:

$$\Delta p = \Delta p_L + \Delta p_a + \Delta p_s + \Delta p_g + \Delta p_b + \Delta p_c \qquad (11.13)$$

where

Δp = total system pressure drop (Pa)
Δp_L = line pressure loss due to air only (Pa)
Δp_a = pressure drop due to particle acceleration (Pa)
Δp_s = pressure drop due to solids friction (Pa)

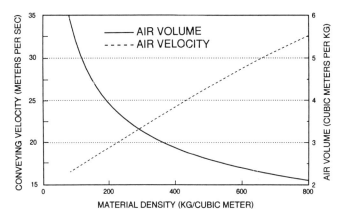

Figure 11.14–Average velocities and air volume for low pressure pneumatic conveying of materials (Redrawn from ASAE Data D273).

Δp_g = pressure drop due to vertical lift (Pa)
Δp_b = pressure drop in bends (Pa)
Δp_c = pressure drop in accessories (Pa)

Line pressure loss. The line pressure loss is the pressure loss due to only air flowing through the conveying ducts. It can be estimated from the following equation:

$$\Delta p_L = \lambda_L \frac{\rho}{2} v^2 \frac{L}{D} \tag{11.14}$$

where
λ_L = air resistance factor
L = length of the conveying duct (m)

For turbulent flow the following equation given by Koo as cited in Marcus et al. (1990) may be used to determine line friction loss factor:

$$\frac{\lambda_L}{4} = 0.0014 + 0.125 R_e^{-0.32} \tag{11.15}$$

where as the Reynold's number $R_e = (\rho v D)/\mu$ and μ is the viscosity of air.

Acceleration pressure drop. As the solids are introduced into the air stream they are accelerated to the solids velocity (c). This requires an additional pressure drop. This pressure drop may be estimated from the following equation given by Marcus et al. (1990):

$$\Delta p_a = \phi_m v \rho \, c \qquad (11.16)$$

Pressure drop due to solids. This pressure drop is due to solid particle interaction and wall friction. The following equation may be used to estimate this value of the pressure drop:

$$\Delta p_s = \phi_m \, \lambda_s \, \frac{\rho}{2} \, v^2 \, \frac{L}{D} \qquad (11.17)$$

Konno and Saito (Marcus et al., 1990) gave the following equation to determine the solids friction factor needed in the above equation:

$$\lambda_s = \frac{0.0285 \, \sqrt{gD}}{c} \qquad (11.18)$$

where g   = acceleration due to gravity ($9.81 \ m/s^2$).

Pressure drop due to lift height. This pressure drop represents the potential energy change in lifting the solids through the desired height. The following equation is used to estimate this pressure drop:

$$\Delta p_g = \rho^* g \Delta z \qquad (11.19)$$

where Δz = lift height (m).

Pressure drop due to bends. As the air/solid mixture goes around a bend, there is some loss of energy due to the friction of air and solids against the wall. The solids slow down as they go around the bend and an additional pressure is needed to accelerate them up to the conveying velocity. The pressure drop in a bend is computed separately for air and solids. The pressure drop due to air only is calculated by determining an equivalent length for the bend. An equivalent length is that length that produces the pressure drop in a straight pipe as that in the bend. The following equation is used to compute the equivalent length:

TABLE 11.3. SOME FITTING LOSS COEFFICIENTS
FOR TURBULENT FLOW (ASHRAE, 1972)

Fitting	Geometry	K
Entrance	Sharp	0.5
	Well-rounded	0.05
Contraction	Sharp $(D_2 / D_1 = 0.5)$	0.38
90° elbow	Miter	1.3
	Short radius	0.9
	Long radius	0.6

$$L_{eq} = \frac{KD}{\lambda_L} \qquad (11.20)$$

where K = fitting loss coefficient.

The fitting loss coefficient (K) can be selected from table 11.3 (ASHRAE, 1972). Equivalent length should be calculated for each bend and added to determine the total pressure loss due to the bends. The pressure loss due to the solids can be calculated by the following equation:

$$\frac{\Delta p_{b,solids}}{\rho v^2} = 0.245 \left(\frac{\dot{m}}{\rho v D^2}\right)^{1.267} \left(\frac{R}{D}\right)^{-0.260} \qquad (11.21)$$

where

$\Delta p_{b,solids}$ = pressure drop due to solids in bends (Pa).
R/D = bend radius to pipe diameter ratio.

Pressure drop in accessories. The pressure loss in accessories is based on their design. No simple equations are available to estimate this pressure drop. Graphs are available in literature that can be used to determine Δp_c for different accessories. Often manufacturers provide pressure drop data which should be

TABLE 11.4. PRESSURE LOSS DATA FOR SOME COMMON
PNEUMATIC CONVEYING ACCESSORIES
(NOYES AND PFIEFFER, 1985)

Accessory	Pressure drop (kPa)
Blower suction	0.7
Inlet filter	0.7
Inlet filter and muffler	1.4
Outlet muffler and check plate	1.4
Discharge cyclone	0.7
Bin vent	1.4
In-line filter	1.4

consulted. Table 11.4 gives pressure loss data for some common accessories.

Power requirements. The blower power requirement depends on the conveying air volumetric flow rate and total system pressure drop. The power requirement may be computed from the following equation for standard air. Correction should be made for altitude, temperature, and humidity.

$$P = \frac{\Delta p Q}{\eta_b} \qquad (11.22)$$

where
   P = blower power (W)
   Δp = total system pressure drop (Pa)
   Q = volumetric flow rate of air (m^3/s)
   η_b = blower efficiency (0.5 to 0.7)

The specific power or power per unit material flow rate may be calculated from:

$$P' = \frac{P}{\dot{m}} \qquad (11.23)$$

where P' = specific power (W·s/kg).

Example 11.2.
   Wheat is to be conveyed through a horizontal distance of 30 m horizontally and 10 m vertically at a rate of 30,000 kg/h. The transport line has four 90° bends and its diameter is 12.7 cm. Assuming standard air properties, determine total system pressure loss and blower power requirement.
   Solution. From table 11.2 wheat density, $\rho = 769$ kg/m^3. Corresponding to this value, it is recommended that the conveying velocity be 35 m/s (figure 11.14).

Volumetric air flow rate, Q $= \frac{\pi}{4} (0.127)^2 \times 35$

$= 0.443$ m^3/s

Mass air flow rate, ρQ $= 1.2 (0.443)$

$= 0.532$ kg/s

$$\text{Mass flow ratio, } \phi_m = \frac{8.33}{0.532} = 15.66$$

This ratio is higher than the required 15 for lean phase conveying. The velocity of air must be increased.

Required air mass flow rate = 8.55/15 = 0.57 kg/s

$$\text{Required air velocity, v} = \frac{0.56}{1.2 \frac{\pi}{4} (0.127)^2}$$

$$= 36.53 \text{ m/s}$$

$$\text{Corresponding Reynolds number is, } R_e = \frac{\rho v D}{\mu} = \frac{1.2 (36.53) (0.127)}{10^{-5}}$$

$$= 5.57 \times 10^5$$

(a) Line pressure loss:

$$\Delta p_L = \lambda_L \frac{\rho}{2} v^2 \frac{L}{D}$$

$$\frac{\lambda_L}{4} = 0.0014 + 0.125 (5.57 \times 10^5)^{-0.32}$$

$$\lambda_L = 0.013$$

$$\Delta p_L = 0.013 \frac{(1.2)}{2} (36.53)^2 \frac{(30 + 10)}{0.127}$$

$$\Delta p_L = 3.24 \text{ kPa}$$

(b) Acceleration pressure loss (use Table 6.1 for dp):

$$\Delta p_a = \phi_m v \rho c$$

$$\frac{c}{v} = 1 - 0.68 dp^{0.92} \rho_p^{0.5} \rho^{-0.2} D^{0.54}$$

$$= 1 - 0.68 (4.08 \times 10^{-3})^{0.92} 1300^{0.5} 1.2^{-0.2} 0.127^{0.54}$$

$$\frac{c}{v} = 0.951$$

or c = 0.951 (36.53) = 34.74 m/s

$$\Delta p_a = 15 (36.53) (1.2) (34.74)$$

$$= 22.84 \text{ kPa}$$

(c) Pressure drop due to lift height:

$$\Delta p_g = \rho^* g \Delta z$$

$$\rho^* \quad = \quad \frac{\phi_m v \rho}{c} = \frac{15\,(36.53)\,(1.2)}{34.74}$$

$$\quad = \quad 18.91 \text{ kg/m}^3$$

$$\Delta p_g \quad = \quad 18.91\,(9.81)\,(10)$$

$$\quad = \quad 1.86 \text{ kPa}$$

(d) Pressure drop due to solids:

$$\Delta p_s \quad = \quad \phi_m \lambda_s \frac{\rho}{2} v^2 \frac{L}{D}$$

$$\lambda_s \quad = \quad \frac{0.0285 \sqrt{gD}}{c}$$

$$\quad = \quad \frac{0.0285 \sqrt{9.81\,(0.127)}}{34.74}$$

$$\quad = \quad 0.92 \times 10^{-3}$$

$$\Delta p_s \quad = \quad 15\,(0.92 \times 10^{-3})\frac{(1.2)}{2}(36.53)^2 \frac{40}{0.127}$$

$$\quad = \quad 3.46 \text{ kPa}$$

(e) Pressure loss in bends:

$$L_{eq} \quad = \quad \frac{KD}{\lambda_L}$$

Assuming K = 0.9 (Table 11.3)

$$L_{eq} \quad = \quad \frac{0.9\,(0.127)}{0.013}$$

$$\quad = \quad 8.79 \text{ m}$$

Total equivalent length for four bends:
$$L_{eq} \quad = \quad 4 \times 8.79 = 35.2 \text{ m}$$

Pressure loss, $\Delta p_{b,\,air} \quad = \quad \frac{3.24}{40} \times 35.2 = 2.85 \text{ kPa}$

Pressure loss due to solids (assuming R/D = 5):

$$\frac{\Delta p_{b,\,solids}}{\rho v^2} = 0.245 \left(\frac{\dot{m}}{\rho v D^2}\right)\left(\frac{R}{D}\right)^{-0.260}$$

$$= 0.245 \left(\frac{8.33}{1.2\,(36.53)\,(0.127)^2}\right)(5)^{-0.260}$$

$$= 1.9$$

or $\Delta p_{b,\,solids} = 1.90\,(1.2)\,(36.53)^2$

$$= 3.04 \text{ kPa}$$

Thus, the total pressure drop is:

$$\Delta p = 3.24 + 22.84 + 1.86 + 3.46 + 2.85 + 3.04$$

$$= 37.3 \text{ kPa}$$

Note that the pressure drop is exclusive of the pressure drop due to the accessories, such as cyclones, etc.

Power requirement.

$$P = \frac{\Delta p\,Q}{\eta_b}$$

$$= \frac{37.3\,\frac{\pi}{4}\,(0.127)^2\,36.53}{0.6}$$

$$= 28.76 \text{ kW}$$

11.2.3 Performance

The performance of a pneumatic conveying system depends on factors related to the equipment, the material being conveyed, and the operating conditions. Proper design is important for efficient operation. The selection of the type of conveying system would depend upon the given constraints on material feeding and discharge. Material properties and the desired feed rate would determine the airflow rate and the power requirements. Figure 11.15 presents performance data for corn for a 11.12 kW (15 hp) positive pressure system. The figure shows the effect of vertical lift and the horizontal conveying distance on the volumetric conveying rate. Table 11.5 gives a comparison of performance of an 60 kW (80 hp)

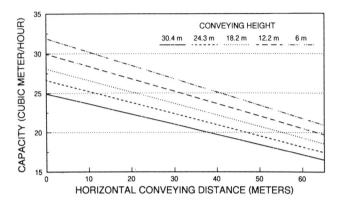

Figure 11.15–Capacity of a pneumatic conveyor as affected by the vertical lift and the conveying distance (Drawn using data by Hellevang, 1985).

positive/negative pneumatic unit with a 15.2 cm (6 in.) screw conveyor (PAMI, 1979). It is evident that a screw conveyor is considerably more efficient than the pneumatic unit.

Grain damage is an important performance parameter. According to a PAMI test report (1977) 0.25% grain damage is caused for each pass through a pneumatic unit. It was also reported that the damage was comparable to that caused by a grain auger. Grain damage increases with conveying speed. Table 11.6 shows the effect

TABLE 11.5. COMPARISON OF 60 kW, POSITIVE/NEGATIVE PRESSURE 20.32 CM (8 IN.) PNEUMATIC UNIT TO A 15.24 CM (6 IN.) GRAIN AUGER (HELLEVANG, 1985)

	Maximum Conveying Rates				Specific Capacities	
	Pneumatic Unit		Auger		Pneumatic Unit	Auger
Grain Type	(t / h)	(m^3 / h)	(t / h)	(m^3 / h)	(m^3 / kW-h)	(m^3 / kW-h)
Wheat	25.1	28.5	37.6	42.7	0.87	10.60
Barley	24.2	34.4	27.9	39.7	1.04	11.77
Oats	33.5	67.1	21.8	43.8	1.79	16.00

TABLE 11.6. DAMAGE IN CONVEYING WHITE BEANS WITH A PNEUMATIC CONVEYOR (HELLEVANG, 1985)

Seed Velocity (m / min)	Germination (%)	Visible Damage (%)
0-control	93.5	0.00
198	91.0	0.40
292	89.7	0.49
440	83.5	0.59
505	82.7	0.70
689	73.5	1.62

TABLE 11.7. Damage in conveying white navy beans with pneumatic conveyor (Hellevang, 1985)

Breakage Due To	Conveying Phase	
	Dense Phase (%)	Lean Phase (%)
Air lock	1.03	0.27
Transport	0.52	1.35
Total	1.55	1.62

of conveying speed on damage for white beans. Grain damage as caused by air lock is shown in table 11.7 for two phases of conveying (Hellevang, 1985).

11.3 Bucket Elevators

The bucket elevator is most commonly employed for vertical conveying of free-flowing materials such as small grain and pellets. A bucket elevator consists of equally spaced buckets mounted on a belt. The belt wraps around two pulleys located at the top and the bottom of a rectangular shaped housing as shown in figure 11.16. As the belt rotates the buckets scoop some grain from the bottom and carry it up. At the top the buckets unload the material as they go around the top wheel and are made to turn upside down. The bucket size varies from a 10.16 cm × 7.62 cm (4 in. × 3 in.) to as large as 35.56 cm × 20.32 cm (14 in. × 8 in.). The bucket spacing ranges from 11.43 cm (4.5 in.) to 30.49 cm (12 in.). The belt speed can vary from 1.2 m/s to 3.3 m/s. The capacity of the bucket elevator depends on the bucket size, bucket spacing, and belt speed. Commonly, the capacity of the elevators employed for agricultural applications is in the range of 7 m³/h to 350 m³/h.

The relationship between head-wheel speed and diameter is very important for satisfactory operation of this type of elevator. When the mass of grain in the bucket is moving around the head pulley it is subjected to the force of gravity acting vertically downward and the centrifugal force acting radially from the center of the head pulley. The resultant of these forces causes the material to be discharged from the bucket into the discharge chute. For clean emptying of the buckets, the start of the flow from the bucket must be delayed until after the bucket has passed its uppermost position on the head wheel. This situation will exist when the gravity and the centrifugal forces are equal. When the bucket reaches the top position on the head wheel, the resultant of the two forces will be zero, and there will be no discharging force on the material. It will neither be thrown vertically from the bucket nor fall out of the bucket.

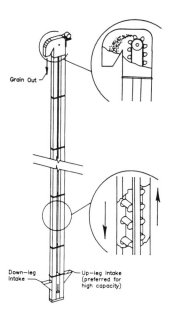

Figure 11.16–Schematic diagram of a bucket elevator (Reproduced with permission from *Grain Drying, Handling and Storage Handbook*, 2nd Ed., 1987 © Midwest Plan Services).

Equating the weight of the grain to the centrifugal force acting on the grain, we get:

$$W = \frac{W}{g}\frac{v^2}{R}$$

or

$$v^2 = gR$$

or

$$v = \sqrt{gR}$$

Using $v = 2\pi Rn = \sqrt{gR}$, the necessary wheel speed may be calculated as:

$$n = \frac{1}{2\pi}\sqrt{\frac{g}{R}} \qquad (11.24)$$

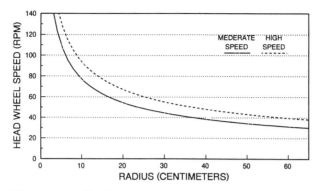

Figure 11.17–Bucket conveyor vs. radius of the path of the center of gravity of the material in the bucket (Redrawn from Millier, 1958).

where

W = weight of material (N)

v = velocity of material (m/s)

g = acceleration of gravity (m²/s)

R = radius to the center of gravity of material in the bucket (m)

n = speed of head pulley (rps)

The graph in figure 11.17 shows the relationship between the head wheel speed and the radius of the path of the center of gravity of the material in the bucket about the center of the head wheel. To find the diameter of the head wheel, deduct from this radius the thickness of the belt and the distance from the belt to the center of gravity of the material in the bucket.

The trajectory of the material from the buckets is parabolic and can be determined from an equation of motion. It has been found that for high-speed elevators, those with head-wheel diameters and speeds determined from the high-speed curve in figure 11.17, the inner lip of the discharge chute should be located as close to the descending buckets as possible and at an angle of 15 to 20° below the center of the head wheel.

Elevator Capacity

The capacity of bucket elevators depends upon the capacity of the individual buckets, the bucket spacing, and speed of the belt or chain carrying the buckets. Bucket spacing is governed by the shape of the bucket and its resulting discharge characteristics.

The capacity of a bucket is considered to be from 85 to 90% of the struck volume for high-speed elevators, if the feed is arranged to allow loading at or above the center of the foot shaft. If loading is below this point, the capacity may be reduced to 80% of the struck volume. On moderate speed elevators the bucket should be expected to fill 90% of its struck volume.

The following equation is used to determine elevator capacity:

$$Q = \frac{V\,v}{s} \qquad (11.25)$$

where
- Q = elevator capacity (m³/s)
- V = bucket volume (m³)
- v = belt speed (m/s)
- s = bucket spacing (m)

Elevator Power

The horsepower required to operate a bucket elevator is that required to lift the material, to scoop the material into the buckets, to discharge the material, to move a small amount of air, and to overcome friction in the bearings and other drive components. In general the bucket elevator has a high elevating efficiency. In practice it has been found that theoretical horsepower required to lift the material needs to be increased only 10 to 15% to obtain the actual power requirement. The following equation is used to obtain the theoretical power requirement:

$$P = \rho_b g Q h \qquad (11.26)$$

where
- P = theoretical power (W)
- ρ_b = material bulk density (kg/m³)
- h = material lift height (m)

It is advisable to use the struck volume of each bucket in determining the elevator capacity. This will eliminate power failures in instances where feed rate is high and the buckets are filling well above the center of the foot wheel.

Example 11.3

Find the velocity of the material being conveyed if the radius to the center of gravity of the material in the bucket is 30.48 cm (12 in.) and then find the speed of the head pulley in rev/min. Determine the power requirement of this bucket elevator:

Given:

bucket capacity = 0.25 kg
belt speed   = 1.25 cm/s
bucket spacing = 20 cm
height   = 15 cm

$$V = \sqrt{gR} = \sqrt{9.81 \times 0.3048} = 1.729 \text{ m/s}$$
$$N = \frac{60}{2\pi} \sqrt{\frac{g}{R}} = \frac{60}{2\pi} \sqrt{\frac{9.81}{0.3048}} = 54.17 \text{ rpm}$$

Elevator capacity can be found as:

$$\text{Capacity} = \frac{\text{Bucket capacity} \times \text{Belt speed}}{\text{Bucket spacing}}$$
$$= \frac{0.25 \times 1.250}{0.2}$$
$$= 1.5625 \text{ kg/s}$$

$$\begin{aligned}\text{Power} &= \text{Capacity} \times \text{height} \times g \\ &= 1.5625 \times 1.5 \times 9.81 \\ &= 22.845 \text{ W}\end{aligned}$$

11.4 Forage Blowers

Forage blowers are commonly used to convey chopped forage by imparting enough kinetic energy to the material to carry it through the conveying pipe. The blowers comprise of a feed hopper, a radial paddle blower, and a conveying pipe. Forage blowers are sometimes called forage throwers because of the throwing action caused by the blower paddles. A schematic of a forage blower is shown in figure 11.18. The material enters the blower housing through an opening in the side. The material is immediately accelerated by the rotating blades as shown in figure 11.19 and blown up the pipe that is located tangentially as shown in the diagram. As the material leaves the blades its velocity is higher than the airflow velocity. Consequently, the air provides a resistance to its movement upward. The materials continues to slow down due to the effects of the air drag, gravity and the friction with the pipe walls. After a time the material slows down sufficiently so that its velocity is slower than the air velocity and the conveying is accomplished in a manner similar to that of a pneumatic conveyor. Therefore, the blower must impart enough kinetic energy to the material so that it will travel to the desired height in the conveying pipe.

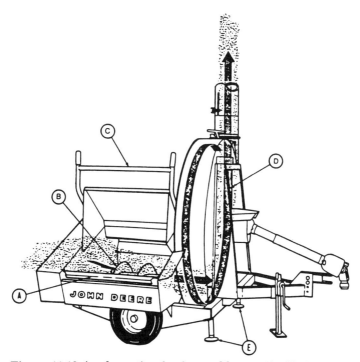

Figure 11.18–A schematic of a forage blower. (A) Shaker pan, (B) transfer auger, (C) clutch lever, (D) blower fan, (E) stabilizers (Courtesy of Prairie Agricultural Machinery Institute, Canada).

Forage blowers are generally driven by the pto-shaft of a tractor. The blower impeller diameters are generally 1.2 to 1.4 m and peripheral speed of about 35 m/s. Most discharge pipes have 22.9 cm (9 in.) diameter. Capacities up to 100 t/h of corn silage are possible.

11.4.1 Theory

Chancellor (1960) completed an analysis of solid particles moving upward in a vertical pipe in an air stream. Based on the analysis and the experiments, he concluded that in the case of a blower, the solids impart energy to the air stream rather than the other way around. The result of air movement in the pipe is to reduce the effect of air resistance. He analyzed three possible cases as discussed below:

Phase 1. The particle is moving faster than the air stream velocity. The forces that act on the particle are inertia acting upward, air drag acting downward, and gravity also acting downward. The total height (H_1) that the material will rise until the particle velocity

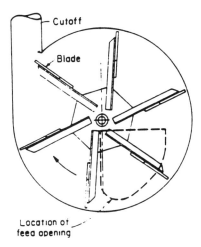

Figure 11.19–Schematic diagram
of an impeller blower (Reprinted
from *Principles of Farm Machinery*, Kepner et al., 1978).

becomes equal to that of the air stream was developed by summing
these forces and solving the resulting differential equation as:

$$H_1 = t_1 (v_a) - \left[\frac{v_s^2}{2g} \ln \left(\frac{v_s^2 + v_r^2}{v_s^2 + v_{r0}^2} \right) \right]$$

(11.27)

where

$$t_1 = \frac{v_s}{g} \left(\tan^{-1} \frac{v_{r0}^2}{v_s} - \tan^{-1} \frac{v_r}{v_s} \right)$$

v_r = relative velocity of the particle in the air stream (m/s)
v_{r0} = initial relative velocity (m/s)
v_s = terminal velocity of the particle (m/s)
v_a = velocity of air stream (m/s)

Phase 2. The particle will continue to decelerate until $v_r = v_s$.
The height travelled in the second phase, is given as:

$$H_2 = v_a t_2 + \frac{v_s}{2g} \ln \left(\frac{v_s^2 - v_r^2}{v_s^2 - v_{r0}^2} \right)$$

(11.28)

where

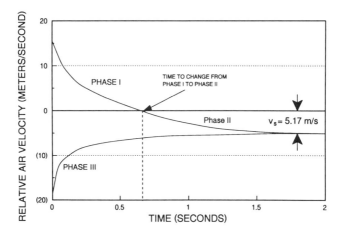

Figure 11.20–Examples of particle velocity changes with time (Redrawn from Chancellor, 1960).

$$t_2 = \frac{v_s}{g}\left[\tan^{-1}\left(\frac{v_r}{v_s}\right) - \tan^{-1}\left(\frac{v_r}{v_s}\right)\right]$$

and v_r is negative.

Phase 3. The final phase is when the relative velocity (v_r) is less than the terminal velocity (v_s) and the air is moving faster than the particle. For this case, the height travelled by the particle is H_3.

$$H_3 = v_a t_3 - \frac{v_s}{2g}\ln\left(\frac{v_{ro}^2 - v_s^2}{v_r - v_s}\right)$$

where

$$t_3 = \frac{v_s}{g}\left[\coth^{-1}\left(\frac{v_{ro}}{v_s}\right) - \coth^{-1}\left(\frac{v_r}{v_s}\right)\right]$$

This phase is similar to that of pneumatic conveying of solids. If the air velocity (v_a) terminal velocity (v_t) and initial relative velocity (v_{ro}) are known or assumed, various values of t may be chosen and values of v_r computed and plotted (fig. 11.20). This plot is then used to construct a plot of total height (H_t) vs time (fig. 11.21).

As the particles travel upward in the pipe, the change in their velocity is caused by gravity and the air-particle interaction. The velocity change due to gravity is $\Delta v_g = g(\Delta t)$. Whereas Δt is the time taken by the particle to travel between locations 1 and 2. The velocity

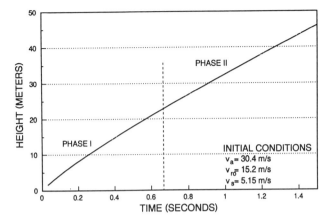

Figure 11.21–Examples of particle height increase with time (Redrawn from Chancellor, 1960).

change due to air interaction (Δv_f) is determined by equating the rate change of momentum to the force of the air in the pipe as follows:

$$F = \frac{dm}{dt}(\Delta v_f)$$

or

$$\Delta P = \frac{1}{A}\frac{dm}{dt}(\Delta v_f) \qquad (11.29)$$

where
$$\begin{aligned}
F &= (\Delta P)A \\
\Delta P &= \text{pressure drop in the pipe (Pa)} \\
dm/dt &= \text{mass flow rate (kg/s)} \\
\Delta v_f &= \text{total velocity change minus } \Delta v_g \text{ (m/s)}
\end{aligned}$$

Example 11.4
    If v_a = 30.4 m/s; v_{ro} = 15.2 m/s; v_s = 5.17 m/s; dm/dt = 4.54 kg/s; pipe diameter = 0.228 m; and pipe height = 12.46 m, find the total pressure drop in the pipe for a forage blower.
    Solution. From equation 11.27 (Phase 1 as plotted in figure 11.20 and 11.21):

$$\begin{aligned}
t &= 0.33 \text{ sc (from 0-12.46 m)} \\
v_r &= 2.8 \text{ m/s (at exit)} \\
\text{particle velocity} &= 30.4 + 2.8 = 33.2 \text{ m/s} \\
\text{total velocity change} &= 45.6 - 33.2 = 12.4 \text{ m/s} \\
\Delta v_g &= 0.33 \times 9.81 = 3.24 \text{ m/s} \\
\Delta v_f &= 12.4 - 3.24 = 9.16 \text{ m/s}
\end{aligned}$$

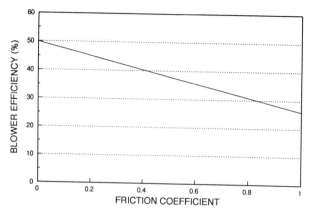

Figure 11.22–Effect of friction on blower efficiency (Redrawn from Chancellor, 1960).

$$F = (4.54)\,9.16 = 41.6\ \text{N}$$
$$\Delta P = 41.6/\pi\,(0.114)^2 = 1018.6\ \text{Pa}$$

The pressure loss due to pipe friction may be computed from equation 11.14. The pipe Reynold's number is 8.3×10^5. Using equation 11.15 the line friction factor was computed as 0.012. These values result in $\Delta p_L = 364$ Pa for $v_a = 30.4$ m/s. The total pressure difference between the ends of the pipe will be $1018.6 - 364 = 654.6$ Pa. Since the top of the pipe is open to atmosphere, the pressure at the bottom of the pipe will be 654.6 below atmospheric pressure.

11.4.2 Energy Requirements

Totten and Millier (1966) suggested that the total power requirements of a forage blower may be computed from the following equation:

$$P = \frac{1}{2\eta}\,\dot{m}\,r_f^2\,\omega^2 \qquad (11.30)$$

where
    P = power requirement (W)
    $\dot{m}$ = Mass mow rate (kg/s)
    η_b = power efficiency of the forage blower
    r_f = paddle tip radius (m)
    ω = angular velocity (rad/s)

TABLE 11.8. BLOWER EFFICIENCY FOR VARIOUS SPEEDS, FEED RATES, AND
AIR INLET CONDITIONS (PETTENGILL AND MILLIER, 1968)

| | | Air-door Conditions | |
Feed Rate (kg / min)	Blower Speed (rpm)	Open	Closed
408	600	24.5	25.7
544	800	28.4	30.7
680	600	24.6	25.9
907	600	25.5	26.9

A theoretical plot efficiency as affected by the friction is given in figure 11.22. According to this figure efficiency increases as the friction decreases.

Example 11.5

The material flow rate of a forage blower is 500 kg/min at 600 rev/min impeller speed. Determine the power requirement if the efficiency is 35%.

Solution.

$$\dot{m} = \frac{500 \ (\text{kg/min})}{60 \ (\text{s/min})} = 8.34 \ \text{kg/s}$$

$$\omega = \frac{600 \ (\text{rpm}) \ 2\pi \ (\text{rad/rev})}{60 \ (\text{s/min})} = 62.8 \ \text{rad/s}$$

$$r_f = 0.6 \ \text{m}$$

$$\text{Power} = \frac{1}{2 \ (0.35)} \ (8.34) \ (0.6)^2 \ (62.832) = 1.7 \ \text{kW}$$

11.4.3 Performance

The blower efficiency is affected by the factors related to blower design, the operating conditions, and the material properties. Blower

TABLE 11.9. BLOWER EFFICIENCY FOR VARIOUS DESIGN CHANGES
(PETTENGILL AND MILLIER, 1968)

| | Blower Efficiency (%) — Air-door Conditions | |
Design Condition	Open	Closed
Normal system	24.60	25.9
Inlet cutoff	24.63	25.22
Teflon paddles	24.08	24.17
Teflon paddles and housing	24.7	26.01

Note: All tests were run at 600 rpm and 680 kg / min.

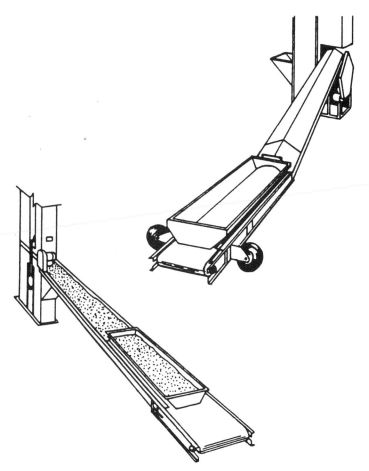

Figure 11.23–Typical farm belt conveyors (Reproduced with permission from *Grain Drying, Handling and Storage Handbook*, 2nd Ed., 1987 © Midwest Plan Service).

design factors include the blower size, number of blades, angle of paddle slant, clearance between paddle tip and the scroll, the location and size of the material inlet opening and the size of conveying pipe. The operating parameters include the conveying height, blower

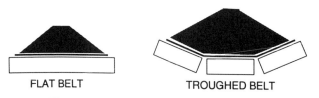

FLAT BELT   TROUGHED BELT

Figure 11.24–Two types of belt conveyors.

TABLE 11.10. TYPICAL HORIZONTAL BELT CONVEYOR CAPACITY
(MIDWEST PLAN SERVICE)

| Belt Width | | Max. Belt Speed | Belt Capacity @ a Belt Speed of 30.4 m / min (100 fpm) | |
| | | | Troughed Belt | Flat Belt |
m	(in.)	(m / min)	(m^3 / min)	(m^3 / min)
0.304	(12)	106	12.5	6.2
0.356	(16)	137	22.7	10.3
0.457	(18)	137	28.1	12.6
0.508	(20)	137	36.2	16.2
0.610	(24)	182	53.1	23.8

Note: To compute belt capacity at any speed divide the table value by
30.4 and multiply by the belt speed in m / min.

speed, and the material flow rate. The material parameters include bulk density and the coefficient of friction.

Pettingill and Millier (1968) conducted studies on the blower efficiencies that are summarized in Table 11.8. From the data presented in Table 11.8 they concluded that higher efficiency can be obtained in every case if the air door was closed. For a constant material flow rate, increasing the paddle speed increases the efficiency. Efficiency increases slightly with an increasing in paddle loading. Table 11.9 shows that the design changes have very little effect on the blower efficiency. Reducing friction increases efficiency.

11.5 Miscellaneous Conveyors

11.5.1 Belt Conveyors

Belt conveyors can carry different types of materials from easy flow to hard to handle, sticky material. They handle material gently with minimum damage. Belt speeds vary from very slow to a high of 300 m/min. Belt capacity can be as high as several tons per hour. Belts come in varying widths. Generally, belt conveyors are not used at angles steeper than 30° while the most common inclination is

TABLE 11.11. TYPICAL BULK FLOW CAPACITY AND POWER
(MIDWEST PLAN SERVICE)

| Conveyor Width and Depth | | Capacity | Power |
m	(in.)	(m^3 / h)	(kW / m)
0.203	(8)	130	0.245
0.228	(9)	164	0.294
0.254	(10)	202	0.343
0.279	(11)	245	0.392
0.304	(12)	291	0.441
0.330	(13)	342	0.515

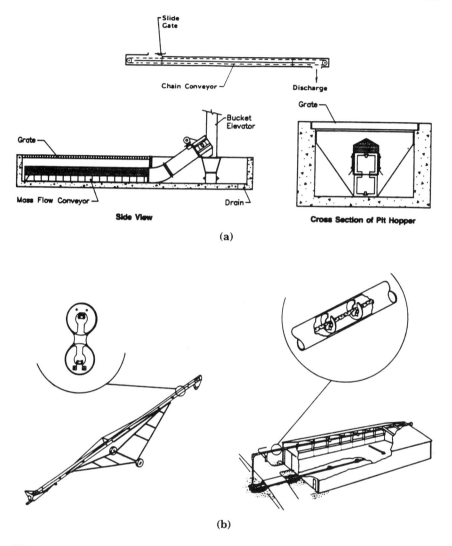

Figure 11.25–Bulk or mass flow conveyors: (a) horizontal conveyors; and (b) inclined and vertical conveyors (Reproduced with permission from *Grain Drying, Handling and Storage Handbook*, 2nd Ed., 1987 © Midwest Plan Service).

around 20°. A general layout is given in figure 11.23. The belts may be flat or troughed. Figure 11.24 shows different arrangements for either belt conveyors. Table 11.10 shows typical values for the capacity of horizontal conveyors. The capacity is affected by belt speed, width, and uniformity of loading.

11.5.2 Bulk or Mass Conveyors

Bulk flow or mass flow conveyors are paddles of various shapes attached at equal distance and housed in a rectangular or circular housing. As the chain moves, these paddles drag material along the bottom of the housing. These conveyors are common in commercial elevators. Figure 11.25 shows rectangular and round mass conveyors. The capacity of these conveyors may be estimated from the data given in Table 11.11.

Problems

11.1   The auger conveyor of example 11.1 is to be used at an angle of 45° from the horizontal. If the desired capacity is to remain unchanged, what changes would you make to accomplish this? What power would be required?

11.2   For the conveyor of problem 11.1 plot the volumetric capacity against the angle of inclination ranging from 0 to 90°. Also plot the power requirements.

11.3   If the material is shelled corn in problem 11.1, determine the volumetric capacity and the power requirements for 0 and 45°.

11.4   If a half pitch screw is used in problem 11.1, determine the capacity of the conveyor. Is the capacity reduced? If yes, what would you do to achieve the same capacity? Is the specific power changed? Explain the results.

11.5   Soybeans are to be pneumatically conveyed in a 15 cm diameter tube at a rate of 1000 kg/h. Determine the minimum air velocity needed to produce dilute phase transport conditions. Determine the apparent bulk density and void ratio during transport.

11.6   Same as Example 11.2 except use shelled corn data and determine the total system pressure drop exclusive of the accessories.

11.7   Same as the previous problem except compute pressure drop for 10, 12.5, 15, 17.5, and 20 cm diameters. Plot the pressure drop and power requirements against the pipe diameter. What would you recommend as the most desirable pipe diameter and why?

Machinery Management

Introduction

Because of the seasonal nature of farm work, farm machinery is used during relatively short periods of the year. With growth in average farm size, machines of high capacity are required to accomplish their task during these short periods. Unlike factory machines, whose costs can be amortized over thousands of hours of annual use, farm machines are typically amortized over hundreds of hours of annual use. The need to amortize machine costs over low hours of annual use puts tight constraints on the manufacturing costs of farm machines. At the same time, since lost time is very costly during the limited periods of annual use, farm machines must be designed to have high reliability and high field efficiency. As early as 1924, it was noted that "time is the essence of farming" and that whatever helps to shorten the time required for planting and harvesting will help overcome the effects of adverse weather (Mount, 1924). Thus, machinery selection and management techniques are of great interest to both the designer and user of farm machinery. ASAE has fostered research on machinery selection and management for many years and currently has three related documents in its standards book. They are Standard S495 on uniform terminology, Engineering Practice EP496 on machinery management, and D497 on machinery management data.

12.1 Field Capacity and Efficiency

12.1.1 Field Capacity

Field capacity refers to the amount of processing that a machine can accomplish per hour of time and was first calculated by McKibben (1930). Field capacity can be expressed on a material or area basis. On an area basis, the field capacity is:

$$C_a = \frac{v\ w\ \eta_f}{10} \tag{12.1}$$

On a material basis, the field capacity is:

$$C_m = \frac{v\ w\ Y\ \eta_f}{10} \tag{12.2}$$

where
C_a = field capacity, area basis (ha/h) (C_{at} when η_f = 1.0)
C_m = field capacity, material basis (Mg/h) (C_{mt} when η_f = 1.0)
v = travel speed (km/h)
w = machine working width (m)
Y = crop yield (Mg/ha)
η_f = field efficiency (decimal)

The term, theoretical field capacity is used to describe the field capacity when the field efficiency is equal to 1.0, i.e., theoretical field capacity is achieved when the machine is using 100% of its width without interruption for turns or other idle time. For cultivators and other machines which work in rows, the machine working width is equal to the row spacing times the number of rows processed in each pass. An operator with perfect steering skills would be required to use the full width of mowers and other machines which do not work in rows. Since operators are not perfect, less than the full width of such machines is used in order to ensure coverage of the entire land area, i.e., there is some overlapping of coverage.

The travel speed of balers, forage choppers, and other machines which process a product may be limited by the C_{mt}, i.e., by the theoretical field capacity of the machine on a materials handling basis. For a given C_{mt}, W, and Y, equation 12.2 could be used with $\eta_f = 1.0$ to find the allowable forward speed. Equation 12.2 is not relevant to machines which do not process a product, e.g., tillage machines; the speed of such machines is limited by one or more other factors, including available power, quality of the work accomplished, safety, etc. Typical operating speeds for various machines are listed in table 12.1.

12.1.2 Field Efficiency

The theoretical time, τ_t, required to perform a given field operation varies inversely with the theoretical field capacity and can be calculated using the following equation:

$$\tau_t = \frac{A}{C_{at}} \tag{12.3}$$

where

τ_t = theoretical time required to perform operation (h)
C_{at} = theoretical field capacity (ha/h)
A = area to be processed (ha)

The actual time required to perform the operation will be increased due to overlap, time required for turning on the ends of the field, time required for loading or unloading materials, etc. Such time losses lower the field efficiency below 100%. The following equation can be used to calculate the field efficiency:

$$\eta_f = \frac{\tau_t}{\tau_e + \tau_h + \tau_a} \tag{12.4}$$

where

τ_e = τ_t/K_w = effective operating time (h)
K_w = fraction of implement width actually used
τ_a = time losses that are proportional to area (h)
τ_h = time losses that are not proportional to area (h)

τ_a and τ_h represent the two extremes for types of time losses and some losses may fall between these extremes. Examples of τ_a-type losses include unclogging of spray nozzles, adding filling fertilizer or seed boxes, or filling spray tanks. For a given yield, time spent in

TABLE 12.1. FIELD EFFICIENCY, FIELD SPEED AND REPAIR AND MAINTENANCE COST PARAMETERS

Machine	Field efficiency		Field speed				Estimated life	Total life repairs	Repair factors	
	Range %	Typi-cal %	Range mph	Typi-cal mph	Range km/h	Typi-cal km/h	h	Percent of list price	RF1	RF2
TRACTORS										
2 wheel drive & stationary							10 000	100	0.01	2.0
4 wheel drive & crawler							10 000	100	0.01	2.0
TILLAGE										
Moldboard plow	70-90	80	3.0 - 6.0	4.5	5.0 - 10.0	7.0	2 000	150	0.43	1.8
Heavy-duty disk	70-90	85	3.5 - 6.0	4.5	5.5 - 10.0	7.0	2 000	60	0.18	1.7
Tandem disk harrow	70-90	80	3.0 - 6.0	4.0	5.0 - 10.0	6.5	2 000	60	0.18	1.7
Chisel plow	70-90	85	4.0 - 6.5	4.5	6.5 - 10.5	7.0	2 000	80	0.30	1.4
Field cultivator	70-90	85	3.0 - 8.0	5.5	5.0 - 13.0	9.0	2 000	80	0.30	1.4
Spring tooth harrow	70-90	85	3.0 - 6.0	5.0	5.0 - 10.0	9.0	2 000	80	0.30	1.4
Roller-packer	70-90	85	4.5 - 7.5	6.0	7.0 - 12.0	10.0	2 000	40	0.16	1.3
Mulcher-packer	70-90	80	4.0 - 6.0	5.0	6.5 - 10.0	8.0	2 000	40	0.16	1.3
Rotary hoe	70-85	80	5.0 - 10.0	7.0	8.0 - 16.0	11.0	2 000	60	0.23	1.4
Row crop cultivator	70-90	80	2.5 - 5.0	3.5	4.0 - 8.0	5.5	2 000	100	0.22	2.2
Rotary tiller	70-90	85	1.0 - 4.5	3.0	2.0 - 7.0	5.0	1 500	80	0.36	2.0
PLANTING										
Row crop planter:										
No-till tillage	50-75	65	2.0 - 4.0	3.0	3.2 - 6.4	4.8	1 200	80	0.54	2.1
Conventional tillage	50-75	60	3.0 - 7.0	4.5	4.8 - 9.7	6.4	1 200	80	0.54	2.1
Grain drill	65-85	70	2.5 - 6.0	4.0	4.0 - 9.7	6.4	1 200	80	0.54	2.1
HARVESTING										
Corn picker sheller	60-75	65	2.0 - 4.0	2.5	3.0 - 6.5	4.0	2 000	70	0.14	2.3
Combine:										
Pull-type	60-75	65	2.0 - 5.0	3.0	3.0 - 6.5	5.0	2 000	60	0.12	2.3
Self-propelled	65-80	70	2.0 - 5.0	3.0	3.0 - 6.5	5.0	2 000	35	0.08	2.1
Mower	75-85	80	4.0 - 7.0	5.0	6.5 - 11.0	8.0	2 000	150	0.46	1.7
Mower-conditioner	55-80	75	3.0 - 6.0	4.5	5.0 - 10.0	7.0	2 000	80	0.26	1.6
Side delivery rake	70-85	80	4.0 - 5.0	4.5	6.5 - 8.0	7.0	2 000	100	0.38	1.4
Baler	60-85	75	2.5 - 5.0	3.5	4.0 - 8.0	5.5	2 000	80	0.23	1.8
Big bale baler	55-75	65	3.0 - 5.0	3.5	5.0 - 8.0	5.5	2 000	80	0.23	1.8
Long hay stacker	55-75	60	2.5 - 4.5	3.5	4.0 - 7.0	5.5	2 000	80	0.23	1.8
Forage harvester:										
Pull-type	50-75	65	1.5 - 5.0	2.5	2.5 - 8.0	4.0	2 000	80	0.26	1.6
Self-propelled	60-85	70	1.5 - 6.0	3.0	2.5 - 10.0	5.0	2 500	40	0.06	2.0
Sugar beet harvester	60-80	70	2.5 - 5.0	3.0	4.0 - 8.0	5.0	2 500	70	0.19	1.4
Potato harvester	55-70	60	1.5 - 4.0	2.0	2.5 - 6.5	3.0	2 500	70	0.19	1.4
Cotton picker or stripper	60-75	70	2.0 - 4.0	3.0	3.0 - 6.0	4.5	2 000	60	0.17	1.8
MISCELLANEOUS										
Fertilizer spreader	60-70	70	3.0 - 5.0	4.5	5.0 - 8.0	7.0	1 200	120	0.95	1.3
Boom-type sprayer	50-80	65	3.0 - 7.0	6.5	5.0 - 11.5	10.5	1 500	70	0.41	1.3
Air-carrier sprayer	55-70	60	2.0 - 5.0	3.0	3.0 - 8.0	5.0	2 000	60	0.20	1.6
Bean puller-windrower	70-90	80	2.0 - 5.0	3.5	3.0 - 8.0	5.5	2 000	60	0.20	1.6
Beet topper stalk chopper	60-80	70	2.0 - 3.0	2.5	3.0 - 5.0	4.0	2 000	60	0.23	1.4
Forage blower							2 000	50	0.14	1.8
Wagon							3 000	80	0.19	1.3

ASAE Standard D497. NOTE: ASAE Standards, Engineering Practices, and Data are informal and advisory only. Their use by anyone in industry or trade is entirely voluntary. The ASAE assumes no responsibility for results attributable to the application of these ASAE Standards, Engineering Practices, and Data. Conformity does not ensure compliance with applicable ordinances, laws and regulations. Prospective users are responsible for protecting themselves against liability for infringement of patents.

unloading harvested crop is proportional to area but unloading time also increases with yield. Many T_h-type losses are proportional to effective operating time, τ_e; these include rest stops, adjusting equipment, and idle travel at field ends if such travel is at normal operating speed. Field shape can have an important effect on τ_h, i.e., τ_h will be much smaller relative to τ_e if the field is long and narrow. Then the machine will make fewer turns at the end for a given field area. Time required to move a machine to or from a field is not included in field efficiency calculations; else the field efficiency would vary widely depending upon distance between fields and distance from the machine storage site. Calculation of field efficiency and capacity is illustrated in example problem 12.1.

Example Problem 12.1

A self-propelled combine with an eight-row corn head for 75 cm row spacing travels at 5 km/h while harvesting corn yielding 9.4 Mg/ha. Losses proportional to area total to 7.6 min/ha and are primarily due to unloading grain from the combine. Neglecting any other losses, calculate (a) the field efficiency and the field capacity on (b) an area basis, and (c) material basis.

Solution. (a) In calculating the field efficiency, consider the time used while harvesting one hectare. From the given information, $\tau_a = 7.6$ min and $\tau_h = 0$. To determine τ_e, note that a row crop header uses the full width, so that $K_w = 1.0$ and thus $\tau_e = \tau_t$. From equation 12.1, the theoretical field capacity on an area basis is:

$$C_{at} = 5 \, (8 \cdot 0.75) \, 1.0/10 = 3 \text{ ha/h}$$

Then, from equation 12.3:

$$\tau_e = \tau_t = 1/3 = 0.333 \text{ h or 20 min}$$

Finally, from equation 12.4, the field efficiency is:

$$\eta_f = 20/(20 + 7.6 + 0) = 0.72$$

(b) Now the actual field capacity on an area basis can be calculated:

$$C_a = 3 \cdot 0.72 = 2.16 \text{ ha/h}$$

(c) Finally, by multiplying by the crop yield, the field capacity on a material basis can be calculated:

$$C_m = 2.16 \cdot 9.4 = 20.3 \text{ Mg/h}$$

Machine breakdowns cause time losses and reduction of field efficiency if the breakdowns occur during planned working hours. The probability of machine downtime is equal to one minus the operational reliability of the machine. One useful way of expressing machine reliability is as the mean time between failures. As shown in ASAE EP456, the reliability of a group or components or machines with a serial relationship is the product of the individual reliabilities, i.e.:

$$R_m = \frac{100 \, r_1 \, r_2 \cdots r_\lambda}{100^\lambda} \tag{12.5}$$

where

R_m = reliability of the entire machine (%)

r_1, r_2, etc. = reliabilities of individual components (%)

λ = total number of components in series

Components are said to be in series if the failure of any one of the components stops the operation of the entire machine. Conversely, reliability can be increased through redundancy, i.e., through use of components in parallel such that, when a component fails, a parallel component will take over the function. Equation 12.5 is valid for calculating the reliability of a single machine based on the reliabilities of its components, or for calculating the overall reliability of a group of machines based on their individual reliabilities. For example, if a successful hay harvesting operation requires the use of a mower, a rake, and a baler in sequence, the overall reliability of the harvesting operation is the product of the individual reliabilities of the mower, rake, and baler. The reliability probability for a machine or group of machines is essentially one for the next minute, but decreases with time. Thus, the probability that a large, complex machine will operate extensively over several seasons without a breakdown is essentially zero. Farmers repair machines during the off-season or trade old machines for new in order to maintain an acceptable level of reliability.

Careful consideration of equation 12.4 leads to the conclusion that time losses are much more critical for a large machine than for a smaller one. As τ_e declines with increasing C_{at}, time losses τ_a and τ_h become larger relative to τ_e. Thus, as a company increases the theoretical field capacity of its combines, for example, it becomes essential to also increase the rate at which the grain tank can be unloaded, decrease the field time needed to service the machine, and decrease any other time losses. Similarly, in increasing a planter size from four-row capacity to twelve-row capacity, for example, it is important to provide a quicker means for refilling seed boxes on the larger planter. Otherwise, the field efficiency will decrease and the effective field capacity will increase less than the increase in theoretical field capacity. Table 12.1 provides a range of field efficiencies and a typical field efficiency for a variety of machines.

12.2 Machinery Costs

Machinery costs include costs of ownership and operation as well as penalties for lack of timeliness. Ownership costs tend to be independent of the amount a machine is used and are often called fixed or overhead costs. Conversely, operating costs increase in proportion to the amount the machine is used. Total machine costs are the sum of the ownership and operating costs. Ownership, operating, and total machine costs can be calculated on an annual, hourly, or per-hectare basis. Total per-hectare cost is calculated by dividing the total annual cost by the area covered by the machine during the year. A custom cost is the price paid for hiring an operator and equipment to perform a given task. A farm operator can compare total per-hectare costs to custom costs to determine whether it would be better to purchase a machine or to hire the equipment and an operator to accomplish a given task. Per-hectare ownership costs vary inversely with the amount of annual use of a machine. Therefore, a certain minimum amount of work must be available to justify purchase of a machine and, the more work available, the larger the ownership costs that can be economically justified.

12.2.1 Ownership Costs

Ownership costs include depreciation of the machine, interest on the investment, and cost of taxes, insurance, and housing of the machine.

Depreciation. Depreciation is the reduction in the value of a machine with time and use. It is often the largest single cost of machine ownership, but cannot be determined until the machine is sold. However, several methods are available for estimating depreciation. One of these is to estimate the current value using various price guides for used equipment. Annual depreciation is generally highest in the first year of the life of a machine and declines each year. The sum-of-the-year digits and the declining-balance methods both give rapid depreciation in the early years and lower depreciation as the machine ages (Thuesen et al., 1971). Rapid early depreciation is used by many machine owners to obtain the income tax advantages associated with such methods. For simplicity in machinery management calculations, straight-line depreciation can be used. With straight line depreciation, the difference between the purchase price and the salvage value is divided by the machine life to obtain the annual depreciation. Alternatively, the cost of depreciation and interest (see Interest on Investment Section) can be recovered through use of a capital recovery factor. The capital recovery factor is discussed in the Total Annual Ownership Costs Section.

Machine life. The life of a machine can be terminated by wear out or by obsolescence. Wear out does not occur at a definite point in time. Rather, the repair costs required to keep the machine operational gradually increase until it becomes uneconomical to continue making repairs. Obsolescence occurs when the machine is out of production and repair parts are no longer available, or when it can be replaced by another machine or method that will produce a greater profit. Table 12.1 gives the estimated life of a number of machines based on total number of hours until the machine is worn out. The number of years of life until wear-out can be obtained by dividing by the annual hours of use. In many cases, because of limited annual use, machines will become obsolete before reaching the wear-out lives given in table 12.1. The term, economic life is defined as the length of time after purchase of a machine that it is more economic to replace the machine with another than to continue with the first, whether because of wear out or obsolescence. The economic life is then the appropriate life to use in calculating ownership costs.

Interest on investment. The money spent to purchase a machine is unavailable for other productive enterprises. Therefore, the cost of ownership includes the interest on the money that is invested in the machine. If a loan is used to purchase a machine, the interest rate is known. If a machine is purchased for cash, the relevant interest rate is the prevailing rate that could have been obtained if the money had been invested instead of being used to purchase the machine. The principal on which the interest is assessed is equal to the remaining value of the machine in any given year. For simplicity, when the straight-line method of depreciation is used, the annual interest cost is assumed to be constant over the life of the machine. It is calculated on the average investment, i.e., the average of the new cost and salvage value of the machine. Alternatively, it can be included in the capital recovery factor.

Taxes, insurance, and shelter. Taxes include sales tax assessed on the purchase price of a machine and property tax assessed on the remaining value in any given year. For simplicity, both kinds of taxes are distributed over the life of the machine. Some states have neither a sales tax nor property tax and, in such states, no tax cost should be included. The machine designer may not know which tax rate to use, especially if a machine can be used in any of a number of different states. If actual taxes are unknown, it is reasonable to estimate the annual tax charge at 1% of the purchase price of the machine.

Machines may be insured against loss by fire or other causes, in which case the cost of insurance is known. If no insurance policy is purchased, the owner has elected to carry the risk himself but an insurance cost should still be included. Insurance costs should be based on the remaining value of a machine. If insurance costs are unknown, a reasonable estimate of annual insurance cost is 0.25% of the purchase price of the machine.

There are no conclusive data to prove the economic value of sheltering farm machines. Nevertheless, providing shelter is often associated with better care and maintenance of machines which can result in longer life, improved appearance and better resale value. If shelter is provided, the cost of providing that shelter can be calculated. If no shelter is provided, there is probably an economic penalty associated with reduced machine life and/or resale value. Thus, a shelter cost should be included whether or not shelter is provided. The annual cost of shelter is considered to be constant over the life of the machine. If shelter cost data are unavailable, it is reasonable to estimate annual shelter cost as 0.75% of the purchase price of the machine.

The total cost of taxes, insurance and shelter can be estimated at 2% of the purchase price of a machine unless more accurate data are available. Although taxes, insurance and shelter are small relative to total ownership costs, they should be included.

Total annual ownership costs. The total annual ownership costs, as discussed above, can be expressed in the following equation:

$$C_{os} = \frac{C_{oa}}{P_u} = (1 - S_v)\left[\frac{I_r(1 + I_r)^{\tau_L}}{(1 + I_r)^{\tau_L} - 1}\right] + \frac{K_{tis}}{100} \qquad (12.6)$$

where
C_{os} = specific annual ownership costs (1/yr)
C_{oa} = total annual ownership costs (dollars/yr)
P_u = purchase price of machine (dollars)
τ_L = economic life of machine (years)
S_v = salvage value as fraction of purchase price
I_r = real annual interest rate (decimal)
K_{tis} = annual cost of taxes, insurance and shelter as percent of purchase price

As noted above, K_{tis} may be assumed to be 2% unless better data are available. The factor in the square brackets in equation 12.6 is the capital recovery factor. The need for capital recovery is reduced to the extent that the machine has a salvage value at the end of its economic life. In the absence of better data, S_v is often assumed to be 0.1, i.e., the salvage value is estimated at 10% of the purchase price.

The real interest rate, as defined by Bartholomew (1981) is:

$$I_r = \frac{I_p - I_g}{1 + I_g} \qquad (12.7)$$

where

I_p = prevailing annual interest rate (decimal)
I_g = general inflation rate (decimal)

Equation 12.7 adjusts the prevailing interest rate for inflation. If there is no inflation, the real interest rate is equal to the prevailing rate. If the inflation rate is greater than or equal to the prevailing interest rate, the real interest rate is zero and the ownership costs are limited to the cost of taxes, insurance and shelter. Purchasing a machine during times of high inflation tends to "lock in" costs and make machine ownership more attractive than leasing. Example problem 12.2 illustrates the calculation of ownership costs.

Example Problem 12.2
    The self-propelled combine of example problem 12.1 has a purchase price of $100,000, an expected economic life of 10 years, and an expected salvage value of 10% of new cost. At time of purchase, the prevailing interest rate is 8.5%, while the general rate of inflation is 5%. Calculate (a) the specific annual ownership costs, and (b) the total annual ownership costs.
    Solution. (a) No data were given concerning taxes, insurance and shelter, so they will be assumed to be 2% of the purchase price, that is, K_{tis} = 2.0. From equation 12.7, the real interest rate is:

$$I_r = (0.085 - 0.05)/(1 + 0.05) = 0.033 \text{ or } 3.3\%$$

Then, from equation 12.6, the specific ownership costs are:

$$C_{os} = (1 - 0.1)\left[\frac{0.033\,(1 + 0.033)^{10}}{(1 + 0.033)^{10} - 1}\right] + \frac{2}{100} = 0.127$$

(b) Finally, the total annual ownership costs are:

$$C_{oa} = \$100,000 \cdot 0.127 = \$12,700/\text{yr}$$

12.2.2 Operating Costs
    Operating costs are costs associated with use of a machine. They include the costs of labor, fuel and oil, and repair and maintenance. A constant hourly labor cost can be determined for hired operators. If the owner operates the machine, the labor cost is determined from alternative uses of the owner's time. If the cost of labor is unknown at the time of the analysis, a typical community

labor rate can be used. Dividing the hourly labor cost by C_a gives the labor cost per hectare of land worked by the machine.

Costs of fuel and oil. For any given operation, per-hectare fuel (or oil) cost can be calculated using the following equation:

$$C_s = \frac{p_L\, Q_i}{C_a} \qquad (12.8)$$

where

C_s = per-hectare fuel (oil) costs ($/ha)
p_L = price of fuel (oil) ($/L)
Q_i = fuel (oil) consumed by engine (L/h)
C_a = effective field capacity during the operation (ha/h)

Of the three independent variables in equation 12.8, Q_i is the variable for which it is most difficult to determine a realistic value. The first step is to estimate the engine power required to perform the operation. Previous chapters in this textbook have considered the power requirements of various operations. Power requirements computed at the drawbar must be converted into equivalent pto power. After the total equivalent pto power is calculated, the specific fuel consumption of the engine can be estimated. ASAE Data D497 provides specific fuel consumption equations for gasoline, diesel or LPG engines but, since most farm tractors now have diesel engines, only the diesel equation is given here:

$$SFC_v = 3.91 + 2.64X - 0.203\ \sqrt{173 + 738X}$$

$$\text{If } X > 0.856, \qquad SFC_v = 0.411\ \text{L/kW·h} \qquad (12.9)$$

where

SFC_v = specific fuel consumption, volume basis (L/kW·h)
X = ratio of equivalent pto power requirement to maximum available pto power

Typical values of X range from approximately 0.2 for spraying operations to 0.85 for primary tillage. Multiplying SFC_v by the equivalent pto power needed for the operation gives Q_i, the estimated fuel consumption to perform the operation.

The per-hectare cost of oil consumption can be calculated using equation 12.8 with the word oil substituted for the word fuel. ASAE D497 gives equations for estimating oil consumption of gasoline, diesel or LPG engines. The equation for diesel engines is:

$$Q_i = \frac{21.69 + 0.59 * P_r}{1000} \qquad (12.10)$$

where
  Q_i = oil consumption (L/h)
  P_r = rated engine power (kW)

Equation 12.10 is based on replacement of oil in the crankcase at the manufacturer's recommended change intervals; it does not include oil that must be added between oil changes, nor does it include hydraulic/transmission oil or other lubricants. Total costs of all lubricants is approximately equal to 10 to 15% of fuel costs.

   12.3.2.2 Costs of repairs and maintenance. Costs for repairs and maintenance are highly variable depending on the care provided by the manager of the machine. Some expenditures will always be necessary to replace worn or failed parts and/or to repair damage from accidents. Repair and maintenance costs tend to increase with the size and complexity, and thus with the purchase price of the machine. The following equation from ASAE EP496 can be used to estimate accumulated repair and maintenance costs:

$$\frac{C_{rm}}{P_u} = RF1 \left[\frac{t}{1000}\right]^{RF2} \qquad (12.11)$$

where
  C_{rm} = accumulated repair and maintenance costs
             (dollars)
  t   = accumulated use (h)
  RF1, RF2 = repair factors from Table 12.1

To correct for inflation, the purchase price in equation 12.11 is multiplied by $(1+I_g)^n$, where n is the age of the machine in years. Note that the accumulated repair and maintenance costs vary from year to year. Average hourly costs of repairs and maintenance can be estimated by estimating the total economic life of the machine in hours, using equation 12.11 to calculate the total repair and maintenance costs over the life of the machine, and dividing the total by the economic life in hours. Then, by dividing the average cost by C_a, one can obtain the average repair and maintenance cost per hectare of area worked by the machine. Repair and maintenance costs are an important component of total costs. For example, use of equation 12.11 with the data in Table 12.1 shows that, for a tractor, the total repair and maintenance costs over the life of a tractor can equal the purchase price of the tractor. Figure 12.1 illustrates the

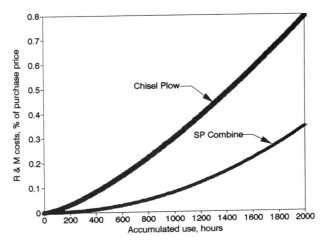

Figure 12.1–Accumulated repair and maintenance costs of two machines as a percent of purchase price of the respective machines.

accumulation of repair and maintenance costs for two different machines. As a percent of purchase price, the chisel plow accumulates repair and maintenance costs much faster than the self-propelled combine. At the end of 2000 hours, for example, the accumulated repair and maintenance costs for the plow are 79.2% of purchase price. The corresponding figure for the combine is only 34.3%. However, the purchase price of the combine is about ten times that of the plow. Thus, in terms of dollars, the accumulated repair and maintenance costs for the combine are over four times those of the plow.

12.2.3 Timeliness Costs

There is an optimum time of the year to perform some field operations and economic penalties are incurred if the operations are performed too early or too late. When harvesting a crop, for example, increasing fractions of the yield may be lost and/or the crop quality may be reduced if the harvest is started too early or delayed beyond the optimum time. In the extreme case, insufficient machine capacity may prevent completion of a harvest before adverse weather destroys the remainder of the crop. It is thus economically justifiable to increase machine costs through purchase of a machine of greater capacity when the larger machine will accomplish more timely work. Thus the term, timeliness cost, is important in machinery cost analyses. The timeliness cost can be calculated by using the following equation:

$$C_t = \frac{K_\tau \, A \, Y \, V}{\lambda_o \, T \, C_a \, P_{wd}} \qquad (12.12)$$

where

C_t = timeliness cost($/ha)
K_τ = timeliness coefficient, fraction of annual crop value lost per day, (see table 12.2)
A = crop area (ha/yr)
Y = crop yield (Mg/ha)
V = crop value ($/Mg)
λ_o = two if operation commences or ends at the optimum time
    = four if operation can be balanced evenly about the optimum time
T = expected time available for field work (h/day)
C_a = effective field capacity of machine (ha/h)
P_{wd} = probability of a good working day, decimal (see table 12.3)

The factor, K_τ, is the fraction of the crop yield that is lost for each day of delay of an operation. It is apparent that the timeliness coefficient varies with the type of operation. Given an optimum planting date, for example, planting earlier or later than that date will diminish the crop yield. Since the actual planting period can be balanced around the optimum date, $\lambda_o=4$ for planting. Conversely, there is no timeliness coefficient associated with tillage unless tillage delays subsequently delay planting. For most harvesting operations, $\lambda_o=2$ because it is often not feasible to begin harvesting until the crop is mature. Note that the denominator of equation 12.12 relates to the rapidity with which an operation can be completed, i.e., working more hours per day and/or using a machine of greater capacity decreases the time required to complete an operation. Use of $\lambda_o=4$ indicates an early start on the operation and thus earlier completion. Weather also affects the number of calendar days required to complete an operation, since the operation must be interrupted during bad weather. As indicated in table 12.3, pwd varies with geographic location and also varies throughout the year in most geographic locations. Example problem 12.3 illustrates the calculation of operating costs.

Example Problem 12.3

The self-propelled combine of example problems 12.1 and 12.2 is harvesting corn in the midwest USA in early September. The crop value is $98/Mg. The combine is used an average of 10 hours per day and 200 hours per year. The 120-kW engine produces 95 kW of power

TABLE 12.2. TIMELINESS COEFFICIENTS

Operation	K_T, 1/day		

Operation	April	May	June
Tillage (depends on whether planting is delayed by prior tillage)		0.000-0.010	
Seeding			
Corn (Indiana, Illinois, Iowa, Eastern Nebraska, Eastern Kansas)			
Available moisture in root zone at planting, cm	April	May	June
10	0.010	0.000	0.002
20	0.006	0.001	0.003
30	0.003	0.004	0.007
Wheat, Utah		0.008	
North Dakota		0.007	
Soybeans, Wisconsin, May & June		0.005	
Missouri, Illinois, June		0.006	
Double crop after wheat, Illinois		0.010	
Cotton, Lubbock, Texas			
April		0.004	
May		0.020	
Mississippi, April & May		0.007	
Barley, Utah		0.008	
North Dakota		0.007	
Oats, Illinois and Michigan		0.010	
Wisconsin after May 6		0.012	
Alabama, Fall		0.000	
Utah		0.008	
Rape, Manitoba		0.003	
Rice, California, May		0.010	
Row Cultivation, Illinois, soybeans		0.011	
Rotary hoeing, Iowa, soybeans		0.028	
Harvest			
Haymaking, Michigan, June		0.018	
Shelled corn, Iowa		0.003	
Ear corn, Illinois, after Oct. 26		0.007	
Soybeans, Illinois (depends on variety)		0.006-0.010	
Wheat, Ohio		0.005	
Cotton, Alabama		0.002	
Rice, California		0.009	
Sugar cane, Queensland, Australia			
pre-optimum		0.002	
post-optimum		0.003	

during combining. Diesel fuel costs $0.30/L, while motor oil costs $1.05/L. Labor costs are $6.00 per hour. Calculate (a) the total operating costs per hectare, excluding timeliness costs, (b) the timeliness penalty costs, and (c) total costs per hectare.

TABLE 12.3. PROBABILITIES FOR A WORKING DAY

Region		Central Illinois		State of Iowa		South-eastern Michigan		State of South Carolina		Southern Ontario Canada		Mississippi Delta	
Soil		Prairie soils		State average		Clay loam		Clay loam		Clay loam		Clay	
Notes		18 yrs. data In early spring and late fall, pwd in Iowa and Illinois may be 0.07 greater in North and West and 0.07 less in South and East		17 yrs. data		Simulation (tillage only)		Simulation (tillage only) Sandy soils can be worked all months and have higher pwd		Simulation (tillage only) Start 7-10 days earlier on sandy soils, 0.15 greater pwd		Simulation (tillage only) Non-tillage field work pwd and pwd for sandy soils some greater in winter and early spring	
Average date	Biweekly period	Probability level, percent											
		50	90	50	90	50	90	50	90	50	90	50	90
Jan. and Feb.	—	0.0	0.0	0.0	0.0	0.0	0.0	0.01	0.0	0.0	0.0	0.07	0.0
Mar. 7	1	0.0	0.0	0.0	0.0	0.0	0.0	—	—	0.0	0.0	—	—
Mar. 21	2	0.29	0.0	0.0	0.0	0.0	0.0	0.03	0.0	0.0	0.0	0.18	0.0
Apr. 4	3	0.42	0.13	0.39	0.16	0.0	0.0	—	—	0.01	0.0	—	—
Apr. 18	4	0.47	0.19	0.57	0.38	0.20	0.0	0.29	0.06	0.07	0.0	0.35	0.08
May 2	5	0.54	0.31	0.66	0.48	—	—	—	—	0.62	0.02	—	—
May 16	6	0.61	0.34	0.68	0.47	0.61	0.32	0.64	0.37	0.60	0.02	0.58	0.28
May 30	7	0.63	0.40	0.66	0.47	—	—	—	—	0.79	0.16	—	—
June 13	8	0.66	0.41	0.69	0.52	0.69	0.42	0.72	0.46	0.77	0.22	0.69	0.39
June 27	9	0.72	0.53	0.74	0.57	—	—	—	—	0.80	0.23	—	—
July 11	10	0.72	0.52	0.77	0.64	0.75	0.52	0.67	0.43	—	—	0.63	0.25
July 25	11	0.72	0.54	0.80	0.67	—	—	—	—	—	—	—	—
Aug. 8	12	0.78	0.64	0.80	0.68	0.74	0.53	0.73	0.51	—	—	0.72	0.45
Aug. 22	13	0.86	0.74	0.86	0.79	—	—	—	—	—	—	—	—
Sept. 5	14	0.81	0.66	0.79	0.64	0.70	0.35	—	—	—	—	—	—
Sept. 19	15	0.65	0.42	0.69	0.46	—	—	0.72	0.46	—	—	0.80	0.58
Oct. 3	16	0.72	0.52	0.71	0.48	0.59	0.26	—	—	—	—	—	—
Oct. 17	17	0.76	0.58	0.79	0.64	—	—	0.61	0.23	—	—	0.76	0.42
Nov. 1	18	0.72	0.50	0.75	0.55	0.42	0.06	—	—	—	—	—	—
Nov. 15	19	0.67	0.47	0.73	0.54	—	—	0.33	0.02	—	—	0.43	0.0
Nov. 29	20	0.54	0.43	0.82	0.70	0.07	0.0	—	—	—	—	—	—
Dec. 13	21	—	—	—	—	—	—	0.02	0.0	—	—	0.10	0.0

Adjust for Sundays and holidays by multiplying pwd's above by 0.86, 0.82, 0.78 and 0.75 for months 0, 1, 2 and 3 holidays.

NOTE: ASAE Standards, Engineering Practices, and Data are informal and advisory only. Their use by anyone in industry or trade is entirely voluntary. The ASAE assumes no responsibility for results attributable to the application of these ASAE Standards, Engineering Practices, and Data. Conformity does not ensure compliance with applicable ordinances, laws and regulations. Prospective users are responsible for protecting themselves against liability for infringement of patents.

Solution. (a) From example problem 12.1, the field capacity of the combine is 2.16 ha/h. Thus, the per-hectare labor costs are:

$$\$6.00/2.16 = \$2.78/ha$$

Next, the per-hectare fuel and oil costs will be calculated. From equation 12.9, the ratio of actual to maximum power is 95/120=0.79. Then the specific fuel consumption of the engine is:

$$SFC_v = 3.91 + 2.64 \cdot 0.79 - 0.203\,(173 + 738 \cdot 0.79)^{0.5} = 0.414 \text{ L/kW·h}$$

The hourly fuel consumption is:

$$Q_{if} = 0.414 \cdot 95 = 39.3 \text{ L/h}$$

From equation 12.8, making use of the effective field capacity from example problem 12.1, the per-hectare fuel costs are:

$$C_{sf} = 0.30 \cdot 39.3/2.16 = \$5.46/ha$$

Next, from equation 12.10, the estimated oil consumption rate is:

$$Q_{io} = (21.69 + 0.59 \cdot 120)/1000 = 0.092 \text{ L/h}$$

Again, from equation 12.8, the per-hectare oil costs are:

$$C_{so} = 1.05 \cdot 0.092/2.16 = \$0.04/ha$$

To calculate the per-hectare costs of repair and maintenance, equation 12.11 is first used to calculate the accumulated repair and maintenance costs after 10 years of use at 200 hours per year. Also, the purchase price is corrected for the 5% inflation rate, that is, the adjusted price is:

$$P_u = \$100,000 (1 + 0.05)10 = \$162,889 \text{ adjusted price}$$

Then, from equation 12.11 and using RF factors from table 12.1:

$$C_{rm} = 162,889 \cdot 0.08 (2000/1000)2.1 = \$55,866 \text{ total repair}$$
and maintenance costs

Harvesting at a rate of 2.16 ha/h for 2000 hours, the combine harvests 4320 ha during its economic lifetime. Therefore, the per-hectare costs for repair and maintenance are:

$$55,866/4,320 = \$12.93/ha$$

The total per-hectare operating cost, excluding the timeliness penalty cost, is:

$$2.78 + 5.46 + 0.04 + 12.93 = \$21.21/ha$$

(b) The timeliness penalty cost is calculated using equation 12.12. From table 12.2, $K_\tau = 0.003$. From table 12.3, averaging values for Illinois and Iowa, $p_{wd} = 0.65$ at the 90% probability level. Harvesting at the rate of 2.16 ha/h for 200 hours per year, the combine harvests 432 ha/year. Then, inserting values into equation 12.12 as given in the three example problems, the timeliness cost penalty is:

$$C_t = \frac{0.003 \cdot 432 \cdot 9.4 \cdot 98}{2 \cdot 10 \cdot 2.16 \cdot 0.65} = \$33.66/ha$$

(c) From example problem 12.2, the $12,700 annual ownership costs divided over 432 ha harvested annually are $29.40 per hectare. Thus, the total per-hectare costs are:

$29.40/ha   ownership costs
21.21/ha   operating costs excluding timeliness penalty
33.66/ha   timeliness penalty cost
$84.27/ha   total costs

Harvesting costs consumed about 9% of the total revenues from growing the corn crop, that is, 9.4 Mg/ha · $98/Mg = $921.12/ha. The combine used in example problems 12.1 through 12.3 may not have been of optimum capacity. In section 12.3, a method for selecting the optimum capacity will be presented.

12.3 Machinery Selection and Replacement

12.3.1 Machinery Selection

Choosing the appropriate field capacity for a machine is an important problem for both the machine designer and the farm operator. From the farm operator's viewpoint, there is an optimum field capacity for maximum profit and the goal is to determine that optimum capacity. Since the farm operator will want to purchase a machine of optimum capacity, the machine designer also has a vital interest in designing machines of optimum size for various farm sizes. The problem of machinery selection is illustrated in figure 12.2, in which machines of various size are considered for a farm of a given size. Three types of costs are illustrated in the figure. The machinery costs include all ownership and operating costs except labor, which are displayed separately. The timeliness costs are also shown. The per-hectare machinery costs increase with machine size because the land area is fixed and larger machines cost more than small machines. Larger machines decrease the labor costs by completing the work more quickly. Thus, if timeliness is not considered, the smallest machines would be most economical. However, timeliness costs rise sharply when machines are too small to complete the work in a timely manner. As indicated in figure 12.2, the optimum machine size is one that minimizes the sum of the timeliness costs and the machinery costs including labor.

Mathematically, the field capacity giving least total cost for an individual machine can be determined by combining all of the cost equations into one equation and differentiating with respect to field capacity. The result is given in the following equation:

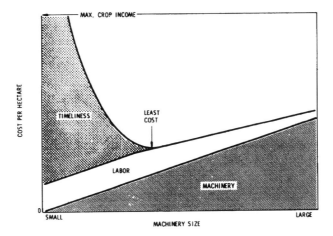

Figure 12.2–Costs related to machinery size for a specific farm (Burrows and Siemens, 1974).

$$C_{aopt} = \sqrt{\frac{A}{C_{os}\, K_p}\left[L_c + T_{fc} + \frac{K_\tau\, A\, Y\, V}{\lambda_o\, T\, p_{wd}}\right]} \qquad (12.13)$$

where
    C_{aopt}= optimum effective field capacity (ha/h)
    L_c = labor cost ($/h)
    T_{fc} = specific ownership costs of tractor ($/h)

A value for T_{fc} can be determined by using the following equation:

$$T_{fc} = \frac{C_{oat}}{\tau_A} \qquad (12.14)$$

where
    T_{fc} = Amount charged to machine for tractor use ($/h)
    C_{oat} = annual ownership cost of tractor ($/yr) (from eq. 12.6)
    τ_A = total annual use of tractor (h/yr)

The remaining quantities in equation 12.13 were previously defined, except for K_p, the unit price function. It is defined as the increased price for one additional unit of field capacity. A value for K_p can be determined by comparing the prices of a group of machines which vary only in capacity. If the sales price is plotted versus field capacity for the group of machines, the slope of the line is equal to K_p. If the increased capacity is expressed on a width basis, as for a tillage machine, then the purchase price should be plotted versus width. The slope of the line is then the price per unit of increased width and K_p can be calculated using the following equation:

$$K_p = \frac{10P_w}{v\, \eta_f}$$ (12.15)

where
$\quad K_p$ = unit price function ($\$ \cdot$h/ha)
$\quad v$ = travel speed (km/h)
$\quad \eta_f$ = field efficiency (decimal)
$\quad P_w$ = price per unit of increased width ($\$$/m)

Equation 12.13 can estimate the optimum capacity of a single machine. Usually, however, a family of machines is required in farming operations and these machines should have field capacities which are compatible with each other and with the tractor. For example, a tractor, plow, disk, planter, combine, and possibly other implements may be required to grow soybeans. Each of the implements has a definite period during the year during which its work should be accomplished. The term, scheduling, is defined as determining the time periods during the year when each operation can be performed. After the scheduling is completed, the required capacity can be calculated by using the following equation:

$$C_a = \frac{A}{\tau_{ad}\, T\, p_{wd}}$$ (12.16)

where
$\quad C_a$ = effective field capacity required to complete the work (ha/h)
$\quad A$ = area to be worked (ha)
$\quad T$ = length of each working day (h/day)
$\quad \tau_{ad}$ = available time to complete the work (days)
$\quad p_{wd}$ = probability of a good working day, decimal (see table 12.3)

The tractor must be large enough to provide power to the implement with the greatest power demand. If the implements vary widely in power demand, the tractor will be used inefficiently on the implements with the lowest power demand. Thus, to provide greatest overall efficiency and profit, it may be best to choose some implements with greater capacity than would be calculated using equations 12.13 or 12.16. The calculations become even more complex when the size of the farm justifies ownership of more than one tractor and/or more than one combine. Further, the use of constant timeliness coefficients, K_t, is an over simplification. Realistically, there is little or no reduction in crop yield if operations can be accomplished during the normally-scheduled periods. The daily penalty for delayed work should be assessed only after the scheduled period. To achieve greater realism, digital computer programs have been developed for scheduling farm machinery operations and for selecting optimum systems of farm machinery (see, for example, Rotz et al., 1983 or Siemens et al., 1990). Except for the simplest of systems, it is necessary to use such programs to obtain realistic results. Example problem 12.4 illustrates the calculation of optimum size of a single machine.

Example Problem 12.4
Using data from example problems 12.1 through 12.3, calculate the optimum combine capacity for harvesting the corn. Assume that, from an analysis of the purchase prices of two self-propelled combines, the unit price function is $20,000 h/ha.
Solution. The required data for use in equation 12.13 are already available. Note that $T_{fc} = 0$ in this example, since no tractor is used with the self-propelled combine. The optimum size is:

$$C_{aopt} = \sqrt{\frac{432}{0.127 \cdot 20,000}\left[6 + 0 + \frac{0.003 \cdot 432 \cdot 9.4 \cdot 98}{2 \cdot 10 \cdot 0.65}\right]} = 4.08 \text{ ha/h}$$

By using equation 12.1, the reader may verify that a combine traveling at 4.72 km/h with a 16-row corn head working in 75 cm rows with a field efficiency of 72% would have the optimum capacity. It would be instructive to rework example problems 12.1 through 12.3 to observe the changes in the various costs as a result of using the larger combine.

12.3.2 Machinery Replacement
All machines eventually reach the end of their economic life and the owner must decide when to replace each machine. There are a number of reasons why the owner might decide to replace a given machine. Machine damage suffered as a result of an accident might be so great that replacement would be less expensive than repairing the damage. The machine might become obsolete. As previously mentioned, a machine is obsolete when it is out of production and repair parts are no longer available, or when it can be replaced by another machine or method that will produce a greater profit.

TABLE 12.4. AN EXAMPLE OF AVERAGE UNIT ACCUMULATED COSTS

End of year	Remaining value	R&M costs	Depr.	Int.	Acc. depr.	Acc. int.	Acc. R&M	Tot. acc. costs, $	Acc. use, ha	Unit acc. costs, $/ha
1	2000	10	1000	200	1000	200	10	1210	100	12.10
2	1400	50	600	136	1600	336	60	1996	200	9.98
3	1000	70	400	96	2000	432	130	2562	300	8.54
4	700	100	300	68	2300	500	230	3030	400	7.58
5	500	200	200	48	2500	548	430	3478	500	6.96
6	350	300	150	34	2650	582	730	3962	600	6.60
7	225	350	125	23	2775	605	1080	4460	700	6.37
8	125	450	100	14	2875	619	1530	5024	800	6.28
9	100	550	25	9	2900	628	2080	5608	900	6.23
10	75	600	25	7	2925	635	2680	6240	1000	6.24

NOTE: ASAE Standards, Engineering Practices, and Data are informal and advisory only. Their use by anyone in industry or trade is entirely voluntary. The ASAE assumes no responsibility for results attributable to the application of these ASAE Standards, Engineering Practices, and Data. Conformity does not ensure compliance with applicable ordinances, laws and regulations. Prospective users are responsible for protecting themselves against liability for infringement of patents.

Combines, balers and other processing machines generally become obsolete faster than tractors, since tractors need only supply power. A machine should be replaced when the anticipated frequency of breakdowns becomes so large that the machine is no longer reliable; large economic penalties can result when field work is delayed and an unreliable machine can cause delays. Finally, a machine should be replaced when it is anticipated that the cost of repairs will begin to increase the average unit accumulated cost above the minimum. For example, table 12.4 shows repair and maintenance, depreciation and interest costs over the life of a $3000 machine which is used on 100 ha annually. The unit accumulated costs reach a minimum at the end of year nine of the machine life in this example. The machine should be replaced before the tenth year unless it is replaced earlier for other reasons.

Problems

12.1   A self-propelled combine is equipped with an eight-row corn head for 75-cm rows. (a) What is the maximum speed the combine should be operated in corn yielding 9.4 Mg/ha if the theoretical field capacity of the combine is 28 Mg/h? (b) What is the theoretical field capacity of the combine in ha/h?

12.2   A self-propelled combine is equipped with a 5-m grain platform. (a) At what speed must the combine be operated to fully use its separating capacity of 28 Mg/h in harvesting soybeans with a yield of 2.7 Mg/ha? (b) Considering the data in table 12.1, what is the maximum recommended speed for harvesting the soybeans? (c) What is the theoretical capacity of this combine, in ha/h, in harvesting soybeans? (d) Is the theoretical field capacity limited by gathering capacity or separating capacity of the combine?

12.3   A company is planning to design a family of self-propelled combines with a range of field capacities. All of the combines will be designed to operate at the typical speed listed in table 12.1. Corn heads and 2, 4, 6, 8, 10, and 12 rows will be marketed, all for 75-cm row spacing and with separating capacities to match the corn heads. (a) If the field efficiency of the two-row machine is 70%, calculate the total time losses, $\tau_a + \tau_h$, that are incurred in harvesting 1 ha. (b) Assuming that these time losses would remain unchanged for the combines larger than two-row capacity, calculate and plot the field efficiency versus size of the corn heads. (c) As an alternate assumption, calculate and plot the allowable total time losses, $\tau_a + \tau_h$, that could be tolerated per hectare if all of the combines were to have the same field efficiency.

12.4   Same as problem 12.3, except that a family of row-crop planters is to be designed. All of the planters will operate at a typical speed of 6.4 km/h and the field efficiency of the two-row planter is 60%.

12.5   (a) Assuming that 100% of the machine width is utilized, calculate and plot the total allowable lost time as a fraction of theoretical operating time, i.e., $(\tau_a + \tau_h)/\tau_t$, versus field efficiency. (b) Repeat part a but with 90% of the machine utilized. Plot both curves on the same graph. (c) Using data from table 12.1, mark the curves to show the allowable lost time for typical field efficiency of a potato harvester and a field cultivator assuming 90% of the width of the field cultivator is utilized.

12.6   Calculate and plot specific annual ownership costs versus economic life for life ranging from 1 to 20 years. Include two curves, one for a general inflation rate of 2% when the prevailing interest rate is 7% and one for a general inflation rate of 20% when the prevailing interest rate is 25%. Assume salvage value is 10% of purchase price, while taxes, insurance and shelter are 2% of purchase price.

12.7   Same as problem 12.6 except calculate and plot specific annual ownership costs versus real interest rate for interest rates ranging from 0 to 10%. Plot two curves, one for a 5-year economic life and one for a 10-year life.

12.8   A tractor with rated pto power of 90 kW is used to perform a tillage operation which requires 75 kW equivalent pto power. The effective field capacity is 2 ha/h. Fuel costs is $0.35/L and oil cost is $1.05/L. Calculate (a) the specific fuel consumption, (b) the fuel consumption in L/h, (c) the per-hectare fuel costs, (d) the oil consumption in L/h, and (e) the per-hectare oil costs.

12.9   Same as problem 12.8, except that the rated power of the tractor is 80 kW.

12.10   Same as problem 12.8, except that the rated power of the tractor is 120 kW.

12.11   (a) Assuming a zero rate of inflation, calculate and plot accumulated repair and maintenance costs as a percent of machine purchase price for a chisel plow. These dimensionless costs are to be plotted versus accumulated hours of use from zero to the estimated life of the plow, as given in table 12.1. (b) Repeat part a, but with an inflation rate of 10%. Put the curves for zero and 10% inflation on the same graph.

12.12   Repeat problem 12.11, except for a two-wheel drive tractor.

12.13   Repeat problem 12.11, except for a self-propelled combine.

12.14   A twelve-row conventional row-crop planter is to be used to plant 180 ha of soybeans with 75-cm row spacing in early June in Central Illinois. The soybeans have an anticipated yield of 2.7 Mg/ha and an anticipated selling price of $250/Mg. (a) Using typical travel speed and field efficiency for the planting operation (see table 12.1), calculate the field capacity, and (b) the timeliness cost assuming the farmer works 10-hour days and wants to be assured of a 90% probability of having the required number of good working days.

12.15   Repeat problem 12.14, except use a six-row planter.

12.16   Repeat problem 12.14, except use the planter to plant 200 ha of soybeans.

12.17   A conventional row-crop planter is to be used to plant 200 ha of soybeans with 75-cm row spacing in early May in Central

Illinois. The soybeans have an estimated yield of 2.7 Mg/ha and an anticipated selling price of $250/Mg. The farmer works 10-hour days. The planter is pulled by a $60,000 tractor that is used 400 hours per year (only a fraction of that total time is used with the planter) with an economic life of 15 years. For both the planter and tractor, assume salvage value of 10%, interest rate of 5% and K_{tis}=2%. The economic life of the planter is 10 years and labor costs are $6.00 per hour. List prices are $21,253, $33,570, and $58,284 for 8, 12, and 16-row planters, respectively. Calculate (a) the total annual ownership costs and (b) specific ownership costs of the tractor, (c) the specific annual ownership costs, (d) unit price function, and (e) optimum effective field capacity of the planter. Assume 30 cm of moisture in the root zone at planting time and a 90% probability of good working days. (f) If the planter works at the typical speed and field capacity given in table 12.1, select the best available planter, i.e., how many rows would it have?

12.18   Same as problem 12.17, except that the planter is used to plant corn (maize) in Iowa in early May. Also, there are 30 cm of available moisture in the root zone. The anticipated corn yield is 9.4 Mg/ha and the anticipated selling price of the corn is $98/Mg.

12.19   Suppose that 10 days were available to do the planting described in problem 12.17. What size planter would be selected to allow such scheduling?

12.20   Rework example problem 12.4, except let the hours worked per day vary from 6 to 16 hours. From the results, plot optimum capacity versus hours worked per day.

Appendix A
Patents Cited
(Chapter 10)

3,858,660   January 7, 1975. William F. Wadsworth. Feed Conveyor Apparatus.

3,896,612   July 29, 1975. Carl Manning McHugh, Byron Kenneth Webb and Clarence Elam Hood, Jr. Fruit Harvester.

3,964,245   June 22, 1976. Charles L. Hecht. Air Pickup System for Strawberry Pickers.

4,166,505   September 4, 1979. Frederick P. West. Method and Apparatus for Harvesting Green Peanuts.

4,185,696   January 29, 1980. Rodney B. Williams and Jerry A. Taylor. Row Crop Harvester with Adjustable Picking Heads.

4,251,983   February 24, 1981. Charles G. Burton. Grape Harvester with Cane Lifter.

4,364,222   December 21, 1982. Barry Ramacher. Nut Harvesting Machine.

4,409,782   October 18, 1983. Rod Westergaard, Lou Morton and Ken Zeiders. Multiple-Pattern Tree Shaking Mechanism.

4,416,334   November 22, 1983. Alain M. Bouillon. Potato Harvesting Apparatus.

4,464,888.   August 14, 1984. Charles G. Burton. Collector Leaf Construction for Harvesting Machine.

4,519,191   May 28, 1985. Richard L. Ledebuhr and Clarence M. Hansen. Strawberry Harvester and Procedures for Growing and Harvesting of Such Fruit.

4,560,008   December 24, 1985. John Carruthers. Root Crop Harvester.

4,584,826   April 19, 1986. Thomas S. Bettencourt and Darryl G. Bettencourt. Tomato Harvester.

4,621,488   November 11, 1986. Gerald L. Claxton. Oscillatory Shaker Rail Harvester.

4,769,979   September 13, 1988. Jean-Camille Merant. Machine for Harvesting Fruit and Berries and the Like, from Fruit Trees and Bushes Planted in a Row.

4,776,156   October 11, 1988. Galen K. Brown, Henry A. Affeidt, Jr., Thomas A. Rech and Richard J. Welthmia. Variable Eccentricity Mass for Mechanical Shakers.

4,793,128   December 27, 1988. Sherman H. Creed. Horizontal Force Balanced Shaker and Method.

4,860,529   August 29, 1989. Donald L. Peterson and Ted S. Kornecki. Shaking Mechanism for Fruit Harvesting.

4,934,461   June 19, 1990. Cecil J. Spears, Sr; Larry Spears and Cecil J. Spears, Jr. Peanut Digger and Vine.

4,975,016   December 4, 1990. Roger Pellman, Jose L. Mestoya, Antonio G. D'Emor, Marc Ronhart. Automated Machine for Detection and Grasping of Objects.

Appendix B

GRAPHIC SYMBOLS FOR FLUID POWER DIAGRAMS

(Partial listing from American National Standard ANS Y32.10, 1966)

LINES AND LINE FUNCTIONS		PUMPS, MOTORS, AND CYLINDERS	
Line, working (main)		Pump, single, fixed-displacement	Out / In
Line, pilot (for control)		Pump, single, variable displacement	
Line, drain		Hydraulic motor, fixed displacement	In / Out
Flow direction	Hydraulic / Pneumatic	Hydraulic motor, variable displacement	
Lines crossing		Hydraulic motor, bidirectional	
Lines joining		Cylinder, single-acting	
Line, flexible		Cylinder, double-acting	
Line with fixed restriction		**MISCELLANEOUS**	
Station (testing, measurement, or power take-off)		Reservoir, vented	
Line to reservoir* Above fluid level Below fluid level		Accumulator, spring-loaded	
Vented manifold		Accumulator, gas-charged	
Adjustable or variable component (run arrow through symbol at approximately 45°)		Cooler (heat exchanger)	
Pressure compensated units (arrow parallel to short side of symbol)		Filter (strainer)	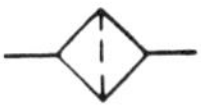
		Component enclosure (may surround a group of symbols to indicate an assembly)	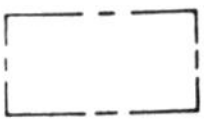
Temperature cause or effect		Direction of shaft rotation (arrow on near side of shaft)	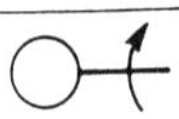

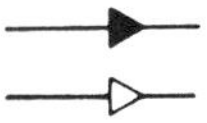

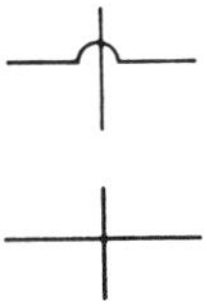

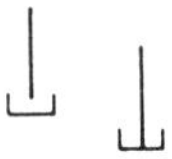

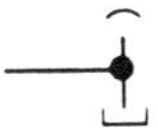

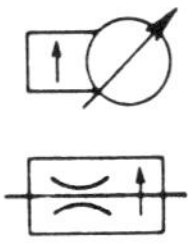

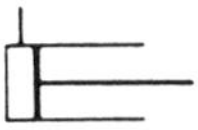

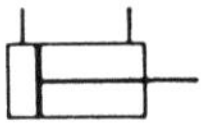

*Any number of these symbols may be used in one diagram to represent the same reservoir.

APPENDIX B

VALVES (See also Fig. 4.3)	
Check	
On-off (manual)	
Pressure relief, direct-acting (indicates infinite positioning, normally closed, for single port)	
Pressure reducing, direct-acting (indicates infinite positioning, normally open, for single port)	
Flow control, adjustable, noncompensated	
Flow control, adjustable, pressure-compensated, with reverse bypass	
Two-way (two ports), two-position	
Three-way (three ports), two-position	
Four-way (four ports), two-position	
Four-way, three-position, closed center	
Four-way, three-position, two-ports open center (tandem)	
Horizontal bars indicate valve capable of infinite positioning within limits	
General (add divisions and internal paths)	

ACTUATORS AND CONTROLS	
Spring	
Manual (general symbol; no specific type)	
Push button	
Push-pull lever	
Pedal or treadle	
Mechanical	
Detent (vertical line indicates which detent is in use)	
Pressure compensated	
Solenoid, single winding	
Reversing motor	
Pilot pressure, remote supply	
Pilot pressure, internal supply	
Pilot differential	

Basic symbols may be combined in many other ways to represent different components. All symbols except accumulators, vented manifold, and lines to reservoirs may be rotated or reversed. In a circuit, each symbol should be drawn to show normal, at-rest, or neutral conditions of the component, unless multiple diagrams are included to show various phases of circuit operation.

Selected Bibliography

Chapter 2

Baumeister, T. 1987. *Mark's Standard Handbook for Engineers*. New York: McGraw-Hill.
Goering, C. E. 1989. *Engine and Tractor Power*. St. Joseph, MI: ASAE.
Liljedahl, J. B., P. K. Turnquist, D. W. Smith and M. Hoki. 1989. *Tractors and Their Power Units*, 4th Ed. New York: Van Nostrand Reinhold.
NFPA. 1990. National electrical code. Quincy, MA: National Fire Protection Association.
Obert, E. F. 1973. *Internal Combustion Engines and Air Pollution*. New York: Harper & Row.
Sprick, W. L. and T. H. Becker. 1985. *The application and installation of diesel engines in agricultural equipment*. ASAE Distinguished Lecture Series. Lecture No. 11. St. Joseph, MI: ASAE.
Surbrook, T. C. and R. C. Mullin. 1985. *Agricultural Electrification*. West Chicago, IL: South-Western Publishing Co.

Chapter 3

Agricultural V-Belt Drive Design Manual. 1976. Denver, CO: Gates Rubber Co.
Chains for Power Transmission and Material Handling. Rockville, MD: American Chain Association.
Kepner, R. A., R. Bainer and E. L. Barger. 1978. *Principles of Farm Machinery*, 3rd Ed. Westport, CT: AVI Publishing Co.
Merritt, H. E. 1976. *Hydraulic Control Systems*. New York: John Wiley & Sons, Inc.

Chapter 4

ASAE Standards, 37th Ed. 1990. St. Joseph, MI: ASAE.
Ayers, P. D. and J. V. Perumpheral. 1982. Moisture and density effect on cone index. *Transactions of the ASAE* 25(2):1169-1172.
Brixius, W. W. 1987. Traction prediction equations for bias-ply tires. ASAE Paper No. 87-1622. St. Joseph, MI: ASAE.
Brixius, W. W. and R. D. Wismer. 1978. The role of slip in traction. ASAE Paper No. 78-1538. St. Joseph, MI: ASAE.
Ellis, R. W. 1977. Agricultural tire design requirements and selection considerations. ASAE Distinguished Lecture Series. Lecture No. 3. St. Joseph, MI: ASAE.
Liljedahl, J. B., P. K. Turnquist, D. W. Smith and M. Hoki. 1989. *Tractors and Their Power Units*, 4th Ed. New York, NY: Van Nostrand Reinhold.
Vomicil, J. A., E. R. Fountain and R. J. Reginato. 1958. The influence of speed and drawbar load on the compacting effect of wheeled tractors. Soil Science Soc. of America Proc. 22:178-180.
Wismer, R. D. and H. J. Luth. 1972. Off-road traction prediction for wheeled vehicles. ASAE Paper No. 72-619. St. Joseph, MI: ASAE.
Zoz, F. M. 1987. Predicting tractor field performance (updated). ASAE Paper No. 87-1623. St. Joseph, MI: ASAE.

Chapter 5

ASAE Standards, 29th Ed. 1982. S414.1. Terminology and definitions for agricultural tillage implements. St. Joseph, MI: ASAE.
Bernachi, H., J. Haman and Cz. Kanafojski. 1972. *Agricultural Machines, Theory and Construction*, Vol I. Published for USDA and NSF by Foreign Cooperation Center of the Central Institute for Scientific, Technical and Economic Information, Warsaw, Poland.
Clyde, A. W. 1954. Pitfalls in applying the science of mechanics to tractors and implements. *Agricultural Engineering* 35(Feb):79-83.

————. 1944. Technical features of tillage tools. Pennsylvania Agr. Expt. Sta. Bull. 465 (Part 2).

————. 1939. Improvements of disk tools. *Agricultural Engineering* 20(June):215-221.

Cooper, A. W. and W. F. McCreery. 1961. Plastic surfaces for tillage tools. ASAE Paper No. 61-649. St. Joseph, MI: ASAE. (Cited in Kepner et al., 1978.)

CRC Handbook in Agriculture. 1988. Volume I: *Crop Production Engineering.* Boca Raton, FL: CRC Press.

Frevert, R. K. 1940. Mechanics of tillage. Unpublished M.S. thesis, Iowa State University, Ames.

Furlong, D. B. 1956. Rotary tiller performance tests on existing tines. Tech. Rept. 1049. Central Eng. Dept., FMC Corp., San Jose, CA

Getzlaff, G. E. 1953. Comparative studies on the forces acting on standard plow bodies. Grundl. Landtech., Heft 5:16-35 (NIAE transl. 6).

Gill, W. R. and G. E. VandenBerg. 1968. *Soil Dynamics in Tillage and Traction.* Agricultural Handbook No. 316. USDA-ARS.

Gullacher, D. E. and W. E. Coates. 1980. Effects of cultivator sweep pitch an tillage forces. ASAE Paper No. 80-1567. St. Joseph, MI: ASAE.

Kepner, R. A., R. Bainer and E. L. Barger. *Principles of Farm Machinery,* 3rd Ed. Westport, CT: AVI Publishing Co., Inc.

Klenin, N. I., I. F. Popov and V. A. Sakun. 1970. *Agricultural Machines.* Moscow: Kolos Publishers. (Translated from Russian and published for USDA and NSF by Amerind Publishing Co. Pvt. Ltd., New Delhi, 1985)

Marling, R. W. 1963. Soil force analysis as applied to tillage equipment. ASAE Paper No. 63-149. St. Joseph, MI: ASAE.

McKibben, E. G. and I. F. Reed. 1952. The influence of speed on the performance characteristics of implements. (Presented at SAE National Tractor meeting. Cited in Kepner et al., 1978.)

Nichols, M. L., I. F. Reed and C. A. Reaves. 1958. Soil reaction: To plow share design. *Agricultural Engineering* 39:336-339.

Randolf, J. W. and I. F. Reed, 1938. Testing of tillage tools: II. Effect of several factors on the reactions of fourteen-inch moldboard plow. *Agricultural Engineering* 19(June):29-33.

Rowe, R. J. and K. K. Barnes. 1961. Influence of speed on elemnets of draft of a tillage tool. *Transactions of the ASAE* 4(1):55-57

Soehne, W. 1956. Some principles of soil mechanics as applied to Agricultural Engineering. Grundlagen der Landtecknik 7:11-27 (NIAE Translation 53).

Sommer, M. S., S. H. Chen and J. F. Bierl. 1983. Disk blade performance. ASAE Paper No. 83-1537. St. Joseph, MI: ASAE.

Wu, T. H. 1966. *Soil Mechanics.* Boston: Allyn & Bacon, Inc.

Chapter 6

Adekoya, L. O. and W. F. Buchele. 1987. A precision punch planter for use in tilled and untilled soils. *Journal of Agr. Engr. Research* 37:171-178.

ASAE Standards, 39th Ed. 1992. St. Joseph, MI: ASAE.

Anonymous. 1968. Finger pickup unit replaces plate in corn planter. *Agricultural Engineering* 49(9):536.

Anonymous. 1971. IH develops air force planter. *Agricultural Engineering* 52(4):182.

Brewer, H. L. 1988. Experimental automatic feeder for seedling transplanter. *Applied Engineering in Agriculture* 4(1):24-29.

Cunningham, F. M. 1963. Performance characteristics of bulk spreaders for granular fertilizer. *Transactions of the ASAE* 6(2):108-114.

Davis, J. B. and C. E. Rice. 1973. Distribution of granular fertilizer and wheat by centrifugal distributors. *Transactions of the ASAE* 16(5):867-868.

Eddington, D. L. and L. N. Shaw. 1987. Singulator for fluid planting of sprouted seeds. *Transactions of the ASAE* 30(6):1569-1574.

Eisener, F. 1930. Das widerstands problem. Proceedings of the Third International Congress of Applied Mechanics, 23-42.

Futral, J. G. and B. P. Verma. 1973. A powered furrow opener for precise seed depths. ASAE Paper No. 73-1543. St. Joseph, MI: ASAE.

Giannini, G. R., W. J. Chancellor and R. E. Garrett. 1967. Precision planter using vacuum for seed pickup. *Transactions of the ASAE* 10(5):607-610, 614.

Glover, J. W. and J. V. Baird, 1973. The performance of spinner-type fertilizer spreaders. *Transactions of the ASAE* 16(1):48-51.

Goering, C. E., L. E. Bode and M. R. Gebhardt. 1972. Mathematical modeling of spray droplet deceleration and evaporation. *Transactions of the ASAE* 15(2):220-225.

Goyal, M. R., L. O. Drew, G. L. Nelson and T. J. Logan. 1980. Soybean seedling emergence force. *Transactions of the ASAE* 23(4):836-839.

Hawk, A. L., D. B. Brooker and J. J. Cassidy. 1966. Aerodynamic characteristics of selected farm grains. *Transactions of the ASAE* 9(1):48-51.

ISO. 1984. Sowing equipment - Test methods. ISO Standard 7256. Paris, France: International Standards Organization.

Mennel, R. M. and A. R. Reece. 1963. The theory of the centrifugal distributor, part III, Particle trajectories. *J. of Agr. Engng. Res.* 43(1):78-84.

Morrison, J. E., Jr. and T. J. Gerik. 1985. Planter depth control: I. Prediction and projected effect on crop emergence. *Transactions of the ASAE* 28(5):1415-1418.

Moysey, E. B., E. W. Lambert and Z. Wang. 1988. Flow rates of grains and oilseeds through sharp-edged orifices. *Transactions of the ASAE* 31(1):226-231.

Munilla, R. D. and L. N. Shaw. 1987. A high-speed dibbling transplanter. *Transactions of the ASAE* 30(4):904-908.

PAMI. 1978. Evaluation report on John Deere 9350 grain and fertilizer drill. Humboldt, Saskatchewan, Canada: Prairie Agricultural Machinery Institute.

Phene, C. J., D. N. Baker, J. R. Lambert, J. E. Parsons and J. M. KcKinion. 1978. SPAR - A soil-plant-atmosphere research system. *Transactions of the ASAE* 21(5):924-930.

Pitt, R. E., G. S. Farmer and L. P. Walker. 1982. Approximating equations for rotary distributor spreader patterns. *Transactions of the ASAE* 25(6):1544-1552.

Richardson, P. and M. J. O'Dogherty. 1972. Theoretical analysis of the seed spacing distribution produced by a fluid drill. National Institute of Agricultural Engineering Report No. 4, NIAE, Silsoe, England.

Shaw, L. N. 1985. Apparatus for metering and dispensing seeds. U.S. patent No. 4,703,868.

Shaw, L. N. and K. H. Kromer. 1987. Revolving spade planter soil opener. ASAE Paper No. 87-019. St. Joseph, MI: ASAE.

Stapleton, H. N. and R. P. Meyers. 1971. Modeling subsystems for cotton — The cotton plant simulation. *Transactions of the ASAE* 14(5):950-953.

Suggs, C. W., T. N. Thomas, D. L. Eddington, H. B. Peel, T. R. Seaboch and J. W. Gore. 1987. Self-feeding transplanter for tobacco and vegetable crops. *Applied Engineering in Agriculture* 3(2):148-151.

Vaughn, D. H. and H. D. Bowen. 1977. Simulation of cotton radicle elongation during emergence. *Transactions of the ASAE* 20(5):810-812, 816.

Wilkins, D. E., P. A. Adrian and W. J. Conley. 1979. Punch planting of vegetable seeds – A progress report. *Transactions of the ASAE* 22(4):746-749.

Chapter 7

Bernacki, H., J. Haman and Cz. Kanafojski. 1972. *Agricultural Machines, Theory and Construction*, Vol. 1. Published for the U.S. Department of Agriculture and N.S.F., Washington, D.C., by the Scientific Publications Foreign Cooperation Center of the Central Institute for Scientific, Technical and Economic Information, Warsaw, Poland.

Bode, L. E. and B. J. Butler. 1981. The three d's of droplet size: Diameter, drift, and deposit. ASAE Paper No. AA-81-004. St. Joseph, MI: ASAE.

Bode, L. E. and S. L. Pearson. 1985. Equipment and calibration: Granular applicators. Circular No. 1240. Cooperative Extension Service, College of Agriculture, University of Illinois, Urbana.

Bode, L. E. and B. J. Butler. 1981. Equipment and calibration: Low-pressure sprayers. Circular No. 1192. Cooperative Extension Service, College of Agriculture, University of Illinois, Urbana.

Crowther, A. J. 1958. The distribution of particles by a spinning disc. *J. Agric. Engng. Res.* 3:288-291.

Cunningham, F. M. 1963. Performance characteristics of bulk spreaders for granular fertilizers. *Transactions of the ASAE* 6(2):108-114.

Deysson, J. Y. and J. Karian. 1978. Approximate sizing of single fluid and pneumatic atomizers. 1st International Conference on Liquid Atomization and Spray Systems, Tokyo, Japan.

Dombrowski, N. and W. R. Johns. 1963. The aerodynamic instability and disintegration of viscous liquid sheets. *Chemical Engineering Science* 18:203-214.

Dorman, R. G. 1952. The atomization of liquid in a flat spray. *British Journal of Applied Physics* 3:189-192.

Ford, R. E. and C. G. L. Furmidge. 1967. The formation of drops from viscous Newtonion liquid sprayed through fan-jet nozzles. *Brit. J. Appl. Phys.* 8:335-348.

French, O. C. 1942. Spraying equipment for pest control. California Ag. Expt. Sta. Bull. 666. (Cited in Kepner et al., 1978).

Frazer, R. P., N. Dombrowski and J. H. Routley. 1963. The filming of liquids by spinning cups. *Chemical Engineering Science* 18:323-337.

Frost, A. R. 1981. Rotary atomization in the ligament formation mode. *J. Agric. Engng. Res.* 26:63-78.

Goering, C. E., L. E. Bode and D. B. Smith. 1978. Characterization of spray droplet size distributions. 1st International Conference on Liquid Atomization and Spray Systems, Tokyo, Japan.

Hughes, H. A. *Fundamentals of Machine Operations — Crop Chemicals*. Deere & Co., Moline, IL.

Inns, F. M. and A. R. Reece. 1962. The theory of the centrifugal distributor II: Motion on the disc, off center feed. *J. of Agric. Engng. Res.* 7(4):345-353.

Keith, F. W. and A. N. Hixon. 1955. *Ind. Eng. Chem.* 47:258-267.

Kepner, R. A., R. Bainer and E. L. Barger. 1978. *Principles of Farm Machinery*, 3rd Ed. Westport, CT: AVI Publishing Co., Inc.

Marshall, W. R. 1954. *Atomization and Spray Drying*. Chem. Eng. Prog. Monogr. Ser. No. 2.

Matsumoto, S. and Y. Takashima. 1978. Design criteria of hollow cone nozzle and prediction of drop size distribution. 1st International Conference on Liquid Atomization and Spray Systems, Tokyo, Japan.

Mennel, R. M. and A. R. Reece. 1963. The theory of the centrifugal distributor III: Particle trajectories. *J. of Agric. Engng. Res.* 8(1):78-84.

Patterson, D. E. and A. R. Reece. 1962. The theory of the centrifugal distributor I: Motion on the disc, near center feed. *J. Agric. Engng. Res.* 7(3):232-240.

PAMI 1985. Evaluation Repot 407. Humboldt, Saskatchewan, Canada.

————. Evaluation Repot 457. Humboldt, Saskatchewan, Canada.

Ritter, D. W., C. L. Griffis and E. J. Mathews. 1980. Computer simulation of rotary spreader distribution patterns. ASAE Paper No. 80-1504. St. Joseph: ASAE.

Smith, H. P. 1964. *Farm Machinery and Equipment*, 5th Ed. New York: McGraw-Hill Book Co.

Spraying Systems Co. 1991. Product Catalogue 40. Wheaton, IL.

VanEe, G. and R. Ledebuhr. 1987. Spray unit for controlled droplet atomization. U.S. Patent No. 4,659,013.

Yates, W. E. and N. B. Akesson. 1973. Reducing pesticide chemical drift. In *Pesticide Formulations: Physical Chemical Principles*, ed. W. VanValkenburg. New York: Mercel Dekker. (Cited in Kepner et al., 1978.)

————. 1963. Hydraulic agitation requirements for pesticide material. *Transactions of the ASAE* 6(3):202-205, 208.

Chapter 8

ASAE Standards, 39th Ed. 1992a. S229. Baling wire for automatic balers. St. Joseph, MI: ASAE.

————. 1992b. S315. Twine for automatic balers. St. Joseph, MI: ASAE.

————. 1992c. S328. Dimensions for compatible operation of forage harvesters, forage wagons and forage blowers. St. Joseph, MI: ASAE.

————. 1992d. S472. Terminology for forage harvesters and forage harvesting. St. Joseph, MI: ASAE.

————. 1992e. S424. Method of determining and expressing particle size of chopped forage materials by screening. St. Joseph, MI: ASAE.

————. 1992f. D251. Friction coefficients of chopped forages. St. Joseph, MI: ASAE.

————. 1992. X498. Terminology for round balers. St. Joseph, MI: ASAE.

Berge, O. I. 1951. Design and performance of the flywheel-type forage-harvester cutterhead. *Agricultural Engineering* 32(2):85-91.

Blevins, F. Z. and H. J. Hansen. 1956. Analysis of forage harvester design. *Agricultural Engineering* 37(1):21-26, 29.

Bonner, J. and A. W. Galston. 1952. *Principles of Plant Physiology*. W. H. Feeman.

Bockhop, C. W. and K. K. Barnes. 1955. Power distribution and requirements of a flail-type forage harvester. *Agricultural Engineering* 36(7):453-457.

Burrough, D. E. and J. A. Graham. 1954. Power characteristics of a plunger-type forage baler. *Agricultural Engineering* 35(4):221-229, 232.

Elfes, L. E., 1954. Design and development of a high-speed mower. *Agricultural Engineering* 35(3):147-153.

Freeland, R. S. and B. L. Bledsoe. 1988. Energy required to form large round hay bales effect of operational procedure and baler chamber type. *Transactions of the ASAE* 31(1):63-67.

Harbage, R. P. and R. V. Morr. 1962. Development and design of a ten-foot mower. *Agricultural Engineering* 43(4):208.

Ige, M. T. and M. F. Finner. 1975. Effects and interactions between factors affecting the shearing characteristics of forage harvesters. *Transactions of the ASAE* 18(6):1011-1016.

Kepner, R. A. 1952. Analysis of the cutting action of a mower. *Agricultural Engineering* 33(11):693-697, 704.

Koegel, R. G., R. J. Straub and R. P. Walgenbach. 1985. Quantification of mechanical losses in forage harvesting. *Transactions of the ASAE* 28(4):1047-1051.

Koegel, R. G., K. J. Shinners, F. J. Fronczak and R. J. Straub. 1988. Prototype for production of fast drying forage mats. *Applied Engineering in Agriculture* 4(2):126-129.

NIAE, 1965. Report No. 445 of the National Institute of Agricultural Engineering, Silsoe, England.

O'Dogherty, M. J. 1982. A review of research on forage chopping. *J. of Agr. Engng. Res.* 27:267-289.

Persson, S. 1987. *Mechanics of Cutting Plant Material*. St. Joseph, MI: ASAE.

Pitt, R. E. 1990. *Silage and hay preservation*. NRAES Publication No. 5.

Richey, C. B. 1958. Discussion on "energy requirements for cutting forage". *Agricultural Engineering* 39(10):636-637.

Rotz, C. A. and S. M. Abrams. 1988. Losses and quality changes during alfalfa hay harvest and storage. *Transactions of the ASAE* 31(2):350-355.

Rotz, C. A., J. R. Black, D. R. Mertens and D. R. Buckmaster. 1989. DAFOSYM: A model of the dairy forage system. *Journal of Production Agriculture* 2(1):83-91.

Rotz, C. A. and Y. Chen. 1985. Alfalfa drying model for the field environment. *Transactions of the ASAE* 28(5):1686-1691.

Rotz, C. A., K. G. Kogel, K. J. Shinners and R. J. Straub. 1990. Economics of maceration and mat drying of alfalfa on dairy farms. *Applied Engineering in Agriculture* 6(3):248-256.

Rotz, C. A. and D. J. Sprott. 1984. Drying rates, losses and fuel requirements for mowing and conditioning alfalfa. *Transactions of the ASAE* 27(3):715-720.

Shinners, K. J., G. P. Barrington, R. J. Straub and R. G. Koegel. 1985. Forming mats from macerated alfalfa to increase drying rates. *Transactions of the ASAE* 29(2):374-377, 381.

Wieneke, F., 1972. Verfahrenstechnik der halmfutterproduktion (methods for forage production). F. Wiekneke, publisher, Gottingen, Germany.

Chapter 9

Arnold, R. E. 1964. Experiments with rasp bar threshing drums. *J. of Agr. Engng. Res.* 9:99-134.

Berry, P. E. 1958. Research on oscillating conveyors. *J. of Agr. Engng. Res.* 3(3):249-259

Bottinger, S. and H. D. Kutzbach. 1987. Performance characteristics of a cleaning unit under various crop conditions. ASAE Paper No. 87-1512. St. Joseph, MI: ASAE.

Byg, D. M. and G. E. Hall. 1968. Corn losses and kernel damage in field shelling of corn. *Transactions of the ASAE* 11(2):164-166.

Cooper, G. F. 1971. Cylinder/concave performance from laboratory tests. ASAE Paper No. 71-625. St. Joseph, MI: ASAE.

German, R. F. and J. H. A. Lee. 1969. Grain separation on an oscillating sieve as affected by air volume and frequency. *Transactions of the ASAE* 12(2):883-885.

Gregory, J. M. and C. B. Fedler. 1987. Mathematical relationship predicting grain separation in combines. *Transactions of the ASAE* 30(6):1600-1604.

Hill, L. G. and G. E. Frehlich. 1985. Effect of reducing MOG/G on combine performance. ASAE Paper No. 85-1577. St Joseph, MI: ASAE.

Huynh, V. M. and T. E. Powell. 1978. Cleaning shoe performance prediction. ASAE Paper No. 78-1565. St. Joseph, MI: ASAE.

Huynh, V. M., T. Powell and J. N. Siddall. 1982. Threshing and separating process – A mathematical model. *Transactions of the ASAE* 25(1):65-73.

Kepner, R. A., R. Bainer and E. L. Barger. 1978. *Principles of Farm Machinery*, 3rd Ed. Westport, CT: AVI Publishing Co., Inc.

Lee, J. H. A. and R. G. Winfield. 1969. Influence of oscillating frequency on separation of wheat on a sieve in an airstream. *Transactions of the ASAE* 12(6):886-888.

Long, D. J., M. Y. Hamdy and W. H. Johnson. 1969. Centrifugal force and wheat separation. *Agricultural Engineering* 50(10):578-580.

Nyborg, E. O., H. F. McColly and R. T. Hinkle. 1969. Grain-combine loss characteristics. *Transactions of the ASAE* 12(6):727-732.

Reed, W. B., G. C. Zoerb and F. W. Bigsby. 1974. A laboratory study of grain-straw separation. *Transactions of the ASAE* 17(3):452:460.

Rotz, C. A. and H. A. Muhtar. 1991. Rotary power requirements for agricultural equipment. ASAE Paper No. 91-1550. St Joseph, MI: ASAE.

Rumble, D. W. and J. H. A. Lee. 1970. Aerodynamic separation in a combine shoe. *Transactions of the ASAE* 13(1):6-8.

Srivastava, A. K. 1972. Grain straw separation in a centrifugal force field. Unpubl. Ph.D. diss., The Ohio State University, Columbus, OH.

Srivastava, A. K., W. T. Mahoney and N. L. West. 1990. The effect of crop properties on combine performance. *Transactions of the ASAE* 33(1):63-72.

Waelti, H. and W. F. Buchele. 1969. Factors affecting corn kernel damage in combine cylinders. *Transactions of the ASAE* 12(1):55-59.

Wang, G., G. C. Zoerb and F. W. Bigsby. 1987. A new concept in combine separation analysis. *Transactions of the ASAE* 30(4):899-903.

Wilkinson, R. L and O. A. Braunbeck. 1977. *Elements of Agricultural Machinery*, Vol. 2. Rome: FAO.

Chapter 10

Adrian, P. A. and R. B. Fridley. 1965. Dynamics and design criteria of inertial-type tree shakers. *Transactions of the ASAE* 8(1):12-14.

Ag Eng 88 Book of Abstracts. 1988. In *Proceedings of the International Conference on Agricultural Engineering*. Paris, France.

ASAE. *Fruit, nut and vegetable harvesting mechanization*, Proceedings of the International Symposium on Fruit, Nut and Vegetable Harvesting Mechanization. St Joseph, MI: ASAE.

ASAE Standards, 40th Ed. 1993. S337.1. Agricultural pallet bins. St. Joseph, MI: ASAE.

Bilanski, W. K., S. H. Collins and P. Chen. 1962. Aerodynamic properties of seed grains. *Agricultural Engineering* 63(6):216-219.

Bower, D. R. and R. P. Rohrbach. 1976. Application of vibrational sorting to blueberry firmness separation. *Transactions of the ASAE* 19(1):185-191.

Cargill, B. F. and G. E. Rossmiller, eds. 1969. *Fruit and vegetable harvest mechanization, Technological implications*. E. Lansing, MI: Michigan State Univ., Rural Manpower Center.

DeBaerdemaeker, J. and L. J. Segerlind. 1974. Aerodynamic properties of strawberries. *Transactions of the ASAE* 17(2):729-732, 736.

Delwiche, M. J., N. Singh, H. Arevalo and J. Mehlschau. 1991. A second generation fruit firmness sorter. ASAE Paper No. 91-6042. St. Joseph, MI: ASAE.

Glass, S. W., III and R. P. Rohrbach. 1980. Driving point mechanical impedance of blueberries. *Transactions of the ASAE* 23(2):298-302.

Goldsmith, W. 1960. *Impact, The Theory and Physical Behavior of Colliding Bodies*. London: Edward Arnold Publishing, Ltd.

Hightower, J. 1972. *Hard Tomatoes Hard Times*. Cambridge, MA: Schenkman Publishing Co.

Meredith, F. I., R. G. Leffler and C. E. Lyon. 1988. Detection of firmness in peaches by impact force response. ASAE Paper No. 88-6570. St. Joseph, MI: ASAE.

Mohsenin, N. N. 1970. *Physical Properties of Plant and Animal Materials*. New York: Gordon and Breach Science Publishers.

O'Brien, M., B. F. Cargill and R. B. Fridley. 1983. *Principles & Practices for Harvesting Fruits and Nuts*. Westport, CT: AVI Publishing Co., Inc.

Persson, S. 1987. *Mechanics of Cutting Plant Material*. St Joseph, MI: ASAE.

Ruff, J. H., R. P. Rohrbach and R. G. Holmes. 1980. Analysis of the air-suspension stem-vibration strawberry harvesting concept. *Transactions of the ASAE* 23(2):288-297.

Soule, H. M., Jr. 1970. Investigations of some aerodynamic properties of lowbush blueberries. *Transactions of the ASAE* 13(1):114-117.

Tsatsarelis, C. A., 1987. Vibratory olive harvesting: The response of the fruit-stem system to fruit removing actions. *J. Agric. Eng. Res.* (38):77-90.

Chapter 11
Screw Conveyors

Brusewitz, G. H. and S. P. E. Persson. 1969. Parametric study of factors influencing screw-conveyor throughput and power requirement. *Transactions of the ASAE* 22(1):51-59.

McFate, K. L. and R. M. George. 1971. Power capacity relationships of nominal 8-inch screw conveyor when handling shelled corn. *Transactions of the ASAE* 24(1):121-126.

Millier, W. F. 1959. Bucket elevators, auger elevators for handling free-flowing materials. *Agricultural Engineering* (Sept.).

Peart, R. M., B. A. McKenzie and F. L. Herum. 1967. Dimensional standard and performance-test procedures for screw conveyors. *Transactions of the ASAE* 10(5):667-669.

Regan, W. M. and S. M. Henderson. 1959. Performance characteristics of inclined screw conveyors. *Agricultural Engineering* (Aug.).

Rehkugler, G. E. and L. L. Boyd. 1962. Dimensional analysis of auger conveyor operation. *Transactions of the ASAE* 12(1):98-102.

Stevens, G. N. 1962. Performance test on experimental auger conveyors. *J. of Agr. Engr. Res.* 7(1):47-60.

Pneumatic Conveyors

ASAE Standards, D273 St. Joseph, MI: ASAE.

ASHRAE. *Handbook of Fundamentals*. New York: ASHRAE.

Cornish, G. K. and L. F. Charity. 1966. Pressure drop in elbows of a pneumatic conveying system. *Transactions of the ASAE* 9(1):29-31.

Crane, J. W. and W. M. Carleton. 1957. Predicting pressure drop in pneumatic conveying of grains. *Agricultural Engineering*.

Grain Drying, Handling, and Storage Handbook. 1987. Ames, IA: Iowa State University, Midwest Plan Service.

Hellevang, K. J. 1985. Pneumatic Grain Dryers. Report No. 13AENG2-3. Fargo, ND: North Dakota State University, Cooperative Extension Service.

Kraus, M. N. 1986. Pneumatic conveying systems. *Chemical Engineering* (Oct. 13).

Marcus, R. D., L. S. Leung, G. E. Klinzing and F. Rizk. 1990. *Pneumatic Conveying of Solids*. London: Chapman & Hall.

Noyes, R. T. and W. E. Pfieffer. 1985. Design procedure for pneumatic conveyors in agriculture. ASAE Paper No. 85-3507. St. Joseph, MI: ASAE.

Bucket Elevators

Millier, W. F. 1958. Bucket elevators, auger conveyors of handling free flowing materials. *Agricultural Engineering* (Sept.).

Forage Blowers

Belvins, F. Z. and H. J. Hansen. 1956. Analysis of forage harvester design. *Agricultural Engineering* (37):21-26, 29.

Chancellor, W. J. 1960. Relation between air and solid particles moving upward in a vertical pipe. *Agricultural Engineering* (41):168-171.

Chancellor, W. J. 1960. Influence of particle movement on energy losses in an impeller blower. *Agricultural Engineering* (41):92-94.

Kepner, R. A., R. Bainer and E. L. Barger. 1978. *Principles of Farm Machinery*. West Port, CT: AVI Publishing Co.

McLeod, H. E. and K. K. Barnes. 1958. Effect of paddle tip clearance on forage blower performance. *Agricultural Engineering* (Aug.).

Pettingill, D. H. and W. F. Millier. 1968. The effect of certain design changes on the efficiency of a forage blower. *Transactions of the ASAE* 11(3):403-406, 408.

Raney, J. P. and J. B. Liljedahl. 1957. Impeller blade shape affects forage blower performance. *Agricultural Engineering* (Oct.).

Totten, D. S. and W. F. Millier. 1966. Energy and particle path analysis: Forage blower and vertical pipe. *Transactions of the ASAE* 9(5):629-636, 640.

Chapter 12

ASAE Standards, 39th Ed. 1992. St. Joseph, MI: ASAE.

Bartholomew, R. B. 1981. Farm machinery costs under inflation. *Transactions of the ASAE* 24(4):843-845.

Bowers, W. 1987. *Fundamentals of Machine Operation – Machinery Management*. Moline, IL: Deere & Co.

Bowers, W. and D. R. Hunt. 1970. Application of mathematical formulas to repair cost data. *Transactions of the ASAE* 13(6):806-809.

Burrows, W. C. and J. C. Siemens. 1974. Determination of optimum machinery for corn-soybean farms. *Transactions of the ASAE* 17(6):1130-1135.

Fairbanks, G. E., G. H. Larson and D. S. Chung. 1971. Cost of using farm machinery. *Transactions of the ASAE* 14(1):98-101.

Frisby, J. C. and C. W. Bockhop. 1968. Weather and economics determine corn-production machinery systems. *Transactions of the ASAE* 11(1):61-64.

Gao, H. W. and D. R. Hunt. 1985. Optimum combine fleet selection with power-based models. *Transactions of the ASAE* 28(2):364-368.

Hunt, D. H. 1983. *Farm Power and Machinery Management*, 8th Ed. Ames, IA: Iowa State University Press.

Mayfield, W., G. S. Hines and L. Roberts. 1981. A new method of estimating farm machinery costs. *Transactions of the ASAE* 24(6):1446-1448.

Mount, F. P. 1924. Farm machinery lowers production costs. *Agricultural Engineering* 5(2):31.

McKibben, E. G. 1930. Some fundamental factors determining the effective capacity of field machines. *Agricultural Engineering* 11(2):55-57.

McKibben, E. G. and P. L. Dressel. 1943. Over-all performance of series combinations of machines as affected by the reliability of individual units. *Agricultural Engineering* 24(4):121-122.

Renoll, E. 1975. Field machine index use and application. *Transactions of the ASAE* 18(3):493-496.

Rotz, C. A., H. A. Muhtar and J. R. Black. 1983. A multiple crop processing machinery selection algorithm. *Transactions of the ASAE* 26(6):1644-1649.

Siemens, J. C., K. Hamburg and T. Tyrrell. 1990. A farm machinery selection and management program. *Journal of Production Agriculture* 3(2):212-219.

Smith, E. S. and J. D. Oliver. 1974. Annuity approach to machinery costs. *Transactions of the ASAE* 17(5):796-797.

Thuesen, H. G., W. J. Fabrycky and G. J. Thuesen. 1971. *Engineering Economy*, 4th Ed. Englewood Cliffs, NJ: Prentice-Hall.

Tufts, R. A. 1985. Failure frequency and downtime duration effects on equipment availability. *Transactions of the ASAE* 28(4):999-1002.

Tulu, M. Y., J. B. Holtman, R. B. Fridley and S. D. Parsons. 1974. Timeliness costs and available working days – shelled corn. *Transactions of the ASAE* 17(5):798-800, 804.

Von Bargen, K. and M. B. Cunney. 1974. Activity ratios for farm machinery operations analysis. *Transactions of the ASAE* 17(2):225-227.

Ward, S. M., P. B. McNulty and M. B. Cunney. 1985. Repair costs of 2 and 4 WD tractors. *Transactions of the ASAE* 28(4):1074-1076.

Subject Index

A

A/F ratio (See Combustion)
Adhesion 136, 182, 191, 218
Agitation 233, 266, 283, 287, 289-293, 322-323, 432, 438
    hydraulic 283, 287, 289-293, 322
    mechanical 289-290, 292, 322-323
Air/fuel ratio (See Combustion)
American Society of Agricultural Engineers (ASAE) 118-121, 129, 132, 136-139, 146,
    352, 355, 385, 450, 452, 550
Angle 479
    bevel 331-333, 340, 344, 398-399
    chip 332
    clearance 332-333, 344, 398-399, 542
    clip 333-334, 399
    cutting 351, 398-399
    oblique 332-333, 351
    rake 332-333
    repose 433, 440
    slant 333, 398, 542
    tilt 155-156, 161, 194, 398
    wrap 60, 62
Anhydrous ammonia 278, 282-284
    applicator 283
Articulated steering 135
Atomization 295, 297-298, 300, 302
    jet break-up 297-298
    sheet break-up 302
    droplet break-up 303
    droplet size distribution 304-305
Atomizers 281, 295, 297
    pneumatic 295
    pressure 281, 295, 297
    rotary 281-282, 295, 297
Auger conveyors 360, 511, 544
    capacity 544
    efficiency 509-511, 513, 516, 543
    power requirements 391, 509-511, 514, 516, 545

B

C

D

I

R

S

T